GREAT WRITERS OF THE WORLD

SAINT PAUL: *ENVOY OF GRACE*

THE APOSTLE PAUL
From a painting by Rembrandt, in the National Gallery of Art,
Washington, D. C. Widener Collection

SAINT PAUL:

ENVOY OF GRACE

By

ROBERT SENCOURT

NEW YORK

SHEED & WARD · 1948

COPYRIGHT, 1948, BY SHEED & WARD, INC.

Printed in the United States of America

67852

*To the memory of my father and mother
whose bequests gave me the opportunity
to write this book*

I am grieved and pained that all men do not know this man as they ought to know him; but some are so far ignorant of him as not even to know the number of his epistles . . . . . It is not through any natural readiness or sharpness of wit that even I know as much as I do—if indeed I do know anything—but owing to a constant drawing towards him and an earnest affection.—ST. CHRYSOSTOM, Proem to Homilies on the Epistle to the Romans.

PREFACE

FOR MORE YEARS THAN I CAN THINK I HAVE BEEN FASCINATED by St. Paul as the first and greatest of Christian writers. This is an attempt to profit by experience as biographer, as critic, as historian to tell his story in the words of our time, and survey with a layman's eye the result of a hundred years of scholarship, not unmixed with controversy.

In this last hundred years since Lewin wrote his excellent life, much has been discovered: but also there have been put forward many conjectures which—however flattering to their authors' combination of ingenuity with learning—cannot rank as established facts. The latest views are not always the most convincing. The broad lines of St. Paul's life and work are known: but there are periods at which we can only guess. Compelled to discriminate between various suggestions, I have sought to show in the notes, when not in the narrative, what the alternatives are. I have been compelled to choose between them: but I do not claim authority, nor write as a controversialist.

The guide of my judgment is the belief that the books of the New Testament are, as documents, more important than the theories of critics about them. That is the conviction of the majority of those who care to read the Bible: a conviction supported by much research, by the power of faith, and by the survival and spread of the Church. It receives support from the lay historian.

The story is meant to interest the layman as it stands. Notes and bibliography will suggest the relation to sources which to the specialist have an interest of their own: but my aim is to follow the design of one of those sacred Hebrew historians who preceded St. Paul.

"To stand upon every point," he said, "and go over things at large, and to be curious in particulars, belongeth to the first author of the story:

"But to use brevity, and avoid much labouring of the work, is to be granted to him that will make an abridgement.

"Here then will we begin the story: only adding thus much to that which hath been said, that it is a foolish thing to make a long prologue, and to be short in the story itself."[1]

[1] II Maccabees ii. 30-32.

CONTENTS

LIST OF ILLUSTRATIONS

PROEM

IN THE SUNSHINE, THE COLOUR, THE VERDURE AND THE CONtours which make the Mediterranean shores a palace of light, there lived from two to three thousand years ago a company of imperishable genius.

Built in stone, in brick, in marble, their monuments, bridges, arches, baths, courts and temples combined elegance with grandeur. Their poets left masterpieces telling of adventure, passion, rivalry, triumph and doom: their philosophers peered into the secrets of thought and of idealism: their sculptors lent to marble the lines and proportions of the naked body: their historians and poets wrote of brave men and high events in apt, sounding and pregnant words: their orators argued the rights of citizenship: their captains conquered empires: their rulers governed by wise laws. Yet—among all their men of genius, none has affected such a number of men, none has been so closely scrutinised from century to century by the scholar, none has been recognised as so intimate, so moving, so august as a Cilician Jew who came among their triumphs with other thoughts, and was often jailed by their police.

Why do his words echo more insistently than theirs? Why does he leave a more vivid impression? The truth is that his personal adventures were more dramatic, his inner experiences both deeper and more distinct: and, as for his ideas, they proved to have such a power over culture, over good men, and even over the masses of the people, that they were able finally to dissolve the Roman ways of thought and take their place.

Nor was this all. This man's life was finely staged. Before he was slain by the sword outside the walls of Rome, he had passed through scene on scene which rivals her majesty. Rome to us is the exordium to the blue gulfs, the white mountains and the lambent marbles of Hellas. Among them he travelled.

He knew the eternal summer of the Isles of Greece. He heard the memorable names. But, a Cilician, he spent most of his years in the Levant. He knew in Syria the snows of Hermon, the gorges of the Lebanon, the dryness of the desert, the anemone scarlet in the spring, the groves of palms, the patronising calm of camels. The central city of his interests was the walled city none forgets, the city on a hill, whose name means peace—Jerusalem. Through these gilded scenes, ringing with evocative names and fanned with living airs, he passed from danger to danger. Yet none of his adventures is so absorbing as the story of his heart, and in self-revelation none approached him. For he was constrained and urged by a great love; he was absorbed in the sense of living in a presence that disturbed him with the joy of elevated thoughts; his trials and perils worked in him, as he himself wrote, from extreme to extreme, a solid weight of glory.

To estimate his greatness, the assessment of the judge is out of place. His power is over those who understand him: their feeling is the veneration of a worshipper, the gratitude of men overcome by their sense of blessing.

The vividness of his personality he set down with a directness all his own; which could become, when his excitement soared, fine art. Among the most eminent of his age, his spirit rises lofty as the cypress above olive and almond in a garden of the Rome which was his final dwelling place, imperial as Rome over the provinces she subdued. Yet he insisted that the mystery of his power was not his own. He lived obscurely; habitually, he earned his living by the craft of his hands; and when he spoke to his followers, spoke not as having dominion over their faith but as a sharer in their joy.

NOTE.—The names of places are in the form in use to-day: the names of people in the classic forms except in the figures so great and so familiar that we know them as our own.
[The two following chapters sketch first the Roman Empire in the time of Augustus, and then the position and life of the Jews at that time. A reader interested only in the personal narrative need not brook the delay; he can pass direct to Chapter III. But for those seeking a fuller understanding, the two backgrounds are given here rather than later.]

IN THE GRECO-ROMAN WORLD

1

A JEWISH BOY GROWING UP IN ANY COUNTRY OF THE MODERN world is hardly more aware of the religion and pride of his race than of the world-power to which he is subject. A young Israelite in the time of Augustus could not ignore the Greco-Roman civilisation. While the Jews as a whole brought their contribution into the Empire, they accepted its civilisation. Since we are considering a Jew who was a Roman citizen and a traveller, we must have some idea of the imperial consummation as a whole.

Julius Caesar had inaugurated for Rome a new epoch. "The stake for which he played was nothing less than the mastery of the world."[1] His eye not only pierced the murk of the North: but after defeating at Pharsala Pompey, who had conquered Jerusalem in B.C.63, he made terms with the Jewish princes.

At his death, Mark Antony, having secured his papers and his funds, had joined Lepidus and Augustus and divided the Empire with them. He then came to Ephesus in Asia Minor as a luxurious, genial and splendid governor. He summoned to meet him the enchanting queen, half Macedonian, half Greek (with a touch of the Iranian), who was reigning in Egypt as Cleopatra VII. Their meeting-place was Tarsus, the capital of Cilicia. It shared with Athens and Alexandria the attractions of a Hellenistic university: it was a centre of trade with the East through Damascus and Palmyra, as well as with the ports of the Levant. It was built on the banks of a sparkling river. A line of peaks, the Taurus, sheltered it from the northern winds.

Subtle and sympathetic as a ruler, her charm glittering with the brilliance of her mind, Cleopatra employed every device of colour, perfu. e, music, picturesqueness to impress the tastes and genius of Antony; and Tarsus received favours from a pair it could not forget. Before Antony fell in B.C.31, he had organised the Levant.[2] He had treated with the Jewish king, Herod, and made him a tributary of the Roman power. This had an urgent importance for every Jew in Tarsus who, whether or not he had received Roman citizenship, was a subject of the Emperor.

2

And who was this Emperor? After the defeat and death of Antony, Augustus prepared the shining lands of the Mediterranean for the culmination of his reign. He aimed at founding an ideal constitution and died in the hope that his foundation would endure.[3] His birth was hailed as that of a Saviour inaugurating a new age. From Cologne to Dendera, from the damp farms of Cumberland to the palms and temples of the Tigris, his Empire enjoyed what Pliny was to call "the boundless majesty of the Roman peace".[4] After the struggles with barbarians, and the distress of civil war, men in their gratitude venerated the central power. Augustus inherited the worship which three hundred years before had been given to Alexander, to Jupiter Ammon, to Antiochus Epiphanes. Nor was this veneration without cause. The central principle of order emanating from Rome in edicts, rescripts, mandates and despatches, established justice, built roads, maintained communications by sea as well as by land,[5] administered colonies, promoted commerce, showed itself generous to subject peoples, and brought down the proud. It realised one aspect of the gilded hope which

Virgil in the year B.C.40 hymned to the names of Pollio and Apollo. From the Mediterranean, under the pressure of Roman flotillas, pirates vanished. To quote Velleius, an officer of the time, "agriculture returned to the fields, respect to religion, to mankind security of possession, old laws were carefully amended, new laws enacted for the general good".[6]

Yet though the base of business was then as always the farm or the workshop, merchants, and some speculators, made fortunes; for Jewish aptitudes now found their opportunity.

The variety of the Empire was amalgamated into one. "The savours," said Pliny, "mingle together".[7] The peculiar Roman character was conquered by its own triumph. The goddesses of Egypt, and the indulgences of the Levant, combined with the spiritual philosophy of Greece[8] to give new qualities to the Roman, the Greek and the Jew. Yet, while some cultivated ideals, many indulged vices.

3

The Romans followed the Greeks in fostering social standards when local patriotism vaunted the claims of Tarsus as of each particular city. The young Jew could see how, throughout the whole Empire, municipal life could develop freely, and every city was encouraged to maintain a standard of cleanliness, of sanitation and of town planning. He saw that the streets were built straight and wide; like those of the highroads their surfaces were paved: conduits and pipes brought fresh water to the houses, drains carried the swill away.[9]

At Tarsus, as in other towns, he could see markets, town halls, basilicas and temples: hotels and inns; and often in the more important ones, public baths with central heating and a promenade; libraries, circuses, theatres and amphitheatres, all built of stone; and besides these, big monuments and imposing arches.[10] The sun of civilization was rising through clear air to its meridian. On the Palatine hill Apollo was enthroned.

Even in Tarsus the world-wide state was already consisting of a number of urban districts, each of which had for its centre an equally well-organized town or city, but all looked towards Rome for those who directed the social and economic life of the Empire.

4

The mere title of Roman citizen itself counted for much: and without it no one could aspire to positions of honour. It gave the right to a boy to enter the special schools and colleges and receive his training in athletics, philosophy, music and the arts of speaking.[11] As soon as he entered this world of culture, with its philosophy, its arts, its games, the young Roman citizen fell under the influence of Hellas: the great achievement of the Caesars followed the example given them a hundred years before by Alexander.

5

For Alexander, who was the pupil of Aristotle—as Aristotle had been the pupil of Plato—had fostered the idea of an elastic personal freedom of the citizen fitting into a concept of a far-reaching Empire.[12] He had regarded himself as one sent to harmonise and settle the whole world, bringing to all men peace, concord and community. He had endowed the Greeks with breadth of mind and toleration. His name and legend evoke admiration still in every corner of the Levant.

Nurtured in the sense of the unity of the world, and of an ideal truth and beauty within and beyond it, the cultured Hellenes had learnt "the great Asian mystery", as Disraeli called it, and explored the reach of intuition; their philosophy was moral, metaphysical and universal.

The cult of excellence and the ideal transcended the limitations of religion, family, class and nation: it needed neither images nor temples.[13] It looked to the reconciliation of mankind. And so its universalism enthroned the individual. By its contact with the East, and its sense of the unseen power of soul and ideal, philosophy became first metaphysical, and then mystical. For it knew already that the things which are not seen are eternal.

When the Greeks were conquered by the Romans, they taught their victors idealism. Cicero writing now about duty, now about the nature of the divine beings, had set out Greek thought in Roman terms.

With art and philosophy came the sense that law was in itself, as Plato had taught, the expression of the eternal truth of justice and order.[14] And a Roman citizen who was a Jew would add these ideas to his own Jewish law.

6

A well-educated citizen of Rome learnt therefore that the alliance of law and order depended on the law's own foundation on reason, and therefore on that prudence which was the cardinal virtue of reason.[15] For the Greek philosophers taught that as reason, illumined by intuition, should guide and control all the human faculties, so law should control the life of the city. Its citizens in turn were trained to these ideals by exercise, assisted by rhythm. For even in music, reason must still be lord

7

and master, and men, in aiming at the ideal, must attune themselves to the eternal laws, the eternal order by which they live.[16]

While, therefore, the young man in the Greco-Roman world was learning of culture and philosophy, he met in Tarsus, as in every city, a series of festivals, of sport and music. Aristides, writing in the second century, compared these celebrations to the sacred fire which must never be allowed to burn out.[17] Rome encouraged the passion for sport; it was firstly innocuous; but shrewd administrators soon saw that the vent for vitality was associated with the honour given to the gods, and above all with the majesty of the Emperor.

But if, on one side, the lure of the ideal encouraged culture and effort, there was a crude physical side to life as well in the world of sport; the clear streams of rhythmical order met the muddier one of pleasure in sport which, meant to make a young man's life both virile and delightful, was not altogether divorced from animal pride; then as now, it was a cult in itself.[18]

7

Yet we must not imagine the Greco-Roman world as a Paradise. It had no conception of a God who loved it; while the nobler kind might aspire to ideals and virtues, there was only doom for the sinner. And though a slave might have a kind master, life was generally hard for him. Both cruelty and uncleanness disfigured society; magic arts were practised, and men had fantastic ideas of worship. Some sought to be initiated into elaborate rites or "mysteries" connected with the names of Isis, Serapis, or Mithra, by which they could escape from sin and death: some worshipped grotesque idols: veneration was sought, not merely for Augustus but for his three powerful but profligate successors, those whom Fisher calls "a madman, a pedant and a monster".[19] Ideals were one thing; custom was another. Carousals, debauches, riots, quarrels were apt to arise even at the temple and the shrine—the Levant wandered far from ideals.

8

Nevertheless, the Hellenistic culture of the time gleamed with subtle and intriguing views. Five hundred years before it had reached its culmination after the age of Pericles. Sublime speculation—as to what was meant by being and reality; what was the origin, what the essence of goodness, truth and beauty; whether the soul was immortal, whether it would reincarnate; and what was the best theory of politics and society—had been both enriched by lofty speculation and subjected to analytical criticism by two immortal lecturers — Plato, and his pupil, Aristotle. These studies were — even after the changes and modifications of four centuries — what the Greeks called the philosophy or wisdom which made the highest life of the mind.

"Wherever literature consoles sorrow or assuages pain," wrote Macaulay; "wherever it brings gladness to eyes which fail with wakefulness and tears, and ache for the dark house and the long sleep: there is exhibited in its noblest form the immortal genius of Athens. . . . ."

"No material advantage", he continued, "is to be compared with that purification of the intellectual eye which gives us to contemplate the infinite wealth of the mental world, all the hoarded treasures of its primeval dynasties, all the shapeless ore of its yet unexplored mines. This is the gift of Athens to man."[20]

9

What was the Hellenic idea of the time of Augustus? It was, if one may put it shortly, to be a gentleman. It was to live according to standards: to run to no extremes: to have endurance, taste, and judgment: to keep the laws, and play the man. The balance and harmony in each man's character should ennoble social life. But how could he attain to this unless the gods were with him? A man must above all bow to the mysterious Governance which so quickly brought humiliation to the man who believed himself all powerful. Sophocles, especially in the "Ajax", had driven home the lesson that man should recognize that he was but man, and show reverence to the Gods.[21]

Nevertheless the picture of Hellas is singularly attractive: in its way it is what we have come to know as singularly English. And it had within it many metaphysical subtleties,[22] which, when they met that curious and ubiquitous people, the Jews, persuaded them to seek for philosophy and reasonableness in their own religion.

10

So much for the Hellenistic culture in which a Roman citizen was trained: but a shrewd Jew would soon see that the Roman rule had a firm grip of common clay. Like the Americans, or the English, the Roman had practical success in view: like them he cherished justice, had a sense that the eternal powers were behind him, and he compromised with superstition. Merchandise could prosper, amenities increase, civilisation rise on wings of culture. Yet however beneficent and progressive, the Empire stood upon its army: it was the officer who had the glamour

and the power. As in Hohenzollern Prussia, the soldier's bearing marked his preeminence; as he moved, he gleamed and
glinted with the flashing insignia of prestige. When all was
said, the Emperor ruled because the army was behind him. To
put it crudely, each Caesar was the head of a military tyranny.[23]

The result of this was dramatic. The Emperors were fascinated by the opportunities of their authority, but fearful of
losing them. And seizing their pleasures while they could, they
plucked poisonous berries in the byways of depravity. But
oppressed with fear, they engaged in intrigue, and intrigue led
on to crime. And by a curious irony, at the same time as they
fell below the standards of their slaves, they allowed themselves to be proclaimed superhuman and divine.[24] But to the
Empire as a whole, worship of the Emperor was a convenience.
"He was a god so long as he governed the state and because
he governed the state."[25] One reason why divine honour was
claimed for him was that it invested with prestige the authority
of his officials and his officers.

The rule of Imperial Rome was sound, just, beneficent: its
cult and culture were not without nobility, but its worship
implied neither moral effort nor mystical communion: it was
an act of homage to the infinite convenience of an established
order, and it, too, was far from that solidity of trust, that veneration of the one personal fount of mercy, that plainness of
command and obedience both for conduct and for custom which
was cherished by the Jews.

THE HELLENISED JEW

1

HOW, IN THE TIME OF JULIUS CAESAR, DID THE ROMANS VIEW the Jews who in former centuries had not gone much further from Syria than Babylon on the one side and Egypt on the other, but were now spreading along the shores of the Levant to Greece and to Italy, Cyprus, Cyrene, Asia Minor, Macedonia? All came to know this race as having a patriotism that thought not of soils and empire, but of a religion, a custom and a law which enabled business men to recognise every scattered pedlar and trader as a brother. These people lived apart: they saved money to be benevolent to their own people and gave nothing to the rest: though their temperaments were passionate, they mixed with no women but their own. They had not only their own quarters but their own courts. They were despised; they were outcasts.[1] Yet somehow they were at home: for among themselves they had the social gift, hospitality, gaiety, and kindliness. The Levant still knows these little communities—not always only Jewish—where, linked together by a common history, common customs, and a common danger, people repeat their gossip and work out their intrigues.[2]

Joined by both their racial passion and their oriental subtlety, the Jews yet remained a puzzle. They seemed like a secret society, a freemasonry working for each other at the expense of outsiders.[3] The food they ate, or the food they refused to eat, their insistence on observing their sabbath and their feasts, the suggestions of smelliness[4] and even dirt, which others noticed in them, their pale complexion, their unmistakable lines of nose and eyes and lips, all combined to make them repugnant to the cultured Roman.[5] Men felt that a people so singular must be sinister, must be the enemies both of mankind and of the Gods.[6]

2

And yet a power, even a dignity, remained. Men noticed a certain standard, a certain elevation. Jews could attract interest or pity, especially from women.[7] Jews could make converts to their religion of trust in the one, true, merciful God they persistently worshipped.[8] Men noticed their fraternal link with one another, their charity, their application, their honesty. Living among the poor and enslaved, they had the pride of princes. In the centre of the whirlwind, their confidence gave them calm: in a polluted world they felt themselves to be superior and pure.[9] Warm feelings, honesty and family affection gave to their lives the flavour and a perfume of a garden of herbs; a patriarchal system, an oriental temper and a sublime tradition—robed them in dignity as the gabbah does the Bedouin sheikh to-day.[10]

3

At the time of Augustus, there were a million of these among the eight millions of Egypt.[11] There were other large bodies of them in Asia Minor, especially at Antioch on the Orontes.[12] But they spread to Arabia, to Africa, to the Crimea, all through Asia Minor, all through Greece, in Cyprus, in Crete; and of course to Rome, the city of central opportunities. "The Jews have found their way into every state," said Strabo, "in the whole world it is not easy to find a single place which has not received this race and found it indomitable."[13] They were estimated at a twelfth of the Roman Empire.[14] Julius Caesar, following Alexander, had seen the prudence of conciliating them. By four successive edicts, he assured them not only their entire independence but other privileges as well.[15] Their laws and customs were recognised: they were permitted to hold assemblies and collect taxes either for local synagogues or for the temple at Jerusalem. They obtained recognition of their sabbath and other sacred seasons. They were even allowed a sabbatical year when they were exempted from taxes. Cicero in his speech for Flaccus said that it required courage to run counter to them, and even judged it discreet to drop the voice before referring to their influence.[16] The privileges granted by Caesar were confirmed by Augustus.[17] Everywhere the Roman Governors treated Israelites with consideration.[18] If it were ever otherwise, if any town denied their prerogatives, or anyone attempted to meddle with their property, the whole Roman Empire would echo to complaints of persecution.[19] They got into their hands the business of the small tradesman: then, quietly and by degrees, they would attain power over the bigger interests.[20] Then their aid would even be required by the Roman administrators in the collection of the taxes: in the region of the Euphrates they had been employed even as ambassadors.

4

Yet their success generally made them unpopular with the common people: in Egypt the oracles of Ammon Ra had denounced them as a curse.

5

Such was the strange drama of their lives: theirs was a lofty religion, believing in one God: worshipping Him in holiness: trusting in Him as the Master of graciousness and pardon: keeping not only His ten commandments, but all those ritual enactments, customs and directions they reverenced as His Law.[21] They had in a word all the qualities they still retain: they added to them the superiority of having the finest and loftiest belief in a Lord whose law was inviolable, and whose power was in His loving-kindness: "Blessed", they repeated, "is the man that trusteth in Him."[22] So everywhere a young Jew learnt that he was one apart.

6

What was the history of his people? He found it set down in a Literature ennobled with a clearer and clearer sense of the goodness of God. It began with a phrase of overwhelming and sublime significance: *In the beginning God created the heaven and the earth.* In epic phrases it traced the story of the ages, of man's original disobedience, of Abraham's place as Patriarch, and the promise that in his seed shall all nations of the earth be blest.[23]

The figures of remarkable Judges, prophets, and kings emerged. Eminent among these was one who had borne the name of Shaul, whose successor David, or Davood, was both king and poet, and whose son in turn—he is still revered from Malaya to Morocco as Suleiman—was the wisest of the Kings of the East.

Later disaster had fallen on the Jews. They had been carried away captive into Babylonia: and from that time we trace their dispersion. When only the fraction had chosen to return, the rest had scattered over lands that became the Roman Empire, cherishing always the conviction that they were a unique race. The next to dominate that region were Seleucus and his house reigning at Antioch on the Orontes. But when the Seleucid King, Antiochus IV, ordered the profanation of the temple, the Jews rose in revolt, under the leadership of the Maccabees. In B.C.63 as we saw, Pompey conquered Jerusalem, and when Caesar defeated Pompey at Pharsala, in B.C.48, the government was obtained by the able ruler of Idumæa, Herod the Great, the head of the Hasmonean house, who treated with Mark Antony.[24]

Thus then, in the time of Augustus, did a young Jew learn of his people; he was one of a race scattered over the Empire but with a sacred capital in Jerusalem: he had a strong and lofty religion which bound him to the keeping of their tradition; and this in turn meant the study of their sacred books; for their code was interwoven with history, with sacred poetry, and with the work of the prophets—and all were venerated together under the name of TORAH — the TORAH of JAHWEH (or Jehovah) the unnamable Lord.

7

The Torah was in the first case the law of Moses, reinforced by Ezra the Scribe,[25] who taught in Israel statutes and judgments leading to a devotion without qualification or reserve, a wholehearted allegiance to the will of God.[26]

But what in the course of ages had that come to mean? All the Jews must uphold the Torah, but, since the Jews had had to accommodate themselves to the House of Seleucus, reigning at Antioch, the party most closely associated with the government, that is to say, the priestly families who had become the nobility, did not want their devotion to the Torah to interfere with their political work for the Hasmonean house. They preferred, therefore, to keep to the letter of the Torah, as Ezra had established it.

Such compromise, however, was by no means enough for the more zealous Jews, who wanted to keep the Torah apart from all worldly considerations. In every act of life they insisted that it was a sacred guide. Now cases were always arising where the written code required an interpretation in order to be applied. In such cases the priests and learned men, the Rabbis, gave their interpretation, and claimed authority for it: this attached to the Torah a sacred tradition, the Halacha.[27]

Above the general run of the Jews, the people of the land— the Am-ha-aretz—was therefore a stricter order of life, an order set apart, the Parushim, an order of laymen, who held themselves apart and insisted on their power to understand, interpret and apply the Torah to every act of life.

They differed on the one side from the Am-ha-aretz, and on the other from the upper class of priests and princes who, finding their model in Zadok, the court priest, suited their religion to the demands of power. Such is the difference between the Sadducees, the devotees of Zadok, and the Parushim— whom the English know as the Pharisees. These were always studying and applying the Torah by means of their living oral tradition, the Halacha; they surrounded it with a body of legend and allegory known as the Haggadah. But their passion was for the Torah as a way of life and of holiness. How strict then was the life of the young Parush!

8

"The Torah of Jahweh is perfect, restoring the soul"[28]: "Blessed are they that are undeviating in the way, who walk in the Torah of Jahweh."[29] This Torah means teaching: it did not mean mere Law.[30]

It meant: "all that God has made known of His character, nature and purpose and of what He would have men be and do."[31] And since this was so, Torah and Halacha, law and tradition, were to the Parushim one. Those who practised it lived apart, a stricter and more conscious life of piety: "Among them, the rabbi and the father of the family tended more and more to supplant the Levite and the priest."[32]

Finally, in the application of the Law to daily life, the Parushim were supreme, and, for an Israelite desirous of devoutly fulfilling his duties, indispensable. Women especially, as Josephus noted, looked upon them as their oracle.

The Parushim represented, from the time of the Maccabees to the fall of Jerusalem, the kernel of Israel.[33]

9

Thus to be a Hebrew and a Parush meant to live in a daily interpretation and application of the Torah, as the greatest privilege and blessing which the unnamable Lord of Mercy had ever given to men, every separate injunction being duty and privilege in one. The fulfilment of the divine precepts was also to lead to earthly welfare and prosperity.[34]

Prominent in the Torah was the sacrifice of animals in the temple at Jerusalem. But the idea of sacrifice was not the only one found in the Jewish religion. For sacrifice could be overdone.[35] It could fail by being either crude or perfunctory. It was not for *God* merely to eat the flesh of bulls, or drink the blood of goats. And so the Israelite could read in one place:

"In sacrifice, and in offering of meat Thou takest no pleasure,

Burnt-offering and sin-offering Thou hast not demanded.
I come to do Thy will."[36]

For to this great worshipper intense prayer had been enough.
And in another place he could read:

"Thou hast no delight in sacrifice, else would I give it
  Thee,
Thou hast no pleasure in burnt-offering:
The sacrifices of God are a troubled spirit,
A broken and a contrite heart, O God, Thou wilt not
  despise."[37]

Before the supreme and awful quality of the most High,
men must bow: "For thus saith the high and lofty one that
inhabiteth eternity, whose name is Holy: I dwell in the high
and lofty place with him also that is of a contrite and humble
spirit."[38]

10

Thus though the zealous Israelite fitted himself to success in
the world, yet before his Maker he must bow to adore and
praise Him whose hands made the skies a tent for the sun, and
who had ordained the moon and the stars that night should
teach knowledge to night, and who yet had made for man's
soul a perfect rule, and enlightened his eyes with a pure commandment. All through the great anthology of Israel was the
idea of a personal God in whom Israel might trust[39] and who
said: "I have loved thee with an everlasting love and with
loving-kindness have I drawn thee."[40]
For here was not, as to Sophocles or Aeschylus, the grim
thought of inexorable fate, only to be endured. All the calam-

ities of man could not cut him off from the solicitude of the All Merciful. "Though he slay me, yet will I trust him."[4]

1 1

If a young Jew went to Jerusalem, he heard, morning by morning, on the steps of the Hebrew temple, the robed Levite raise his voice to pronounce the ancient blessing: "The Lord bless thee and keep thee, the Lord make his face to shine upon thee and be gracious to thee, the Lord lift up the light of his countenance and give thee peace."[42] The idea of a blessing spreading like the light of sunrise mingled with a hope that on a great day the Lord would come to establish his reign of happiness and good in a city where "the streets of the city would be full of boys and girls playing",[43] where the vine should give grapes, and the earth her increase, where the gates would be open continually.[44]

Nowhere in Hellenic classics, from the flashing heroes and fair women, the wine-dark seas and the bold exploits of the Odyssey to the weight of pathos in Euripides or doom in Aeschylus, or in the exact and soaring thought of Plato and his followers, is there a style so powerful, a conception so exalted, a moral law so pure, a trust so solid in God and His goodness to men, a hope so constant in His blessings and mercies, as those treasured by the tribes of Israel:[45] nor were they to be found in what the greatest of Romans had been writing: nor even if one went over the Himalayas to the Ganges would one have found in the Bhagavad-Gita, or the Vedas, a voice so intimate, a law so spiritual, a vindication at once so august and so personal of the character and fate of men.

If there was drama and travail in their life, it was but the absorbing story of a call to holiness, and the earnest of an

(*Kersting*)

JERUSALEM——LOOKING TOWARD THE MOUNT OF OLIVES
(*From the old walls; the so-called Tomb of Absalom is on the right*)

nheritance of glory: here then would be goodness for the poor,
freedom for those chained in prison: God Himself, with the
ender sympathy of a healer, would bind up the broken-
hearted:[46] He would rise like a sun of righteousness, with
healing in His wings.[47]

The story had been long, and had passed through many
phases of human passion and merely human interest; but to the
Israelite of the time of Augustus, the jewels could be taken at
will.

12

By that time, however, a young Jew in the Greco-Roman
world would learn how the very Torah itself had undergone
a subtle change. The Jews, always elastic and adaptable, had
suited their mentality to the Hellenistic world in which they
lived,[48] and its Platonistic philosophy: their veneration of the
Torah was associated with those qualities of which they read in
the works of the wise king: wisdom and understanding.

What was their attitude to these non-Jews, whom they called
the Goyim, or in Greek, the nations? Were they to be regarded
as men benighted and corrupt, spreading a dangerous infection,
or were they by gracious and accommodating views to be won
towards the Torah? The inclination of the Jews naturally was
to take a favourable view of any that gave them opportunities.
On this ground, they were less favourable to the Romans than
they had been to the Egyptians or Ethiopians. But naturally
the families who had been given Roman citizenship or other
considerations found much good in the ways of Rome.

13

Besides, these Israelites desired to gain adherents: they

21

wanted to Judaize those whom they taught to venerate their Torah. They recognised those who followed it as good men; they called them "the God-fearing".[49] But they could go a step further: they could actually receive them into the promises and covenant of Israel by applying the act of initiation which was performed on their own flesh: Jews were marked with their sacred character by the definite rite of circumcision performed on all their males. This act, with its sacrifice of pain and blood, with its mark lasting, intimate, peculiar, was the sacred, the crucial, the significant test.[50]

The divine origin they claimed for circumcision, its association with the act by which the race was renewed, its intimacy, its particularity as the sign and act of initiation among the elect combined to fix their insistence that it was the touchstone of rightness both among the Jews and before the Lord.[51] Those who lacked it were beyond the pale, in outer darkness.

The Greeks and Romans found this rite as distasteful as they found the Jews. To them it was a disfigurement: they held it in derision.[52] They were just as anxious not to be among the circumcised as the Jews were to cherish their initiation, and to eat their banquets alone.[53]

14

On the one side, then, for the young Jew, exclusiveness, on the other, if not compromise, at least elasticity. It developed an aptitude for discussion and explanation of the Law. "The Israelites of the Dispersion struck just the right balance, for they discarded the hard literalness of the letter, they were modest with regard to their own wisdom, they were ready to hold arguments, to listen to the opinion of others, and to consider every question that might be raised."[54] Their religion was modified, but at the same time they felt more than ever that it was worth spreading.

Their Scriptures were translated into Greek, in the form known as the Septuagint. It received this name because according to the current legend, Ptolemy Philadelphus desired to have a translation, and seventy-two scholars, retiring to the island of Pharos close to Alexandria, made the translation in seventy-two days. This form of Hebrew literature was charged with a different atmosphere, just as the English Bible has its English atmosphere. And even for those who spoke Hebrew there was an equivalent change, for the ancient Scriptures were translated contemporarily to the Aramaic: this translation, the Targum, was a Jewish parallel to the Septuagint. New books were also written, and came to be accounted sacred by the Jews.

15

A distinct Hellenist influence can be traced above all in the new love of the quality of wisdom, an almost personal quality,[55] appreciated by the Jews as far back as 300 B.C.

A new genius summed up, in the "Wisdom of Solomon", the essence of this religion as the gift which God had given in irradiating the secrets of His own mind; the study of the Law went hand in hand with the cultivation of wisdom. A power pointed man upwards to something in him which was infinitely more august than himself:

> "Wisdom that is the artificer of all things taught me.
> For there is in her a spirit, quick of understanding, holy,
> Alone in kind, manifold,
> Subtle, freely moving,
> Clear in utterance,
> Unrestrained, distinct, unharmed,

Loving what is good, keen, unhindered, beneficent,
Loving towards man, steadfast, sure, free from care,
All powerful, all surveying,
And penetrating through all spirits that are quick of
understanding, pure and most subtle."[56]

Above all, at Alexandria, the Hebrews had learned the meta-physical subtlety of wisdom, and Philo, the ablest of them all, spoke not only of that but of a Word which came forth from God as the thought and expression of His Mind.[57]

As he did so, he taught that the highest quality of man was that breath of life which came from the in-breathing, the inspiration of God. A new conception was added to Greek thought. The breath, the spirit was the highest faculty of man, rising far above that principle of natural life, the psyche—the life which was in the blood.

At a centre of culture like Tarsus, a young Jew inevitably became aware of the steps already taken in this sense at Alexandria.

16

He saw how everywhere the mind and religion of Israel had become less tribal and personal. "The Bible in which God is called Jahweh is the Bible of a race," wrote Deissmann, "the Bible in which God is called the Lord is the Bible for the world".[58] If this is true of the word Jahweh, it is not less true for the word Torah. When Torah became translated into the word which represented to the thinking mind not only the majesty of Roman law, but the ideal principle of order and justice, it suggested no longer a merely Jewish code, but the moral order which was one with the Spirit and Wisdom of the

Universe. The words "Blessed are they that are undeviating in the way who walk in the Torah of Jahweh"[59] implied that all that mattered was to be a good Jew. But when a man read the words: "Blessed are they who are undefiled in the way who walk in the Law of the Lord", they thought of a moral standard for the whole world.

Since they could not change the sacred formularies they looked on as eternal, their method was to read into them by explanation, by comment, by allegorical interpretations the meaning they required.

17

Not least was this true of their expectation of him for whom they hoped, their Machiah, their Anointed One, or as the Septuagint called him, the CHRISTOS, who was to lead to final glory the Israel of God. A liberator, he was to save and preserve his people by the power of the ineffable I AM.

In the Book of Samuel, it was written

"The Lord shall give strength unto his King,
And exalt the horn of his Christos."[60]

The Seventeenth Psalm of the Septuagint hailed the triumph of the Christos. He was to be the Judge, the Ruler and the Conqueror. This prince of promise appeared both in the Psalms and in Isaiah as the Son of David[61], endowed with the spirit of wisdom and counsel.[62] Yet as time went on, he appeared as a selfless hero sacrificing himself to expiate the sins of his people, and save them from the avenging justice, ready to offer in their stead his body and his life.[63]

The Second Psalm spoke of the Christos meeting the crafty opposition of kings: "The Lord said unto me, Thou art my

Son . . . and I will give Thee the uttermost parts of the earth for Thy possession". In Daniel, the Son was the Son of Man, triumphant: "I saw in the night visions and beheld one like unto a Son of Man came with the clouds of heaven and came to the Ancient of Days, and they brought him near before him, and there was given him dominion and glory and a kingdom that all peoples, nations and languages should serve him. His dominion is an everlasting dominion and his Kingdom that which shall not be destroyed".[64]

What form the Christos should take, the Rabbis could not decide. But, as a recent authority attests, "it is no exaggeration to say that in the reign of Augustus, speculations as to the date and duration of the Messianic reign, the coming of the Messiah, the day of Jahweh, the Resurrection, and the last Judgment were central in Jewish thought and occupied the chief place among the politico-religious questions which engrossed the inhabitants of Palestine".[65] It was natural for a Jew to expect that the Christos would make them paramount in the Roman Empire.[66]

Everywhere, as in Europe in the Elizabethan time, the air was alive with expectancy; Virgil's prophecy of Apollo returning to reign over a bland earth in a golden age, restored in leisure and blessing, mingled with the Jews' conviction that a great power was about to appear among them. Prophets, enthusiasts, agitators arose. Each of these claimed to be the Anointed, the Messiah, the Christos.[67]

18

Into this dawn and expectation, into this new epoch, into this interplay of East with West, with the majesty of the Roman peace, with the honour of Roman citizenship, with the inheritance of a fine Hellenic training for the body and the mind, was born the Jewish child who was to develop with outstanding character and genius his acceptance not only of the sacred heritage of Israel, but, in that, of a mystery hidden from the foundation of the world.

YOUTH SEEKING HOLINESS

1

AS A YOUNG CHILD WAKES TO CONSCIOUSNESS, HE LEARNS HOW to use every weapon of the social joust. The young Israelite in Tarsus soon learnt what it was both to be a Roman citizen and to be a Jew. He was proud of Tarsus, proud therefore of its history, proud of its university, proud of its trade, proud of its views. It had been founded by a great Assyrian: it was granted privileges by Pompey the Great; it had received still more from Antony and Cleopatra[1]; it was a centre for elegant youth learning rhetoric in its schools, learning through the thrust of question and answer in the "diatribe",[2] learning the tradition of the gentleman not only in the training of words, but in musical competitions, races and sports. In all these things a youth of the more honourable classes would absorb the atmosphere, just as a quite orthodox young Jew in the English nobility seeks at Eton the triumphs of an Etonian. All these things were his *métier*: he grew up to enjoy his privileges as naturally as he saw a servant class—the slaves—appointed to look after him, give him his early training, and, as time went on, take him to school.

But as he did all these things among other boys born to enjoy the prestige of citizenship in the Empire, he learnt from a devoted father how he was marked with more sacred privileges; he belonged to the sacred race; he inherited the traditions of the Jews who had been settled in Tarsus for nearly two hundred years; he was brought up to the zeal not merely of the Jews but of the Rabbis and their Parushim. He knew that far above all else in importance were his law, his religion and his God.

2

Tarsus then—he called it Tersous—on the one side showed him what the world was: "loaded with favours by Rome, free and exempt from taxes since the time of Pompey the Great, and the metropolis of Cilicia since the reign of Augustus, it was a chief emporium of the Levant":[3] to it came therefore caravans of camels and donkeys laden with stuff they had brought over the desert to Damascus from Babylon, Baghdad and Persia; at its wharves were moored white-sailed ships from the Mediterranean: to the North, as giants to sentinel the land, marched the host of Taurus peaks; through their rough gorges and jagged heights, a pass, known as the Cilician Gates, led the traffic of merchantmen, after the snows had melted, into the rough interior of Asia Minor. Around the city, a fruitful plain, intersected by ditches and canals, grew produce for the market-place. Through the blue air above, pearly wings marked in spring and autumn the migrations of battalions of storks: and as it drew towards evening, the sky assumed a golden blush and the clouds, scarlet like the anemone, flashed flame.

It was a scene to fill an imaginative boy with a sense of the wealth of life. In the spring, when the meadows burst into flower, the scent of jasmine and orange blossom added the charm of perfume, while in the evening, the harp, and the cadences of the voice taught his spirit to vibrate; the sense that life was good, that the world was made in wisdom, that it pointed to a Creator of endless power and beneficence came to him both from his eye, and from early lessons in which literature and religion were one.

In such a town as this an able man of business found his opportunities, and it is easy to see why a Jew of enterprise should come there from the hill land of Galilee. The Jew who had prospered, however, was apt to ascribe his prosperity to the Lord who blessed him, and he found the secret of his success in his traditions. Fortune, therefore, instead of beguiling him from religion, strengthened him in piety; and living strictly as a Jew, he not only gave his son the name of his tribe's famous king, Shaul; but he was well content that his resources should enable the boy to grow up as a Rabbi, a master of the Jewish law, who could as such be advocate, counsellor, magistrate, lecturer or man of letters.[4]

It was the Jews' rule, furthermore, that every boy should learn a craft. The craft chosen for this boy was that of a weaver of goat's hair, and in fact a maker of tents, such as were in demand by the traffickers who brought and led their camels afar. From his earliest years this boy knew, with the clatter of the loom, the art of being creative: his work also gave him an interest in travel, and all it taught. His world swarmed with variety, and he had, to a phenomenal degree, the sensitiveness of perception, the adroitness of mind, and the elasticity which enables a boy to develop in many directions. This boy tasted early of the fruit of romance, but he was more interested in things of the town than of the country, and fully aware of the world and its distinctions: one of those who knows best the milieu in which he lived suggests that to his Jewish name, Shaul, he, as a Roman citizen, had added from childhood a Roman name, such as Gaius Julius Paulus.[5] What came to him from the Hellenic world was simply the effect of his environment on a highly-strung, vigorous, impressionable, daring and brilliant boy: his training was that of an Israelite: his loyalties to the Parushim; his belief and canon those which took him back to Abraham, to Isaac and to Jacob.

From the beginning, he had been aware also of the buffoonery, and the scurrilousness of the general youth, who turned from philosophy, or from the gentlemanly standards of the Stoics to sheer vulgarity or to the crude worship of Sandon, or to the elaborate, savage ritual by which the worshippers of Mithra sought courage and virility. A habit of silly and dirty talk which has survived among boys of all countries in all ages was certainly not wanting in Tarsus; [6] it mingled with the gentlemanly standards of the University of Athenodorus; it was apt to arise in the exercises of the stadium, where boys stripped naked to jump, to run, to box; and where the mark of circumcision reminded others that the young Jews had deliberately branded themselves apart from others. [7]

4

What was the boyhood of Shaul in Tarsus? Conscious to a certain extent of sex, he yet recoiled from its impurities; aware of pagan worship, he shrank in horror of its error and its blasphemy; breathing the atmosphere of what the Stoics still taught of Platonism, he made no direct study of it, feeling that the poetry of Israel knew of a Wisdom which was subtler, purer, and more personal.

Proudly recognising that the Roman power, whose might was indisputable, and which everywhere brought law and order, had set his family in a position of personal privilege, he enjoyed the additional sense that this supreme power respected his race and his religion; touched—as who could not be?—by the Hellenic culture around him and its ideals of taste and beauty, his deep trust was in that Lord who had made heaven

31

and earth, whose mercy was over all His works; vaunting the tradition and prestige of Tarsus and its culture, he turned with grateful awe to a Jewish Torah which, as the Law, was dearer to him than thousands of gold and silver, and which taught him to say, "The zeal of thy house has devoured me":[8] thus the young Shaul, of the tribe of Benjamin, a Parush, breathed the air of Cilicia—learning all it had in common on the one side with Athens and Rome, on the other with Syria, with Egypt and with the desert.

5

The tastes and excesses of culture and commerce made Tarsus already a rough model of what Lorenzo dei Medici was to see in Florence. But it was a town of the Orient and of the South. The air was suave, at times close. The sun shone brilliant from a sky filled with light and colour: the plain on which the sturdy boy rode on his donkey was green in summer, gold in the autumn with corn and maize; through it, from the glaciers and ravines of the Taurus, he saw the river Cydnus flowing down till just above the city it cascaded in speed and foam over rocks in a shallow waterfall; it then resumed its transparent flow to where the boats came into its quays from Tyre, from Alexandria and from Ephesus. Further down, it spread into a lake.

From this striking scene, the young Jew gathered memories of its Assyrian founder, Assur-bani-pal, of battles of Cyrus and his Hellenes with the Cilician Queen, of the Roman conquest, of the dalliance and prowess of Mark Antony. Among the scholars of Tarsus, one Athenodorus had been the tutor of Augustus,[9] and he was not the only man of learning to show that learning can bring wealth and honour. Where learning pays, not a few will study: and some of them will be Jews.[10]

But the hearts of Shaul and his family were in other things. While touched in a thousand ways by general impressions, from his earliest years he was drawn towards piety and the study of the Torah.

How did the boy learn this? Very early he was taken to the bare house of meeting, which the Jews in their own language called the Kenishta; in Greek the word for meeting was Synagoge. There the faithful came together, not to offer sacrifice, but to hear read from parchments in embroidered vellum the translation of the Law and all the other scriptures which were the masterpieces of their literature.[11] These recounted the dramatic story of their race, which told of its customs, its ideals, its mysteries, its hopes of the coming of an anointed chief, the Messiah, the Christos. There he was trained in a great literature, there he learnt of all the developments of his religion, from the Scriptures themselves, generally in the Septuagint, but sometimes was read one of those renderings in contemporary Hebrew which was called a Targum; he learnt the repetition of them—the Mishna. There he heard the traditional prayers, and sometimes a priest voicing his own thanksgiving, or his own plea for mercy.

Indeed this worship of the Kenishta, the Synagoge, though oriental, had resemblances to the Presbyterian or Wesleyan service of to-day: in the Scriptures, it had the background of traditional forms which affected its style and tone: it was a ministry of the word—bible worship with little ritual and no sacrifice.

Yet his Jewish Law, the Torah, was always telling him of the sacrifices it required; the sacrifice of animals was, as he soon learnt, an essential part of the ritual and worship of the central shrine of Israel, the temple at Jerusalem; the temple was built by Solomon, and rebuilt in the time of Cyrus, as Paul learnt from the sacred writer he knew in his Septuagint as Esdras.

He had a genius for words, and from his earliest days the poetry of the Septuagint was stamped on his memory. It is the key to his culture. In the Mishna, he learnt long passages by heart.[12] And with it he learnt its history, and its meaning; for was it not already being adapted by an elastic application and by allegory to meet the changing and growing needs of the human spirit, such as they were known to citizens living in a Hellenised world, under Augustus?[13]

6

How long he stayed in Tarsus, one cannot exactly say: one authority says till he was thirteen, another till he was fifteen, a third till he was twenty.[14] The time came in his youth, sooner or later, when it was fixed that he should leave Tarsus for Jerusalem. He went down the Syrian coast past Alexandretta, Latakia, Beyrout, Acre, seeing every evening the chain of Lebanon light up as the sun set over the sea, till, above Haifa, it was succeeded by the rounder mass of Mount Carmel, and finally at Caesarea he found himself at the port for Jerusalem.

When he had been travelling for some hours up gently rising land, he found above him the declivities steepening. It was up through rough and moutainous country that he passed into the traditional home not only of his race but of his own particular tribe; he was among names he already knew. After traversing a deep gorge, his caravan wound up long miles of hill till they were in sight of an eminence marked with the rose-coloured outlines of a city. This hill was Sion. This city was Jerusalem.

Earth offered him no greater privilege than to enter it: "The

Lord loveth the gates of Sion more than all the dwellings of Jacob".[15] That he had learnt long since. And already many other cherished verses came to his lips: "I was glad when they said unto me, we will go into the house of the Lord: our feet shall stand in thy gates, O Jerusalem. For thither the tribes go up, the tribes of the Lord". There, he believed, was the earliest shrine of God's mercy: there was the fullest and finest exposition of the Sacred Law: there was the Holy of Holies; had he not already prayed for the peace of Jerusalem, that there should be plenteousness within her palaces; did he not know that they who loved her should prosper? if he forgot Jerusalem, might his right hand forget its cunning!

And there he could gratify his heart's desire to study the books which were the most inspiring open to the study of mankind.

He was to search their meaning under a scholar of the highest authority and eminence; there was never a better Rabbi than Gamaliel. Gentleness and graciousness marked the temper of his bearing: his aim was to reconcile mankind to the Law. His method was not the dispute of exact points, but an enthusiastic comprehension and elucidation of the whole.[16] A father of conciliation, and of pardon, lofty, generous, such was the Master in Israel chosen to form the mind of the zealous and brilliant youth who had arrived from Cilicia to be his most gifted pupil.

Here the young Shaul learned to be what the son of Sirach had painted: "He who giveth his soul to the law of the Lord Most High searcheth the Wisdom of the Ancients, and meditateth upon the prophecies. Revolving in his mind the words of holy men, he delves into the winding path of allegories, scrutinises the meaning hidden in proverbs, and meditates upon the enigmas of parables."[17]

And Shaul insisted upon living according to the strictest

rules available: his passion was nothing short of perfection: he wished to keep to the model of the Torah in the most exact and minute manner he possibly could:[18] in everything he was a Hebrew of the Hebrews:[19] his zeal carried him to the extremes: both in learning and in practice, he was the eager pupil of his master.

Breathing the bracing air of Jerusalem, delighting in its intense sunlight and the wild scenery which led down so sharply into the valley of the Jordan and the Dead Sea, steeped in all the associations of his race and particularly of his tribe, the young Shaul, standing for hours below Gamaliel,[20] and engaged with him in earnest discussions, often interrupted, in a way which orientals have never abandoned, with ejaculations of piety and praise, the eager youth watched year after year the spring cover the hills with wild flowers, red as blood, to be followed by a summer of scorching noons and refreshing nights; the autumn gradually brought its torrential storms; alternations of shower, wind and sun made the winter change-ful.

While nature showed him these things, religion trained him in a succession of fasts and feasts: in the spring the fast days were in general preliminary to the feasts and were associated with sacrifice, the Passover: the feast of weeks to celebrate the harvest: and the feast of tents later in the year for the final gathering of the fruits, joined to a remembrance of the Flight from Egypt.

Lesser feasts celebrated the Dedication of the Temple, the Reading of the Torah; for on the feast of Purim was read the story of Esther prevailing on Mordecai to secure the prosperity of the tribe. Each week was sanctified by the Sabbath.

"I had looked for Thee in holiness that I might behold Thy power and beauty."[21] Here in the domain of the spirit was the noblest triumph of the Torah. It began with ritual prescriptions, including the observance of special seasons: but it was always allied with, and was gradually replaced by, a moral and spiritual accordance with the will of God Most High. "The Holy God shall sanctify Himself in righteousness,"[22] and men of the world must do likewise till a certain impress of the loftiness and purity of the Master of Spirits was reflected in a spotless life and in an illumined mind—a mind illumined by Holy Wisdom, for the Saints had a very great light,[23] while unnurtured souls went astray. But apart from this there was the reading and study of the Law, the practice of prayer, the search for purity of soul. With these high aims was associated the idea of sacrifice, and the ritual life of the Levites. For Jerusalem faced the young learner with a startling spectacle; to put it brutally, their temple was a slaughter house.[24]

7

Such then was the young man as found in Jerusalem. He lived in an inspiring scene and bracing air; he breathed in an atmosphere of learning, enthusiasm, effort, adoration; he was imbued with pride in the traditions and qualities of the chosen race; he paid a minute observance to a life of ritual and ceremonies, centering on the temple on the naked rock Mount Moriah; he enjoyed the advantage of an excellent memory and a fiery mind, joined to the readiness of a born speaker, trained in Hellenised Tarsus; his mind had a supple and enthusiastic quality which put him rapidly in touch with different types. He had not forgotten the surrounding world, the Hellenised world of gentlemanly culture and sport in which the rites of strange gods survived; he was also aware that the supreme power, the power that maintained law and order, was the power of Rome and of the successors of Augustus. He was as ready to accord to the Roman Emperor the right claimed by the Roman Emperor as he was to render the worship which his religion told him was due to Him who said: "Thou shalt have none other gods but Me".[25]

Wearing on his robes the broad leather phylacteries and two cases of small leather, the tephillin, one on his forehead, the other on his left arm, attached by a broad and ostentatious strap[26] (as a good churchman of Britain might wear on his watch chain a golden cross), dressed in the flowing robes of the Jew—and a Jew's taste is for excellent and noticeable dress—the refined, eager, brilliant, exemplary and highly-strung young Rabbi from Tarsus completed his training. He learnt by heart the picturesque history of his race, he learnt it still more from religious poems, which combined with a passionate devotion to the Most High a strong element of human feeling, sometimes of doubt and strife, sometimes of exaltation and mysticism. For as he caught from the Psalms their spirit, he felt that God was mysteriously near: "Thou hast holden me by the right hand," he read, "thou shalt guide me with thy counsel and afterward receive me with glory. Whom have I in heaven but thee? And there is none upon earth I desire in comparison of thee. My flesh and my heart faileth, but God is the strength of my heart and my portion for ever".[27] He developed his passion for poetry, learning great passages of literature, from the prophets, and especially from the writer, or writers, he knew as Isaiah, and psalm after psalm. And above all he learnt to interpret the Scriptures through allegory and parable, as the Rabbis were interpreting them.

To Jerusalem came Greek-speaking Jews of the Dispersion with the new books, *Maccabees, Wisdom, Ecclesiasticus.* These modernised and refined the mind of the young Rabbi. Who either by zeal or temperament or by training was better fitted to win converts? So it was that when he had completed his first training at Jerusalem, he could carry back to Cilicia a knowledge to fortify his zeal; he hoped to persuade many more to "the fear of God": and he believed that Israel would dominate the Roman Empire at the coming of the Christos.[28] Was not the time ripe for that triumph? Yet the deliverer was still to come.

8

Nevertheless, while Shaul was away from Jerusalem, the districts of Judaea, Samaria, Galilee bore the imprint of a Presence. One who spoke with authority, who impressed the people with signs and wonders, came among them, taking his language from the simple and sublime things of nature, expounding the prophecies, and saying: *Come unto me.*

More than once he had rebuked the Parushim, the Rabbis, and the Levites. "God is a Spirit", he said, "and they that worship Him must worship Him in spirit and in truth."[29] Forgiveness to the uttermost, going hungry that one's enemy might eat, a universal benevolence, a sincere and selfless life were the ideas that he enforced from the Hebrew scriptures, but he spoke of a kingdom of heaven to set up on earth, a kingdom that would grow as the mustard tree from its seed. It seemed that in his claim to fulfil the Scriptures, he was inaugurating a religion that was new. His powers were so arresting, his authority so profound, his claims so exalted that the simple people among whom he worked would ask, "Is not *this* the CHRIST?"[30]

And, indeed, his claims were such that men must either denounce him as an audacious impostor, or admit that he belonged to an order of being new to earth. Which? He was accused of blasphemy: and, after a protest from the Roman Governor, he had been utterly disgraced: the very mob had clamoured for his death. He had been thrashed and finally nailed up, naked and dripping with blood, between two thieves; he had died, in the place of a skull outside the city wall, the death of a criminal slave.

Yet that was not the end. A day or two later, a new story, which—pay as they might[31]—the Jewish authorities could not hush up, echoed through Jerusalem. The tomb of this man, whom his followers called their Lord, was empty. *The dead man had risen again!*

After being seen at first by a few, and finally by many, he had finally ascended in a cloud to heaven, as the Elijah of Jewish history had been carried to heaven in a chariot of fire.[32]

Such was the story they told of Jesus.

THE REVELATION IN THE SAND

1

LIKE MANY A GENIUS AND LEADER SHAUL HAD BEEN A YOUTH of conflicting tendencies. On the one hand, he was all correctness, with that superiority which comes with the discipline and rigidity of a youth with a spiritual ambition. He will scale the angels' ladder by hard training: he will keep every rule. For a young Jew this meant to follow out the Hebrew law with passionate precision, and to seek for satisfaction by combining ritual with morality. "Great", he read, "is the peace of those that love Thy law."[1] Yet Shaul had *not* found peace.

Every kind of excellence brings its peculiar selfishness which is known to some as superiority, and to others as pride. The trouble with his sort of zeal was that self was still in it. A man who is strong to excel does not easily lose himself in the thought and lives of others: and those others feel their grudge. Shaul was in himself a socially gifted and a warmly sympathetic nature, but excel he must: this meant a conflict which in him resulted in a nervous strain, and that led finally to a crisis, in which every effort seemed fruitless. A man on the verge of a nervous breakdown feels his will paralysed, and his thoughts tend to become fixed ideas. Haunted by a sense of ineffectiveness, the man with tired nerves feels not only that nobody loves him, but that he is a complete failure. If he is a religious man, what will strike him most is that he is a religious and moral failure: in one word, a sinner; faced with the highest standards, he sees them only to see how far he falls below them; and to

hear of them is to think of release in the opposite direction.
If told "Thou shalt not feel violent desires for this or that",
he begins immediately to feel them. And then a scrupulous
conscience makes him miserable. The very commandment,
wrote this man long afterwards, which was meant to point the
way to life, pointed to death. The signpost was twisted round.
"With the consciousness of the commandment," he wrote, "sin
came to life"; its very excellence made him feel hopeless about
his own state: he was, he said, a man of human weakness,
bought as a slave by sin. And sin was death. "I died."

What was this mysterious power of mind which decided his
will, which dwelt within him as a master enslaving him? It
made his heart a battle-ground. He chose one thing and made
resolutions accordingly, yet, when it came to the point, he acted
differently. A man can no more control his temper and his
feelings than he can control all his physical mechanisms. If he
is tired and hungry, he becomes irritable. "Not what I will do
I practise," confessed Shaul, "but what I hate I do that: for
I fail to do the good thing I would: the evil that I would not,
this I practice. In me, that is in my weak human nature, no
good thing dwells. Wretched man that I am!" he burst out,
"who will deliver me from the body of this death?"[2] It was
all very well for the Jewish Rabbis to assure him that, if he
were penitent, God would forgive: a man who is being led
through the most passionate religious experiences can still be
haunted by the sense of ineffectiveness and of sin. Despair torments him; he asks, "what rests? Try what repentance can,
what can it not? Yet what can it, when one cannot repent?"[3]
The more a man is ashamed of himself, and the more he suf-
fers from the inner conflict, the more inclined he will be to
wreak the strain on other people.

2

With this sense of ineffectiveness working havoc in his nerves, Shaul came back to Jerusalem to hear talk from the Parushim of an appalling blasphemy. The man who among two thieves had died naked, bleeding, and disgraced, had claimed not only that he fulfilled the prophecies concerning the Christos, but that he was greater than Abraham[4]; that he was in some unique sense of the very nature and being—the *Son*—of the Unnamable,[5] the JAHWEH who in the Septuagint was called THE LORD.

3

The young Rabbi from Tarsus was outraged. He could be nothing less. He was strictly trained: he was in his way a member of an aristocracy: on the one hand he wore the badge of a gentleman—Roman citizenship; he added to his social and political position a most precise Hebrew training: and he looked forward to a consummation when his training in learning and sanctity would be associated with a great prince and prophet—such as David had been and more still—one who would make the dignity of Israel universal, who would bring the Jews to dominate the Roman Empire.

What did he find? An obscure group of little education, no training and of no social consequence: people who had come from a humble and a doubtful milieu, setting up a new movement, starting out as a new and revolutionary sect, with the most extravagant claims centred on one who, after being charged with blasphemy, had been ignominiously executed. Had anything been wanting to scandalize an impeccable teacher, it was the claim that this so-called prophet was more than a prophet, and that, in fact, after death he had arisen from the sepulchre, and given authority to his chosen twelve to go and teach all nations, baptising them in the name of the Father, the Son and the Holy Spirit.

The novelty was startling: a new cult, a new and mysterious formula, a new way, different, obviously from the Torah which it claimed to fulfil: the learned and zealous Parush was as shocked by it as a rigid Sabbatarian Calvinist Scot of a hundred years ago would have been shocked by the claim of Irish labourers in Glasgow that their garish chapel, with its images and bells, was the holy place of the one true Church.

4

The course was clear: they must be scourged out of the way: the movement must be suppressed ruthlessly. The orthodox convention must be vindicated with every rigour. It was even more blatant than that: it was the case not merely of a false religion but of a criminal offence. You might as well have expected the Dean and Canons of Winchester a hundred years ago to have approved a cult of Tess of the D'Urbervilles after she had been hanged in the county gaol for the murder of a man with whom she had been living as his mistress, as that a Parush would believe that the scourged agitator was GOD.

5

Such an example, such a scandal could only lead the correct and virtuous to live more exactly, even if more humbly, their life of correctness and virtue, keeping to every iota of their rules and standards in sacred reading, in worship, in almsgiving,

in good works, in scrupulous attention to the code and tradition
in standards of clean lives and simple living. For the Pharisaic
type is a perennial type and is always conservative, cultured
and rigid. It is so excellent and its temptations are so subtle
that it recurs in the very religion which denounces it.

Self-righteousness is like a clean, lavender-scented handker-
chief: it gives the flavour of taste, or exquisiteness, of superiority to all around it: it will not tolerate that those whom it
despises should claim to be holier than its own sort.

What choice was there but to try by every means to suppress
the movement? The offenders must be scourged out of existence: the orthodoxy, and the dignity of Israel, the expectation
of a triumphant Messiah vindicated ruthlessly and with devouring zeal.

6

Of the many Hellenised Jews in Jerusalem one of the most
gifted was Stephanos (his name meaning a Crown). Just at this
time this young man began to preach with an extraordinary
power that Jesus was the Christ. Like Shaul, he knew the
Jewish Scriptures well: his personality was singularly elevated
and attractive: he seemed less a man than an angel. His learning, his power as a speaker, the influence he exerted (for it
was said that he had certain miraculous faculties) made him on
the one side an object of love and admiration, on the other of
outrage and scandal.[6]

Plans were made, as they had been a year or two before in
relation to Jesus. A plot was completed: it was planned to trap
him into some blasphemous expression, and finally he was
brought before the supreme council of the Jews, the Sanhedrin.
To them he spoke at great length: he showed himself fully

45

aware of the story of Abraham, of Isaac, of Jacob, of the migration into Egypt, of the birth and career of Moses. After reminding them that the attitude of the Children of Israel towards Moses had often been scornful and insulting, he came to the story of David and Solomon, and the building of the temple. He quoted the Book of Isaiah:

> The Most High dwelleth not in temples made by
>   hands.
> The heaven is my throne, and earth is my footstool.
> What manner of house will ye build me, saith the
>   Lord,
> And what is the place of my rest?[7]

Warming to his theme, the ardent young Hellenist turned in a fury of impatience on the purblind people who always refused to live according to the highest inspirations of the Spirit. Jews they might be formally: but where was that change of heart which the act of circumcision symbolised? In heart and mind they were *un*circumcised, and their necks were obstinately stiff. "Which of the prophets", he asked, with pressing intensity, "did not your fathers persecute?"[8] These had told long before that after them would come the Man of Righteousness, whom, he said to the people before him, "you have betrayed and murdered.—You who received the Law as it was ordained by angels and kept it not."[9]

7

This was a declaration of open war; as such it was accepted by Shaul and all his party. They were furious and showed their fury with a snarl like that of a dog. Stephanos was facing deadly danger; but the prospect of it only increased his religious exaltation. His mind was absorbed in a rapture: "I see the heavens opened," he cried out, "and the Son of Man sitting at the right hand of God."

The vision and the claim inflamed in the Jews the sense of scandal. Shouting at the top of their voices, till a single impulse of excitement frenzied the seething mob, they rushed at him, and tearing off his clothes thrust him out of the city towards the deep valley of Hinnom below.

Then they let restraint go. They flung off their own clothes and as a pledge of their loyalty they laid them at the feet of the young leader whose zeal had roused them. Naked, they took up stones to hurl at the naked young man before them. He had soon fallen while the mob, rushing nearer, increased the weight of their assault. Stephanos, still in an ecstasy, but knowing that the end had come, cried out to the Master whose presence he felt: "Lord Jesus, receive my soul." And then in a last effort he rose on his knees, and exalted by a rapture that changed all bitterness into joy, he called on Jesus to forgive the men who were about to kill him. "Lord," he cried, "lay not this sin to their charge." Even as he spoke, a last stone had struck him down for ever.

8

Shaul had not thrown any of the stones, but he had not attempted to hold back the crowd. On the other hand, he had first joined in the denunciation and then urged them on. Sharing in the excitement of the mob, he went back to the city and made fresh inquiries as to where the pernicious movement could be found. Accompanied by his minions, he forced his way into the houses of the followers of Jesus: and dragged off both men and women to jail. The more he succeeded the more hotly burned his angry zeal. One idea consumed him—to root out the new growth. It was not enough to scorch the sapling in Jerusalem. The mysterious plant was spreading in every direction, and he heard that it was shooting vigorously up in the fertile Syrian city where the waters of Hermon irrigated the border of the desert. He went to the high priest at Jerusalem and demanded authority to work in the synagogues there, planning first to make his arrests, and then to bring the innovators bound back to Jerusalem.

The mild old Rabbi, at whose feet year after year he had learnt wisdom, counselled a milder course: it was not the Hebrew way to rage furiously like the heathen; the God who was all merciful was almighty: against His will nothing could prosper. The truth was that with this new movement the old man's gracious soul felt a secret sympathy. In his mildness and holiness, authority was endued with charm: the people as a whole gave him reverence. To them he spoke advising care: would it not be more wise to confide the thing to God Most High? This Jesus was not the only teacher who had arisen: there had been a certain Theudas: there had been in Galilee still another man. Both had met their death and their followers had scattered. "What I say," said Gamaliel, "is this: leave these men alone for if their ideas or their work is simply another movement of agitators, it will come to nothing." But on this point the wise old Rabbi felt a benevolent doubt. "If it is from God," he said, "you will not be able to overthrow it, and perhaps you would be found to be fighting against God."

The old man's serenity lent his words influence. The followers of Jesus had had much success till Shaul returning—impetuous, fiery, eloquent—had taken the view more generally held by the Parushim and given a new impulse to the persecution which was encouraged by the Chief Priests.

9

Such was the position when Shaul obtained permission to go and attack the followers of Jesus in Damascus. He had suffered already too much from his inner conflict and its resultant exhaustion to take any line but that of violence: and besides, in his intense nature, so sensitive and yet so strict, there was a vein of revenge, which led him to ask that others should suffer as he had suffered.

The journey before him might have cured a more normal case of strain.

As the zealot rode away from Jerusalem with the cavalcade of camels, he passed over a rough, hilly region: he came gradually in Samaria to Jacob's well at Sichem; then winding on through Nablous he reached the green plain of Esdraelon, bounded at the west by Carmel and Sharon. At the northern end of it on a high hill was Mount Tabor: above was the village of Nazareth. The road then turned round eastward through the hills down to the Sea of Galilee where a settlement had been named after Tiberias, and an older one, Capernaum. He was now 500 feet below the sea level: all the more bracing the climb up to the hills above with the fine sight of Hermon and its snows and the beauty of the attendant hills. Shaul was to wind round Hermon: he had a choice of two routes, either to cross the turbid Jordan below the lake or to wind on towards Caesarea Philippi and go over a higher shoulder of the mountain. In either case he must soon be again in the desert, and looking out over a copper-coloured earth, the air dry and bracing in the fierce glare of the sun on the sand, while in the far distance he could vaguely discern the outlines of the city of Damascus, famous already as a city of desire, famous still among all the Bedouins of Arabia.

Damascus is one of the most ancient cities of the world. It

67852

still survives when Tyre has become a fishing village, and Babylon a heap of dust. The desert is its defence. It has Hermon and Lebanon for neighbours. Their snows feed the rivers which give it bloom and life; and these have made a legend, and produce a thrill.

> Oh brother; 'mid far strands
> The palm-tree cinctured city stands.
> Bright white beneath as the heaven bright blue
> Leans o'er it while the stars pursue
> Their course.[10]

No minaret yet thrust its spires upwards from the green, but the waters flowing from Hermon had long since made fruitful gardens there; gardens not alone of vine and fig, but of peach and cherry; and through the desert came caravans and camels from the palms and bazaars of Mesopotamia.

As the avenging Jew wound down over the mountain into the dry heat, his nerves were already keyed up by a more than usual tension. There was electricity in the air. His exhilaration stripped naked the soul which he had long since exercised in the feats and gymnastics of the inner man. In his course upwards and inwards to the height where the soul moves, not of its own volition, but led by the hand, and held by the right hand, of the Spirit of God, the illusions and barriers of sense were dissolved, as finally, with a flash, the lightning of sudden heat blinded him; he and all with him fell to the ground. He was confronted by immense personal power, which carried his soul upwards and inwards beyond all imagining into the heart of reality; and through the thunder he heard a voice, speaking to him in Aramaic: "Shaul, Shaul, why persecutest thou Me?"[11]

10

He had now passed to those depths of experience which rule supreme. The voice that spoke to him was one whose command he could not question. Raptures, and the sense of marvel, his mystic sense had known—but what were they to this? Its command was absolute and so were its serenity and solicitude. He strove with giddy wits to question the instant Presence:

"Who art thou, Lord?"

With the same kingliness came the words:

"I am Jesus whom thou persecutest."

Then, comparing him to a harnessed animal to whom each movement of sulking haunches means a prick from the waiting goad, fixed there to prevent it, the Voice continued: "It is hard for thee to kick against the pricks".

The authority implied was accepted. He felt he was a harnessed animal, and that this new authority could control his impetuous genius as a master controls the simple donkey or the stubborn mule. He was filled with awe of the power that mastered him. Wondering where the rein was to guide him, he sought only to obey. "Lord, what dost thou wish me to do?" The answer came imperial: "Arise and go into the city and it shall be told thee what thou must do".

11

Like an Arab blinded and choked by the whirling sand of the Khamsin, a blankness, a complete humiliation, a long prospect of obedience, and with all these the glow and intimacy of trust, brought him a conviction of reality which he regarded for the rest of his life as final.

His Pharisaism had misled him: Gamaliel's warning had

pointed to the inner truth: the disease of sin needed a healer. The words and demeanour of Stephanos were not merely those of Stephanos: through him and in him was a mystery: Stephanos, and all those men and women whom Shaul had arrested and cruelly thrashed in Jerusalem, and whom he planned to bring bound from Damascus, all these *were actually Jesus*. They had the same air, the same atmosphere, the same spirit as the Master who had subdued him. And Jesus was alive in them, through them, beyond them.

Here was the reality of the Messiah, the Christos on whom he had meditated for so long. The Judge, the man of power, who was the Master of the world—here He was at last, beyond all question, and more mysterious than any had even dreamed.

Gigantic certainties paralysed the zeal of genius. The man who had seen the lightning found that he was literally blind!

ubinski)

DAMASCUS—THE STREET THAT IS CALLED "STRAIT"

(Kersting)

AQUABA—ON THE TRACK FROM DAMASCUS TO ARABIA

FILLED WITH THE SPIRIT

1

AS A PARUSH, HE HAD HAD HIS MYSTICAL AIM. EVEN FOR THE Parushim, "The need of the soul", as a contemporary Jewish scholar reminds us, "was for harmony with God, perfect accord between the human will and the divine. To attain to that harmony was the constant aspiration of the soul: and the idea was a harmony, perfect and unbroken. That which broke the harmony was sin and the means of restoring the harmony was repentance answered by forgiveness."[1] "Look how high the heavens are in comparison with the earth," said a famous Psalm, "so great is his mercy towards them that fear him. Look how far the East is from the West, so far hath he set our sins from us."[2]

Such was the more gracious side of the Parush system as it had been set before Shaul in Tarsus and Jerusalem. It naturally seemed to him that the new figure from Nazareth had been utterly unjust to it. But he was shown in a flash, blinding as noonday sun on glittering sand, that in its loftiest moments, his Jewish piety had been far from what he found as from Hermon he came down upon Damascus. Suddenly his standards had been altered, his aspirations transcended, his ideals outshone.

Thus Jesus, by appearing from the unseen, won the allegiance of the man who, at that time, was the most brilliant both in gifts and training of any in Syria, or indeed in the world.

A genius who had been developing the surrender to God of the deepest impulses of the heart, found that his own efforts were as nothing to that reach and grasp of God which approached him, claimed him, received him, embraced him, and led him forward blindfold from darkness to darkness, from grace to grace. To see was to believe; to believe was to surrender his will. Long afterwards, he summed up the whole experience in one phrase: "I was not disobedient to the heavenly vision."[3]

2

It is too common to speak of visions as though they were materialisations: even in the more outward and imaginative form, they are a faculty to understand reality with the imagination: in their inner form they are more: they are a faculty of intellectual vision when the inner mechanism of interpretation receives an impression: to this mystical power of vision, words might well be added: for words go far into the inner consciousness.[4] The vision of Shaul on his way to Damascus was an immense addition to his mystical powers already accorded, an addition which left on all his subsequent life its authority and weight. He had seen through the telescope of the soul an astronomy which, in relation to other readings of the stars, was sovereign. And so intense was his light and his glass that it paralysed, as we saw, the physical nerves of sight.

Still surrounded by his party of conservative Jews, who had seen the light, but had not seen the heavenly vision which had overcome him, Shaul stumbled on through the afternoon and evening, blind to the sparkling waters, the delightful gardens, the gleaming domes, the quiet though crowded streets of Damascus. Many and many a time in the travel he was afterwards to take, he was so absorbed in his sense of inward life as not to notice the brightest scenes of beauty.

3

It happens with men of abnormal nervous energy—men of genius—that their whole physical organism responds to the desires and will. A need for action and they know no fatigue; their food is their enthusiasm. On the other hand, a shock, a disappointment, and they are exhausted; their appetite is gone, their physical life arrested. So it was now with the most dynamic Jew of the age: his whole nature—with its training, its learning, its energy, its zeal, its devotion to the Parushim, their Torah and their Halachoth—had received a shock. He had lived for Jahweh, as the Master of the heavens: now from the heaven itself in a brightness which he saw yet more clearly with his soul than his eyes could see the sand before him, there had appeared, with a voice of authority, Jesus, identifying Himself with the Jews who believed in Him.

4

As the senses of Shaul revived, he became aware of the outlines of his dilemma. How could he give orders to his attendants? How could he present the letters he had brought from the High Priest, if he must at the same time announce that he had become one of the very infidels he had come to arrest?—Had Hess when flying over Germany come to a sudden fervour for the British cause, he would not have been in a more awkward position. To his former friends, he became a traitor: he had nothing to convince the other side who had good reasons to distrust and punish him.

The convert remained helpless. First he was humbled: so grievous an error showed that his conscience was awry. On the other hand, he had promised obedience, and was told to wait.

He had long been accustomed, at moments of high spiritual tension, to lighten body and spirit by fasting. As night and day succeeded in quiescence, the lowering of his physical life was accompanied by a clearer insight into the nature of truth. Clearly this talk, as he had considered it, of the Resurrection of the Crucified Man he had despised, was simply the assertion of a fact. Jesus lived, and with a Caesar's authority. "It shall be told thee what thou must do."

5

After three days and nights of dependence, his expectancy was not surprised when a stranger came to his door in the long street at which he had found a lodging, the street called "strait." He had grown confident that the Lord who summoned his obedience would find a means to put him in touch with his new companions. The follower of Jesus appeared not to upbraid but to welcome the converted man. "Brother Shaul," he said, "the Lord Jesus who appeared on the road by which you came has sent me that you may receive your sight and be filled with the Holy Spirit."[5]

To his strain and waiting, this welcome gave swift relief. Suddenly he could see, he could move; at once Ananias decided that he should receive the rite of initiation on which those who walked the New Way already insisted. The community of Damascus was even then not devoid of teaching and of formulas, and Paul had opportunity to learn the meaning of the new religion and its forms.[6] Among these not the least important was that he should be immersed in water, in the name of the Father, the Son, and the Holy Spirit. Through this symbolic act, uniting as it did with faith, he received a gift, a gift which, as he had learnt from the heavenly vision, made the believer one with Him in whom he believed. From this washing he came forth not only refreshed but as one who had within him the springs of an unfathomable love. He had made the act, he had given the choice which bore him into courses beyond any he had asked or thought, to where even

Desire perishes of its own exceeding fire.[7]

He had done in a word that which was to be shown him to do. Forgiven, restored, illumined, and touched to the heart's quick, he came back to eat and to drink.

Again and again he was to refer to this baptism, combining it with the idea of faith as a fact (enforced by experience) which received him into Christ and raised him to newness of life. As an event it was critical. It transformed him.

6

The new mystical life into which he had been born now demanded a long spell of lonely communion with the Redeemer who had appeared and called him: he longed again for the solitude, the sand, the dry bracing air, the prodigious empty distances, the curious significance and atmosphere of the desert, its life of dependence upon Him who ordained the heaven above it, by day the sun, by night the moon and Orion. For month on month of solitary contemplation, in the silence and the sounds of the sandy wilderness and irresponsive air, he renewed his whole life in the mysteries of his new knowledge.

How far he journeyed none knew. Many think he remained in the desert between Damascus and Petra: others that passing the blue gulf of Akaba, he wandered on past Kadesh Barnea to the Sinai where the Lord Jahweh had given the Torah to Moses; for that, as they rightly say, was what the Parush and the Jew understood by the word Arabia.[8] The all-important point was that, absorbed in solitary communion with God in the dry air of the wilderness, he watched the heavens till his own soul was renewed. Applying the precise instruction he had received at Damascus, he fitted the religion he had adopted into all that he knew of the Jewish Code and of the prophets.

For years he had prayed, for years he had sought to love God with all his heart and mind and soul and might, for years he had felt and known that the Lord was his shepherd, and that goodness and mercy would follow him all the days of his life—for years he had looked for the Messiah.

Now the yearning of those years was consoled. God's Holy Spirit had come to dwell within him, to give him the fulness of faith: he believed that by this Holy Spirit he had found the path of life; he had been led to a baptism which washed him clean from sin and made him live anew: he lived not only with but in the conscious power which had arrested him in the thunder flash; it was that of none other than the Messiah, the Christos of all their hopes.

Gradually he was to accustom his eyes to these immense vistas. For how could he have been born again of water and the Spirit into the life of this power within him unless the Jesus who had appeared between Mount Hermon and Damascus had been united as man with that Divine Word which, when all things were in silence, resounded from the Eternal Throne, and at whose vibrance the eternal hills and stars, with presences enthroned among them, had sprung to being and life? Such was the Power within him come to make captive every impulse and faculty of his genius and his heart till he could say, "I live no more: Christ lives in me."

For what was the gift within, unless, giving him his faith, it was the Spirit which united with the I AM the CHRIST who was the wisdom and glory of the universe, the Light of Light, and God of God?

COMING TO THE ROCK

1

HOW FAR THE FOLLOWERS OF JESUS HAD THEN MADE THEIR religion precise, it would be hard to say. There is no record from that time; it was only after many years that an account was given; but scholars are satisfied that the Way had already its marked lines, and even told something of the life of Jesus.

After the Ascension of Jesus, His Apostles had received the Divine Spirit which Jesus had promised them: they were filled by this Holy Spirit so that they were endued with power, and they preached the Resurrection—which also meant the death—as a proof of the supremacy of Jesus. "Let the house of Israel know assuredly", said the Apostle Cephas, "that God hath made Him both Lord and Christ this Jesus whom you crucified."[1] It is according to a general tradition they repeated such formulas as "Jesus is Lord" and "God has raised Him from the dead."[2]

This Cephas everywhere stood forward as the most prominent of the Apostles of Jesus. He exerted a miraculous healing power; he insisted that the revered leader whom God had raised from the sepulchre was the Prince of Life. The Lord Jahweh had sent Jesus to bless them; "Change your hearts therefore", he pleaded, "and be converted that your sins may be blotted out and that there may come seasons of refreshing from the Spirit of the Lord."[3] Christ the Rock was the foundation-stone, and there was neither health nor safety in any other: for there was no other name under heaven given among men, in which men must be saved.

Everywhere the Apostles spoke boldly and were filled with the Holy Spirit, and so great was the prestige of Cephas that they brought the beds of the sick out into the streets that at least his shadow going by might overshadow some of them: when it did so, they were healed every one.

2

Such were the circumstances in which the young Stephanos had spoken with wisdom and with power.

In all places Cephas and his company insisted that the power of the Holy Spirit had been given to them: they went each day into the temple, they went from house to house, and, says the chronicle, ceased not to preach Jesus Christ.

All their adherents they initiated by immersion in water, and by this mystery the initiate was baptised into the Christ. The whole community had a fixed life, repeating what the Apostles taught, sharing in the community, communing with God in prayer, and in that breaking of bread which, so Jesus had told them, they would do in remembrance of Him, as a mystical shewing forth of His death. This in turn they handed down to one another. He had said: *"Where two or three are gathered together in my name, there am I in the midst of them."*[4]

Such was the community which the converted Parush had joined; such were they who followed Him whom he followed; the fervour of his temperament and the force of his ability, strengthened by a grand visionary experience and contemplation, had in him followed the inner training of years under the mild influence of a saintly Master in Israel.

3

To his eagerness it had been given, as it had already been given to Stephanos and others, to realise how everything in the Law, the Prophets, and above all the Psalms, combined to show that the Messiah for whom the Israelites had been looking was greater than they had dreamed; that He would come to suffer tribulation: but that none the less, and in fact even the more for this very reason—that it proved a love undreamed of—this Messiah was more than a prophet. When Shaul came back from the desert to Damascus, his conviction was supported with a completeness of Hebrew learning far beyond theirs.

He could prove from passage after passage, with the addition of apt illustrations and arguments, and with all the force of mystical insight, not only that they were guided by the Holy Spirit, but that the Holy Spirit had shown him that in a unique sense Jesus was the Son of God.

4

The doctrine, we have seen, was stupendous. That in the mystery of the heavens the unnameable and eternal Lord had in His own order a Son, begotten from the beauty of holiness in the womb of the morning, and that this Son had assumed into Himself the nature of Man; this Son of God, in a word, was the Christos. But to hear this daring doctrine from the man who had been scattering and destroying the followers of Jesus; from the man who had come to Damascus for this very purpose that he might bring them back as prisoners to the High Priest at Jerusalem—this indeed left them astounded!

It was not only the followers of Jesus who listened: others came also and asked a similar question: "Isn't this the man who

in Jerusalem was attacking those which called on this Name?"
To these Jews Shaul turned his argument. His words were
weighted with the power of conviction: far from yielding
before them, he faced them with reasons so strong as to amount
to proof.

5

Some were won over: others, furious, conspired with the
Arab officials of the King of Petra, Aretas. To a movement they
distrusted, Shaul added a force which produced suspicion alike
from civil officials and Jewish zealots: the universal law which
sets national standards against the inward and supernatural
powers put him in danger of his life. His friends became aware
of hostility and suspicion; by the curious mixture of swift
observation with intuition which, through the centuries, marks
the oriental mind, it was understood that Shaul who came to
arrest others was himself to be arrested. He had betrayed the
order he came to serve: he had produced an enthusiasm which
seemed to undermine known prestige and order with new
values. The distrust was natural. He must be silenced.[5]

His house was watched: the guards were waiting for him to
come out to preach yet once more: his friends saw everything
that was happening. How could they save him?

There was only one way. The house in which he lodged had
an aperture in the city wall. The minds of his friends were soon
at work: a basket was brought, a rope attached, provisions
gathered, the eloquent and learned Rabbi was placed in the
basket, and then gradually, in the night, the rope was lengthened till he found himself outside the wall, and before long
he was on his way back to Jerusalem by the very road he had
travelled in such different circumstances three years before.

6

Whether he walked alone, or whether, as is more probable, he waited for a caravan, we cannot tell. But now once more he traced his way back through the scenes of Galilee, past Capernaum, past that level in the hill where Jesus had fed the multitude, past Nazareth where for years He had served as a craftsman in wood and metals, past Tabor where He had been transfigured, past Nain where He had raised to life a widow's dead son, past Jacob's well at Sichem where He had told a woman all the things she had tried to keep hidden in her past life, and where He had said "God is a Spirit, and they that worship Him must worship Him in spirit and in truth", past the spot where, as a boy, returning from Jerusalem His parents had found that He was missing, till he came to Jerusalem where He had been Crucified and Risen again.

But now Shaul found difficulty confronting him once more —the followers of Jesus, naturally surmising that this conversion was a new trick to entrap them, were all afraid. On the other hand, he—the most promising Parush and Rabbi of his age—had gone against all his former loyalties, had gone over to the Man whom other Rabbis and Parushim hated, and whom the High Priest had contrived to have executed. Again he was in a quandary: again he prayed: again a convert appeared and helped him.[6]

7

The man who now came to his rescue was like himself a man of position, and a Hellenised Jew of the Diaspora. While Shaul came from Tarsus in Cilicia, this Yusuf, who was to be called the Son of Consolation, Barnabas, came from Baffa in Cyprus.[7] He had surrendered all his resources to his new community: to it he offered his life and with it his kindliness, his wisdom and his generosity.

Training, judgment, and intuition combined to show him the value of the ardent genius who in the beginning of manhood had come back from Damascus changed from persecutor to protagonist. The Cypriote learnt his story: and then decided to lay it before the man who by the ardour of his temperament, and the firmness of his faith stood out preeminent among the Apostles of Jesus, and who was now known as Cephas, the Rock—among the Hellenists by its translation—Petros. He had lived in close intimacy with the Master who had found him on the shores of the Lake of Gennesareth busy with his nets, and who had promised to make him a fisher of men. He was one of those born amid simple surroundings to be a leader. Warm-hearted, impetuous, direct, his open face fitted with a rounded beard to give an impression of spontaneous yet spiritual radiance. He gave himself whole-heartedly, reserving nothing: yet like all impetuous people, he would at times recoil from his own swift advances, lest they had been rash. But, with his trust and expansiveness of nature, he received with ardour all that he heard from the wealthy Cypriote convert of this other and more brilliant adherent, who had received the personal call of that Master who, by a word at Gennesareth, had changed the whole current of his own life. He knew in the depths of his being the miraculous power of Jesus over the soul and heart that He had chosen. Cephas did not hesitate for a moment, but, receiving Shaul as a brother, asked him to come and share his own house, and told him what he himself knew from his intimacy with Jesus.

A more absorbing story never fell upon a more attentive ear. Shaul longed to tell others his own story: but it was too much to expect of flesh and blood that the friends of Stephanos should listen to the fierce Parush they looked on as his murderer. Shaul sought rather to argue in Greek with unconverted Jews who spoke Greek: but hardly had he begun when his words produced a storm.

How could the Parushim resist a feeling of indignation at this renegade? How could the Hellenist Christians forget the part he had played in the murder of Stephanos? In both came a fury of hatred; which made it natural to recall and to apply to himself his own arguments in favour of persecution. There was in his personality something too dynamic to ignore. Everywhere he was as disturbing as a typhoon: the feeling was so violent that it was seen that Shaul might well be treated as he himself had treated Stephanos.

Then again he had a vision of Jesus. He heard the voice of authority saying: "Make haste and get quickly out of Jerusalem."[8] He recalled in answer how he himself had taken a lead in persecution and was warned now that he was to be sent among the nations.[9]

From this second vision came convictions and impulses not incomparable to the first. He was being shown with blinding clearness what to do. Escaping over the hills to Lydda and Caesarea, he there took ship to return to the mouth of the Cydnus. Barnabas went to argue the new case on the river Orontes in the Seleucid capital, Antioch. For several years he stayed there while Shaul, passing from mature manhood to middle age, had ample time to reflect on all he had learnt from James and Cephas[10] while he preached the New Way in his boyhood's home at Tarsus, and accommodated his new thought to their Hellenised centre and university which had mingled with all the earliest impressions of a fascinating world.

THE PROBLEM OF THE MYSTERIES

1

NOW, HOWEVER, HE FACED ANOTHER PROBLEM. AS A BOY, AS A youth, it was how to live as a Jew, keeping the Torah in a Hellenised centre of culture: as a young Rabbi, it was to win others to Judaism. Now it was how to win over both Jews and Hellenists to a new conception: to live by the power of the Spirit in the Christ. He recalled the voice that he was to travel far and carry a message to people other than his own: his elastic mind began to take a passionate interest in views that he had once despised: he developed to the full his natural Jewish adaptability: he became all things to all men:[1] to the Jews he spoke as a Jew. As for the non-Jews, he must seek out every possible affinity between their views, their systems and his own: he looked therefore at Hellenic culture with a new interest; a great general must have enough sympathy to understand his enemy, if he is preparing an attack on those whom he could not hope to subdue unless he duly appreciated their resources.[2]

2

The Hellenistic Jews had been subtly influenced by the atmosphere which they breathed. But the aim of the converted Rabbi was something new. It was a scrutiny of the lives and ideals of all around him for something on which he could build up the appeal of a new mystery.[3] Before this time his unconscious sympathy with any friends who were not Jewish had been atrophied with a sense of superiority, which inclined him to recoil. The Torah—even when most significant and most sublime; the idea of Wisdom—even when most subtle—had been constricted and dim in comparison with the light and love beaming from the Holy Spirit now dwelling within him.[4]

3

The problem with which all the cults of the time set out to deal was the fear of death and the craving for eternity. The people of the time were one with Cleopatra in feeling immortal longings. The cult of Mithra satisfied this at the same time as it gave a philosophical explanation of the universe: like the Greeks, it made time a God: it identified the idea of a first cause with the Sun; in its reverence for the stars and the elements, it exalted the physics and the astronomy of the Greco-Roman world into a spiritual system.[5] While this appealed to the intellectuals, Mithraism taught also that

> Holy were the haunted forest boughs
> Holy the earth, the water, and the fire—[6]

that the simple man could find in the nature which sustained him powers to venerate or to fear. "The stars that shone in the sky, the wind that whispered in the foliage, the spring or brook that bubbled down the mountain side, even the earth he trod under his feet were in his eyes divine, and all surrounding nature provoked in him a worshipful fear." So writes M. Cumont.[7] The writer of Wisdom had said of others like them "that the whistling wind, the waterfall, the roaring of wild beasts, the melodious noise of birds among the spreading branches, the echo rebounding from the hollow of the mountains had made men craven with fear";[8] but a good Hebrew could be thankful for such things: for "at the commandment of the Holy One the glory of the stars will stand in their order as the beauty of heaven, and never faint in their watches."[9]

When Shaul looked out on the worshippers of Mithra, he could see that like those of the way of the Christ, they purified themselves by baptism: that they expected from a holy meal salvation of body and soul. They practised renunciation, and encouraged not only continence but chastity. Like the Jews, too, they knew of a heaven and a hell: they remembered a great flood; like the Parushim, they believed in the resurrection of the dead, and they taught that this was to follow the last judgment and the conflagration of the universe.[10]

4

But the God he worshipped had come down to give life to all men and was the light of every man coming into the world, even of those who sought him in what they called their mysteries. These mysteries had many different rituals and senses. From Egypt came those of Isis, and of Serapis who under Ptolemy I had taken over the qualities of Osiris. In Phrygia there were those of Sabazios, in Syria those of Baal and Adonis, in Asia Minor those of Cybele, and from Persia the great mystery of Mithra.

What did they offer? A symbolic path from things outward to inner powers, from dullness through emotion and ecstasy to more reality and more inspiring experience, from the fear of death to life eternal. They all taught that man has within him an element of the divine, and that by an appropriate ritual and discipline he could enter on that path to things eternal which was the way of life and salvation; in each there were rites of purification, in each a ritual leading to a gift of strength and power, in each some form of communion, in each a sense of partaking of eternal life. The mysteries, Cicero had written, have given "not only good cause why we should live joyously, but also a better hope in death."

Isis personified all that is sacred in the woman and the mother. Often she bore her babe in her arms. Those who worshipped her lived as guests in her temple: there they were given an initiation which revealed her grandeur, and then, dwelling with her image, they were honoured when it was honoured.

Apart from sacrifices, there were rites or mysteries which were thought to procure, either for time or eternity, a magical advantage, or a delirious excitement. Sometimes it was a feast —such as that which drew the Carians together before the Zeus of Panamara to share benefits alike with one another, and their deity. Sometimes in frenzied dances they coursed wildly through the forests to the sounds of flute and tambourine. Other devotees, excited by their wine, sought ecstasy in the cult of Dionysus: sometimes, the more sophisticated, cultivating theories about the etheric nature of the soul, adopted an elaborate symbolism to indicate the progress at which the soul had arrived.

In the mysteries of Isis the devotee was invested with robes figured with stars; in those of Mithra, he passed through a succession of doors, signifying the planes or spheres through which the soul reascends to the ether. A little later, in an arcaded temple at Rome, they engraved among butterflies and winged victories, figures of Eros and Hermes to symbolise their hopes of overcoming death and attaining resurrection. Sappho, after diving into the sea, was shown to attain it in the presence of Apollo.

In every case the mysteries were a means of assisting the soul to free itself from gross matter and ascend to higher levels: few, however, insisted on a moral effort to accompany the ritual act.

But the idea that Shaul owed his own teaching to a study of Mithraic mysteries in Tarsus cannot be sustained.[11] Some scholars have avowed such conjectures: none have come near to providing proof. "The connexion between the Mithraic doctrine and St. Paul's teaching", says Mr. Patterson after an exhaustive study, "is very dubious."[12] Dr. Kennedy agreed with him long since: "The central Pauline conception, which we have just examined, has no real equivalent in the Mystery Religions".[13]

Reitzenstein himself insisted how absurd it was to think that Paul, either as a pious and exclusive Parush, or as an enthusiastic convert to Christ, had been initiated into heathen mysteries, or had been likely to have won the confidence of Mithraic worshippers.[14] It was not the study of Greek philosophy that influenced the faithful Hebrew, but rather the ideas of philosophy and revelation which were coloured by it in certain byways between theosophical speculation and the works of the magicians. Such speculations were current among the Jews of the Diaspora.[15] In spite of many differences, they can be more easily understood by undeniable resemblances in one memorable case.

5

At Alexandria, in Shaul's early years, or before, an illumined Israelite was explaining his religion to the Greek-speaking Platonists.

Philo had a profound knowledge of the Septuagint: he interpreted it not only as the Torah of Jahweh, but as the νόμος τοῦ κυρίου —the law of the Lord: and as the Book of Wisdom recommended, he worked out Hebrew history in parable and allegory. For him in fact history had become philosophy. He harmonised with Platonism the Law and the Prophets. To him God was above all a mind, a Mind with ideas which were the archetypal forms of things. He taught that the Divine Mind, completed in a perfectly expressed idea, was the Logos which was at the same time conceived and generated.[16]

Judaism was presented in a way to suit the Platonic idealists. As for man, Philo taught that he was a compound of body and vital principle, but he had in him also a divine power of intuitive reason to which God had given the breath of life.[17] To the Jews, the mind of Philo seemed almost Greek, while to the Greeks he remained a Jew. Here was a model for Shaul to use in later years when he was approaching minds moulded by the idealism of the Stoics.

6

Above all Philo believed in the goodness of God. If one asked what is the principle of the created universe, the most accurate answer would be God's grace.[18]

What was this grace? The word was not found in the Septuagint, except for one or two passages. "The Lord will give grace and glory and no good thing will He withhold from those that live a godly life."[19] Or in Zechariah one might read that God would "pour forth a spirit of grace and compassion".[20] These were enough, however, for Philo to develop his sense of a divine love and favour which are the source of all those inward blessings that give us a share in God's perfection.[21]

The idea was sketched in Philo, but nowhere else.

As Philo taught the meaning of grace, so he taught also the meaning of faith.[22] Just as the word "prophecy" first means a knowledge of the future, and then goes on to emphasize the relation to God implied by the knowledge, so the confidence of faith in the promises of God implies that God is the master of every event, and events themselves are of value only in so far as they are the signs of God working within them; it is this mystical fountain of trust in God which Philo calls faith. "To rid oneself of learning and believe in God only is the act of a great and Olympian thought, which is no longer overwhelmed by the nothing which surrounds us."[23]

Yet no doubt Jowett was right when he said there were very bizarre notions in the mind of Philo, and passages as tedious as the platitudes of a modern sermon![24]

7

Whether Shaul had actually read the works of Philo we can never know; we do know that his ideas were current in the air of the time, and whether by direct knowledge, whether by the study of papyri which have since perished, or by a general wave of enthusiasm they reached Cilicia and the Orontes Valley. They were acted upon by a mind of impetuous swiftness, and searching eagerness; its poetic power raised these to the standard of genius.

But to emphasize the human genius of Shaul would be misleading. He was a man transformed by spiritual experience: he had received immense favours which often came as revelations. He joined to his unique power of rapid and enthusiastic apprehension, both as scholar and as man of the world, the insight of an advanced mystic: a mystic living by his faith.

What is a mystic? To be precise, it means one who had given up the human modes of knowledge and activity to a certain quiet in which he caught from afar the echoes of heavenly voices; the passiveness of his own mind and will allowed the will of God to act upon him more directly. Why had Shaul wished to be a Rabbi but to learn the secrets of holiness? They had been opened to him with his reading of the holy books and poems. To the command: "Be still and know that I am God",[25] he had answered: "Open Thou mine eyes that I may see the wondrous things of Thy law".[26] And now that he saw them more and more in the Christ, these things were wondrous indeed. In his surrender of his own faculties in adoring calm, the inspired words had remained in memory as the echo of the heavenly voice. The high poetry which he had learnt by heart became the living Spirit telling of immeasurable truth.

In the loneliness of the desert, he had already gone from height to height of contemplation: his intense convictions came from those depths of mystical consciousness which have a sovereign authority.

In ordinary relationship a thing seen passes from the sense impression to an image which is interpreted by the intelligence: in intuition, the intelligence can grasp a direct impression, or add so much to memory and impression that knowledge is both more intimate and more distinct than by the other processes of knowledge. But besides such modes of apprehension there is the life where intuition itself is exalted by the direct action of the Holy Spirit. Then the mind is enlarged to use faculties not its own. Its will and constancy are strengthened: it receives a guidance: it enjoys an intuition into the being and nature of things: it lives in loving confidence and confiding love: it is able to perceive the relation of things to one another, and to the divine purposes: it concentrates on the things of God and, above all, it savours the meaning of life and the universe: for it discerns it to be God's creation. All these powers intermingle with one another through acts of thanksgiving and praise which lift the soul to adoration.[27]

9

As Shaul received these gifts, they mingled in his life with that central revelation in the sand outside Damascus, with the mysterious presence of Him for whom he had always longed, the priest, the prophet, the judge, the King, the Lord's Anointed, the CHRIST.

In his mystical apprehensions, the two facts were supreme. The Christ had been crucified. The Christ had risen again.

Accustomed to allegorical interpretations which read theological implication into history, his mind saw these events flashing with light. The Resurrection proved the Divineness of the Man of Nazareth; and yet this man of sovereign power died in torment the death of a disgraced slave. That meant that the Christ had chosen to sacrifice Himself that He might put others right with God by pouring His life, His blood into them, by accepting themselves into this mystery. The desire for initiation and redemption, the seeking for communion through a sacrifice, the belief that the life was in the blood, were joined together, consummated and satisfied in this Christ into whom he had been taken.

Shaul went in his orison from height to height. He received visions and revelations from the Lord till he was caught up into Paradise, and in the third heaven saw things which it is not lawful for man to utter. He knew that in those heights of prayer he was led and taught directly in what he called revelation.[28] Whether he was still in his body, or out of the body, he knew not. All heaven was at his feet, and he was amazed at the riches of the glory with which he had been endowed. He enjoyed already those experiences of union which were to return to mystics through the ages.[29]

10

"And in the soaring track of revelation, lest I should be excessively exalted," he wrote, "there was sent to the flesh a pricking point, an angel of Satan to smite me, to prevent me being excessively exalted. Three times I begged the Lord on account of this that I should be released from it, and He said to me, 'Sufficient to thee is My grace: for power is made perfect in weakness'."[30]

Through the centuries men have debated what this "angel of Satan" was. They have seen in it, on the physical side, sharp physical pain, malaria, ophthalmia, epilepsy, nervous disorder: on the moral side trials and temptations. For malaria, with its stabbing pain in the head, its bouts of prostration and shivering, and its acute attacks of depression, Sir William Ramsay has made out the most excellent case, and to this must be added the fact that Shaul afterwards said he was compelled through weakness to go to Galatia, as though obliged by his malaria to quit the coast and go inland. But, on the other hand, we must remember that his habitual use of the word flesh meant the weakness of human nature. "He was wont to call by the name flesh not the natural body," says St. Chrysostom, "but the depraved will . . . for by the flesh he does not mean the body— it is the earthly mind, slothful and careless."[31] This view is well borne out by the use of the word flesh in the Old Testament.

Let us also remember that in Mediterranean countries animals are to this day often goaded on with a sharp-pointed stake. Shaul was a man of furious temperament: his early zeal had taken the form of cruelty: as his temperament had little of the normal inclination towards women, this nervous excitability may well have taken the form of either extreme irritability, or some more obscure and unusual temptation, which at times was as painful and humiliating as a blow——. If this is so, the Latin translation, *stimulus carnis*—the spur of the flesh —may well carry this idea of a torment to the weakness of his nature.

If it had been an illness, it would have been natural to ask for a cure, especially in a day when the Apostles displayed the gifts of healing. But here the answer, which itself came as a revelation in direct words from the very Christ who had arrested in the sand his rage for persecution, was: "Sufficient to thee is My *grace*".

It is just possible that his main meaning, however, was the physical humiliation of persecution. That, when he said he was smitten, he meant this literally. He may quickly have come into conflict with the strict Jews among whom he had lived. For he related afterwards that he was scourged many times; and it was possible that this hideous and disfiguring torment was in his mind, as a humiliation to counter his ecstasies.

Whether, then, the angel of Satan came to him in the form definitely of a scourge, or of a germ, or of his own excitable temperament—or, as is not impossible, in the reactions of these on one another—researchers may continue to conjecture, but they will not determine. Ruthless as the scrutiny has been, it cannot lay bare the humiliation that Shaul trusted to delicacy to veil. But not the less plain is the essential meaning he intended to convey: at the same time as he was far advanced in the mystical life, with revelations, with visions, with raptures and ecstasies so lofty that they raised him to paradise and shewed him things too sublime for words and images even to hint, he had some human failing — or disability — or chastisement — from which he longed and prayed to be free: on the other hand, through divine grace, this enabled him to live more supernaturally; as his self-confidence failed, he leant more on faith: as his own faculties weakened and died, the Christ lived in him.

This is a story which many souls and mystics have repeated: and most of them look to him as their master.

11

Therefore he could in deepest truth say that he lived *in Christ*. He had, by study, come on such words as grace and faith, and seized and grasped them, till in his hold they gained such a shine and ardour as few words had had before; grace was a joyful participation graciously accorded in the inner life of Christ in God; faith, as a quality of this grace, was not merely an assent through the mind of the whole being to trust in God's promises and His word until it became a sharing in the mind and sureness of His Christ. But it meant also a divinely accorded inclination of heart and will to a fidelity embracing every instinct and every faculty of the believer's nature.

12

To this man, thus prepared, came the invitation from the cultivated Cypriote who had come to his rescue in Jerusalem to join him in a great populous capital, as crowded and varied in relation to Tarsus, as New York is to Princeton, Frankfort to Heidelberg, or Marseilles to Aix. Whether Barnabas felt that Shaul should be rescued from persecution, or that his gifts would receive full play only in the opportunities of the capital of the Seleucid dynasty, no one has related. All we know is that some time in the nine obscure years after his return to Tarsus from Damascus, his Cypriote protector, who combined enterprise with magnanimity in a genial expansive nature, summoned him from Cilicia to the Orontes—and he came.[32]

IN CYPRUS AND LYCAONIA

1

A JOURNEY OF SIXTEEN MILES UP THE ORONTES FROM SELEUCIA brought him to the most impressive site of the Levant. At that point the last extension of the wild Taurus range terminated, cut by the broad sparkling river. From the opposing side of this, the Lebanon threw out in final grandeur the lofty and abrupt declivities of Silpius. Unabashed by the crags and ravines of the mountain, the Syrian kings of the House of Seleucus had stubbornly raised a wall so that over bulwark and bastions of impregnable strength the castellated line of lofty heights threw a startling picturesqueness against the southern sky. Such was the site which Seleucus Nicator had chosen. For close on three hundred and forty years, his house had glorified it.

The city the Syrians had made splendid was yet further enriched after the Roman conquest. Where many pointed minarets now proclaim the greatness of Allah, then aqueducts, baths, basilicas and temples gave to the architecture ʾe rounded completeness of the Roman. The traffic o   ntred on a corso more than a league long, paved   ; and marble, too, was a double row of columns set   side to form an arcade. The city was unique in Asia .   ng an admirable collection of statues—masterpieces of   approached sculpture of Hellas at its finest bloom; here the beautiful mythology of Greece called cosmopolitan fancy to delight in the classic fable. Again and again a shrine or statue called for fealty to Apollo, and a delightful spot some two hours' walk above the city took from Achaia the name of Daphne.

With these poetic fancies of the world of gods and heroes, renewing the inspirations of Ida, Parnassus and Olympus, the Syrians brought their own cults and mysteries as at Tarsus. Certain quarters of the city bore oriental-sounding names — Gandigura, Charandana. The island on which the Kings had built their sumptuous palace was known by the Arabic word *Ghisira;* while, with an eye for effect, the ruling citizens built their villas in the declivities of the mountain where, among torrents and waterfalls which plashed down the depths of the ravines, the fresh verdure of laurel and myrtle spread their polished leaves above hyacinth, anemone, and cyclamen. Here at night one might imagine the hanging gardens of Semiramis. Such was the enchantment which power and wealth had added to the grandeur of mountain and river.

The crowd of inhabitants gave its undeniable culture other flavours. At certain games, bands of damsels performed their rhythmical exercises in the lightest attire. The cosmopolitan crowd which thronged the length of the Corso with the songs, the parodies, the jests in which frivolousness found vent, made it like a pantomime. Beneath their occasional wits was a temper of fickleness, of faction, of indulgence: for they were people less virtuous than voluptuous.[1]

Thus silky Syrians and versatile Greeks combined to surround with the spirit of carnival an immense colony of Jews. Of these not all were pious. For there, as elsewhere, Jews could revel, and find their pupils, in corruption: but the stricter could not but feel a grim superiority as they passed beside the naked statues of the gods of Hellas to worship in their austere synagogues. There, in answer to the question: "Who shall ascend into the hill of the Lord or who shall stand in His holy place?"[2] came the reply: "He that hath clean hands and a pure heart, and who hath not lifted up his soul unto vanity".[3]

2

Thus, to the crude contrasts of a capital already as populous as was Paris itself in the reign of Louis Philippe, came Barnabas to call the Hebrews to the New Way. His movement had some distinguished converts among many humble ones. Among the leaders was a foster brother of King Herod. Here Barnabas could offer a fitting field for the versatile and soaring genius of his Cilician protégé.

Here then they lived the life of contemplation, of piety, of charity, of reading the Scriptures, of recounting the story of the Christ, of Breaking the Bread which showed forth the mysteries of His death, and of finding in all they taught and all they had a mind to do the direct illumination of the Divine Spirit. Knowing that man does not live by bread alone, they refined their natures with fasting, and sought for an eternal light that they might worthily minister the Holy Mysteries: through prayer and contemplation, they sought how best to serve the Most High. They were assured that the Holy Spirit was guiding them with His counsel. They felt that they must spread afar the glad tidings of their good things.[4] They planned to return on the wings of the morning to the smiling beaches, the wooded valleys and mountains, the temperate, delicate air of the island where Barnabas had been a boy.

3

The scene of their departure was sublime. Before them lay the open sea in brilliant colour; behind them, the Jebel-el-Akrab rose above declivities luxuriously wooded to a peak some five thousand feet high. At dawn on a clear morning, the blue outlines of Cyprus could be discerned across the water. With a favourable wind, a voyage of a few hours was enough to bring them to Famagusta.

No one can fail to enjoy travel in this delightful island. What route these travellers took we do not know. Whether they saw Nicosia and the indented northern coast, whether they crossed the mountains at Troödos, or whether they took the southern road past Limassol, they travelled westwards through the island till they came to Baffa, then called Paphos. Suave airs, sunshine, and woods were the background of their message that the King of Glory had come down to dwell with men.

But at Baffa, new adventures were awaiting them. For there, a Roman Proconsul, Sergius Paulus, had set up his praetorium. At Baffa, therefore, they found themselves for the first time in direct touch with the Roman administration.[5] The Romans even then were an urbane, cultured and tolerant people, slightly sceptical about mysteries, profoundly attached to institutions. This proconsul was not merely cultured: he was a man with an open mind. As one who knew how to govern in the East, he was far too shrewd to ignore the occult. He heard that two cultured Israelites had come to the island with new, far-reaching and powerful ideas: he summoned them to an interview that he might satisfy his search; Shaul appeared before him, able to claim the dignity of Roman citizenship; and his fine mind, trained in the Cilician capital, could not but make an impression on the able Italian.

4

But he was not the first Jew to have attracted the benevolent curiosity of this Proconsul. For Sergius Paulus had already in his little court one of those men—partly conjurors, partly wizards—who combine trickery with the black arts. This wandering Jew was naturally infuriated at seeing his own influence threatened by the arrival of fellow-countrymen of a different order. He did his best to discredit them, and their teaching. He attacked it before the Proconsul. The conflict was not merely personal, it was occult.[6] The forces in the two systems had come into direct collision.

With the swift and dynamic intuition of a man living in Christ, Shaul not only sensed the sinister mixture of power and cunning, but declared battle against it with temperamental fury. "Son of the Devil," he said with emphasis, as he fixed upon the sorcerer the mesmeric power of his eyes, "you man full of every deceit, of every trickery, you enemy of everything straightforward, will you not cease to impede the noble ways of the Lord? Look now, the hand of the Lord is upon you and you will be blind—so blind that for a time you will not see the sun itself."

A paralysis, kindred to that which had paralysed Shaul himself outside Damascus, now, and for kindred reasons, raised a mist before the eyes of the Syrian magician. The dark force he had controlled failed him; facing a power and will immensely stronger than his own, he found that he could do nothing. His whole imposture failed like a mirage. As Shaul had done approaching Damascus, he sought some one to lead him by the hand.

Conscious not less of supernatural power than of furthering the truth he was expounding, Shaul continued his appeal to the Proconsul, who was both impressed by the miracle, and touched by the nobleness of what he heard.

5

Whether either openly or secretly he entered the New Way has been a subject of dispute. Again Sir William Ramsay pro-

(xclusive)

THE LIFE OF ST. PAUL

From an illuminated MS. of the IX Century in the Library of St. Paul, Rome

St. Paul explains the Scriptures to the Jews
St. Paul hears the voice of God
St. Paul, blinded, is led to Damascus
Ananias heals St. Paul's sight
Ananias receives inspiration from God
St. Paul preaches to the Gentiles
St. Paul is let down from the wall in a basket

duces a brilliant case for the contention that he did so: but other scholars remain sceptical. Through the ages there have been many men of culture and position who see the truth and power of the Catholic Church without joining it; this Italian Proconsul in Cyprus may have been among the first of them. That would not prevent him employing for his new friend the many resources of his position and his experience.

However that may be, the fact is clear that only after this time did the great convert make much of his Roman citizenship.

Yet more remarkable is it that from henceforward the chronicler drops the Hebrew name, which alone had been employed up to now; henceforth he writes Paulos. Did the benevolent Proconsul suggest this? Did he attach his own name? Or should we prefer the coincidence that the first Roman to listen to Christ's ambassador had the very name that his ambassador had first taken as a Roman citizen? So vague is our information that it is even possible that though, in later years, this Jew claimed that he inherited Roman citizenship, the Proconsul had first shown to the man who had so deeply impressed him and satisfied his search the citizenship's full value in Roman eyes.

The word Saulos, however, is not a pleasant word: it means not merely a conceited or affected person, but a conceited person who shows off certain protuberances of his figure by his way of walking: it was not merely a ridiculous word: it was a word that had a faint flavour of something more acrid. An Italian man of the world, who knew the Hellenes, would be the first to counsel a change.

When Jews change their name, they generally like to keep some connection, if it is a mere initial, with the name they have borne as Jews.[7]

But if they changed the initial, they could keep the rest. And if the name of this powerful patron would enable him to make this convenient change, was not this as providential as his victory over the Syrian magician? The fact that Sergius Paulus and his family remained in Cyprus would counsel a certain reticence in relating the change.

The conjecture that the great preacher owed to Sergius Paulus a knowledge of how to avail himself of the Roman citizenship with which he was born must then be placed with the others to explain why he, who afterwards claimed the Roman citizenship, had nevertheless at some time in his life been punished with two Roman scourgings, as no Roman citizen could be. It would explain also why henceforth he and not Barnabas became the leader.

6

From the shrine of Aphrodite in the ancient Paphos, ships sailed across the sparkling waves of the Mediterranean to a shrine on the blue shores of Pamphylia. But Paul was making for the mouth of the Kestros; to the right, the waves tossed laughter all the way to the blue Karamanian coast, where the peaks of the Taurus stood in absolute light. Some ten miles up the little river another temple had been built for Aphrodite. Around this had been built a flourishing little town.

Here the rapidly developing cosmopolitanism of Paul, or his taste for travel, or the calls of a Jewish home, proved too much for one of the party. The young cousin of Barnabas, Marcus, who had come from Jerusalem, and travelled with them through Cyprus as an attendant, declined to go further in the way of enterprise.[8]

And Paul himself fell ill. Those whom the enervating and malarial air of the coast had weakened were advised to take the cure. It was to ascend through the pass of the Taurus to the high Lycaonian plain which, set well over 3,000 feet above the sea, enjoyed a dry and bracing air. The journey up long valleys, past groves of walnuts into the pines, was delightful. They could not begin their journey from Seleucia till spring had calmed the sea. And the season was now so far advanced towards summer that the people began to move into the mountains for their Yailah. With camels and donkeys, with flocks and herds, the families have for centuries migrated at this time of the year into the cool heights of the mountains. If the health of Paul was affected, he would be the more constrained to go. Even in those days tombs and inscriptions marked the road, which was made partly of artificial pavement, and partly of natural marble. In the earlier part of June the oleanders spread out their branches over the banks of the watercourses in flashes of brilliant crimson. As the travellers climbed up the track, the fruit-trees gave way to oak-woods and these to pine and walnut, and these again to the cedar and the juniper, while the plane tree spread its broad leaves over the stream which dashed down the ravine, crossing and re-crossing the dangerous road. On the lower ground the crocus was in bloom; in the higher altitudes, the scarlet anemone.

The air freshened, and the nights grew cold, and before long clouds were seen floating among the precipices, and at times the wind blew fierce and sharp. As they passed into the wild cliffs of the mountain, separated from each other by valleys of sand, they came into regions infested with bandits. So they passed onward to the treeless undulation of the Phrygian plain. In places the ground was burnt and volcanic, in others green and cultivated. Among the rare pools storks would fish and feed. Here there was pasture for the flocks and herds; the people dwelt either in primitive flat-roofed villages, or in tents of goats' hair such as Paul himself had woven. As night grew chill, they would gather round a blazing fire; when the moon was bright it lit up the snow on the heights of the Taurus. The air, indeed, was crisp, but the scene bare. Here on the banks of the little river Anthos, between the two lakes of Limnai, and above a chain of hills, the Shillian Dagh, in a settlement once known as Mygdonian and now as Yalovatch, the House of Seleucus had established a provincial capital, naming it, like the great city on the Orontes, after Antiochus their King.[9]

7

In this Phrygian centre, Paul and Barnabas had the next adventure in their mission of grace. They found here an important and supple colony of Jews who had already attracted a number of the local inhabitants to come to their synagogue and hear of their religion of righteousness, of mercy and of trust. The Hellenised rabbis of this settlement could not but be impressed by these strangers who had come among them, one a Rabbi brilliantly trained by masters in Jerusalem, adding to an expert knowledge of their great literature and its Torah a profound personal conviction. After their customary reading of the Miqra, the local leaders turned to the visiting Rabbi to speak.

At first sight, his appearance hardly inspired enthusiasm. Bald and with a narrow head, the eyebrows meeting above the nose, he was not handsome; he was bow-legged, his figure had no command, but there was in his presence both charm and power. As he spoke, also, his expressive gesture, his burning eyes, his gift of eloquence were associated with that nameless force which is the power of those possessed of the Spirit of Holiness. They change and dominate the atmosphere.

As always, he reassured his hearers by his knowledge of the sacred history of his people. He reminded them of the great promises given to Abraham and to the seed of David. He proved to them that the Christos they expected was to suffer without a cause. He reminded them of the powerful preaching of the prophet who baptised in the Jordan, who prepared the way for one infinitely greater than himself. And this greater, having appeared, and having been sent innocent to his death, had RISEN AGAIN. . . .

There had been many witnesses of this. And this too had been prophesied: for the Holy One of God was not to see His body corrupt. And from Him, if only men would believe in Him, flowed out a power of healing and forgiveness, which put men right in the eyes of God, as the Torah could not put them.

He finished his speech by quoting a great warning from the prophet Habakkuk:

> "Behold, ye despisers, and wonder and perish,
>   For I work a work in your days, a work in which
>   you in no way believe,
>   Even if anyone should put it clear before you."[10]

His words were not without effect. Many were persuaded to accept the grace of God. The following Sabbath, Paul and Barnabas filled the synagogue to overflowing.

8

But this was a success for which the ruling Jews were unprepared. They were extremely jealous; jealous first at the popularity of the travellers; jealous still more that their own particular prerogative should be offered to mere uncircumcised Phrygians: they made an open attack on the new-comers and all that they had said. These answered them with equal vigour:

"We must needs speak first to you the word of God. But if you reject it, and deem yourselves unworthy of eternal life, we will turn to the other peoples. For so the Lord hath given us the command: 'I have set you up that you should bring healing to the farthest ends of the earth!'"

Those words were from the prophet Isaiah. They rejoiced the simple Phrygians who accepted them as divine; and the great offer spread among the people like fire through dried wood, till they were aflame with the joy of a new hope.

But the Jews, already in touch with the Romans who made the upper classes, craftily worked up these against the new religion, and the missionaries were compelled to flee some five days' march to the East, to the town of Konieh.

Here the same trouble rapidly arose with the Jews. Paul and Barnabas fled therefore round the bare black volcano, the Kara Dagh, which dominates that part of the Anatolian plateau, to two little towns on the northern foothills of the Taurus.

Here, in the humble settlement called Lystra, they healed a lame man. The simple people of the place were awestruck: already initiated into the myths and poetry of Hellas, their imaginations had awakened to prospects of hope and healing. Aware that great powers had come among them, they believed that the fading hierarchy of Olympus had passed over sea and hills to glorify their sequestered lives. The patriarchal Barnabas they took for Zeus himself, the father of gods and men: and Paul, being a prince of eloquence, they hailed as Hermes. The priests of Zeus came forward with calves and garlands and flowers to offer sacrifice to them.

Appalled at the innocent blasphemy, yet deeply touched by the warmth of enthusiasm with which they were received, they spoke of the goodness of God in simple terms which they hoped these simple Phrygians would understand: "We are but men akin to yourselves," they said, "come to give you a blessed message to turn you from these vain things to the living God, who made the sky and the earth and the sea and all that lives in them; in the generations that have passed, He allowed men to walk in their own ways: and yet He did not leave Himself unevidenced, for He showed goodness and kindness, giving you from heaven rain and fruitful seasons, filling your hearts with food and gladness." Then, as always, Paul's broad sympathy and cultured insight encouraged every tendency towards good: he sought to answer from every quarter the quest for the Divine. So deeply touched were the people at the touching assurance that God had made Himself known to them, and that He loved them, that those who set out their spiritual philosophy could hardly restrain the people offering them sacrifices. Before the people could be prepared to understand the mystery of Christ, however, furious Jews arrived from the towns they had already visited, and worked up the crowd to throw stones at them; Paul, struck by a stone, fell down as dead.

It was plain then that if men would work and live in Christ, they must pay the price of Christ for the heavenly treasure: and "through many tribulations enter into the kingdom of God". Nevertheless, Paul persevered on his high embassy. A document has come down from the second century connecting this mission of Paul with two enthusiastic converts; the name of one was Onesiphoros, of the other Thecla: and the legend tells of miracles. But what is more important to know is that Paul and Barnabas worshipped, they fasted, they built up their Church, they ordained "ancients" or priests to act with authority: and so the time passed till they retraced their steps through the valleys of Taurus, came to the coast, took ship, sailed past the blue Cilician hills back to Seleucia: and so to Antioch from which they had been sent forward with their high romance.

Nor had they been disappointed. Amid the hazards of the

Taurus, amid the dangers of unbridged rivers, amid assaults by stone and stick, amid insults and abuse, through bruises and blood, amid sickness and hardship, amid the waves and the storms, they had maintained their courage. They had shown not merely to the scattered Jews, not merely to the ignorant and poor, but to those touched by the beauties of the Hellenic mind, to those exercising the august beneficence of Rome, how much these were all loved by the Father of them all. The Divine Sovereign had chosen them to be the heirs of His riches and His court.[11]

Who would not be Romans in such a Rome—or Jews in this Jerusalem?

9

Eyes fascinated by these sweeping and comprehensive views had once more to contract their gaze, however, to the sharp, small blade used for the rite of circumcision. The alternation of the widest sweep of thought with the loftiest mystical experiences, with the pushing bigotry of fools, with the hard suffering of daily life, and with the sharp claims of common sense in the world of common things and common men: this is but one of the things that make it hard to be a Christian.

FAITH AND THE LAW

1

WHEN PAUL RETURNED TO ANTIOCH FROM HIS JOURNEY IN Pisidia, however, he found that the question of the full rights of the Church being given to converts who were not yet initiated by the Jewish operation aroused the most furious distrust among the believers of the chosen race. They had accepted the new way as a perfecting and fulfilment of the Torah, but the Torah must still be applied to and accepted by all: it was the foundation. So strong was this feeling that it looked insuperable.

Nevertheless, the inclemency of nature provided the fertile mind of Paul with a way out. A Jew among Jews, he learnt that the believers in Jerusalem were short not only of money but of food.

Realising then that the famine showed them not only a duty but an opportunity, the two leaders of the Church in the wealthy valley of the Orontes decided themselves to travel to Judaea's barren hills; they took with them an uncircumcised Greek called Titus, whom they had converted in their missionary journeys: and they did not arrive with empty hands.

The case of Paul certainly needed support. He had been received on sufferance eleven years before as a persecutor: and now he had to plead a difficult case: that of receiving the uncircumcised into the Church. He thought he would less scandalize the Jews if he put his case confidentially only to those most competent to judge, Cephas, with James and John.

Cephas, long since convinced that his great message was for

all the world, yielded to the impassioned arguments of the two men whom he had already befriended: Paul and Barnabas might go to the Gentiles, as Cephas and the others to the Circumcision: and they "should be mindful of the poor."[1]

What would be more natural than that Cephas, knowing that the famine was not affecting Antioch, should go back with them to this city of plenty—that, being there, he should mingle with the Gentiles and eat with them? Afterwards, however, when certain exclusive Parushim, acting on their own initiative, arrived from Jerusalem, and accused him of eating with the uncircumcised, he decided not to scandalize them.

2

For centuries men have read into the account that follows an account of a direct quarrel. They take it that Paul had affronted Cephas to the face when the man of Rock, in an access of weakness, had failed to maintain his settled policy of accepting the outside peoples into the Church and was refusing to sit at table with them.

It may be so: to Westerners the explanation seems obvious: but those who, having worked in the East, know the diplomacy which is second nature to the oriental mind prefer the little drama described by St. Chrysostom. According to him, Cephas was nervous about scandalizing the Jews freshly arriving from Jerusalem, and blaming him: *he therefore pretended to give way to them*, as did also the other Jews in Antioch! he pretended to be unwilling to eat with the Syrian Christians. Barnabas, too, says the account, was carried away by this dissimulation, this play-acting, this pretence. But now Paul brings it out into the open. The question demanded by the situation was: "Why are you, a Christian, living with the old rules of a

Jew?" When, before all, Paul confronts Cephas, the question he does ask is quite another: "When you, yourself a Jew, live as a non-Jew, why do you compel the non-Jews to live as the Jews?"

Now as St. Chrysostom points out, Cephas was not compelling the non-Jews to act as Jews, nor did he wish to do so: but Paul by his question had shown up the real attitude of Cephas. The question whether Cephas himself was to keep the strict rules of a Jew, Paul diplomatically takes for granted; he so shows what Cephas really felt; thus they both gained their point. Paul then went on with his argument that it is by faith and trust in Christ, and not in carrying out the enactments of the Torah, that men are set right in the eyes of God.[2]

Such is the oriental explanation: and thoroughly Jewish would such a drama be. It was the explanation not only of Chrysostom, but of Jerome, and, Jerome says, of Origen before him. But it shocked St. Augustine, and his explanation of the impetuousness and weakness of Cephas has gained currency among controversialists who contest the dignity of Cephas —but not only among those.

Whatever the truth of this negotiation, it is certain that the ultra-Jewish faction among the Churches was making things difficult for the others: and this too was to be repeated for years in every centre of the Church.

The Jewish Colonies were closely bound together and the trouble at Antioch appears at once to have spread further. Paul now heard that his own Jewish converts in Pisidia and Lycaonia, which he knew to be incorporated in the Roman province of Galatia, had fallen victims to the same propaganda as the troublesome Parushim had been making in Antioch. These Jews not only insisted for themselves, but they demanded also from the Gentiles, a full observance of their Torah—including circumcision. They were impugning the rights of Paul and

Barnabas to allow them freedom. They were, in fact, undermining his teaching about the faith.

3

His mind surging with his recent argument, Paul at this point turned to the Galatians with all the excitement he felt about the Jews. "Senseless Galatians!" he cried, "who has laid you under a spell?" He must make the whole thing clear, beginning with his own story on the Orontes, and it would govern the argument he must perforce employ against the Judaizers.[3]

His was no human choice: he had received the truth not from men but by revelation from the Christ Himself. He recapitulated his experiences—his conversion: his delay of three years of solitude in the desert before he went back to Jerusalem. Even when he went thither, he went to meet Cephas, and the only other of the twelve was James. The notion that he had taken his ideas from the twelve as a whole was absurd: he swore that he had done nothing of the sort. And then eleven years had gone by before he went to Jerusalem again, to deal with false and interfering Jews who were again slipping in as spies to disturb the freedom of his converts. His references to the famine were discreet: he only mentioned that he was asked to make a contribution: but he could boast that he had won his case.

4

Then he relates the drama in Antioch. It was much, it was a sacred privilege to be a member of the Chosen Race, and live according to the Mosaic Law. But had he not come to the Galatian region with better news than that? He had argued, had he not? that the secret of life, the vindication of the soul, was not to act according to the Mosaic code, but to believe in the Christ. He plunged into his great mystery of redemption. "By the Jewish Law", he cried, "I am dead to the Jewish Law that I might live to God."[4]

What could that mean? It meant that he was one with Christ, that Christ—seeing how the Jewish code meant an effort and a system of sacrifice that could not give man a wholly free life in God—had died to show what a life-giving sacrifice was: and that as He poured out His blood on the ground, so in the mysteries of grace He poured His life into men's souls till they were one with Him. "I have been crucified with Christ," said Paul, "and if I live it is no more I who live; Christ lives in me."[5]

The only way to live the life of perfectness, and to walk the way of lasting health of the soul, which meant eternal life, was to accept within oneself by the trust and assurance of faith that outpouring of Divine life which is the blood of Christ.

5

Then what was the relation of the Jewish Law—the Torah —to the life of faith? Did not the Jews trace the fount of their blessings beyond Moses—to Abraham? Was it not he to whom had come the words: "And in thy seed shall all the nations of the earth be blessed"? But why had Abraham received the promise of blessing? Because he had faith, and this faith was counted to him as righteousness.

"The man who lives aright will live by faith." That phrase of the prophet Habakkuk stated the profound principle, and

only on the foundation of faith and trust could one work out the enactments of the Torah into a vital principle: "he that doeth them", said Leviticus, "shall *live* in them."

But, said Deuteronomy, the Torah brought with it a frightful sanction—a curse: "Cursed is he who is not constant in carrying out all that is written in the book of the Torah". And since no one could perform it all, a Jew's conscience was in peril of a curse; even the most scrupulous Jews were troubled. They strove with constant effort, as Paul himself had done; but what was the result? They were never free from the fear of this curse: this curse which in the crucifixion had fallen upon Christ. But if only they would trust in Him. To Him the promise was made, Him the Torah pre-figured, He had redeemed men from the curse implied by the Torah. The Torah had served as an exalted rule of right living till from the descendant of Abraham should come that promised mediator ordained by angels. As a slave, being something between a nurse and a tutor, led boys to school, so the "Law"—partly nurse, partly tutor, partly slave—had led them to Christ: but after faith had come, men no longer needed anyone to lead them to school:—"*You are all the children of God by faith in Christ Jesus: for all of you who have been baptised into Christ have put on Christ. There is neither Jew nor Hellene, there is neither slave nor freeman, there is neither a stronger sex nor a weaker: for you are all one in Christ Jesus.*" The promise made to Abraham is fulfilled in you because of faith in the Christ and baptism into the Christ; these fulfil in one another the gifts of grace. "You are in Him. He has adopted you into Himself. You are His heirs: His sons; because He has sent into your hearts the Spirit of His Son that you might call Him Father."[6]

6

How, when his converts in Phrygia had enjoyed this glowing privilege of freedom, could they turn back to notions so elementary, so rudimentary, as the observance of times for ritual acts? Did not Abraham of old have two families, one of slaves, one of freemen? Hagar, the slave mother, was like the Sinai which had given the "Law" for the Jews: but the promise given to those that believe was no barren mountain of the desert: it was that heavenly city, that spiritual Jerusalem which is the mother of us all.

It was all very well then for Jews to think of circumcision as an initiation into the complexities of the "Law": but it is by faith through the Holy Spirit that we await the hope of right living which vindicates us in every place of judgment. For in Christ Jesus neither circumcision in any way avails, nor uncircumcision—but faith working through love, faith that makes a new creation: "as many", Paul concluded, "as walk in a straight line according to this canon, peace be upon them and mercy, and upon the Israel of God".[7]

7

Paul had worked out the principle of his thought: he had shown where he placed the "Law" and, indeed, the whole Jewish race which practised it—as a preparation for the coming of Christ: Christ who came to receive into Himself all men who having trusted in Him, all who believing in Him, would be baptised into Him.[8] And what was this life of faith? To answer that, Paul mentioned two opposing principles in men: one, human nature and its weaknesses; the other, the Holy Spirit and His graces.

"The supreme end for every human creature was to be linked to the Life Divine."[9] "The Son of God has come among men, and was made man that He might carry out this design. He desires that by adoption we should be brought to share in His privileges as the Son of God."[10] This is the plan which Paul had disclosed. "Walk by the Spirit", he pleads therefore, "and you will not fulfil the lust of the flesh. For the flesh might live the Spirit, and the Spirit against the flesh and if I live it is contrary to one another so that you may not What things you desire. Now the works of the flesh are in and recognisable: fornication, impurity, furies of evil desire, idolatry, sorcery, quarrels, strifes, jealousies, divisions, heresies, envyings, drunkenness, carousals and things like those: about those again I tell you plainly, as I did tell you plainly already, that those which do such things shall not inherit the kingdom of God. But the fruit of the Spirit is love, joy, peace, magnanimity, kindliness, goodness, fidelity, gentleness, self-control; against these the Law can say nothing.

"If we live by the Spirit, by the Spirit let us also walk."[11]

Such was the teaching which the most powerful writer of his age wrote to those whom he had brought to share his new conception of life, and it was worked out in a profound inward change in which all his nature, desires and impulses had been sacrificed to the mystery of life in the Christ. "Far be it from me that I should vaunt myself, unless in the Cross of our Lord Jesus Christ by whom the world is crucified for me, and I unto the world."[12] All the things of the world had been sacrificed, all his inclinations towards them mortified, that he might live a new selfless life, the life poured out by Christ through His blood that He might live in men's hearts by faith.

Such is the tenor of this first formal pronouncement of the man of genius who was to prove himself the most absorbing and influential writer of the age. His style was moulded to some extent by the Septuagint, and echoes it: but it had a tone ▓▓▓▓▓ conversational, confidential, and, when arguing, ▓▓▓▓ came to arguing to press a point home, his pen had ▓▓▓▓ e of a quick and trained talker:—"There is just one thing I w▓ to learn from you. Was it by the works of the Law you received the Spirit, or by the hearing of faith? Are you so brainless as this? having begun with the Spirit, were you finishing with the flesh? Have you had such great experiences for nothing?"[13] Here is the debater or the disciplinarian: but also he had to relate the Jewish religion to other mysteries.

Paul's tone was that of a man who poured out his whole heart in the absorbing subject of his interest: a man so eager and full of his subject that he did not stay either to polish his expression or to work out his thought to the clear sequence of logic. His tone was impetuous: it was peculiarly frank: on the one side, his style was vigorous: on the other, he was so much alive to every nuance of the situation that the flow was interrupted by the inrush of one gushing tributary after another. In this vast mystery of redemption there were so many things to keep in mind. The claims of the Jews, the claims of the other nations, the personal revelation, the intercourse with the apostles of Jesus, then the relation of the "Law" to faith, and, through the grace which included faith, his own incorporation into the very Lord he worshipped—here was a wealth of subjects which, with all his desire to argue and prove his case, led to subtleties so profound and thoughts so rich that however impetuous, however incisive he might naturally be, he was overborne by their complexity.

9

The electricity of thoughts came pouring on his mind like flashes of lightning over a canopy of stars: what he had seen in the twinkling light was now flooded with sudden flashes, each showing a glory, each too absorbing for him to relate to another. "By the Law I am dead to the Law that I ~~live~~ to God. I have been crucified with Christ, and ~~it is no~~ more I who live but Christ who lives in me. ~~What~~ I live now in the flesh, I live in the faith of the Son of God who has loved me and given Himself up for me. I do not put aside the grace of God, for if the good life could be attained through the Law, then Christ has died for nothing."[14]

"The Epistle to the Galatians", writes a French scholar who lived long in Jerusalem, "is not only a document beyond price for the history of the origin of the Church. It is not only a Charter of freedom in relation to the Jewish law. It is the expression torn from Paul by a deep religious conviction and by the tenderness and torments of his heart. His sight had been cleared; on humanity in its different aspects and stages, on the Old Testament, on Christ Himself and on His never-ceasing operation on the souls of men, he now projects something of the light which had streamed in on his own soul. And this epistle, which establishes his rights among the Apostles is also that which shows the feelings of a spiritual Father for his sons in Jesus Christ."[15] In it, now as always, advanced souls have found the power to strengthen and sustain them.

FROM THE TAURUS TO THE TROAD

1

THE DISPUTES IN ANTIOCH, THE DANGERS IN PHRYGIA, THE general insistence of the Parushim on all the points on which they had always insisted made Paul and Barnabas wonder whether they should not go back to Jerusalem once more. It was more tactful not to mention Cephas or any other of those who had come down to Antioch. It was better therefore to state that the turmoil had been fierce, the strife acute. Before they had gone with the strong persuasiveness behind them of provisions for famished people: this time they could claim in addition to that debt of obligation the addition of many converts—and converts are potential contributors. For this mission Paul may have also prepared a learned and persuasive argument such as was afterwards used in his Epistle to the Romans.

Paul and Barnabas went down the coast from Seleucia, passing Beyrout, Tyre, Sidon to Acre, and then upwards through Samaria; they were able to proclaim the success of their evangel everywhere as they passed; this thought of men living in the Christ caused deep joy. At Jerusalem they were received with honour; the Apostles, the ancients and priests, and the mass of believers heard what a wonderful number of people had been attracted to the new religion. There was a feeling of exhilaration and triumph in the community: but still the Parushim insisted on their two questions: Did you circumcise them? Are they keeping the Torah of Moses?[1]

At this point there was a feeling that all the chief authorities should hold a council and decide.

The Israelite rigorists pressed their case with characteristic confidence and vigour. They were answered with no less characteristic impetuousness by the Parush they had so often observed as Shaul: but present also was the impulsive and generous figure who had so often taken the lead, who had been the first to recognise the true uniqueness of his Master, who enjoyed a prestige that made the first recorders of the inception of the new religion always put his name first on the list of Apostles, who had received from his Master the assurance—through that prayer which was an omnipotent decision—that his faith should fail not and that, when he was confirmed in it, he should strengthen the rest: he now stood up in the debate and gave a decision.[2]

It was wholly on the side of Paul. He declared that the Holy Ghost had been given to others just as to the Jews.—"Purifying their hearts by faith, He put no distinction between us and them. Why do you press God that He should put on the neck of these learners a yoke that neither our fathers nor we were able to bear? But we believe we shall be saved just as they are, through the grace of the Lord Jesus."[3]

Both in his speech and in the man who made it there was an authority which stilled further dispute. Paul and Barnabas told their great story: a story not merely of conversions but of signs and wonders. Then the other great figure of the Twelve who had been with Jesus spoke to tell of his assent to all that Cephas and Paul had argued. He abrogated the crucial test of circumcision.

3

He did ask them, however, in their eating not to outrage those Jewish rules which were as much a matter of health and of taste as of tradition, and of significance. They must not eat meat already offered to idols: they must not eat the flesh of animals which had been strangled, nor take their blood. And as they must maintain these decent rules in eating, so must they maintain the rules of chastity which are so often outraged in the purlieus of the temple. Decency of self-restraint, decencies in the eating of meat, and a definite dissociation from the crude rites of idolatry, with all that they implied, surely this was not too much to ask?[4]

4

A letter in this tenor was taken back to Antioch. The great principle was authoritatively settled. The Community had already grown into a Church, a separate community from the Jews, a community centred on Christ, a way of holy men to live in Christ. And the Romans recognising them gave them their name from Him in whom they believed. The Way of the Pupils (or Initiates) became the Church of Christians.[5]

5

Paul had now before him new and finer adventures in his lofty cause. As soon as the Church at Antioch enjoyed the advancement he desired, he thought of setting out with his old friend to revisit the communities he had founded in Cyprus and Lycaonia; his journey was to carry him farther than he dreamed.

Knowing that the journey was to be hazardous and its demands severe, he was therefore taken aback when Barnabas told him that as for himself he would not think of starting out without his nephew Marcus. What? The youth who having put his hand to the plough looked back at Perga, and proved himself unfit for the Kingdom of God? Was it fear, or was it family affection? Marcus was in either case branded in the eyes of Paul as one of those who prefer human ties to their loyalty to the King of Heaven.

To Paul every human cord had long since been burned in the flames of his love for the Christ. He had been crucified to the dearest things in human life: he had formed countless intimacies with souls. For all he had given up, therefore, he had received in this life a hundred-fold. Between Barnabas and himself the issue was no small one, and each clung to his contention.

To Barnabas, patriarchal, paternal, mild, the company of a relation he trusted was all important. The friend whose cause he had espoused twelve years before at Jerusalem was impetuous, uncompromising, exhausting; the man dreaded then for his persecutions retained still some ruthless quality of disposition. Long years together had shown Barnabas the strain of living with so supernatural a genius. To suit himself to this companion without the service and support of his young relative was more than he could face. There was, says the chronicler, an outbreak, a "paroxysm". It was the final cleavage between two men who had come to live on different scales. Barnabas took Marcus and sailed away—out of history—to Cyprus, to that delightful island which was his home; Paul chose for companion another, a cultured Roman citizen like himself, a man of courage to share his heart and his travels, "a man of marked personality and recognised position", both in the

Church and the Empire. The name of this new companion was Silvanus.[6]

6

It was spring weather and the journey before them led them first upwards about 2,000 feet to the Syrian Gates, which travellers crossed from the Orontes Valley to the road around the picturesque gulf of Iskanderun. It is still a road with hair-pin bends that unnerve travellers in motor cars. Around them were bare hills and the wooded valleys, the myrtle and the pine, made more charming by vineyards and orchards; distant below them lay the tideless, satin sea; above them the snowy line, sublime among the clouds in their glows of dawn and evening. They passed Issos where Alexander the Great had fought his great fight. They came down to the flat plains and on to Messis, then Mopsuestia, and Adana and so to that region of Cilicia which Paul knew so well. Yet it was not of climate, of scenery, nor of old associations that he thought; his mind was absorbed in men, who lived—in faith and hope and love—the life of grace which filled him with joy and peace in the Christ. All were one in that new society which was not only human but divine: all divisions were done away; neither cir-cumcision availed nor uncircumcision, but a new creation: and to as many as walked in a straight line according to this Canon, "peace be upon them and mercy and upon the Israel of God".

Such was the message which the fervid preacher carried, while the sun strengthened and the mosquitoes bred, through the plains which the Taurus sheltered from the northern breeze.

His cavalcade of mules or of camels, the nightly shelter in the khans, the group gathering round the fires, the sudden storms, the return of sunlight, these passed over or by him, unrecorded; all that he remembered was those things which bore upon his mission. Everywhere alike he found his communities built up on welcome for the mercies of heaven and on praise. Day by day, hour by hour, he in solitude adored; then with his converts he sympathised, he encouraged, he explained. Hour by hour, he dispensed the mysteries of the Christ.

As the traveller's journey had passed from the defile to the sunny meadows and the cornfields, so all these little communities had moved from rock and desolation to green pastures beside a refreshing stream.

From Tarsus there was more than one track over the Taurus to Lycaonia. But we cannot doubt that Paul and Silvanus chose that which Cyrus, Alexander, Cicero had travelled before them into the heights and cliffs of the pass known as the Cilician Gates. The road was at times so narrow that only one camel could pass at a time. Then again came the risk of bandits: but Paul and his friend travelled the long leagues past the hills and valleys of the Northern Taurus, and then on to Podanos, Kybistra, Kastabala—where the Turkish train now runs—to Karaman, then called Laranda. From there they had an easier journey to Derbe and Lystra, with the wild heights of the Taurus still stretching out of sight on the left hand and in front once more the dark bare mass of the Kara Dagh.[7]

7

Here he met the friends of his earlier visit. Here he took to himself a new companion. A devout Jewess, named Lois, had married her daughter Eunice to a Greek in Lystra: the pair had a gifted son whom they named Timotheos.[8] Trained in the Septuagint, he was drawn to travel with Paul, taking the blessed message. Silvanus agreed that Timotheos was meant to join them. The enthusiastic youth declared his faith; and the local ancients with Paul laid their hands on him. Lest any Jew should cavil, he generously underwent the painful rite of circumcision, which the Council had wisely abrogated.[9]

This youth was to Paul the most charming and faithful companion. Timid at times and delicate, yet he worked with the fidelity and affection of a son. From the first he followed and sought to copy his great leader: his warm and sensitive temperament might at times have led him astray; but Paul could call him at the last his son faithful and loved, and say that he sought the things of Christ.[10]

8

Thus the three travelers went on and on with their work and their evangel. They passed out of the bare uplands and came to those delightful lands of mountain and valley which lead for hundreds of miles down to the coasts of the Aegean Sea. What route they took none can determine. They may have reached Chonas on the river Lycus, and then turned back:[11] they felt they must not preach in the Roman Province of Asia:[12] passing through Phrygia and the Galatian region, they journeyed towards Bithynia: but there the inspired intuition, which guided their counsels, took them from the Bithynian Olympus, from the Lake of Nicaea, from the shores of the Sea of Marmora. An imposing body of scholarship holds that it was now Paul first met and converted those whom he addressed as Galatians: the contention cannot be ignored; nor can we ignore the fact either that though the chronicler met Paul soon afterwards, he said nothing of it, or that the researches of Sir William Ramsay have provided another and better conclusion.

We do not know what the travellers said nor what course they took. Perhaps they went down the valley of the river Rhyndacos,[13] but finally they traversed the fabled plain of Troy, perhaps along the great road through Smyrna, or more directly through Thyatira, and Pergamos to Edremid, then known as Adramyttium.

An instinct of haste pressed them on through days growing always hotter. As they travelled their observation suggested to them that they were leaving Syria and the East: the new scene was already like that of Europe, or at least like Greece or Southern Italy.[14]

For the approach to the Troad had led them through country which, after the high tablelands of Lycaonia, was singularly refreshing. Not only was food easy to find—and milk—but from countless springs there sparkled a thousand rills of foam and diamonds. At point after point, the horizon was closed in by the varied and striking outline of the ranges, one behind another, sharp sometimes as the teeth of a saw, with here and there a cone or cliff which displayed the stone formation with the marble beauty of a giant statue. From the stretching mountains came the cool delicious water which fed the valleys and nourished the plane trees and the avenues of poplars. The march was tiring often: but each resting-place a Paradise: a draught of this pure water, and a morsel of bread; with here and there, perhaps, honey, or a new-laid egg, made travelling a very different story from the thirst, the hunger, the cold winds which the pilgrims had endured through the weeks before.

9

At last the scene was dominated by a new and separate mountain. This was the famous Ida, on the flanks of which, as he poets told, Zeus had embraced the Queen of Heaven, Oenone had loved Paris, and Paris had given to Aphrodite he prize of beauty.[15] Famous too were the streams, Scamander and rocky Simois, sauntering towards the sea, which now the ravellers crossed. Above them over the plain was the city of Troy from which, as Virgil had so finely told, Aeneas had set out to plant the seed of history in Ausonian land. But all this country's charm of nature, of legend and of living poetry was of little or no concern to a man whose inward eye had gazed on more brilliant prospects. In the Lord he had been given his heart's desire; in darkness, in weariness, in hunger, in thirst, in cold, in nakedness and in danger, he could recall such marvels as neither ear had heard nor eye had seen nor had entered into the heart of man to conceive; these in his visions and revelations, through ways he dared not tell, he knew to be his own, since God had laid them up for them that love Him.

XI

ON TOWARDS OLYMPUS

1

WHILE STAYING IN THE BUSY PORT OF ALEXANDRIA TROAS, THE party of three, Paul, Silvanus and Timotheos, was joined by another. The fourth was a physician or healer. He had had a thorough training in writing Greek: he was absorbed in the whole Christian story, he—as almost all will admit—was the chronicler of the journeys of St. Paul. His name was Lucanus or Lucilius.[1] Though others say he was a Macedonian, Eusebius says he came from Antioch.[2] He may well have been the brother of Titus. He may have been converted already: or he may have been brought to persecute Paul and then won over to his Way.

He was also a traveller who had learnt a good deal about sailing: it was said that he could draw and paint. But that he was a skilful compiler with a sound judgment, a delicate taste and a fine gift of style, this no scholar will deny. He was to be in fact one of the most memorable, perhaps one of the most inspired writers of an epoch-making company. That he at once proved a sympathetic and agreeable young man, we cannot doubt, nor that he had already been in Macedonia.

When Paul and his party reached Troas, they found the harbour full of ships. He was to sail over the seas in one of them, but whither? In this uncertainty, his doubts were resolved in a dream. In the suspension of active consciousness, his mind lay open to the unseen world: and as he slept, he met with one, it may have been Lucanus himself, who called, "Come over into Macedonia and help us".[3]

A ship was sailing northward. It was full summer weather, and the breeze blew freshly from the South, till at the mouth of the Dardanelles, having passed Ceos and Tenedos, they found themselves under the mountainous island of Samothrace: on the northern side of this island they could shelter from the wind till their sails were set for the Island of Thasos and the gulf it also sheltered. Facing it on the mainland is the port of Kavalla (then called Neapolis) and here the travellers landed. At a port now busy with the export of Turkish tobacco for cigarettes, the Apostle of Christ first brought to Europe the truth and powers of the new mystery.

2

That shore of Macedonia was not at first sight markedly different from the lands of mountain and sea on which Paul had seen a warm sun shine for the preceding forty years of his life. The colours were high, the light intense, the sea sparkling, the mountains wild and lofty as they rose into the intense blue. Thasos closed his view into the Aegean: bare hills rose above the harbour to the East. To the north-west the hills culminated in the lofty triangle of Pangaios, while against the southern sky stood out at the extremity of the coast the Matterhorn of Macedonia, the lofty peak of Athos.

The people, neither in themselves nor in their customs, nor in their language were vastly different from those Hellenists whom he had known always: and still among their settlements were colonies of Jews.

Taking the great Roman Road, known as the Via Egnatia, which already connected Durazzo with the Dardanelles, they had arrived after three or four hours' journey at a settlement colonised by the Romans, on the border of a stream called the

Angites. In this town a triumphal arch commemorated the victory of Augustus over Brutus and Cassius. As a Roman colony, it was a centre of the imperial administration with which Paul had had such happy relations at Baffa.[4] Its name was Philippi.

3

Here he met a striking woman, who had enriched herself in the dyeing trade. Coming over from Thyatira, and taking the name of its province, Lydia, she had inherited or developed a business which appealed to the tastes of the wealthy. It was to extract from the murex, a shell fish of the coast, the tincture favoured as the Roman purple. The province of Lydia in Asia Minor was the province of luxury, of wealth, of Croesus himself. She had no doubt developed a special knowledge of the shades, violet, heliotrope or mauve, which would make silks or wools look most attractive or most splendid.[5] This able woman was a power among the Jews, and admiring the unique gifts of St. Paul, she soon pressed him and his company to share the comforts of her house.

He had first found the worshippers with some Jewish women at the river bank after he had passed the fine triumphal arch. Such a rest in the summer weather, after the long fatigues of the journey, was most welcome: and in this atmosphere, he met men of loftier ideas of worship than other pagans he had known; the culture, the order and the charm of Italy gave their mark to the colony; he formed here, therefore, a company of prosperous and generous converts, who were always ready to come to his assistance, and who in later years filled his mind with thankfulness and joy. Here he found them living in the order of a Roman colony in a Roman province on a great Roman road. He could savour once more that Italian amenity which had attracted him a year or two before in Sergius Paulus at Baffa.

But this did not mean that the sojourn in Philippi was free from the violence and the drama which had always marked his travels.

4

For the competent Lydia was not the only woman the missionaries noticed at Philippi. There was also a young woman who, suffering from a nervous disease, or obsession, uttered strange noises and cries. Some enterprising sharpers had exploited her as a sort of prophetess. Now it often happens that a person mentally deficient or deranged still has an intuitive sense of good and evil in personalities: in Paul, this poor girl felt the presence of great powers of good. It was just such cases as hers which the followers of Christ were specially apt to treat. They exorcised the spirit troubling her: they cured her nervous malady: by this, however, her masters were deprived of a source of income. They were then, naturally enough, furious. They could not bring before the courts of Rome the story of what had been done: they could nevertheless plot and plan a revenge. So they decided to accuse the new-comers of agitating the city, and spreading doctrines that were disturbing to Roman citizens. The idea of an outrage on the veneration of the Emperor by wandering Jews provoked so much uproar that before any case had been heard, the lictors had seized Paul and Silvanus, torn their clothes off and thrashed them with their rods, a bundle of which, the fasces, they always carried with them. They then thrust their victims into their gaol, of which the inner part seems to have been a cave hewn out of the rock;⁶ here the gaolers made their prisoners' feet fast in the stocks.

At this new tribulation Paul was consoled by one of those accesses of exaltation which he had so often enjoyed: at midnight he, with Silvanus, hymned the Resurrection: and, as he did so, an earthquake broke open the dungeon doors and freed them from the stocks.[7] The gaoler, terrified at the earthquake, was yet more horrified to find the dungeon doors open. In this mood of terror, he heard from the prisoners that they were Roman citizens. To fetter a Roman citizen was crime enough: to flog him, and without a trial—this was a shameful outrage.[8] Whatever gods there were had plainly taken vengeance.

Conscience-stricken, the gaolers realised that their prisoners had behind them the powers of truth and life. How could these be propitiated? How could the men be saved? Paul answered them with the name of Jesus. Let them put their whole trust and confidence in Him. He explained to them the mysteries of the Way, the Secret of the Church. The gaoler understood: he believed: he took Paul with him, and washed his weals and bruises. And then, in that water in which in faith men were born again, they were received into the Church.

What had won over the gaolers had impressed the duumviri. Better let these men go. But "No," said Paul, seeing his opportunity, "we have the power to threaten now. You have fettered, you have scourged Roman citizens. You are yourselves offenders against the majesty of the Law." Such was the message with which he charged the lictors. The Romans understood, and begged them to depart. Stiff, bruised, but triumphant, the three once more set out upon their journey, leaving Lucanus behind.[9]

5

Though in the full heat of summer, travelling was hardly less delightful than it had been on the other side of the Aegean.

binski)

ATHENS—LOOKING THROUGH THE COLUMNS OF THE
PARTHENON TOWARD LYCABETTOS

The same springs of sparkling water, the same road paved with marble, the same villages, the same background of mountain and hill marked the scene of their progress along a smiling valley, over a verdant plain. So wiry was Paul's constitution that he was already recovering from his torment and his wounds.

They came first to Amphipolis on the river Strymon at the base of high Pangaios. From here their path led them close to the shore from which they could again see Mount Athos and later Thasos across the glittering waves. They crossed the stream which led to the wooded shores at Stavros. Then they passed through the Aulon of Arethusa near which is the grave of Euripides. About them fluttered storks, and bee-eaters; pale green "rollers" were swaying in the air. On the ground were tortoises and scorpions. Most numerous of all was a large copper-coloured grasshopper, the size of a mouse, which as they drew near discharged in fright a canary-yellow liquid.[10] The cool air, the flowing stream, the growth of shrubs and stalks had been gay as an Alpine valley, but they were placed at the edge of a furnace.

For the next stopping-place, Apollonia, is in the centre of a stretch of flat ground between Lake Beshik and the Hortiach range; in the month of June this stretch will burn with torrid heat. From the exhausting sun, the flocks of sheep, and the herds of oxen sheltered beneath the trees, while the ducks sought shelter among the reeds at the edge of the lake. All slept but the buzzing insects or a few noisy birds. The travellers took their rest in the heat of the day: but before long they were rising once more over the hills, and after passing the peak of Hortiach they saw a view more superb, more significant than any they had yet seen. At the head of a long inlet a noble town was built on the edge of still water which mirrored many masts. Beyond it, over the water, rose through the mists a lofty outline which they would have thought itself a cloud but that its form was fixed, while its colour changed from rose through every shade of pearl to dazzling white.

That was the mountain on which the soaring surmise of Hellenic imagination had placed the court of Zeus and all his hierarchy: it was Olympus: to the left of it stretched Pelion and Ossa: the city—which faced this earthly counterpart of heaven in a place where navigation had long meant, and still means, wealth and what that brings of monuments and beauty —was Salonika.

Here the Jews had already built their synagogue. It was these to whom Paul was before long to address his exordium to a new literature for Hellas, to whom he was to tell a story which would guide them, as common men, to a far higher heaven than that which the great Homeric epic had pictured as the privilege of those Olympians whom Cicero declared already to have vanished when he came along the Egnatian Road from Durazzo some hundred years before.

6

Travelling here for refuge during his exile Cicero referred to the citizens of Salonika as "placed in the lap of the Empire".[11] Strabo and Lucian had noticed it as the most flourishing city of Macedonia.[12] Gibbon tells us that it was afterwards thought of as the capital of the whole Roman world.[13] Yet it had never been so Romanised as Philippi: it remained a Greek city, ruled by its own Greek politarchs. In view of its place on the great Roman road to the Bosphorus, its large colony of Jews, above all its close relation to Hellas, and not least its superb views and situation, it was to the Jewish traveller the entrance into European civilisation.[14] From that moment he had to prepare to place his message before the thinkers of Athens and of Rome.

Yet he began as usual with the synagogue, and while waiting to do so, he set to work as a craftsman to earn his living.[15] When he spoke, he again based his case on the Septuagint and its promise of a Christos. He showed how there were words pointing to a Man of Sorrows, and to One who should rise again. He told them how he had himself, in the intense reality of inward vision, seen this Risen Man. Those who had seen Him die and rise again Paul had himself known; now the power of His Spirit was with those that believed—to give them in holiness and in everlasting life the fulfilment of every mercy.

The beauty and persuasiveness of his teaching convinced many, not only of the Jews, but of the wealthier women, and of the Greeks who, in their search for a religion purer and more vital than was offered by their poets or their philosophers had been turning, and not in vain, towards the Septuagint.

But Paul was in danger, and he knew it. Thrashed at Philippi,[16] he might here be thrashed again. Conventional bigotry and racial vanity combined to exacerbate the unconvinced Jews. With their usual subtlety they laid their plans. It was to induce the crowd of ne'er-do-wells, gathered in the market-place, to make a riot in the streets. Singing, shouting, this horde of riff-raff was led to the house where Paul, Timotheos and Silvanus had their lodging: as they could not be found, their host was seized and dragged before the politarchs. He was accused of harbouring revolutionaries, men who having disturbed other parts of the Roman Empire had now arrived in Salonika, to impugn the authority of the Emperor, and to set up as rival sovereign their Jesus.[17]

Now it was just at that time that in Rome itself the Jews had been expelled by the Emperor Claudius, for making tumult and strife in the city, at the instigation, as Suetonius records it, of Chrestus;[18] this sounded very like the Christos about whom Paul was speaking. The rumour of any revolution against the power of the Emperor was highly disturbing both to the politarchs and to the Greek populace they represented. A pledge was extracted from their host not to keep Paul and his friends in Salonika. Secretly and at night Paul (still with Silvanus and Timotheos) was led out of it across the Vardar valley to make his way some forty miles across the plain to Verria, then called Beroea: on this plain they saw herds of oxen, flocks of sheep, and ducks among its pools and marshes.[19]

Verria is a little town fronting Olympus at a height of 600 feet from the north side of the Haliakmon valley: a town noisy with watercourses from the fresh springs above it, pouring down to nourish the pomegranate, the fig and the vine. Here there were also Jews, but Jews of a higher class than those in Salonika. These, and Greek men and women of some position, Paul again succeeded in persuading. Here his most enthusiastic adherent was named Sosipatros. How did he put forth a teaching to appeal both to Jews and to educated Greeks?

7

The Greeks, still mingling the Stoic philosophy with crude anthropomorphic conceptions associated with their sculpture, might indeed have listened with interest to what the Jews could tell them of the mercy of the one true Lord of Life: both they and the Jews were disturbed by the fear of death, and by fear of the wrathful judgment of heaven. They spoke of Nemesis and the Eumenides. A sense of doom and vengeance had made them full of fear. Paul placed before both Jew and Greek a conception infinitely nobler than this grim obeisance before the justice and wrath of the divine powers. He taught them that God was their Father: that He had called them to His own kingdom and glory. Paul spoke with mingled gentleness and sympathy, a swift and radiant affection.[20] He promised them that cure of the soul which would give them power and glory at once and for ever: he freed them from the fear of death.[21] Jesus had not departed from them. He had said: "I am with you always even to the consummation of the age", and who knew when He would come in glory in the clouds of heaven, taking to Himself those who were awaiting Him, raising the bodies of those who had died with Him. All would be caught up to meet Him.

This was the exciting promise, partly mystical, partly allegorical, partly imaginative, which he set forth to satisfy the anxiety and curiosity of his hearers. Primitive people want things put in ways they can understand.[22] Paul made his subtle doctrine as simple as he could: he spoke as a babe to babes, or rather baby-language as a nurse speaks to the baby she loves.[23]

Above all he taught them that they were in the Church, and the Church was in Christ and Christ was in God. They must, therefore, be holy and blameless: they must above all purify their affections so as not to bring them down to the crudities of sex and its looseness, as they, like the Syrians, were only too prone to do—rather must they be blameless, honest, living with one another in unselfishness, in patience and in peace.[24] And beside all these gifts of the Spirit came those three virtues which were always echoing through his mind: faith—to turn with undying trust to Him who could give them what they hoped for: hope—which gave them a confident expectation of blessings enriching them from day to day for eternal things: and love and charity which made them one both with one another and with God.[25]

Such, as Paul afterwards recalled, was the teaching which,

with his genius and fervour, he preached in the busy port and in the quiet country town beyond where the Vardar flowed from the Rhodope ranges to meet the traffic of the Empire of Claudius at the foothills of Olympus.

8

A doctrine so spiritual, so pure, so radiant, could not but appeal to those who had already felt within their hearts the holy inspiration which showed them the truth and promises contained—though in form and degree how different!—both in the literature of Israel, and in the epics, the tragedies and the philosophies of Hellas.

Nevertheless it could not but infuriate those who took their religion as an exclusive claim to personal superiority, as the proud legalism of the hypocrite, or as a cloak to the greed of the Levantine haggler and trickster. The Jews who had persecuted the envoy of God in Salonika sent their messengers to Verria: and before long Paul was again on the sea shore, driven to escape; and this time neither Timotheos nor Silvanus was with him.[26] He now planned to make his way along the coast of Thessaly to Attica, to that shrine of Pallas Athene which rose over against Parnes and Hymettos above the Ilissos and the Kephissos—the home of Plato and of Aristotle, of Myron and Praxiteles, the ancient capital where Pericles had gathered the most brilliant genius that not only Europe but the Mediterranean had seen, the very heart of Hellas which was "the nurse of man complete as man" before he became "pregnant with the living God".[27]

IN ATHENS AND CORINTH

1

FROM THE MOMENT HE HAD ARRIVED IN MACEDONIA PAUL HAD been travelling through a country as much marked by its mountainous surface as by its indented outline. Not yet in his life had he seen, nor was he ever to see, anything in nature more remarkable than the view which met him as, with the sun rising upon Olympus, he saw against the dawn beyond the deep gulf the distant height of Athos. The nights were warm with the softness of late summer: the dawn was the one fresh moment: the outlines of the heights rose in signal majesty over the intense colour in air and water. Pelion and Ossa emerged in more distinctness as the boat tacked southward, till between Skopelos and Skiathos his boat turned westward between Euboea* and the great Gulf of Volo.

He was learning for the first time the nature of the true Hellas. The mountains grouped themselves into distinct chains, with well-marked summits and delicate outlines. For Greece is a country of blue and white, like her flag: at every turn the deep inlets of her coast take the bright blue of the sea into the scene with the white summits of her mountains. He was approaching that angle of Thessaly where the Othrys range diverges toward the East from the Aetolian mountains which run south-west. Between these another range passed on to rise to Parnassus, to Helicon, and above the Gulf of Aegina as Parnes and that of Corinth as Cithaeron.

*Now pronounced Evvia.

This continuous presence of the mountains and the sea had left its mark on the genius and temper of the Hellenes. The delicacy of the outlines, the purity and brilliance of the colour of every scene made

.... interminglings mild
Of light with shade, in beauty reconciled.[1]

The alternation in one view of land and water, of plain and mountain, of wild ravine and shining tableland, of fertile valley and snow-decked crag, all deepened in effect by the sparkling blue coming into every wide view from the indenting sea, stamped on the soul of the lover of Hellas the taste for beauty. It made the people like the country temperate and many sided; it gave them independence. The simple rugged mountaineer was never far away from all that the seafarer brings from his travel and his changes.

The Greeks therefore were as versatile as they were moderate. Humanism came naturally to people living in the long summers in scenes where variety made every vista as interesting as it was symmetrical. Trained also to hardihood at the same time as they had every pleasure of climate, the natives of Greece had been constantly affected by the neighbouring shores of Asia till the very energy of their minds was projected into metaphysics and mystery.

Philosophical, athletic, cultured, versatile, the Hellenes had been for centuries the humanist civilizers of the world: their language was the language of culture and cosmopolitanism; but, though endowed with infinite charm, with taste, with gaiety and with intelligence, they had failed to attain to the loftiness of the Hebrew religion, or to the governing power of Rome.[2] Indebted to them as Paul was for many conceptions, and for the easy adaptable language which made his project possible, how was he to speak to them, how use their culture to preach the evangel he brought? Such was the question implicit in the fascinating scenes which unfolded as he sailed on to Chalkis and Euripos where every six hours the tide flows in a contrary direction. A few hours later, passing Kynosura, his boat had sailed from the calm waters into waves as it made its way on from the Boeotian coast to where Marathon looks on the sea, and on again to the silver mine of Laurion, where Themistocles had built his fleet for Athens.

As he came round Cape Colonna and entered into the delightful panorama of the Saronic Gulf, he saw in all its beauty the marble temple of Sunion raise its columns direct above the sea. After the course turned to north-west there gradually came into view a crest of rock glistening with marble temples, and as he came nearer he could see that near the largest and finest of these rose a colossal statue of a goddess with helmet and spear flashing in the sun. Then he came in sight of the Acropolis of Athens. In this city of monuments, amid this populace of marble (elegant in the Empire of Claudius as the Cambridge of Longfellow in the States of Abraham Lincoln) he must now procliam the mystery of the Christ.

3

Five hundred years before, under Cimon, the Athenians had taken from Ionia not only her merchandise but her civilization, which meant both her arts and her philosophy. Cimon had planted trees and dressed them, laying out among them walks and fountains. Pericles, succeeding Cimon as ruler, followed him in the protection of the arts, and, as Plutarch records, thought to make Athens the capital of a federated Hellas. But the fame of Athens rested on her supremacy in culture, on the achievements not of warriors, but of the poet, the sculptor, the builder and the sage. "Revolution after revolution", wrote Newman, "passed over the face of Europe as well as of Greece, but still she was there—Athens, the city of the mind—as radiant, as splendid, as delicate, as young as ever she had been."

"Many a more fruitful coast or isle is in that blue Aegean; many a spot is there more beautiful or sublime to see, many a territory more ample, but there was one charm in Attica which in the same perfection was nowhere else. The deep pastures of Arcadia, the plain of Argos, the Thessalian vale, these had not the gift. Boeotia, which lay to its immediate north, was notorious for its very want of it. The heavy atmosphere of that Boeotia might be good for vegetation, but it was associated in popular belief with the dullness of the Boeotian intellect: on the contrary, the special purity, elasticity, cleanness and salubrity of the air of Attica, fit concomitant and emblem of its genius, did that for it which earth did not—it brought out every bright hue and tender shade of the landscape over which it was spread, and would have illuminated the face even of a more bare and rugged country."[3]

4

In this city, steeped in electric air and sparkling with the influence of genius, there was of course a Jewish colony and a synagogue where the zealous, if fatigued, Israelite would find the religion in which he had been brought up, where he could hear of the Law of the Lord, and sing His mercy and His praise.

But what grieved and impressed Paul in the city was that at every point the most admired statues were named after the denizens of Olympus. House after house had, in its tanagras, miniature representations of these. Above Salonika Paul had been able, on a hill which gave him a superb view of the town and harbour, to survey at leisure the mountain where those gods and goddesses had been said to hold their court. Climbing now above Athens on to Lycabettos he could see not only Parn , r Hymettos commanding the plain of Attica, but full in view he eminence which, as he sailed up from Sunion, had first arrested his attention, the shrines of Pallas and her company.

That Doric simplicity, that subtle proportion of line and column, those tinctures of blue and red and yellow on the marble, those reliefs and statues, what in their classic elegance did they convey to the trained Jew who looked at them more than an outrage of the first commandment: "Thou shalt have none other gods but Me"?

5

How, he asked, sick at heart, was he to convey to a people nurtured in this mythology and trained by the Stoics in the Platonic tradition, the idea of a heavenly Father who had sent His Son to save them?

Yet, as he looked at the Athenians more closely, he was reminded that their philosophy was still feeling after God: it still taught that in the world of timeless being reigned a Mind, that this Mind was mirrored in every human being, and that above the unseen and the seen was the majesty of an unalterable Law. Along such lines he could preach to them, he could argue —could he not?—the Majesty of this great God and Lord, whom even the Athenians felt in some dim way to be their master, and who in the life of mystic contemplation not only gave them communion with the ideals of truth, of beauty, and of love, but showed them justice, prudence, temperance, fortitude as the basis of character, and for them always the love of the ideal was the crown of the life of thought. But he could appeal to something more scientific: the grouping of nations, the ordering of the world, the idea that the very nourishment of life came from an inward Spirit; and surely he could argue from all these to the need of a spiritual renewal, and so to their adoption into that Incarnate God who had raised them to heavenly places when He had risen with His human nature and ascended into heaven.

Along such lines Paul was thinking out his persuasion for the philosophers when, among the statues of naked and perfectly formed young men in which the great sculptors had depicted their ideals, he saw on a tablet the inscription Αγνωςτοι θεωι : "To the Unknown God". This could mean either of two things: "To one or other of the tutelary powers" or "To the Great God, sought, but abiding hidden". In a surge of pity and hope, the envoy of the Church attached to it the richer meaning; and then he began to set out his argument.

Like fashionable and idle people of culture everywhere, the young Athenians craved always to be at the crest of novelty's wave. Their passion was fashion. And this eloquent Hellenist from Syria provided certainly the last sensation. They led him up from the market-place towards the marble crest of their Acropolis to give a more connected discourse. Below the entrance to this was a lower eminence hanging on a cliff above the city; it overlooked the Theseion and the Agora, and beyond these the busy streets and quiet Colonos; one could see afar against the sunset Daphne and Eleusis and Acro-Corinth and the sea, till gracious outlines faded into luminous sky. Such is the view from the Field of Ares, God of War, where the Cilician Jew was to introduce to classical culture the scheme of his evangel.

The actual words he employed we do not know: the record of his speech is in the words of a suaver and more ordered diction than that ever used by the restless subtlety, the torrential fervour, the inconsequent and arbitrary expansiveness of Paul himself. But a record of his speech recalls how apposite was his argument to men of thought who cherished in their imaginations a sense that Zeus was the father of Gods and men.

6

"Gentlemen of Athens," he began, using the formula of Socrates, "I observe that in all things you are extraordinarily preoccupied with the unseen. For as I was passing through your streets, and looking at your objects of worship, I found a tablet which bore the inscription *To the Unknown God*. What therefore ye unknowingly worship, that I expound to you. The God who made the world and all that is in it, He being the Lord of Heaven and Earth, dwells not in temples made by hands; neither is He served by man's hands as though He needed anything, seeing that He has given to all men life and breath and all things. For He made of one species all nations of men to dwell on all the face of the earth, having determined beforehand their appointed seasons, and the boundaries of their habitations."

So far Paul had established them on these grounds they could understand:—the unseen power who was the giver of life and who gave to men their place according to climate and natural conditions: and what was the object of the Divine Being in thus ordering the Universe but that they should attain to His mystery?—"To seek God if haply they might feel after Him and find Him, seeing He is not far from every one of us. In Him we live, and move, and have our being, as certain of your own poets have said. For we also are of His race." Thus in his argument Paul united with the soaring instinct of the poet the metaphysical account of the life and genius of man to the sustaining source of all things. "Being therefore of the race of God," he continued, "we should not worship Him with gold or silver or stone in the handiwork of art and of the conception of man, as though God were such as that. Now having seen from on high those times of unawareness, God at this time cries aloud unto men that all men, in all places, should remould their minds: for He has established a day on which He deems to establish in the inhabited world the decision of justice in the Man whom He has appointed, claiming from all men confidence in Him, for He has raised Him from the dead."[4]

7

As he led his exposition to its climax, the voice of the preacher gathered in power till, with awed yet triumphant conviction, he told of the infallible proof that he could place before them: a man who, after he died, *rose again*.

But as through the warm evening air the voice of the Syrian enthusiast rang on the ears of his sophisticated listeners, it failed in its effect. When the preacher brought forward the argument of an historic fact which transcending their experience offered a new explanation of the universe, they thought it but a naif return to the crudities of poetry and of mythology, which they had long discarded; others, hesitating between incredulity, a fear of ridicule, and a desire not to seem discourteous said: "We will hear you on this subject another time". And Paul, passing through the crowd, came down the hill, baffled, crestfallen and alone.

When a man has surpassed himself in eloquence on a unique theme, and has met with derision, the reaction is bitter and exhausting, but still more difficult for him is the superiority which is too courteous for more than a smile. To continue his mission in Athens was more than he could face. Yet not in vain if from its votaries of wisdom and the arts, some man, some woman, heard, understood, and received in grace the gift that opened the heavenly treasure and drew them to the warm heart of Jesus.

8

Exhausted, yet consoled, that from Athens one soul and yet another, a Damaris, a Denys, had come to the feet of the Redeemer, Paul made his way past Eleusis and Megara to the great modern city of business where at a narrow isthmus the traffic of the Eastern Seas met that of Italy and of Rome in another scene of sapphire and silver, of snowy mountains, of wide prospects and of sparkling sea, of autumn days still mild and warm, of purple nights of stars, of bees, of cicadas, of grapes green and purple, where the breeze turned the olive from sage-green to silver, and where the cypress raised against the azure the tawny splendour of her plume.

Here, where nature was so perfect, ships brought their own beauty and mystery, and the traffickers untied their corded bales.

9

Yet, though so finely set, Corinth was no paradise. Athens had been a shrine of elegance and associations: this was not. It was a big, crowded haunt where many evils had gathered and many vices were indulged. To the temple of Aphrodite Urania which stood on the heights above, with shrines of Helios and Eros, were dedicated a thousand courtesans.[5] Wearied by his months of adventure, and solicitude, saddened by the paganism and evil surging round him, weakened at the end of the summer by a return of malaria, and depressed by poverty, Paul felt all exhilaration leave him. Turning to Jesus for consolation, he found in Him above all the Man of Sorrows. And leaving the high argument he had so masterfully prepared for the cultured society of Athens to speak something more suitable to sailors and to shopmen, to worldlings and voluptuaries, and to Jewish pedlars and their women, he turned to the Cross: he preached nothing but Christ Crucified: he longed that men might die to sin for the sake of Him who died to save them.

He gave up what he called excellency of speech: he said nothing for the philosophers: he lost all personal confidence. He was shaking from the ague: he was feeble and sore broken: his strength failed him. But Paul owes his place in history to the fact that he could make of Christ Crucified a theme more eloquent than the highest speculations of the Platonists: more telling than a tragic oration written by Sophocles or Aeschylus to tell of the stuff that weighs heaviest on the human heart.

DIVINE FORCE AND ENERGY

1

HOW WAS THE TIRED TRAVELLER TO LIVE? THE SAME EDICT OF Claudius which had accentuated his difficulties in Salonika and Verria now supplied him with the aid he needed. Among the Jews expelled from Rome was an Armenian Jew, who had taken his name from the eagle, Aquila: he had married a woman of a certain rank and cultivation, for she had the elegant Roman name of Priscilla. These were already Christians.[1] And Paul, providentially, came on them soon after his arrival. So began one of his happiest friendships. They understood the weaving of goats' hair, and soon the three friends were working together at the same craft. Such was the occupation Paul found for his hands while his nerves rested: on the sabbath day, he went as usual to the synagogue. And there, adding the training and authority of a Rabbi to his force of Christian conviction, he had soon won over the very Ruler of the Synagogue, Stephanas; there were several other new names: Gaius, Quartus, Fortunatus, Crispus, Titus, Justus, Chloe: to write into the book of life.[2]

But one morning the loom was still. Silvanus and Timotheos had arrived from Macedonia. How much they had to say, explaining just what the difficulties were—the doubts, the failings—the curiosity about the new life, and the rising of the Christ. Since Paul dared not go back, all he could do was to write a letter; and this, though not one of his masterpieces, was to be read, studied, quoted, as no great passage of prose or verse yet written in Attica.

Did Paul write it himself? He never wrote with his own hand; at the appointed hour his amanuensis would appear with writing materials. The ink was made of charcoal, gum and water, compounded so skilfully that, after nearly 2,000 years, enough of the colour remains to make the writing legible. The pen was a reed, cut and trimmed to a point like a quill. The material to be written on was manufactured from the pith of papyrus, a plant growing beside the Nile. In texture and colour it was not unlike the smooth, whitish-brown paper used in modern times by shopkeepers as a wrapping for parcels.

Papyrus could be bought in either separate sheets or rolls. The average size of a single sheet for private use was about 10 inches by 5 inches. The rolls were composed of a number of sheets joined together by the maker.

The writing was not continued in long lines across the papyrus; it was set down in narrow columns each about 3 inches wide, and there might be five such parallel columns running down the roll with an interval of an inch or two between them. Many words were written in a contracted form. There was no punctuation, no division into chapters and verses and no space between words. The papyrus on which it was written would be rolled very tightly and either tied with a thread or fastened with a clay seal.[3]

Such then was the way his words were set down.

What were their claims to attention? Even in its opening salutation, this letter told of conceptions richer and more elevated than Hellenes, with all their genius had heard: "Paul and Silvanus and Timotheos to the Church of Salonika in God the Father and the Lord Jesus Christ. Grace be to you and peace".[4] Those simple Macedonians were then in God and *God was their father!* They were the inheritors from Him of grace and peace! Paul went on to speak of faith, of love, of hope. The evangel had come to him not in word only, but in ower, and in the Holy Spirit, and in much abundance so that his converts became an example to all that believed.

Therefore also, he said, "We give thanks to God constantly hat taking up the spoken word of God from us, you received t not as the word of men, but as it truly is, the word of God who is a force and energy working anew within you who have he faith".[5] He spoke, in words of intense ardour, of his love for his people: he pleaded his own example: he spoke of his longing to see them again: he was taken from them in presence not in heart. "We would have come to you, I, Paul, once and again, but Satan hindered us. For what is our crown of triumph f not you, in the presence of our Lord Jesus in His coming? For you are our glory and our joy."[6]

Had Athens in the age of Pericles, or Macedonia in that of Alexander, heard so warm a language of the heart, so great confidence and thankfulness, so vital an identification of man with man, so full and deep a sense of the relations of himself with others, that it was "glory and joy"? "The Lord make you to abound in love one towards another and towards all, as we also do to you, so as to establish you all unblameable in holiness in the presence of God our Father at the coming of our Lord Jesus with all His saints."[7]

2

What was God's plan for them? That they should be made holy. Freed from lust and passion, their hearts should catch fire with the love of God, who had taught them to love one another. Love with faith was their breastplate: their helmet the hope of salvation. All were to be in Christ who died that, whether we wake or sleep, whether we live or die, we should be with Him: for in His presence is life. So the Christians'

ways were to be transformed till they ever followed that which
was good, both among themselves and with all men: "Rejoice
evermore: pray constantly: in every happening give thanks . .
and the very God of peace sanctify you wholly, and may your
whole spirit and soul and body be preserved blameless in the
coming of our Lord Jesus Christ. Faithful is He who calls you,
who also will accomplish this. Brothers, pray also for us. Greet
all the brothers with the holy sign of love. The grace of our
Lord Jesus Christ be with you all."[8]

Such was the first letter he sent to be read in Europe to all
the Churches: he mentioned those of Salonika: he must have
had in mind all his converts in Macedonia: all who had come
to live in Christ since he had heard the voice of the pleading
Macedonian in that dream which he had dreamed in the harbour close to Troy.

The thought of them made even his persecution among them
seem a gain: what were tribulations but a cause of glory? In
his sense of triumph he forgot the many things that grieved
and disturbed his soul in the tainted life of Corinth, which was
to owe to his presence and his work a new celebrity; gathering
to itself associations that mingled oddly with those which otherwise made its name familiar to the world—fluted columns and
dried grapes.

3

The Emperor Claudius had decided at this time again to
send a Senator to govern Achaia; his new Proconsul was a man
of unusual culture and unusual charm. Son of a well-known
speaker, elder brother to an essayist and thinker famous still
as Seneca, Marcus Annaeus Novatus took an interest both in
nature and in books; this combined with his delightful manners

nd his wit to fascinate all who knew him; his polished culture made him eminently suited to govern for Rome the province which contained Tiryns, Argos, Epidauros, Eleusis and Athens. As a boy, he had been adopted and trained by another well-known orator, Lucius Junius Gallio, and at adoption, he had taken his foster father's name.[9]

Such was the writer before whom the recalcitrant Jews of Corinth now led the newcomer who had converted the former leader of their synagogue. After the conversion of Crispus, another had been appointed ruler of the synagogue in his place. This new man, Sosthenes, complained that whereas by the edicts of Caesar the Jews were guaranteed freedom of worship, they were being disturbed by a new sect that had no such privileges of immunity.

In an argument of Jew against Jew, why should a Roman interfere? As soon as the Proconsul had heard the complaints of a man whom he must needs regard as another Jewish fanatic, he made the answer that every experienced administrator of that time or this would make. He was there to uphold the Roman law: to exercise administration, not to take a part in personal quarrels or in arguments as to what this ubiquitous and insistent tribe made of a peculiar religion. "If it were a question of a crime or irregularity, I should hear you in the proper way," he said, "but if this is a dispute on a matter of your teaching, or the interpretation of your authority, or a controversy over your books, you must settle that yourselves. I do not want to pass judgment on such matters."[10]

Imperturbable, shrewd, urbane, but perfectly clear as to his authority, the cultured Roman gave orders to clear the court. There was an uproar and Sosthenes, obstinately refusing to give way, soon felt the blows of the lictor's rod, perhaps of others. The greater the uproar, the more decided the unconcern of Marcus Annaeus Novatus Gallio. Convinced of his

superiority, he turned with his habitual urbanity to more congenial and more practical affairs. So it was that the man of
genius who was to play a part in Roman culture for century on
century made no impression on the Roman who was the most
cultured and advanced of any that he ever met. Charming manners, worldly experience and literary culture may easily leave
on one side him whom history afterwards recognised as the
great reformer of society, and the master of spiritual truth.
But in later years Gallio was to have, after a distinguished and
honourable life, the same fate as Paul. Nero gave each their
reward.

4

Though silenced, as he was about to speak to the Proconsul,
Paul learnt from him a significant thing: he learnt that to the
Roman administration his evangel was to be considered not a
new religion, hostile to the Emperor, but as a variant of the
Jewish religion which Caesar had sanctioned long since by edict
after edict. He was therefore legally free to preach as he
wished: if the proconsuls were not all as favourable as Sergius
Paulus in Cyprus, yet he need not expect them to be more
hostile than Annaeus Gallio in Achaia. The conclusion was
simple: he should remember that where proconsuls had set up
their provincial capitals, he had the Roman law to guarantee
his freedom.

At Cenchrea, the Eastern port of Corinth, Paul again found
Jews and among the women a convert whom he trusted,
Phoebe. While there, whether in thankfulness for a favour,
as a pledge for future blessings, or to complete a ritual preparation, Paul had his head shorn. Thus marked as a Jew, set apart
for a special purpose, and strictly observant of the Jewish re-

igion, he set sail from Corinth for Ephesus, the Roman capital
of Asia, on his way to report to Jerusalem the result of years
of enterprise.[11]

5

Before he did so, however, he wrote a second time to
Salonika. Silvanus and Timotheos, returning, had brought back
a fresh account of persecution and afflictions. Paul though
touched was not dismayed. Such afflictions were but the sure
sign of God's favour. "We pray always for you", he wrote,
"that our God may make and count you worthy of your calling,
and may fulfil every inclination of goodness and work of faith
in you."[12] His prayer was that Christ might be glorified in
them and they in Christ.

He had heard that they were still absorbed in the idea of a
fresh advent of the Redeemer. He had to speak of it much
when he was with them: he had already once written at length
about it: he must now write once again to warn them that
before Christ came, the lawless one should display his power
to deceive in signs and portents. But the great mystery of
Christianity was independent of such events as these. "God
chose you from the beginning for salvation in the hallowing of
the spirit, and in believing the truth, and for this He called
you through our evangel to encompass and embrace the glory
of Christ our Lord."[13]

If therefore they talked much, as the Jews had been in the
habit of talking of the great coming of the Lord, when he
would return like a monarch making a state visitation to some
region of his territory, Paul would answer them in symbolical
terms such as they would understand. The nurse, he said, when
she explains things to a baby, must talk in baby talk. But

though he had not forgotten what, as a Jew, he had once gathered from the Talmud or the Midrash, the importance of the distinction between this world and the world to come, or the age to come, was, in the power and intensity of his inward vision, dying away. "The writers of the New Testament", says Prat, "give the present age or present world only a moral value: the present age has lost its notion of duration and the present world its idea of space; henceforth, the present age and the age to come can interpenetrate each other; there is no chronological interval between them; there are only opposing influences. On the one hand the idea of a sudden catastrophe inaugurating the reign of the Messiah, and of an instantaneous cataclysm caused by God alone, without the co-operation of man, who will be only a passive instrument, gives place to that of a Messianic Kingdom, developing by degrees till the consummation of all things. In these conditions the Jewish concept of the age or the world to come was almost inapplicable, and it was necessary to replace it by eternal life."[14]

"This idea of a world which was gradually to become the realm where corruption was done away and the spirit ruled was the fruit of a belief rich in the gifts already given. It made them the pledge of immortality and glory. The Spirit of Life is already within us. The pledge we have received is not distinct from the Holy Spirit, it is the Holy Spirit; it is a gift we already possess, though by more closely identifying ourselves with it, by making it more intimately our own, we can bring it as we bring ourselves to perfection."[15]

Grace flowers out into glory. Between the one and the other, who shall too sharply distinguish?[16] "Whoever is grafted into Christ is by that very fact associated with His immortal life in glory."[17]

Such was the assurance which Paul proclaimed from the beginning to the end.

6

It had been the achievement of Paul to have arrived at this scheme from the strictest intelligent appreciation that a cosmopolitan Jew could give to the gradual unfolding of the Old Testament. He was born into its tribal code: he was steeped in its superb literature from which he could draw treasures at will: phrase after phrase he had found most precious: phrase after phrase had shown itself elastic and alive: as he put his hand into the jewels he found infinite riches in a little room: and from them he could draw at will things which flashed like an opal with hidden lights and fires. But what excited him in the Jewish Scriptures was their expectancy. For wisdom in her subtlety told him that "while all things held quiet silence, wisdom came from her hidden throne". Like those around him, he was waiting for the King who would force Rome and all the world to acknowledge that the Jews were the people God chose.

Then, to his human mind was added a gift of spiritual experience so overpoweringly real as to lift him into another order: that of faith, of revelation and of mystery; so it is through these that he is led to his knowledge of the Christ, and of holiness, and of both in the fulness of the Church.

7

To manifest and irradiate this glory: such was the task he had accomplished in Macedonia and Achaia. Where Thasos and Athos rose from the deep gulf of Kavalla, where the Roman arch marked the triumph of Caesar's successor on the Egnatian Road at Philippi, where that road came to a great harbour over against Olympus; in the quieter country town in

the valley below the mountain, in his journey past the shore
of Thessaly and Boeotia, among the sculpture and the pillar
of the city of Plato and Praxiteles, in the traffic, the volatility
and the vice of Corinth, he had brought not only the news, but
the power, of a new way of life. Men, to escape from the
dangers which they feared and the defilements which dis-
heartened them, should lift the everlasting doors to the King
of Glory. But how manage such engineering as this? By the
electric current of holiness—which came to them as divine
grace, which grew among them as peace.

Yet his depression at Corinth, his repugnance to what he saw
there, his recoil from the culture of Athens, all leading as they
did to an insistence on the Crucifixion, left a danger behind.
The Corinthians were given to cliques and factions. When,
after his departure, they heard from men of Jerusalem of
something more personal of the life of Christ: when they
heard from Alexandria of the philosophic line given by the
School of Philo, there were many who questioned whether
Paul was really the man to follow.

8

But his memories of his crude converts in Corinth mingled
with many others, as in the Spring weather he sailed between
the Isles of Greece, which floated like leaves in the blue sea,
till after two or three days of sailing he reached Ephesus, and
on through the Straits between Samos and Trogyllion, past
many a hilly island and sandy bay, past Calymna and Kos to
Piskopi. After passing Rhodes, he went out of sight of land
and harbour into the vast void of the Lycean and Egyptian
Sea: day after day he sailed on beneath the mast and ropes
through wind and calm: through hours of choppy water,

through ease and discomfort, through navigation and through danger. In it all, as the sails flapped or filled, he was absorbed in the sense of the power that mastered him; associating it with memories of the great poems he had learned from the Septuagint as a boy. In more senses than one he was exercising his business in great waters: he saw the works of the Lord and His wonders in the deep: at times he was at his wits' end: and in the movement of the ship, as it staggered like a drunken man, he remembered that more than once he had been ship-wrecked, and once spent a whole night and day before he was picked up: and again he was in perils of great waters. But he never doubted that if they cried to the Lord in their trouble, He would deliver them from their distress.[18]

And so indeed it proved. Again the Lord showed his loving kindness. Again the waves subsided; and at last at Caesarea Paul with his company reached the haven that they desired.

From thence over familiar paths, he made his way once more to Jerusalem.

INTRIGUE AND CONSOLATION

1

WE KNOW BUT LITTLE OF WHAT OCCUPIED PAUL WHILE HE was now again in the Holy City. But he was evidently anxious to keep his missionary enterprise in close touch with the Jews he had won over to his side at the Council. Nor did he forget the contribution he had sent three years before. He carried back a very clear idea of the importance of that means of persuasion when he went back to Antioch for a stay, in which some authorities think he wrote again to the Galatians. And from here he set out once more to face the hardships of travel on land: once more he faced the cold, the insufficient clothing, the exhausting days of travel, the danger from bandits, the hunger, the thirst, the disturbed nights, the encounters with infuriated Jews. Whether at this time or another, Paul was twice beaten by the fasces of the Roman lictors as he had been at Philippi: and on five separate occasions he was counted strong enough to suffer the full thirty-nine blows of the leathern thongs of the Jews. He spoke afterwards of being treated shamefully at Lystra and Derbe: and perhaps where once he had been chastised, he was chastised again.[1] He may well have travelled down the course of the Hermus through Philadelphia and Sardis. All that we are told, however, is that after passing through the region of Galatia and Phrygia he arrived finally at Ephesus, which the Romans had made the capital of their province in Asia Minor. Paul, having abandoned the Orontes, transferred thither his centre of interest. He settled in its capital now for three years.

2

Ephesus had by now displaced in the traveller's predilection the claims which Miletos had established on the conjunction of its excellent harbour with the neighbouring mouth of the Mæander. Ephesus was on a smaller river, the Cayster; its mouth afterwards silted up, and by now the city, which was three miles from the sea on the banks of a lagoon communicating with the river, is but a humid swamp. Only a few scattered columns remain to speak of the ancient capital: only white swans on the marsh remind us that in Homer's time swans were already there.[2]

The Romans ruled in Ephesus; to rule there was no sinecure; in spite of some admirable statues by Greek sculptors, its streets combined with cosmopolitanism the aspect of a crowded but rather ramshackle, oriental bazaar: the traffic was extremely busy: many traders were wealthy: some no doubt were cultured. But in spite of the views of mountains to the East, and of islands against the sunset, the spirit of the Ephesians was debased; their obeisance to the Roman power was servile. They shared much with the people of the Syrian capital which Paul had left.[3]

No one in the town was better known than Balbillus the astrologer.[4] The streets were crowded with magicians, with chapmen selling amulets and medals, with jewellers, with dancers, with youths playing on the flute, and novelists creating lurid love-stories. Men searched for the lightest pleasures, and they found them—till even the Greeks were shocked. Dancers were accompanied by soft Lydian airs: at times the flutes or trumpets rose shrill, and the trumpets jangled; maenads, their hair flying in the wind, and androgynes, uttering wild cries, danced through the streets.

Orgy, frenzy, gluttony, lust, drunkenness and violence were

the outcome of the torchlight festivals and crude rituals in which men pressed towards the temple of their favourite idol —a deformity, who above her legs and thighs, stiffly encased in a garment bearing meaningless inscriptions, showed multitudinous teats and crude features surmounted by a crown in the shape of a tower. In her hands were a trident and a club. Such was the effigy to whom Ephesians had given the name of Artemis, worshipping as a goddess of fertility, whom the Greeks honoured as a huntress chaste and fair. To house it the Ephesians had built a temple, with columns of jasper on a base of Parian marble. Each of these was sixty feet high. Countless lamps lit up statues of carved ivory decorated with gems, while a purple curtain veiled the famous idol.

In this centre, which shared much on the one side with Syria and on the other with Hellas, and was mastered by Rome, there was of course an important colony of Jews: busy in all the trafficking of the bazaar—busy where the smooth waters of the lagoon mirrored many masts—busy, some of them, in the law and the prophets of their religion.[5]

Such was the capital to which the tireless Paul now came to organize Churches amid the valleys watered by the Mæander, and the Lycus, valleys sheltered beneath the lofty line of Tmolus, or the peak of Cadmus, as, above the Mæander valley, it rose into the blue. The whole province was to hear his evangel: he established Churches as far north as Pergamos; at the great port of Smyrna, as at Ephesus itself, inland at Sardis, Philadelphia, Laodicea and Thyatira.

The climate of Ionia was delightful; life was easy, leisure common. The whole country then, as even now, breathed gaiety and charm.

In this atmosphere of pleasure, of leisure, sometimes of indulgence, Paul, offering to the natural goodwill of the people that spiritual joy which melts the hardness of the heart, began

bring their gifts and his own to fruition. This Asian province
f the Roman Empire became a province of the Kingdom of
Ieaven.

3

When he arrived at Ephesus, he found there not only the
ultivated Priscilla with her Armenian Aquila, who had mi-
rated from Corinth, but a new convert, Epainetos; with them,
man of a higher order of gifts, an Alexandrian of the School
f Philo, a man who taking his name, Apollonius or Apollos,[6]
rom the God of Sun and Genius, added eloquence to a pro-
ound knowledge of the Septuagint. From the time of his
rrival in Ephesus, he had been expounding his belief that the
Messiah had come: but he had not yet learnt the inner teaching
f the Church, the belief in a Holy Spirit pouring out gifts of
race: Paul's friends from Corinth had been explaining to him
he mystery that it was from the Spirit of Christ that love was
pread abroad in men's hearts to make them holy: and that
his gift was given in the mystery of regeneration when they
vere by baptism born into Christ.

Such was the company Paul found on his return to Ephesus;
ome twelve converts were received into the Church, and after
Paul had laid his hands on them, the mysterious power,
escending, moved them to speak as the oracles and inspired
reachers of God.

4

The early Church moved in the exercise of psychological
henomena. A belief in demons and spirits was general: and

not uncommonly these entities obsessed the souls of men with effect we can parallel to-day; for demonology is not an outmoded fashion.

The ideas of obsession and of illness were as definitely linked, to their minds, as those of error and illness in any Christian Scientist of the twentieth century: cures are still effected to-day: cures were effected then. The very garments that Paul had worn were used as channels of his power: they took the handkerchiefs with which he wiped his face dry in the heat, the aprons he wore at his work, and, like a psychometrist of to-day, they found that, with this means of contact, those who were diseased in mind and body could be healed.[7]

Those who practised magic arts recognised that in Paul was a force greater than their own: his method of power over the unseen they recognised to be the true one: and many of these occultists were won over to the new faith. Many of them brought their books to a bonfire: and so highly were these books valued that those sacrificed in the fires were valued at no less than fifty thousand silver drachmas.

5

Paul's sojourn in Ephesus coincided also with a drama in Roman history. While he had been travelling the Emperor Claudius had died — to be succeeded not by his own son, Britannicus, but by his stepson, Nero, the son of his wife Agrippina by her former husband Germanicus. Agrippina was the ablest and most unscrupulous of mothers. Since the Emperor's son was in the way of her own son's succession, this Roman lady felt no scruple in plotting; and before long some one had poisoned Brittanicus.

In the experienced Proconsul of Asia, M. Junius Silanus

ST. PAUL IN PRISON
From a painting by Rembrandt at Stuttgart

she detected another possible rival to this young usurper. He did not look dangerous; so stately was the bearing of the Proconsul, so ample his resources, so sluggish his mind that he was known as "The Golden Sheep".[8] But he was also a descendant of Augustus and that, as Tacitus said, was cause enough for a crime. As Agrippina had murdered his brother, so she determined to give him also a dose of the tincture which she had found so efficacious in the case of Britannicus. Two Roman equites, Aelius and Celer, were sent from Rome to offer him a banquet, and he died.[9]

Such was the event which now disorganized life in Ephesus; it presented the acute Paul with a double problem. He had already learnt from the favours of Sergius Paulus, and from the refusal of Gallio to interfere if the Jews were troublesome, that he might expect protection from the Roman law. But here was a difficulty: if that august law were compromised and the Roman Court itself stained with crime, he dared not refer to any help received in Ephesus by the murdered proconsul.

6

Again, if the Roman order were itself in abeyance, might not the Jews seize the opportunity to press their opposition? What steps they took, we cannot tell: but from many references to an imprisonment, it seems reasonable to think that Paul was now arrested.[10] The Philippians had heard he was in trouble. Shortly after he left Ephesus he was to write that he had been in prison many times—more often than any other apostle. He wrote before leaving Ephesus that he "was in danger every hour"[11] and, in arguing for the Resurrection of the dead, asked at the same time "If I fought with wild beasts at Ephesus, what does it avail me if the dead rise not?"[12] He wrote after leaving Ephesus of terrible trials in Asia Minor, trials by which he was so crushed that he despaired.[13] He wrote after arriving at Corinth a few months later, and (almost certainly) to Ephesus, "Salute Andronicus and Junia, my *fellow prisoners*".[14]

Apart from his own evidence that he had been in prison several times more than when he was arrested at Philippi, St. Clement of Rome who knew him personally speaks of seven arrests; Marcion in his prologue to the Colossians said that "the Apostle, already in chains, wrote to them from Ephesus". There are even legends that Paul was thrown to a lion; and the ruins of a tower at Ephesus, known as Paul's prison, also point back to the belief that he was imprisoned there.[15]

Evidence to contravene all these assertions is insufficient; even if they do not amount to proof, the biographer should state them. For if St. Paul did not undergo any of these imprisonments at Ephesus, where did he undergo them?

7

The mention of these imprisonments always leads to the conjecture that during his sojourn at Ephesus, Paul wrote his Epistle to the Philippians. The idea is far from new. It was advanced by Goguel. When Dr. Maurice Jones produced his commentary on the Epistle in 1918, he found much to say in support of it. Professor Duncan's work which appeared in 1929 argued strongly for it. Dr. Manson, though he does not accept Professor Duncan's evidence of an Ephesian imprisonment, entirely agrees that the Epistle was written at this stage of Paul's career.[16] There is nothing to refute his contention. The reason why it was not current earlier was that St. Paul said that his imprisonment was known to the whole "praetorium":[17]

in the Authorised Version "praetorium" is translated "a palace": but this word, although applicable to the Emperor's palace refers more often to the "Government House" of a praetor in a colony, and is used in two Gospels in this sense. Nor was "Caesar's household" necessarily all at Rome. Many members of it might be attached to a kinsman such as was M. Junius Silanus in his colony.

It was never easy to see first how the Philippians got news of Paul's imprisonment, how they then could send Epaphroditos, how Epaphroditos and Timotheos are to be sent back, and how he himself counts on coming to see them again, if the background were the long expensive journey from Philippi to Rome. A place in the boat coming down the coast of Asia Minor from Cavalla was a very different matter. Furthermore, since Paul himself speaks of coming again,[18] it must be remembered that his hopes of doing this in Rome were slight, in Ephesus they were almost certain.

Finally, there is in the third chapter a bitter attack on intriguing Jews as dogs, and evil workers; there is a defence of Paul himself as a Hebrew of the Hebrews. Both of these would be out of place at the end of his career in Rome when other cases were more insistent: both fit into their place at a time when he was dealing with each of these points in arguments addressed to Corinth, and which would particularly apply if, as at Corinth, the Jews at Ephesus had reported him to the authorities.

8

What is the gist of this epistle? It is written as a relaxation from *factious converts at Corinth*. Its note is joy. Again and again, the example of the wealthy Lydia, and the open generosity of the Italians had come to support him in his need. "I thank my God", he began "on every remembrance of you . . ." from the first day till that moment they had helped him to spread his evangel; they all shared with him the gift of grace: he prayed that they should abound more and more in knowledge and discernment, being filled with the fruits of righteousness, which come through the Christ, to the glory and praise of God.

He went on to explain how his very arrest had helped the advance of the evangel. Not only was this so among the praetorian guard and the rest, but others had seen that they might dare fearlessly to speak the word of God. Some did so, because they regarded Paul's arrest as a proof of Roman goodwill; others falsely, hoping to embarrass him by causing disquiet among the Romans. But in either case, the Christ was made known, and Paul was confident in his hope that in his own body, whether he lived or died, the greatness of Christ would be made manifest. "To me," he wrote in one of those reverberant phrases which take us to the heart of his mysticism, *"To me to live is Christ and to die is gain"*.[19]

On the one side he longed to die and be with Christ, which is far better; but for their sakes the greater necessity was to live; and as for him the grace of faith had been made nobler by the heroism of affliction, so for them also affliction had brought to faith a more glorious crown. "To you", he said, "it has been given as a grace, for Christ's sake, not only to believe in Him but also to suffer on His account, having that same contest which you saw me wage—and now hear that I engage in."[20]

The thought of this unity of life and feeling in the Church in Christ was a theme which moved him to wonder and joy, as these in turn moved him to eloquence:—

If therefore there is any encouragement in Christ
(he wrote),

If there is any consolation in mutual love,
If any communion of the Spirit,
If any tenderness and compassion,
Ah, fill my joy full,
That you may have minds alike, that feeling alike
  you love one another,
Linked in life and soul, your thoughts on the one
  thing;
Do nothing for rivalry or vainglory,
But live modestly, accounting one another as excell-
  ing yourselves.
Each regarding the other's interests rather than his
  own,
Among yourselves have the mind which was in
  Christ Jesus,
Who, though really in the fashion of God,
Thought not His equality with God a prize to be
  grasped.
But He allowed Himself to suffer loss,
Taking the fashion of a slave,
Having been made in the likeness of men,
And being found in the form of a man,
He made Himself low,
Being made obedient unto death,
The death, indeed, of the cross,
Therefore also God has raised Him to transcend,
And granted Him as grace the name above every
  name,
That in the name of Jesus every knee should bend,
Of those in heaven, and those on earth, and those
  beneath the sod,
And every tongue make music to proclaim
Jesus as Lord and Christ, to give glory to our Father
  God.[21]

He is repeating the words of a hymn, such as the new believers had already begun to sing: an anthem which believers have celebrated through the ages.

> Who is this so weak and helpless,
>   Son of lowly Hebrew maid,
> Coldly in a stable sheltered,
>   Rudely in a manger laid?
> 'Tis the Lord of all Creation
>   Who this wondrous path has trod,
> He is God from Everlasting,
>   And to everlasting God.[22]

Paul's rhapsody of adoration sprang from the thought of the Christian life, as men in the faith were living it with one another in Grace.

9

Faith in Christ, not as merely distinct from, but as actually opposed to, the rules and system of the Hebrew Law—that was to him the dawning of the eternal day — "that is my object," he says, "that I might join Christ and be found in Him—not with my own rightness of living—that which comes from the Law—but that which comes from the faith of Christ —that of knowing Him and the power of His Resurrection and the communion of His sufferings, when I share with Him in the nature of His death, if by any means I might attain to the Resurrection of the dead. . . . For our citizenship is really in heaven, from whence also we await a redeemer, the Lord Jesus Christ, who will transform the body of our earthliness that it may share in the nature of the body of His glory by the energy which enables Him to marshal under Himself all things. Therefore, my brothers, dear and desired, my joy and my crown, stand like that, ah! firmly in the Lord, my dear ones. . . . Rejoice in the Lord always and again I say rejoice: may your reasonableness be recognised by all men. The Lord is near. In no case be anxious, but in all things, by worship and petition with thanksgiving let your requests be made known before God. And the peace of God which passes all understanding guard your hearts and minds in Christ Jesus.[23]

"Finally, my brothers, whatsoever things are true, whatsoever things are worthy of veneration, whatsoever things are right, whatsoever things are stainless, whatsoever things are lovely, whatsoever things are of good report, if there be any excellence, and if there be any praise, let your thoughts dwell on these."[24]

Paul saw mystical perfection concordant with the finest things of classic culture. Trust, thanksgiving, rejoicing, adoration steeped the natural movements of claims for justice, of irony, of impetuousness which marked his tense and strenuous nature. He spoke of himself as the athlete training and striving, not yet successful, as pressing towards the winning post to gain the prize: but realising that the divine purpose was being perfected in him from hour to hour, he was at peace even in his effort and his straits. "I have learned in whatever state I am to be content. I can live in lowly circumstances: I can live in plenty. In each and everything have I learnt to have more than enough, and to be hungry: to have sufficient and to run short. I can do all things in Him who strengthens me."[25]

THE MASTER OF ELOQUENCE

1

WHETHER IT WAS THE TRAINING OF APOLLOS, OR WHETHER IT was the ripe development of something he had learnt in earlier years at Tarsus, or whether pleading developed his native eloquence, Paul now becomes a finished and artistic writer, inserting in his letters passages of eloquent rhetoric and sustained power. His fervour, his conversational acumen, his mysticism, his sympathy—these he had shown in writing to Salonika and Lycaonia—these with tenderness, with moments of indignation, with waves and storms of feeling, combined with revelation; but while he was at Ephesus he began to write passages of more distinct style: though he is often occupied with little local questions, questions peculiar to the time, the highly wrought and continued passages of eloquence, which, by now, occur in his writings, make a special claim on a man of letters.

He was not naturally a classic essayist carefully composing an ordered whole: he does not scruple to descend from the heights to bathos. He has some minute affairs to discuss: how men and women should wear their hair: and some distasteful ones: how to deal with a man who has made his step-mother his mistress: one problem common to the time when animals were killed not at a slaughter-house but at the altar (the question discussed already at Jerusalem of eating the flesh of animals which were killed, not according to Jewish rules but definitely as a sacrifice to heathen gods). Such questions were temporary and local, not universal: and they give literature little scope.

But joined with these were the highest themes: the power of love and charity: the meaning of the Resurrection; the unity of the Church: and, at the very beginning, he wishes to explain how this great question overrides any sense of faction, and how it was a mystery which could not be discussed but by a special initiation, a special *grace*, so that men should rise above their own natures and share the perfect things of God.

2

We have seen how in his former visit to Corinth he had, in his reactions from Athens and from his journey, emphasised the Cross and the Crucifixion: now his converts saw facets of the truth of which he had shown nothing.

New experiences and more exciting ones crowded upon their turbulent consciousness. They began to feel the psychological effects of a new inrush of life. They had fresh tastes of that ecstatic utterance known as "glossolalia" or "speaking with tongues". This had been accepted at Jerusalem as evidence that the Spirit was poured out on them. Nor was an experience of the kind unknown in the religious excitement of pagan rites.[1] Under the influence of strong emotional excitement a thrill passes to the nervous system: and the impression of ecstasy is relieved, the current of nervous or electric energy is released by speech. As Kirsopp Lake puts it, "inhibitions are removed under the stress of great emotion and the words flow out with no more logical consequence than the events of a dream".[2]

It is no uncommon experience in dreams and trances that the soul feels itself in possession of a highly significant secret: again and again men have tried to keep for waking consciousness some phrase that would signify the wealth in their possession, but the phrase is sometimes an illusion. Poulain records an attempt to do this: a man astounded by the splendour of an experience in dreams sought to write down a key word to turn the secret doors. He found on coming to himself that when he had taken up his pen the words he wrote were: "There was everywhere a strong smell of turpentine".[3]

3

If the pen was not at the disposal of the person in ecstasy, his tongue was. When the subject of the afflation became frenzied, he (or she) "began to babble and utter strange sounds", inopportune, unnatural. This phenomenon appeared in England itself in the nineteenth century. Greville listened to a woman in Edward Irving's chapel:—"The speaker, after ejaculating three 'Ohs', one rising above the other in tones very musical, burst into a flow of unintelligible jargon which whether it was in English or gibberish I could not discover. This lasted five or six minutes, and as her voice was silenced, another woman, in more passionate and louder tones, took it up. This last spoke in English, and words, though not sentences, were distinguishable.

"She spoke sitting under great apparent excitement, and screamed on till from exhaustion, as it seemed, her voice gradually died away and all was still."[4]

In Mrs. Oliphant's *Life of Edward Irving*, this experience is described again in relation to a certain R. Baxter.[5] Once again we have an account of ecstatic utterance both in no known language, and in languages unknown to the speaker. The effect was very great.

These modern revivals had each their early counterparts,

when men proclaiming that they were divine, or divinely inspired, spoke unintelligible ravings, which however were as thrilling, and unearthly, as they were unaccountable.[6]

Besides these expressions of religious excitement there was violent intellectual curiosity. Some sought truth in the exercise of metaphysics, and this was known as the search for wisdom or philosophy.[7] Others sought their end by initiation into mysteries, and for these it was the inner knowledge, the *Gnosis*, that gave power. The Jewish women in Corinth felt the emancipating example of Greek and of Roman women.[8]

4

Such was but one of the experiences of the community of converts at Corinth. Few of them were well off, or well educated, or well born; many of them were, no doubt, marked with the peculiar quality of the Jewish pedlars scattered through the Empire, while others knew already in Corinth both the frenzy of its religious processions and the corruption of its central shrines of Aphrodite. Such a community—avid for experience, little exercised in the discipline of emotion, and familiar with the traffic and looseness of the Levantine immigrants in a Corinth already corrupt—could easily develop extravagances: apart from their ecstasies and their fashions, there were some who would ill-distinguish Christian requirements from their old pagan habits; others who would still hold themselves apart with the proud exclusiveness of the Jew. Some of the women developed ecstasies that might impress a congregation or they might annoy it: others, discarding their veils, would parade themselves in bare heads, thus causing scandal to messengers from Asia who never saw women unless veiled, and disturbing too the holy intentions which come to

pure minds from those angels who behold the divine glory—
disturbing perhaps to the deacons who administered the sacra-
ments.[9]

5

Into this fickle and excitable lot of converts came two novel
influences. One was friendly to Paul: it was the brilliant and
eloquent Egyptian who, in flowing utterance, poured out the
explanation of parables and facts in the Alexandrian way so
congenial to the Hellenic mind. He could make Christianity
philosophical. This had its effect: and since it was itself just
what Paul had avoided in Corinth, it provoked invidious comparisons. But it was not the only difficulty. Open enemies had
arrived from Jerusalem to belittle Paul and to claim that the
true way was not his, but quite another, which they pretended
to identify with that Cephas, who to Paul, and to all, was a
leader undisputed.[10]

Paul therefore had much to correct among his converts. He
first wrote a letter which has been lost: some think they have
discovered part of it in the second letter that remains. And
then he addressed himself to Corinth a second time, in that
letter we know as the First Epistle to the Corinthians. From
the very beginning, this shows the writer and thinker in all
the reach and grasp of his devouring genius. It is plain that
Paul now saw that preaching Christ crucified, in terms simple
or eloquent, was not enough. He must preach the whole Christ
in all His sublimity; he must write in a style fitting to the
noblest subject ever spoken of by man. He began with a passage echoing in the long vowel sounds of the genitive the names
of God and Christ and Lord, and mingling these with the
sibilant in his own name and in words of hallowing and grace,

in an interweaving of kindred sounds, these were broken only by the word *Eirene*, translating the Hebrew *shalom* and meaning peace. Taking up the word *grace*, he then reminded them that through this grace they were called into the Communion of the Son of God.

Then comes the word of adjuration: he had heard that there was strife among them: "each of you says I am of Paul, or I am of Apollos, I am of Cephas; but I am of Christ! Is Christ divided? was Paul crucified for you? or were you baptised in the name of Paul?"[11] Again he interrupts his argument for one of those conversational asides which were so typical of his personal tone: but this done, he bursts into great paragraphs of superb style in which, now with poetical quotation, now with irony, but always with consistent art of arrangement, he develops his theme: he sought to show that his message was of a spiritual mystery so sublime as to surpass philosophy, so transcendent as to defy their standards.

The themes of mysticism arrest by paradox on paradox and culminate in that love which proved itself divine by giving its life for men. That was the message which in fear and trembling he had brought to Corinth as Christ crucified: that was the superb theme to which, even while disdaining eloquence and philosophy, he now returned in a passage as consummately literary as any in Plato or Demosthenes:—

"The word of the cross to those in the way of perdition is crudity: but to us in the way of salvation it is the power of God. And so it is written, 'I will destroy the philosophy of the philosophers, and bring to nothing the knowledge of the able.' Where is the philosopher? Where is the man of letters? Where is the scrutineer of this scale of existence? Has not God turned the world's philosophy into crudity? For when the world had failed by its philosophy to gain the knowledge of God in the philosophy of God, it pleased God by the crudity of our announcement to save those who believe. For the Jews require a miracle for proof, and the Greeks seek for a philosophy: but we announce Christ crucified: to the Jews a scandal, to the Greeks crudity, but to those who are called, both Jews and Greeks, Christ the power of God and the wisdom of God. For the crudity which had God behind it is wiser than the philosophy of men, and the weakness which had God behind it is stronger than the power of men.

"For regard your calling, brothers, that not many are in the human way philosophical, not many in position of influence, not many of high rank: but the crude things of the world God chose that He might humiliate the philosophers: and the weak things of the world God chose that He might bring down the strong things: and the things of low order, and the despised things, did God choose, and the things that have no being, that He might bring to nought the things that are, that no human nature should vaunt itself before the face of God. Yet of God you are, in Christ Jesus who became to us wisdom from God and rightness and hallowing and redemption; that, as it is written 'he that vaunteth, let him vaunt in the Lord'."[12]

This is a passage of consummate literary skill: "No Greek orator", said the German scholar, Blass, "would have regarded this passage with other feelings than those of the highest admiration".[13] Apart from style, historians might praise it for its acumen. For again and again in history, from the time of Moses to that of a Napoleon or a Hitler, the power of leadership has escaped from categories;[14] "the great gardener grafts the excellence on wildings where he will". This command of style is then a new thing which Paul owed not merely to practice and to training, but to a new realisation of what the Corinthians' taunts implied—and again to Ephesus itself.

For Ephesus was no unsophisticated place. The capital of Ionia had known the presence of many an Hellenic genius:

many masterpieces may have been echoed in the school where Paul now taught: for he left the synagogue to lecture in "the tyrant's school":[15] the class-room, perhaps, of an exacting master. He had also every opportunity to learn the arts of eloquence from the gifted Alexandrian who was now the ornament of the Ephesian Church. Whatever the reason, Paul now adds to his intensity of feeling the arts of a finished rhetorician, arts which he can drop as soon as he enters on the discussion of other and lower subjects, and which fall short of making his discourses into an ordered whole. It is in special passages that he becomes finished and august: and here, where he expounds the transcendence of the divine in relation to the human, he anticipates all that in later centuries the mystic called Denys the Areopagite, and a great line of contemporaries would write of the dazzling darkness of God, of the soul's pregnant silence, and of the night of the soul.

Never was the quality of Paul's mind more manifest than when after this superb passage, so well illustrating his eloquence, he says: "And when I came before you, brothers, I came not according to excellency of word, or of philosophy, proclaiming to you the mystery of God".[16] His claim on their attention was not the persuasiveness of a finished system of thought, like that of Plato or the Stoics, but the manifestation of the Spirit and of power.

"Wisdom, nevertheless," he continued, "we do speak among the perfect: wisdom not of this age, nor of the rulers of this age, for they will soon be nothing: but we speak in a mystery the secret wisdom which God preordained before the ages to be our splendour, which none of the rulers of this age knows; for had they known, they would not have crucified the Lord of Splendour: but, as it is written:

What eye saw not, nor ear heard,

Nor entered into the heart of man,
Such things did God prepare for them that love
Him.[17]

6

Such secrets, mystical, interior, ineffable, transcendent —
because they were the revelation of God's unique perfection—
man had come to behold, and by beholding to share. This was
the mystery of *grace* by which men lived not of themselves
but by the Spirit which was Divine. "For the Spirit fathoms
all things, even the depths of God. For who has known all
that belongs to man except the spirit of man within him? And
likewise none knew the things that belong to God except the
Spirit of God. But we received not the spirit of the world, but
the Spirit which is from God that we might know what is given
us by grace from God. And this it is we speak, not in the words
and teachings of human philosophy, but in the teachings of the
Spirit, explaining the things of the Spirit to men of the Spirit.
But the man who is living merely as a man does not receive
the things which are *peculiar* to the Spirit of God. For they
are crudity to him, and cannot be known, because they are
received spiritually. But the man who is living with the grace
of the Spirit sees deep into all these things, though no one
sees deep into him. 'For who hath known the inner mind of
the Lord that he should instruct Him?' But we have the mind
of Christ."[18]

7

The writer went on to compare himself first to a sower of
seed, then to an architect laying foundations. Another might

water where he had sown: another might build up walls on his foundation-stone: but the secret of the growth came from elsewhere, came from within. "God giveth the increase."[19]

"Do you not know that you are God's temple?" asked the Apostle, "and that you form a shrine where God's Spirit dwells within? If any man ruin the temple of God, God shall ruin him: for the temple of God is holy: and holy therefore you . . . both life and death, things present and things to come — all are yours — but you are Christ's and Christ is God's."[20]

While kindling from the light within him living phrases (each with its own flame to be a lantern on the paths of faith), Paul had been building up his case. His argument was that he and Apollos were delegates of a mystery which no mind could judge by human faculties; nor could Paul pass judgment on himself. His conscience was clear, but that did not mean that he was free from faults. "He that passes judgment on me is the Lord. So judge not before the proper time, until the Lord comes; for he will bring to light the things now hidden in darkness and disclose the counsels of the hearts, and then the praise shall come to each from God."[21]

What was the lot of the Apostles? They had to play the parts as in a theatre before the world and angels and men. They had to appear contemptible. "Still to this very hour", he cried, "we are hungry, we are thirsty, we are stripped naked, and scourged, we are homeless, and we toil, working with our own hands. Even though we endured patiently, even though we answered with consolations and encouragements: we are insulted, persecuted, calumniated, scoured out of the world, swept away like dirt."[22]

Ironical yet impassioned, the man made perfect through heroism pleads as a father with the children for whom he had obtained the gift of life but who had learnt so little.

He went on to speak of the case of incest at Corinth, pointing out the force of an example: taking an image he had used more than once, he demonstrated that a little yeast could make all the difference in a big lump of dough. Then the word yeast reminds him that before the Passover, the Jews ate bread without yeast, unleavened bread: and at once he soars again. "Christ our paschal lamb is sacrificed for us: therefore let us keep the feast; not with the old leaven, neither with the leaven of vice and wickedness, but with bread free from all leaven, the bread of sincerity and truth."[23]

The thought of the case of scandal led Paul on to discuss the morals of sex.

His point of view is that of the Church to-day. Marriage is lawful, and if people are married they must not pretend to avoid its sacramental fulfilment: for husband and wife have each a claim upon the other. For those that can attain it, celibacy, the unmarried life, is better: but in any case people must maintain the moral law, knowing that the body is sacred and must not be profaned. No sin, says St. Paul, does such intimate harm as sins of impurity: for the magnetism of love is the means by which we cleave to God and His laws. The body of the Christian is the temple of the Holy Spirit, and must not be profaned. He who believes must on the other hand use his body to glorify God.

Fully then the Apostle works out his teaching: God has given men their appointed place in his order: some slaves, some free, some circumcised, some uncircumcised: some in marriage, some in single life. What matters in each case is that they should fulfil the duties of their state. That there are in the single life special opportunities for freer devotion to God and His work is obvious: but there are also special temptations:

and each Christian must do as he is guided first by nature and common sense, then by his spiritual aptitudes; but people must remember that if they marry, they accept the obligations of a household which is apt to impede the spiritual life.

No teaching on this subject has ever been more definite or more reasonable, and it is a teaching which is accepted universally by those who want to live a moral life.[24]

9

Among the questions Paul had to discuss were, as we saw, some of much concern to that time, of little to this: such questions as meats coming from animals offered in sacrifice to the gods of Olympus, and the question whether or not women should wear the veil when in Church. For both he gives his judgment of common sense; yet he sees both in the light of principles: the first is that though what a man eats does not as such matter, yet it is most important to respect other people's scruples, and not to let them think that the worship of an imperfect religion does not matter:[25] on the second point, the oriental idea of a woman being veiled to show that she was not at the disposition of every man to look at her and desire her was sound also in Church.[26] Women, he thought, must show a certain modesty, duly considering their sex and function.[27] A woman appearing in public without a veil seemed to him as bad taste as one cutting her hair short: people must not forget the customs which marked the distinction of sex.

10

Another point he had to consider was his right to have contributions from his converts.[28] Could it be denied that he was an Apostle: that he was free from man's authority: that he had seen Christ the Lord: that finally it was to him that the Christians at Corinth owed their conversion? He bursts with all the energy of his temperament into one of his great argumentative climaxes to establish his claim:—The sower sows to reap: the herdsman drinks of the milk of his herd: and when a preacher sowed the seed of divine things could he not claim the wherewithal for merely human needs? So the Lord had ordained: they that proclaimed the evangel should live from the evangel. "Muzzle not the ox," he quoted with a typical mixture of irony and humour, "Muzzle not the ox that turns the mill to grind the corn."[29] And yet he himself had not asked for money even to be maintained: he had first earned his living at Corinth, as, before he came there, he had done at Salonika. And not only earned his living but with ungrudging effort he had adapted himself to every kind of demand: "I am become all things to all men, that somehow I might save some, and for the evangel", he added, "I do all things that I may share in it with others".[30]

Then he suddenly thought of the athletes in the stadium, such as the Corinthians had often seen at the Isthmian games: all run in the race, Paul wrote, one wins: yet you must all run hard to get the prize. But every runner has to discipline himself in every way for his training: even to win a crown of pine. We, however, expect a crown unfading, "I run as one not uncertain of my goal: I box not as one striking at empty air: but I get in deft blows at my body, and treat it like a slave, lest having summoned others to the contest, I myself should lose my claim to honour".[31] The meaning is clear: but the connections and the metaphor have been forgotten. The man's mind was, again too swift for his meaning, too complex for finished points of expression.

In a short time he was back again on the question of food.

Again he repeats his rule: eat what you like as far as eating is concerned, but always consider whether you will shock people who do not quite understand. Even if it was not a question of committing a sin or breaking a law, one must be exceedingly circumspect among people who love to make a scandal.[32]

11

The next subject on which he had to give directions was the Eucharist. Already taking bread from their baskets, and wine brought up from the rich plain between Argos and Nauplia, he had offered them the mysterious ordinance which was the Communion of the Body and the Blood of Christ. This was the central mystery of Christian worship then—as it has been ever since: *"As often as you eat this bread, and drink this cup you shew the Lord's death till He come"*.[33] How carefully therefore must all worshippers be prepared, with what reverence must they eat, lest their spirit should weaken and drop to sleep, lest, ignoring the power of a mystery which took its awfulness from the Crucifixion, they should even eat and drink their own condemnation![34]

For this was no mere symbol. In this sacrament, the sign is identified with what it signified. And what was signified here? The presence, the majesty, the judgment of the Figure who had arrested him before Damascus. "The chalice of blessing which we bless, is it not the communion of the Blood of Christ?"[35]

From those tremendous words about the Eucharist, Paul proceeds to his great doctrine of the Church: for this too is a great mystery: it, too, shows the Divine Presence. The Church is the Body of Christ: as in a body each organ and limb has its part, so in the Church each member has a special gift: some for one thing, some for another. "Be intensely eager for the best gifts: and now by the supreme standard I shall show you the way."[36]

12

The passage which follows is the most famous and the most admired which Paul ever wrote. Almost—but not entirely—faultless from the point of view of style, it is arranged with patterned skill of the highest order, and illumined with a profound insight into not only love but beauty. It is a hymn in honour of that virtue or power which in the glow and enlargement of the heart comprehends ideal passion, warm affection, and sacrifice of self for others. It tells of the means by which we find our good in that of another. It directs that elevated and hallowed affection which by its magnetism moves the depths of man's being with desire to consummate in joy a creative union in every exercise of noble end. In all its blessedness, it is love.[37]

By the standard of excellence it is the way, as it is the picture, of Christ; and since Paul was the imitator of Christ, it is the picture of him also as he, soaring up towards his ideal, is hallowed by grace into perfection. For how could he know these things unless he had received them in receiving the spirit of Christ and of glory? And how could he have spoken of this secret unless it was one that a taste for beauty in its perfection would draw the chosen to understand?[38]

Let us then first read this famous passage in relation to Corinth, to its taste for ecstatic utterances, to its pride in a gnosis,[39] or esoteric knowledge, and its delight in powerful preaching; let us follow the Greek composition as closely as we can:—

If I speak in the ecstatic utterance of men, and of
angels,

Yet have not love, I become like metal reverberant
or cymbal tinkling,

And if I have eloquence and know all the mysteries
and all the inner knowledge,

And if I have all faith so as to move the very mountains,

Yet have not true love, I am nothing.

And if I divide out in morsels all things that belong
to me,

And if I give over my body that I be burnt,

Yet have not true love: nothing do I earn nor gain.

Love is long to last: good and kind is love,

Not jealous is love: it vaunts not itself; love swells
not up:

It does not offend in manners: it seeks not the things
of self:

It is not provoked to sharpness: it bears no malice:

It has no joy in wrong: but it takes a friend's joy in
the truth.

Over all things it throws its covering: it believes all;
it hopes all, in all it perseveres.

True love never falls away.

If there are speeches of divine eloquence, they shall be
brought to an end,

If utterances of ecstasy, they shall grow silent,

If an esoteric knowledge, it too shall be brought to
an end.

For in part we have the inner knowledge, and in part
we speak our eloquence;

But when comes the completion, the part comes to
an end.

When I was a child, I spoke as a child,
I thought as a child, I discoursed as a child,
When I became a man, I had done with the ways of
   a child,
For we see now in a glass dimly: but then face to
   face.
Now I know in part, then I shall know even as also
   I am known,
And now abide faith, hope, true love, these three,
But the greatest of these is love.

1 3

This passage is arranged in three distinct "strophes", the
first pointing over religious exaltation and learning to the
excellence of love, the second depicting its character, the third
its excellence above its divine sisters of faith and hope, for
their lights shall be merged in this final refulgence: as Shakespeare tersely wrote long after: "Love's not time's fool".[40]

So much for the meaning in English: but one Greek word
after another has such reach and elasticity of meaning that
words are taken to convey a reach of significance quite new to
them. "The wisdom of the great Paul", said St. Gregory of
Nyssa, "could arbitrarily employ words for the intention in
view, and to suit his peculiar train of thought. By the force
of his expressions, he could turn words from their established
use, and employ them for other purposes."[41] So vast an effect
could not be conveyed by a style perfectly polished: the jagged
mountain and the trackless valley are sublimer than the path-
way, the lush pasture, and the level highroad.

There is, for example, one word which is repeated three
times: to be done away. Renan thinks this a fault of style, but
Johann Weiss sees it as a clever means of echoing and binding

together different conceptions.[42] On this point, two opinions are possible; but no one can fail to observe in the Greek the extremely subtle arrangement of consonants and sounds, like those of an excellent musical composition. The passage is the more extraordinary in balanced echoes and cadences because the word *agape* is not in itself musical: the effect must be achieved by the choice and composition of other words: and the echoing is superb.

The result defies analysis: it melts the particular meaning of words in a general impression which exalts and transforms our sense of each in the music and interweaving of the whole. The pattern of sound connects one suggestion with another and takes us from strength to strength. Finally, we understand only in so far as, foregoing criticism, we yield and we admire.

"What passes our thought", said Longinus, "wins our wonder."[43] Vanquished by so pure a goodness, we may well turn back to a translation which has played a leading part in the history of English literature to soar in the music of pure cadences and learn once more how beautiful words are the very light of the mind.

Wilamowitz-Moellendorff, writing as an authority in Greek literature, assessed Paul's writing as a classic of Hellenism because in a time when conventional forms and beauty of style led to commonplaces, there was something refreshing in the very lack of finish which never prevented him from giving an adequate expression to the force and meaning of his thoughts and ideas.[44]

Such a brilliance of success does not necessarily mean that Paul was at the time employing the general devices of rhetoric consciously. His eloquence, thinks St. Augustine, was spontaneous.[45] He was, wrote Lagrange, "too much the Apostle to seek the charm of style, but also too much of the Apostle to forego the opportunity of preciser expression offered him by his imagination, and his knowledge of the finer shades of things. The idea that, like a trained rhetorician, he persistently searched for suitable figures of speech, or poetic lines of phrase, or followed rhythm for its own sake is belied by every chapter he wrote, and is indeed far from the impetuous eagerness of his speech."[46]

Though consciousness may polish, the highest triumphs of words come from the depths and height of a man's mystery. It is by no means impossible that, having studied in youth till his taste was cultivated, he revived his interest when he came in touch with the schools of Ephesus, with the finished eloquence of Apollos. The fact remains that if we date *Philippians* from this period, and if both *Galatians* and *Thessalonians* preceded it, we can trace from the beginning of *Philippians* a definite elaboration of balanced style which is from time to time worked out to elaborate effect in the succeeding epistles.[47]

14

No sooner had Paul inserted into his epistle the immortal encomium of love, than he turned back to the questions out of which it had arisen, the question first of lofty eloquence, and second of unintelligible ecstasy. It is with the second of these that he is now occupied.

None, wrote St. Paul, had more of this gift than he himself had. With him the electrical stimulus of vibrant spiritual experiences was particularly strong: and naturally he was familiar with it in others. This gift might build up a man's own spiritual life: but it was not difficult to have too much of it. How far did it help other people? If the notes of a musical instrument are indistinct, who can fit them to a tune? If the trumpet gives an uncertain sound, who will prepare himself for battle?[48]

Therefore a man who has this ecstatic utterance should also pray to interpret it. Suppose you are blessing God in ecstasy, how is another, who can have no idea of what you mean, to get any good of it? Better to say five words intelligibly to others than to utter thousands of meaningless sounds. A good sermon awakens another man's conscience and shows him the power of grace. Strive then after a mighty eloquence: certainly, if a man utters ecstasies, do not silence him. But in your worship, look for order as well as for what satisfies individuals.[49]

15

Before he terminates St. Paul considers it essential to remind the Corinthians of his *central* argument, the Resurrection. He insists on the evidence for it: first in the prophecies of the Old Testament: secondly in Christ's various appearances, now to Peter alone, now to many, and finally to Paul himself.

This appearance to Paul invites him into one of his typical digressions. Christ had appeared to him as to an abortion—an abortion, or to put it more gently, to him who among the Apostles was least, because he had persecuted the Church of God. "But by the grace of God I am what I am, and His grace towards me did not become vain, but I toiled more abundantly than they all: (and yet it was not I but the grace of God within me). Whether I or they, however, toiled more, so we proclaimed to you the Resurrection, and so you accepted and believed it."[50]

After this digression, Paul launched himself with strong logic into a further argument:—"How do some of you say there is no resurrection of the dead? If there is no resurrection for any, then Christ is not risen: and if Christ is not risen, vain is what we proclaim and vain too your faith."[51] The messengers would in other words be impostors from beginning to end: for how could they swear that God had raised Christ, if He had done nothing of the sort? And yet, he asked once again, "if no dead man could rise again, how could Christ rise again? But now, consider it the other way, if Christ was not raised, then your faith is a delusion: you have not risen with Him from your sins. And the dead too have no hope."[52] The whole scheme of salvation breaks down. No plan could be so cynical: none occasion such dismay as to hope in Christ, finding life with its significance and splendour enhanced, if after all we are to lose it for ever in the grave.

The logic of the position had been put ruthlessly.[53] If no man could rise again, death sounds as the trumpet note of despair: and the Christians were promulgating a huge delusion: but if their evidence was true, Christ's resurrection *is* a beacon and a promise for all who live in Him.

At this point the energy of dialectic gives way to a freshet of eloquence so brimming with inspired conviction that it floods persuasion:

> Christ has been raised from the dead,
> The first fruits of those who have fallen asleep,
> For since by man came death,
> By man came also the resurrection of the dead.
> For as in Adam all die
> So also in Christ shall all be made alive,
> But each in his own order,
> The first fruits Christ,
> Afterwards they that are Christ's in His arrival.
> Then shall be the end,
> When He shall give up the kingdom to God who is
>   also the Father,
> When He shall have brought to an end all rule and
>   authority and power,

For He must reign till He has put all his enemies
    under His feet . . . .
But when He said that all things were put in order
    under Him,
Manifestly He who put them so excluded Himself.
So when all things have been set in order under
    the Son,
Then the Son Himself shall put Himself in order
    under Him who put all things in order under
    the Son,
That God may be all in all.[54]

Argument had been suspended while the vision of faith
spoke certainties in great harmonies of phrase, poetically arranged like the inspired Scriptures he knew, and in reach and
manner not less sublime. Then once again the visionary flow
was interrupted. His thoughts rest for a rapid moment on a
current custom of baptism for the sake of the dead: and then
he thinks of his own dangers at Ephesus: "I am in peril from
hour to hour: from day to day I face death: if here in Ephesus
I had to face wild beasts in the arena, why should I do it
unless I rise again? If the dead do not rise, we might well say:
let us eat and drink for to-morrow we die."[55]

"Make no mistake," he went on, implying that such views
are only too plausible, "fair characters are marred by foul com-
panionships: waken to the effort of an upright life: avoid your
sins: for some of you have no idea what such a word as God
means, and—I speak frankly—you should be ashamed of yourselves."[56] He meant that instead of striving to gain their
reward in the life after the grave, they were living each a life
as self-indulgent as if after death there was no reward for
either good or evil.

After this characteristic combination of confession with
reproach, his hurrying thoughts lose all sequence of style: it

had been for a time only the rush of feeling that had pushed the words together. But now he rises once again in sublime and ordered eloquence to another of those illumined declarations in which faith showed the substance of things hoped for. Some, he said, will ask what is the meaning of a risen body? Why, he answered, any man must know that a seed must be sown before it can germinate—and what you sow is not the form the growth will take; but just a bare grain, wheat perhaps or one of the other grains. But God gives the growth the form He wills, and to each seed its appropriate growth. And as there is a difference in plants, so there are differences in the animal world.[57] But at this point he leaves the illustration of seeds and breeds:

All flesh is not the same flesh
But there is one flesh of men,
Another flesh of beasts,
Another of fishes,
Another of birds,
And bodies celestial and bodies terrestrial,
But the splendour of the celestial is one
While the splendour of the terrestrial is another.
There is the splendour of the sun,
And another splendour of the moon,
And another splendour of the stars,
For star from star differs in splendour.
So also is the resurrection of the dead:
It is sown in corruption,
It is raised in incorruption;
It is sown in indignity,
It is raised in splendour.
It is sown in weakness: it is raised in strength.
It is sown a body of a merely natural order,
It is raised a body of an order one with the Spirit of
God.

For as surely as there is a body of a merely natural
    order

So surely is there a body of one order with the Spirit
    of God.

For thus it is written: the first Adam became a soul
    enjoying a natural life,

The second Adam however is a Divine Spirit which
    irradiates life.

Clearly the first in order is not the divinely spiritual,

But first the natural life, and then the divinely
    spiritual.

The first man is from the earth, an earthly being—

The second man is from heaven.

As the earthly man was, so are all earthly men,

And as the heavenly man is, so are they that are
    heavenly,

And as we have borne the image of the earthly,

So also we shall bear the image of the heavenly.

This I say, my brothers,

That flesh and blood cannot inherit the Kingdom of
    God,

Nor can corruption inherit incorruption.

Behold, I tell you a mystery:

We shall not all sleep

But we shall all be changed.

In a moment,

In the twinkling of an eye,

At the last trumpet sound.

For the trumpet shall sound,

And the dead will be raised incorruptible,

And we shall be changed.

For this corruptible must put on incorruption,

And this mortal shall have put on immortality.

Then shall come to pass the saying that is written,

Death is swallowed up in victory.

Where, O death, is thy victory?
Where, O death, is thy sting?
The sting of death is sin:
The power of sin is the law:
But thanks be to God who giveth us the victory,
Through our Lord Jesus Christ.[58]

If the Resurrection of the Body appears incredible, says St.
Augustine, it is because "he looks simply to what the flesh is at
present, while he fails to consider what it shall be hereafter.
For at that time of angelic change, it will no more be flesh and
blood, but only body . . . . In the case of celestial bodies there
is no flesh, but only those simple and lucent bodies which Paul
calls spiritual, and others, ethereal . . . . Philosophers who
assert that no terrene body can possibly exist in heaven, yet
concede that any kind of body may be converted and changed
into any other kind of body."[59]

The great pæan had reached its climax: "As in Adam all die,
even so in Christ shall all be made alive".[60] That was the
keynote of it all. In lofty similitudes, acceptable to reason,
Paul has stated his belief in the glorified body of Christ as the
model and the power of what man may hope to be.

It is not, however, with this flight of soaring inspiration that
this letter ends. He speaks again of collections, of plans, of
individual friends. He takes up his pen to write the accustomed
greeting: it ends with the touching words: "My love be with
you all in Christ Jesus."[61]

16

Here then was a masterpiece to win the most recalcitrant. It
has opened the gate of heaven to centuries of mourners: its
triumphant hymn of love tells the ages how good and perfect

SAINTS PETER AND PAUL
From a painting by El Greco at Barcelona

a thing it is when we love one another with a pure heart fervently. In it the renown of a writer was established for ages.

But it did not win back to Paul the allegiance of his converts at Corinth. He hurried over there to reinforce its literary splendour with words from his own lips. But he was most coldly received. Virulent enemies flung in his face the boast that they had learnt a better Christianity than his. Contemptuous words were spoken both about his appearance and his way of speaking. Envoys from Jerusalem had undermined his power over his own, bringing against him the charge of being an impostor. What right had he to call himself an Apostle when all he knew of the Messiah was a vision known to none but himself?

Other charges were made: that he came to take their money: that he was a speaker far beneath Apollos: that he lacked the ability to teach the exact truth, and the power to call his hearers to the trance of ecstasy. An *Apostle* was surely something more than this: and the new-comers claimed to having behind them "the super eminent apostles": of the Rock, of James and John who spoke with eloquent authority. The Church of Corinth, already divided, was more divided than ever. They accused him of being crafty and of twisting the prophets to suit his own purposes. Paul was overpowered by the new excitement and returned from Corinth as miserable as after his sermon at Athens, he had gone onwards to preach nothing but the Cross.

And in Ephesus itself how arduously he lived. He toiled with his own hands to support not only himself but others. Night and day he worked among his converts with a sympathy and fervour that brought tears into his eyes. Walking from house to house in heat and bad weather, through the Agora, at the wharf, at the open theatre, among the hovels of the poor, on the heights of Pion and Koressos, there passed this bald and bow-legged Jew with his sweet expression, his perfect understanding, his alternation of tact and urgency, his well of tears and joy. And still the Jews tried to capture him. Yet, whatever his jeopardy, he equalled it with courage; whatever his toil, it could not exhaust him. And he had his reward, for from many a quarter he heard of men and women coming to the Christ and being baptised into His Church.

Yet even his success added to his anxiety.

FROM EXTREME TO EXTREME

1

IN THE SPRING MONTHS, HOWEVER, PILGRIMS CAME FROM ALL over Asia to the Artemision, the feast which was dedicated to Artemis, to her temple, and to her shrine. But the worship of Artemis was not the only reason why they flocked thither. While the devotees gathered at the shrine, traffickers exchanged their merchandise, the younger men gave themselves up to sport in the stadium and the arena. So great was the concourse that it and its ceremonies were ruled by certain local officials, the Asiarchs, who supervised the cult of the Emperor: and these had soon to fulfil their responsibilities: for the silversmiths noticed among the crowds that many not only refused their mementos, but even scorned them.

One of the silversmiths, a certain Demetrios—already annoyed, doubtless, by the demeanour of the converts—decided to take a stand. He called together the members of his craft. There was no need to remind them that to it they owed a lucrative living: "You can see for yourselves," he said, "you can hear from plenty of others that not only here in Ephesus, but through the whole province of Asia, this man called Paul argues and converts a lot of people. He says that those are not gods which are made with hands. Now there is a danger not only of our craft getting a bad name, but of even the temple of Artemis, of our great goddess, being counted as nothing: of her being deposed from her magnificence, her whom all Asia worships, and practically everywhere in the world."[1]

The furies of fanaticism, of local pride and of business

interests mingled in an outbreak of indignation from an excited crowd; they repeated the cry which had so often turned a vast concourse to uproar: "Great is Artemis of the Ephesians".[2] It did not fail to produce the accustomed frenzy; a frenzy which Demetrios and his gang soon turned to their purpose. They hunted for Paul: but while he was kept hidden, two of his travelling companions were found. These, Aristarchos and Gaius, were dragged off, not to the stadium but to the terraced theatre built into the side of a hill; their life was in deadly danger, and Paul in his valour, argued vehemently with the friends hiding and protecting him that he must himself address the crowd. Both the Roman officials and his own converts, however, urged him not to go out.

Meanwhile the streets had filled, and in the movement of excitement, men crowded to the open-air theatre where a single speaker could address some twenty thousand spectators: the crowd rushed there, too excited with the movement to know what it was all about. The Jews were terrified: they pushed forward one of their men to make a defence. But the excited crowd had no wish to listen to a Jew: the answer was to shout him down, and again they raised their voices in the familiar shout: *"Great is Artemis!"*[3]

The officials were growing nervous. Neither Asiarchs nor Romans ever liked to see the crowd get out of hand: they put forward the Recorder of the City who made an adroit speech: who, he asked, could question the privileges of Ephesus in relation to Artemis, and her image? They were in no danger. "You ought to be quiet", he said, "and do nothing rash. Here they have brought men who have never attacked Artemis or despoiled her temple. What has Demetrios to complain of? If any has a complaint, the assizes are held from time to time, and there are Roman proconsuls to preside at them. Let those that wish make their accusations, and plead their cases. If any has other enquiries to prosecute, let it be done in the regular way. Couldn't you see that such a noisy demonstration might easily produce a punishment from the Roman authorities, especially if no one could bring forward a reason for it?"[4] So adroitly able a speaker won the ears of the crowd, and induced it to disband.

The natural course for the officials to take after this was to tell Paul that since they had saved his life, he must put them to no further inconvenience. He could not but agree. He had been in despair of life: he had been weighed down beyond his endurance. If he had asked whether he could possibly escape, his heart would have answered the question with death, but for the mysterious assurance of his faith that God would deliver him. Soon afterwards he made his departure for the North, secretly no doubt, as he had made it from Damascus in that basket he vividly remembered from so many years ago. Many have suggested that he first escaped with Trophimos to Miletos, only to find that Trophimos fell ill there. Once again he was greatly perturbed. Disappointed, wearied, disgusted, doubtful of his Corinthians, doubtful of his Galatians, doubtful whom he should endanger by his presence, he wondered if the whole world had not turned against him.[5]

2

A great door of opportunity had been opened in Asia Minor: the Churches had been founded: the Jews had been countered. He had been able to continue his preaching and to make converts. Yet now, once more, the whole movement in Asia Minor was in peril. But where could his eye turn? Everywhere there was trouble from the orthodox Jews. He had been hounded out of Salonika and Verria: he had found fierce hostility at Corinth:

unless he could send back his contribution to Jerusalem, his prestige would vanish there also. His friends had been placed in jeopardy on his account: and he had been in danger of a fearful death, of being torn limb from limb as by a devouring lion. Hope vanished. Nerves and courage were exhausted. Once again he was a disguised fugitive. But he dared not delay. Finding a place in a boat for Troas, he hoped that Titus would bring better news from Corinth and that he might yet again find an opportunity to spread his blessed message.[6] But no Titus came. His mind was in torment. "I found no relief for my spirits", he wrote, "because I found not Titus my brother."[7] His mind turned back towards what he had suffered in Corinth. "With many tears, in affliction and anguish of heart,"[8] those are his very words, he wrote to the Corinthians a third time, and in this letter he opened out the story of his heroism and his anguish, but his anxiety still pressed hard: What was he to do? Where could he go?

At last he found a means to pass over again to Macedonia. But where he went none dared to say, and to this very day, therefore, his movements at that time remain a mystery.

He moved from danger to danger: his nerves could not recover under the constant menace of attack. He felt extremely lonely. He wanted Timotheos to join him and bring back the books he needed. Without, he said, were fightings, within were fears. Even with his dear Philippians, he could find little rest. But at last Titus did arrive from Corinth, and the news he brought was encouraging: Paul's last letter had not failed in its effect, and to add to his consolation, Timotheos came from Ephesus.

3

Yet a fourth time he addressed himself to Corinth for a personal apologia, and this, beginning on the notes of consolation in affliction, became a pæan of his adventures on the recurring themes of danger and glory. "Thanks be to God who leads us as bearers of censers in a triumphal procession in Christ and through us in every place pours forth the incense of His knowledge. For we are the aroma of Christ in God."[9] And like a voice in that triumph he gives his message: "as from God, in the very sight of God, in Christ, we speak."[10]

Was he once again advertising himself? Did he need letters of recommendation to them, or from them? Ah no—not for *them!* "*You* are our letter, written in your hearts, a letter known and read by all men, for you are clearly a letter of Christ, written by us as His secretary, written not in ink but in the Spirit of the living God, not on tablets of stone but on the tablets of the hearts of flesh."[11] And it was not the literary form that mattered, but the intention and inspiration. The letter kills: but the spirit instils life. When Moses, receiving the commandments on tablets of stone on Sinai, came down to tell the revelation of a law that threatened death, he was yet transfigured by his splendour. With how much greater glory comes the revelation of the Spirit! Indeed, the law which once had splendour has come to have no splendour, in view of the new splendour surpassing it. When the law of Moses was read, a veil lay upon the hearer's heart; but when a man turns to the Lord, the veil is lifted at every corner.[12] "For that Lord to whom he turns is the Spirit; where the Spirit of the Lord is, there is freedom. But we all with unveiled face beholding the glory of the Lord are transformed from glory to glory into the same image, as by the Lord the Spirit."[13]

He had seen the veil lifted: he had seen the dawning of the evangel of the glory of the Christ who is the image of God. Light, he had said, "shall shine out of darkness and shine in our hearts as the sunrise of the knowledge of God",[14] the sense or vision of the presence and the commandment of Christ. On the one side, then, every sign of weakness and contrariety: on the other side the sustaining splendour. And so there comes the paradox of the mystical life: "In our battles we suffer heavily but are never utterly defeated: often hard pressed yet never driven to surrender: in desperate plight but not in despair: chased from the field, yet not left to the mercy of the foe; beaten to the earth, but not killed outright."[15]

4

Every day he was in danger of being done to death as Jesus had been done to death. Yet always by his escapes and deliverances, as by his courage and faith, he proved that Jesus was alive within him; his sacrifices and perils were wearing out the outer man only that in his spirit Christ should reign, and the Church should live.

"I believe and therefore did I speak."[16] Taking up this verse from a psalm, Paul applied it to his trust and confidence that the final victory was sure. "He who raised the Lord Jesus from the grave will, in the power of that Resurrection, raise us up also, and will bring us into His presence side by side with you."[17] All his sufferings helped to spread the power of grace till both from him and from his converts there poured high tides of thanksgiving and of adoration to the glory of God! "Therefore, do not lose heart; I may be worn out; but, inwardly, I am being made new from day to day. I mean to say that the light affliction we are actually enduring is working out for us from excess to excess an everlasting weight and abundance of glory—for my eyes are open not to things seen but to things unseen: for the things that are seen are those of time, but the things unseen are those eternal."[18] By the ever-increasing power of his will and his soul this mystic was moving deeper and deeper into the secret and majesty of God.

We know, he continued, that what we dwell in here on earth is, as it were, a tent. He thought of life on earth as a Bedouin might think of his encampment in a desert: but when the tents are struck for the last time, it is because men have come back to the solid buildings of their homes. And so when the tent-like body is discarded, it is for a house not made by hands, but from God—a house eternal in the heavens.[19] And we long for it, as in the heat and in the cold of a tent in the Levant one longs for solid roof and walls. Then he added, with one of his characteristic turns in which the freshets of wit and mysticism combined, "when we are clothed with that, we shall not be discovered naked."[20]

By the time Paul wrote this he was again near those simple men of Salonika who had pressed him so hard on the subject of the future and the judgment: he therefore insists that what matters is that—whether in the body or out of it—we should be found pleasing to God.

What, they had asked, was his motive power? The power that moved Paul was Christ's love for men acting within him.[21] The Christ had died for all not that all in Him should die for Him but that those who lived should live for Him who for their sakes died to rise again. "If a man is in Christ, he is a new creature. The olden things have passed away, look, they are all made new."[22]

5

At this point in the letter, a novel word is introduced, the word 'exchange'; it could be applied particularly to that change from bad terms to good terms which we know as reconciliation.[23] Through Christ God had taken Paul to Himself as good money; and then made him His servant to bring good exchange —but a majestic sort of servant, an envoy, an ambassador— bearing great letters from a King, the very King of Heaven:[24] "We therefore beseech you, as though God were entreating you," he pleaded, "for the sake of Christ be reconciled to God: let Him accept you as good coinage."[25] Then Paul uses one of his boldest expressions: "Him who knew no sin He made sin for our sakes that we should become the righteousness of God by being merged in Him."[26] "Co-operating we also beseech you not to receive the grace of God in vain."[27] The meaning is plain. Christ as a personage of infinite power can give of that infinity to make right in the eyes of God those who, through grace, live in Him. "He was made man", said Athanasius, "that we might be made gods."[28] "He chose the Incarnation", says Abelard, "as the most effectual appeal to the love of those whom He had made." At the same time, as Anselm showed in *Cur Deus Homo*, the law of the universe was vindicated when suffering was accepted to save others, and the blood of life poured out that they might live. But whether Paul implied so much is not certain: what he here wrote was: *God was in Christ reconciling the World unto Himself.*[29]

6

With echoes from the Psalms, his favourites, Paul now bursts again into rhythmic speech on one of those paradoxes of the Christian life on which he had lately been writing. The Apostles were, he said, giving no offence to anyone lest the ministry should be blamed for it, but in every particular combining to prove themselves as ministers of God.[30]

In manifold endurance, in afflictions, in hard necessi-
    ties, in need, in straits,
In scourgings, in arrests, in riots,
In sleepless nights, in spells of hunger, in pureness of
    life, in inner knowledge,
In patience, in kindliness,
In the spirit of holiness, in love unfeigned,
In the word of truth, in the power of God,
By the weapons of right living for the right hand and
    for the left,
Amid glory and contempt,
Amid bad names and good names,
As impostors and truthful,
As unknown and famous,
As dying and see! we live,
As chastened and not done to death,
As steeped in adversity yet always rejoicing,
As poor men yet making many rich,
As having nothing, yet possessing all things.[31]

So did he hymn once more the story of adventure, danger,
hope and consolation which was his own biography and a picture of the experiences of those who through the ages live like
him in Christ. They see life in two scales of value, those of the
world and those of grace.

Nor can the style of this passage be ignored. The stream
which in the first enumeration of trials had begun to swell
reaches its full volume and flows on in more stately clauses.[32]
St. Paul had seen what St. Chrysostom was to call a snowstorm
of afflictions; but he looked from these to the clear noonday of
his triumph.

7

He had to warn the Corinthians about living on easy terms

with those who still worshipped the Olympians. What partner-ship, he asked, can right living have with lawlessness? How can light associate with darkness? What concord can there be be-tween Christ and Belial? What portion can a believer have with an unbeliever? What agreement can the sanctuary of God have with idols? [33] "For we are the temples of the living God. . . . My dear ones, let us purify ourselves from all that can defile flesh or spirit, bringing our holiness to perfection in reverence for God."[34]

This warning breaks in on an appeal for a return of the generous confidence Paul himself had given: "My heart is open wide to you: open yours wide to me. As one might say to children, that is a fair bargain. I have not wronged anyone, nor ruined anyone, nor cheated anyone. I do not speak to say anything against you: I said to you before that you are in my heart to stay with me through death and stay with me through life. Full is my trust in you: high is my vaunt of you. My heart brims with consolation, I overflow with joy in the midst of all my torments."[35]

We have seen what those were: the back-biting, the open mockery, the gibes and taunts, the treachery, the danger, the hardships, the hunger, the thirst, the weariness, the exhaustion, the recurrent harrying and persecution, the hunting from place to place, the toil and peril of the sea, the incessant disappoint-ment brought on by unworthy converts and their controversies, their fickleness, their scandals, and the toil and moil of their lives.

But always in Paul's mind there was another anxiety. There were the Jews at Jerusalem, and their need of subscriptions; only by that could he count on their not trying to turn the nations out of the Church.[36] Besides, he continued—taking up the argument of his earlier letter—if the nations made a return of this world's goods to those from whom had come the good of heavenly things, was not this, firstly, reasonable; and, secondly, a proof of the unity of all in Christ, who had become poor that men might be rich? Generosity in giving not merely supplies a need: it calls forth thanksgiving to God. And in this spirit of gratitude, those who receive help would praise Him that the Corinthians had adhered to their Messiah: besides, they would make intercession for the Corinthians, thanking God for the overflowing grace manifested in their generosity. In the Church all would be one, and this unity was a gift unspeakable.

8

So did the faith and charity of the Apostle raise into the romance of grace his business of collecting money for the doubters at Jerusalem.

Twice already he had spoken of the drama and paradox of his life: but not yet was the vindication complete. Charitable, forgiving, generous, encouraging, at times almost enthusiastic, he yet felt he must deal once more, and more completely, with the accusations which his enemies at Corinth had brought against him.

He insisted therefore that the weapons of his warfare were not simply those of human nature, for his own nature might in itself be weak: his weapons, however, had the strength of dynamite. They could crash every stronghold; they could cast down the loftiest turret of proud argument or calculation standing in defiance against that inner knowledge which God gives to His own, bringing every device of the mind into captivity to make it obedient to Christ.[37]

At this point, the letter proceeds to an impassioned vindication of Paul's own career: and it leads up to one of his most memorable passages.[38]

"Not he that commendeth himself is approved, but he whom the Lord commendeth," wrote Paul.[39] That was plain truth both in the judgment of the world and in the demeanour of the Christian: any kind of self-praise, any kind even of excuse, very generally has the effect of not increasing but lessening confidence; and yet might he not defend himself against his enemies? Surely those who owed the faith to him, those who were in themselves his very letter of recommendation, his letter written in their hearts not in ink but by the Spirit of God, would understand that it was not for selfish reasons but for those of grace that he wished to vindicate himself. "Do you put up with me," he pleaded. "I am jealous for you with the jealousy of God, for to the Christ I betrothed you as a pure bride to her one husband: but I am afraid lest, as the serpent beguiled Eve with his knavery, your thoughts should be led astray from that simplicity and purity which lead to Christ.

"For if he who comes proclaims another Jesus whom we did not proclaim, or you receive another Spirit which you did not receive, or another evangel which you did not accept, you put up with that finely. For I count I am in no way behind these excessively precious Apostles. If also I was unskilled in my way of speaking I was not so in the inner knowledge, but in every point for every man I made things clear for you within."[40]

And was it a matter of offence that to save them making contributions, he either earned his living as a craftsman, or lived on a subscription sent from Philippi? It had been his rule, and it always would be, never to ask money for himself from his converts: but the time had come when he would tell his own story, even if it did sound like commending himself. "For with

pleasure you put up with senseless men, being so sensible yourselves: you put up with it, if anyone enslaves you, if anyone
preys on you, if he entraps you, if he gives himself airs, if he
gives you a slap in the face. It may be a disgraceful confession
to make, that in those matters I behaved ineffectively. But if
any is courageous, speaking as a fool, I am courageous too.

Are they Hebrews? so am I.
Are they Israelites? so am I.
Are they seed of Abraham? so am I.
Are they servants of Christ? (Speaking like a mad-
man) I more.

In labours more abundantly, in scourgings more
abundantly:
In imprisonment beyond comparison, in perils of
death again and again.

From the Jews five times I received the forty lashes
less one.

Thrice I was beaten with the lictor's rods, once I was
stoned,
Thrice I was shipwrecked, a night and a day I was in
the open sea.

In journeyings again and again.
In perils of rivers, in perils of robbers,
In perils from my own race, in perils from other
nations,
In perils in the city, in perils in the wilderness,
In perils on the sea, in perils among false brothers,
In toil and travail often, in nights without sleep.
In hunger and thirst, in fasts often,
In cold and nakedness.

Beside the things which happen fortuitously
There is a thing that grips me every day—
Solicitude for the Churches.

Who is weak and I am not weak?
What brother stumbles, and I burn not with his
    shame?

If one must vaunt oneself, I shall vaunt myself in
    the things of my weakness,
The God and Father of the Lord Jesus, who is
    blessed for evermore, knows that I lie not.[41]

For a moment his great catalogue was halted by the remin-
iscence of being let down in a basket from a window in the wall
of Damascus; and then his memory soared to his visions and
his revelations, joining them with his own peculiar trials from
within his own temperament and constitution: but the strength
of Christ super-invested his weakness with power. And therefore he was well pleased with weakness, with insults, with dire
needs, with persecution, with straits of all kinds, for the sake of
Christ. For when he was weak, he said, then was he strong.
"Christ was crucified because of His weakness, but He lives
because of the power of God. And I", said Paul, "am weak in
Him, but I shall live with Him because of the power of God,
till it reaches to you: test yourselves to see whether you are
living in faith, consider yourselves: or do you know yourselves
so little as not to recognise that Christ is within you also?"[42]

The Lord had given Paul authority to build them up and not
to cast them down. He insisted only that when he came away
then he should praise them. His letter was finished. He himself
took the pen to write from a full heart his closing words:

"Finally, brothers, rejoice. Be perfected, be encouraged, be
of one mind, live in peace: and the God of love and peace shall

be with you. Greet one another with a holy kiss. All the saints send you greeting. The grace of our Lord Jesus Christ, and the love of God, and the communion of the Holy Spirit be with you all. Amen."[43]

WHAT FAITH ACHIEVES

1

WE DO NOT KNOW THE PRECISE SPOT FROM WHICH THE MAN of genius painted this fadeless picture of his incomparable story. But none question that it was written in Macedonia—a province torn at times by the fierce Vardar winds, as his heart was swept by conflicts and emotions—but a province Greek in its combination of the stretching plain, the wild mountain and the indenting sea—a province which set Salonika as its capital in the quiet azure water of the long sun-swept gulf, shut in on the one side by the Chalcidic promontory and on the other by Mount Olympus, with the heights of Pelion and Ossa near at hand. Over the whole province the mighty mountain always towered, sublime in beauty, sublime in imaginative inspiration—the picture which, as we saw, Greek naïveté had taken as the throne of Zeus, and for which Paul might well quote from the Septuagint, "Thou shinest wondrously from the everlasting hills".

We do not know, we repeat, how far Paul had travelled along the Dalmatian coast in the hot summer days: but though he says nothing of it, we may again recall what it meant at that time to be in Macedonia and Hellas. We should remember the names of heroes, Philip, Alexander: we should remember the ceaseless preoccupation with sports and games of shapely athletes: remember also the background of Roman power, with its administration, its army, its reasonableness, its justice and its order.[1]

For it appears that Paul now came nearer to Rome than ever before. He said himself that he travelled from Jerusalem in a circle as far as Illyria.[2] We may take it to mean that travelling on from Macedonia by the Via Egnatia, he reached Durazzo; he went possibly up that Dalmatian coast which offers such beautiful views at Cattaro and Ragusa, and then making a round journey came on by the western coast of Greece to Corinth, stopping at Nicopolis for the earlier part of the winter, from which to sail in calm sea or travel by the coast till at a safe moment he reached Corinth. When he reached Illyria, he would serve a double purpose by not returning on his road: he would save his friends in Salonika from further embarrassment, and in new ground he could both more freely and more widely preach his glorious evangel. Here then we may suppose his journey to lead among the Western Isles of Greece and the mountains of Epirus in a wilder variety of the Hellenic scene, but on a shore which kept him always in closer touch with Rome. For thence sailed the ships from Corinth to Brindisi, and there was much traffic on that famous coast.

Many were the thoughts that filled his weeks at Nicopolis as he prepared to come once more to Corinth, to reconcile the Church there, to gather the collection, and to preach the mystery of the faith. And with so much on his mind, his nerves swayed to and fro between exaltation and weariness. He had never written comments on the scene before him, and we must not now expect him to tell us that he was passing along one of the finest seas in Europe: that to the South rose Erymanthos and the great Peloponnesian chain in the wild scenery which led down to Lacedaemon and Taygetos among the gathered hills and valleys: or that Alphaeus came down through its deep gorge to the grove and temples of Olympia, or that among those bays was the gorge leading to Megaspelion. Nor even that fifteen hundred feet above the sheltered inlet at Itea, there was, in an air which Plutarch called "as close and fine as silk", the shrine of the Delphic Oracle on the cliff, and above it the Parnassus from which the poets of Greece drew their inspiration as they looked with naïve delight upon the Helicon as the home of Clio and Melpomene, and seven muses more. Yet all these things passed before him, brilliant in colour and magnificent in form, as he sailed on from Nicopolis to Corinth.

With him were two more learned adherents, Zenas, a lawyer, and Apollos, that great reader and expounder of books, to prime him afresh with the latest masterpieces of Alexandria and the Book of Wisdom which showed how much Hellas had refined the conceptions of the Jews;[3] in both he could see already with what lofty inspiration the piety of Israel exalted metaphysics into poetry.

3

When he arrived at Corinth, therefore, his mind was full of projects of more writing and of further travel. It was his way to think in provinces;[4] his aim to spread his Church as a new unit of the Roman Empire. Greece with all its glory was not enough. His mind was consumed with the traffic with Italy of which in his latest travels he had seen much: he must preach and deepen this life of grace in the Empire's capital: in central and imperial Rome. He felt that there was something peculiar about the Church there. "I long to see you," he wrote, "that I with you may be encouraged in joy, each of us by the other's faith, both yours and mine."[5] Again and again the purpose had haunted him. As a preparation for this, he began to prepare a profound treatise of theology.

He would set out in all its subtlety, a subtlety beyond that of any Platonist or Stoic, the whole scheme he preached; the great alliance, as he had been persuading alike Jew and Greek, with Syrian, Galatian, Roman, Macedonian, in his travelling embassy of Christ. His evangel was the power of God for everyone to attain salvation who had the gift of faith: in it was revealed, from faith unto faith, a power of right living which came from God—certainly revealed to the Jews first, but by no means hidden from the Greeks.

Therefore he would establish the claims of God upon the whole race of men, for the truth had been dawning on them all. And he would describe the world as he saw it in the light of this dawn of truth illuminating the good life.

Everywhere he found men choosing as standard their own selfishness; though everywhere God had left the imprint of His majesty. Reason saw in the beauties of Nature the work of the Primal Artist; in the working of natural law an argument for a Primal Cause; and in the very constitution of man's nature there was something spiritual which, as it surveyed the splendour and beauty of the world, felt a mystical elation which raised the mind of man in love and worship, in gratitude and praise—but men, alas, rather than take the strenuous exercise of this communion, preferred the gratification of a corrupt worship, where festivals and excitement around favourite idols led to orgies and to vice.

To Paul it was no new theme. It was set out with fine poetic power in that Book of Wisdom which he and Apollos had studied together.

> By the greatness and goodness of the creatures
> Proportionably the maker of them is seen.
> Surely vain are all men by nature who are ignorant
>   of God,
> And could not out of the good things that are seen
>   know Him that is;

Neither by considering the works do they acknowl-
edge the workmaster;
But deemed either fire, or wind, or the swift air,
Or the circle of the stars, or the violent water,
Or the lights of heaven to be the gods which govern
the world.
With whose beauty, if they being delighted, took
them to be gods:
Let them know how much better the Lord of them is:
For the first author of beauty hath created them.[6]

Paul, whose soul breathed poetry as its native air, condenses
and paraphrases the verse from poetry to prose: but he follows
the argument closely, and uses kindred words, though he never
quotes directly. He had read that

The worshipping of idols not to be named
Is the beginning, the cause and the end of all evil.[7]

He had read a catalogue of vice in which were set down the
results of idolatry: he paraphrases both the denunciation of
idolatry, and the appalling record of the result.

No sooner had he set down this list of horrors than, realising
the inevitable reaction of self-righteousness that they would
occasion in Pharisees, and among Jews in general, he turns to
make a sharp indictment of those that judge others while yet
themselves deserving the severity of the Judge. God would send
tribulation and anguish upon every soul that works evil, the
Jew first and the others also. The Jews had their coded system,
the others however had their consciences. Each must live by the
highest standards he knows, in the light and truth of the Spirit.
"For he is a Jew which is one inwardly, and circumcision is that
of the heart, in the spirit, not in the letter."[8] The word Judah

means praise,[9] and this praise comes not from men, but from God.

That everywhere was his doctrine. What is the use of being a Jew nominally, or nominally attached to any favoured company, even the Church? The whole question is not merely whether as a sincere penitent one trusts in God's loving forgiveness, as a good Jew would do, but whether one lives the life of the spirit, in sincerity and truth.

4

Writing to the Galatians, Paul had already set out his scheme of redemption. We do well to recall it. "The law was that nurse, guide and slave which led us to the school of Christ that we might learn the way of right living from faith. And since the faith has come we are no longer under the slave's tutorship. For you are all the sons of God through the faith in Jesus Christ. For as many as have been baptised into Christ have put on Christ."[10]

That was the simple way he had put it, as he thought of his difficulties with the Jews at Antioch, or the Jews who troubled his converts on the plateaux of Asia Minor. It is highly probable that before the Council at Jerusalem he had stated his case in a style both more conciliatory and more learned, and in doing so prepared the first draft of the Epistle now written.[11] Some years had gone by, and through them the problem had been re-arising. It had caused trouble wherever he went: it lay behind all the factions raised against him at Corinth: it was a question that he would naturally wish to settle before arriving at Rome: it was a subject which he would like profoundly to elucidate in a letter that might be read anywhere. So now in what we know as his third and fourth chapters, he deals with the subtlest controversial difficulties of his recurring theme.

The first question, of course, was what was the good of being in the chosen race, if a non-Jew who believed were better than a Jew who did not believe? What in other words were the advantages of circumcision? Many, answered Paul, but for the time being he spoke of the promises or prophecies, which God *would* fulfil, no matter how unworthy certain Jews: for on the one side, His truth and justice are inviolate: on the other, all men have sinned; and men are never free from responsibility for what they do. How then are men to be set right? The Jewish Code, though it might point out where man has gone wrong, was not the *means* of perfect living. A new means must be found, therefore: it was found not in fulfilling the Jewish system, but through that gift of trust in Christ and that fidelity to Him which change the soul. In other words, a man is put right in the eyes of God neither by the works of the Torah, nor by God's loving forgiveness of a repentant sinner but by his faith.[12] Does that deprive the Jewish system of efficacy? On the contrary, it gives the very reason why it was established.

Paul argues, as he had argued in *Galatians*, that God's goodness was proved not so much by the Law of Moses as in His promises of mercy and of grace, given to all men—as they were given to Abraham—for and by *faith*. Abraham was endued with power in his faith, giving glory to God.[13] And, by the same generosity, we too shall be right in the sight of God, if we put our whole trust in Him who raised Jesus the Lord from the dead. Faith, as we saw, was an agreement of the mind which implied first trust and then fidelity; it was not a mere intellectual agreement: but a gift of personal inner affinity leading to a communion so full and so divine that its enthusiasm reached to the deeps of life and the soul.[14] It is a principle of knowledge that cannot be analysed by mere intelligence but is the secret, inexplicable, spontaneous adaptation of the mind

to the Eternal Word. It implied a deliberate choice of the will
which in its turn was moved by the mystery of grace.

5

The theologian had now painted the shadows of his picture,
the strict theory by which he related himself to the Jewish dispensation.

*Set right in the eyes of God by faith, we have peace before
God through our Lord Jesus Christ, through whom we have
had our access by faith into the grace wherein we stand*[15]—that
summed it all. Now his theology rose to mysticism. "Let us
triumph in the hope of the glory of God, and not only in that,
but let us triumph also in our tribulations, for tribulation gen-
erates strength of character, and out of strength of character
comes proof, and out of proof hope: and hope does not dis-
appoint because the love of God is poured forth into our hearts,
through the Holy Spirit which has been given us."[16] Here is
one of the wide ranging phrases of his mysticism, a phrase that
opens a panorama of the finest scenery of the country of the
soul; a phrase which takes us to the heart of St. Paul and
reveals the secret of his thinking. "The Spirit of Love dwells
in our hearts, a flame that kindles us till we are radiant with
the hope of glory."

The absolute certainty that God loved His chosen in the
Church and made them one with the Church, made everything
plain to Paul. Few care to die for others, even for a saint;
Christ nevertheless had died for sinners, and not only died for
them but taken them into Himself to share His life (the life
signified always by the blood).[17] Set right in the eye of God
by being in that life, that blood, we are saved by Him from
wrath. Those who receive the abundance of the grace and of

the gift of rightness shall reign in life. This grace, this gift of rightness, is a gift to the believer; it is his life. It establishes his rightness: for grace reigns within him. Christ's death showed a reconciling love, while we were hostile. How then is man set right? By receiving in faith a share in the rightness of Christ. How much more are we saved in his *life*, in which we share: we are not only free from danger and from judgment but we may proclaim our triumph in God through whom we have received the reconciliation. One man, the type of what we were all to be, went astray, but if that weakness is general, how much more abundant, how excessively rich is the grace of the man who takes us into Himself that His grace may reign as King to lead us into eternal life through rightness of living —he is Jesus, our Messiah and our Lord. The justified—those who are set right—are those who are in Christ Jesus—His Spirit dwelling in them in His Church, which they love, trust and obey.

What then, we ask, is the rightness which is accorded to faith? Newman, in adroit answers which reconcile many controversies, answers that to be pronounced right is to be both forgiven and made new. Prophets and Apostles revel in it as the great gift of Divine Mercy, or the rich garment of salvation, as linen clean and white, as the enjewelled robe of righteousness, or, as it is elsewhere expressed, as "Christ in us" and "upon us" and around us; as if it were a light streaming from our heart, pervading the whole man, enwrapping and hiding the lineaments and members of our fallen nature, circling round us, and returning inward to the centre from which it issues. The Almighty Father, looking at us, sees not us but His sacred Presence, even His dearly beloved Son spiritually manifested in us, with His blood upon our door posts, in earnest of that final abolition of sin which is at length to be accomplished in us.[18]

6

To have God's loving forgiveness and to acquire merit in keeping the Torah was enough for a Jew; but Paul asked for more. Are you, or are you not, *living in Christ?* That was the question which underlay the whole argument on "justification". "Do you not know that all that have been baptised into Christ were baptised into His death? We were then buried with Him to go down into death that as He rose from the dead in the glory of the Father, we should walk in newness of life."[19]

This newness, which is a completely different mode of viewing life, a life on another scale of being, a life so filled with the consciousness of being loved that we are made partakers of a mystery which changes us and all our standards—this is what to St. Paul it meant to be *christened*. "For if we died with Christ, we believe that we shall also share with Him in life. Knowing that Christ being raised from the dead meets death no more. Death no more lords it over Him. For in that He died, He died once in that ruinous state which is the sphere of sin: but in that He lives, He lives in the sphere of God: so you also must reckon yourselves to be on the one side dead as corpses in all that relates to sin, on the other pulsing with life for those divine opportunities which you find in your life in your kingly redeemer; change your life, moving from the impulses of self which turn every faculty and function of your nature awry, to make each of them a weapon of the good fight for God."[20]

You need not bother about the Jewish system any more, he went on. You are now in the realm of *grace*, and grace is that favour direct from God which makes us sharers in His rightness, His goodness and His mind. You are freed from sin; you are a *new creation*.

7

Some would say then: "Can't we do what we like? If we are in grace, will not God cover everything in His forgiveness and His power?"[21] "Ah," answered Paul, "that idea is intolerable, absurd. You are always under a master, sin enslaves you to death and destruction. But the one who has a claim on your obedience will make you free to live aright. I must speak in a plain, human way because of the tendencies of your nature. As you once made every faculty and function of your nature the slave of impurity and license to sin and doom with uncleanness, so now you must devote them to rightness of living that may climb to holiness. There is a service which is freedom. What did you gain by that old life of indulgence? The end of it is the corruption of death. But if your service is given to God, you have at once the gain of living in holiness, and finally you will have life eternal. For the wages of sin is death, but the gift of God in grace is life eternal in Christ Jesus our Lord."[22]

In other words, effort in the Christian life is accompanied by such a change of atmosphere that grace gives both a sense of freedom, and a confident hope of joy and glory—though we owe the pledge to Christ's redemption, yet it is already clear in a believer's own consciousness.

8

Paul's argument was both subtle and condensed. He had sacrificed clearness to brevity: in itself, the arrangement is confused, and shows a sense of strain at facing a complexity of issues. But one can piece out the contention—in the first place, of course, his argument is not one which every man will follow. People will not accept it, unless they have the gift of an inclination to believe, unless they know inwardly what he means by grace, and the gifts of grace.

But, apart from this, he had two great difficulties: on the one hand he had to face controversy from two separate quarters: from the Jews, with their insistence on their Law, an insistence in which their proselytes would share: from the other, the other nations who were accustomed to the debased worship which followed on idolatry, and which made Corinth a haunt and source of vice. But these two standards were not wholly separate. The Jews were by no means always models; and had they not tended to assimilate themselves everywhere to the conceptions around them?

It is plain that as the argument of this diatribe proceeds, Paul has to some extent forgotten the Romans he intends to visit: he is overcome by the number of arguments he has to meet, and especially by the knowledge that, though the Jewish law was superseded, yet before that it had been not only the highest system the world had known, but a preparation for the Messiah, and the dispensation of grace.[23]

It is to this point he now turns, and turns with characteristic subtlety. "You know, my brothers," he said, "for you are acquainted with the Jewish system—that a man is subject to it as long as he is alive. A woman is bound to a man as long as he lives; but if he dies, she is free to marry again."[24] Paul then says to his Jewish converts: you likewise have died with Christ in His death, and you are therefore free to enter new engagements.

Paul's general idea is clear, though the illustration hardly helps. But no sooner had he brought it out than he breaks into a yet more subtle disquisition; his former experience mingles with his sense of present weakness, and of the weakness of those converts for whose stumblings he blushed.

First of all, he reflected, thinking of his own experience, that to tell a man he should not do a thing at once suggests to him that he should do it: secondly, he reflected, that if he had done it, when he did not know it was forbidden, he had no sense of guilt. The Jewish system was excellent in what it commanded: it was not merely good and a guide to right living, but even to holy living. And yet, in the double way, which he had just explained, it led a man to corruption and made a tender conscience miserable. A man felt sin within him, luring and goading him into the very life he wanted to avoid. That reminded Paul of all the anguish he had suffered before his conversion: an anguish which returned in moments of exhaustion: "Wretched man that I am!" he cried out: "who will deliver me from the body of this death?"[25]

9

There is but one way to escape from this torment and anguish of the soul. It is to turn to Jesus, and through that spirit of love which dwells within us, to live in Him by faith. Then one need have no more fear for the weakness of human nature: if the flesh of man was weak, it had paid the price.

> When all was sin and shame
> A second Adam to the fight
> And to the rescue came.[26]

And this second Adam was the Son of God. He by His death and passion; and by His glorious Resurrection and Ascension, had in His love for man both taken for Himself the death which is implicit in the ways of sin, and raised those who lived in Him to the realm of the Spirit. Though the weaknesses of human nature (which Paul called "the affections of the flesh") are enmity to God, yet if the Spirit dwells within you, that is life and peace, and will ensure your resurrection.[27]

10

In scattered sentences, the Epistle had shown the marks of a great stylist: but the argument as a whole had been far the most confused and dense that Paul had set out. He seemed stifled by the complexity of the problem before him, like the autumn fire smothered by the mixed heap of burning weeds.

His sweeping canvas of the sinful world was not original: it was, as we have seen, but a new draft of certain passages of Wisdom. He had put in three quotations from the Psalms which gave little help to the argument. The remaining doctrines had not been new: they were but a more complex restatement of what he had written to the Galatians. He had restated his current teaching, but were these chapters his introduction to a new community, the subtlest of them might have been puzzled. They would have recognised—in phrase after phrase —the impact of a saint and genius: they would have felt him like a thunder-roll, but he would have made the new teaching yet more difficult to understand. The impression was one of strain, torment, weariness, in a spirit of mighty energy. But now at last the clouds were clearing, and the vision opened with a sense of calm.

As many as are led by the Spirit of God, these are the sons of God.[28] They need not be afraid as slaves, but they might have the loving confidence of adopted children to say to the King of Heaven, Father. "The Spirit Himself bears witness with our spirit that we are children of God: and if children, then heirs—heirs of God and joint heirs with Christ—if we suffer with Him, that also we may be made to share in His glory." [29]

His imagination soared, as on the one side he reviewed what had to be endured, and the glory that was opening on his inward vision. With the insight of St. Francis of Assisi, he felt within himself an intuitive sympathy with the growth and stress of all creation. [30] On the one side, it too seemed to be enslaved, as each single thing fell away to death and ruin—the beast, the flower, the tree. Each seemed to feel within itself the throes of travail and to cry aloud in pain—as man does in the pathos of his existence:—

> I saw wherever light illumineth
>   Beauty and anguish walking hand in hand
> The downward slope to death. [31]

But when he searched the rending storm he saw the clouds coloured to crimson and fire by a sunrise beyond them; for a sun arose with healing in its wings.

In the pathos of life, it is the Spirit of love which speaks: this Spirit intercedes within us "in yearnings which can never be expressed in sighs or groans or tears", [32] yearnings so intense that their very force becomes hope, yearnings which cry into the ears of heaven. The serried argument has changed for the sonorous music of an immortal hymn to the heavenly King, "For we know that to those who love God—to those who are called according to His purpose—all things work together for good. For those whom God had foreknown, He predestined to share a likeness in the image of His Son that, among many brothers, He should be the first-born. Those whom He had destined, He also called to hear and accept His promises; and those whom He called, these He set right in His eyes: and finally to those whom He had set right, He gave His glory." [33]

Such is the triumphant vindication of the sovereignty of God.

"What then shall we say in the face of these things? If God is for us, who can be against us? He who spared not His own Son, but delivered Him up for us all, how shall He not with Him accord us all things as His graces?"

> Who shall bring any charge against God's chosen?
> It is God who has declared them guiltless. Who will find them guilty?
> Christ Jesus, who died, nay rather who rose from the dead,
> Who is on the right hand of God,
> He also intercedes for us.
> Who shall separate us from the love of Christ?
> Shall tribulation? or anguish? or persecution?
> Or nakedness? or peril? or sword?
> As it is written, "For thy sake, we are killed all the day long
> We are regarded as sheep for the slaughter".

"But in all these things, we are more than conquerors through Him that loved us. For I am persuaded that neither death nor life, nor angels, nor principalities, nor powers, nor things present, nor things to come, nor height nor depth, nor any other creature, shall be able to separate us from the love of God which is in Christ Jesus our Lord."[34]

This hymn of triumph in the power of Divine Love is literature immortal, like the passage on charity written at Ephesus a few years earlier. It is not only consummate in the art of words but visionary and sublime: the change of height and atmosphere is so sudden that one asks whether the passage was inserted, or whether a swift excitement overpowered the writer. He takes flight suddenly, and an eagle in high skies, he wings the dawn.

11

Then, as before in Ephesus, he resumes the argument with which he was occupied—but in this case, not without an added tension of feeling. "I speak the truth in Christ, I lie not; my conscience being a fellow witness to me in the Holy Spirit that my sorrow is great, and unceasing pain is in my heart. For I could wish to be anathema from Christ for the sake of my brothers, of those who, humanly speaking, are of one race with me: for they are Israelites, and theirs is the adoption, and the glory, and the covenant, and the giving of the Law, and the worship, and the promises, theirs are the fathers, and from them, humanly speaking, is born the Christ, He who is God over all, blessed for evermore."[35] The words of Deuteronomy, Joel, Ezekiel, the Psalms, but especially Isaiah, haunt him as he develops his theme for his people. Yet the covenant and the promises, he insists, were not enough without answering to the Divine call, the call which comes to other nations too. It was like grafting: if the trunk of the tree is sound and it gets root and soil, it will give its sap to the branches grafted in —so with the alien nations; but their wild branches when grafted in could not bear more than the original branches of the tree if the original tree were sound. And neither will be of use, if they bear no olives.[36] But the very recalcitrance of the Jews gave the others their opportunity, and for those who are called according to God's purpose all things work together for good. He makes them work to the good of those that love Him. He has showered mercy on them all.

The poetry of Isaiah, of Ecclesiasticus and of Wisdom echo in Paul's mind to the swelling and reverberating chords of his impassioned close: "O the depth of the riches both of the wisdom and of the knowledge of God! How unsearchable are His judgments and His ways past tracing out. For who hath

known the mind of the Lord? or who hath been His counsellor? Or who hath first given unto Him, and it shall be
recompensed unto him again? For of Him and through Him
and for Him are all things. To Him be glory for ever and
ever, amen."[37]

12

His argument had ended. His previous disquisition had been
steep and unequal like the peaks and cliffs of a sierra. Logic, to
tell the truth, was not his strong point: he shows everywhere
the lack of a thorough Hellenic training in dialectic; the theory
is rough, not polished: and many a stray thought, a sharp
animadversion, or a personal peculiarity trips and stays the
reader. But now that Paul has only to portray the life of grace,
he does so in outlines as full and clear as his logic had been
jagged.[38]

"And so I encourage you, brothers, through the mercy of
God, to offer up your bodies as a living sacrifice, holy, well
pleasing to God, as your logical service and worship. Do not
model yourselves on this age in which you live, but renew and
remould your inner mind completely till it bears the glory of
that will of God which is one with goodness and nobleness and
perfection."[39]

That would mean harmony and adjustment as the organs
and muscles of a healthy athlete are instinctively co-ordinated
for his purpose: in the Church there are some to serve, some
to teach, some to encourage, some to distribute charity, some to
preside, some to show kindness: let each show his special gift
in the excellence it requires. Let love be perfectly sincere: let
men be full of affection for one another, showing consideration
for one another's position. Rejoice in hope, endure trials, be

assiduous in prayer, generous to Christians in need, and cultivate hospitality. Have that sympathy which joins as much in
the joys as in the sorrows of others. Bless those that persecute
you: and if you have an enemy, do all you can to help him:
go hungry that he may eat. Overcome evil by doing more good.
Christians are members of one body. Love is the fulfilling of
the law.[40] "The night is far spent: the day is at hand. Let us
cast off like soiled clothes the works of darkness: let us robe
ourselves in the armour and weapons of the light. Let us go
forward honourably, as in the daytime, not going to excess in
eating and drinking, or to self-indulgence and indecency, to
quarrels and to jealousies. But wear as your robe Christ, your
Lord and King, and take no thought for your lower nature, to
satisfy its inclinations and its passions."[41]

13

There were vegetarians (he does not mention teetotallers):
well and good, if their conscience told them so; but let them
not force their opinions on the whole Church—nor the Church
on the other hand deride them.[42] And let no one come in conflict with the Roman administration, government, authority or
courts of justice: these were benefits, which came from on
high: the taxation to maintain them, therefore, was perfectly
reasonable and right. Give all Romans their due: taxes, tribute,
submission and respect.[43]

And then "turn back to the Scriptures: for what has been
written in them has been written to instruct that we, through
that patience and that consolation which come from the inspired
word might have hope; and cultivate these feelings towards
one another for the glory and praise of God. May He, the
God of hope, fill your hearts with all joy and peace in the faith

that you may overflow with hope in the power of the Holy Spirit."[44]

Such to all intents and purposes was the end of the long instruction in this document, which had become as practical, as intimate, as warm as Paul's habitual writing.

14

He had still his personal things to say: his plans to tell. He paid his compliment to the mind and character of the saints at Rome, and yet he was justified in renewing their memories, and fulfilling his mission.[45] He hoped to see them when he passed on towards Spain. For the present, he must take the offering to Jerusalem from Greece: and he knew that he must face prejudice and opposition: but their intercessions would help him so that he might go on to Rome with joy and, when he came among them, find refreshment.

FROM FOES TO FRIENDS

1

THIS GREAT DOCUMENT TELLS US LITTLE OF WHAT PAUL FOUND in Corinth: nor do we hear from any other source. We can conjecture only: but though no doubt, his own converts received him warmly in their gratitude for his letters, and though he had many consolations, he felt everywhere that many Jews hated him: not only the unconverted Parushim, but also those Jews who, though they accepted Jesus as the Messiah, felt that His saving work was for Israel only and who were utterly unprepared to see in a universal Church the Israel of God.

Everywhere they had persecuted Paul, and they were now determined to do away with him. Their plan was to wait till he embarked and then quietly have him thrown overboard. And who, when the boat arrived, would be the wiser?[1]

The only way he could escape their gentle plan was to surround himself with proved companions, and travel by land. And of these he had seven with him, seven on whom he could rely completely: three of them were Macedonians: the others were from Asia Minor: for Timotheos had with him a certain Gaius from Derbe; from Asia Minor there were two faithful Hellenists, Tychicos and Trophimos. Such was the party which in the spring weather set off from Corinth on the road which leads past Megara and Eleusis to Athens, where they would have found again Damaris, Denys and a Church. But they were unlikely to have tarried in the electric air which played upon the honey-coloured marbles: if Paul could impart some of those encouragements and flashes of illumination which it was his gift to spread he would have been satisfied. We do not know if he tried again to speak in Athens. But to be in Athens was always an event.

For it was still the centre for the flower of youth from all the countries round. And Paul had realised that he had a debt to Athens.

For all through the favoured land the tradition of Athens was present and alive, both in the marbles and bronzes of the sculptor, in the fluted columns on which the architect set his pediments, in the verses of the poet and the wisdom of the sage. Though they remained apart, the Israelites were not ignorant of these things: and they too had lived among hills and sunlight, with the tempering Mediterranean in view. They too had sheep and goats: they too had fishermen, and fig-trees and the vine. But to an Israelite these fine things of nature were as familiar as, to an Indian, the lotus and the pipal. And it would hardly occur to him to note the more impressive beauty which nature had given to the deep gulfs and glistening mountains of Achaia. "What he would not think of noting down was that the olive tree was so choice in nature and so noble in shape that it excited a religious veneration; and that it took so kindly to the light soil as to expand into woods upon the open plain, and to climb up and fringe the hills."[2] Paul would not think of telling his converts at Corinth or Salonika how, from Athens to Corinth, the delicate and brilliant atmosphere freshened the colours till the olive forgot its monotony, and an Italian might see how its cheek glowed like the arbutus of Etruria or the beech on Umbrian hills. He said nothing of the thyme and other fragrant herbs from which the bees from Laurion or Eleusis, to the heights of Helicon and Parnassus would draw their honey in the long summer hours: he hardly heard their humming; he hardly noticed the violet or narcissus, or the bloom on almond and peach, or the freshness of colour on Parnes or Hymettos: but as the spring advanced while he followed on through that land of names and glory, his eye rested on all these things; till he again arrived from Corinth in Macedonia.

He had become debtor, he said, both to Greek and to Barbarian. He realised the distinct detail: the refined colouring, the graceful outline of the Attic scene were before him against a sky coloured at morning and evening with intensest brilliance of cloud and light; after he had arrived at Corinth, he had looked westward from the heights towards Parnassus and Erymanthos, and the long Corinthian gulf, or backwards towards Athens over the Aegean. Now at Athens, he could follow with his eye the chain of islands "which starting from the Sunian headland seemed to offer the fabled divinities of Attica when they would visit their Ionian cousins, a sort of viaduct thereto across the sea; but that fancy would not occur to him, nor any admiration of the dark violet billows with their white edges down below; nor of those graceful, fanlike jets of silver upon the rock, which slowly rise aloft like water spirits from the deep, then shiver and break, and spread and shroud themselves and disappear in a soft wisp of foam, nor of the gentle incessant heaving and panting of the whole liquid plain, nor of the long waves, keeping steady time, like a line of soldiery upon the hollow shore."[3]

For all those things which here are thus poetically noted were always before him and around him. They mingled with his life, with his praise of God, with his sense of the marvel which, in the triumphal procession of Christ, his life had become till it poured forth love, as the censer pours forth incense. But his soul was absorbed in the drama of his relation with other souls, with the spread of the evangel, with the problem on the one side of sin, and on the other of grace, the problem of redemption which he must elucidate both for his Jews and for all nations. And besides he had his special preoccupation. He was in haste to safeguard the money he carried with him to win accord for his work at Jerusalem.

2

Apart then from the Jewish plot to throw him overboard, this gave a second reason why it would be safer to travel on by land: and by land therefore we may guess that he passed on to Thebes in Boeotia, past Parnassus and Thermopylae over the Ochrys range to the plain of Thessaly with Olympus square beyond, white beneath sun and stars; he went up the long road between the coast and the snow-crested ranges: and so through the fair vale of Tempe, till once again he came to the Haliakmon valley, and saw across it Verria, which had received him with honour some seven years before. There his companion, Sosipatros, knew the best ways of approach. From Verria, he must have passed back to Salonika, and so on past Mount Hortiach and the lakes of Beshek, till, beyond Apollonia, he again came down to the shore at the Gulf of Rendina. At that season, Macedonia is brilliant with hyacinths, crocuses, anemones; above them the asphodel shows its pallid veins. The sun gathers warmth every day. Yet the thoughts that absorbed Paul and his company were still the safeguarding of their money, their prospects at Jerusalem, and their preparation for that Easter celebration of the Passion and Resurrection in which the meaning of the Passover was completed: when the Paschal Lamb for sacrifice was Christ Himself,[4] when they would meet in the communion of His Body and His Blood, and when the unleavened bread signified a life free from the leaven of vice and wickedness to worship an immaculate Redeemer in sincerity and truth.

"How tenderly I love you in the mercies of Christ!"[5] that was the feeling of grateful expectation which echoed on through his heart since he had written it from Ephesus a few years before. Surely when he met them he would find them—as he urged them to be—rejoicing; joy and amenity would make them know, above all, that they had received the gifts of the Spirit: the peace of God, which passes all understanding,[6] would have given a mystic quality to that exquisite taste which fixed its thoughts on things honourable, pure, true, and beautiful,[7] till, like the most spiritual of the Corinthians, they were changed from glory into glory, as by the Spirit of the Lord.[8]

It was thoughts such as these on which his mind rested rather than on the storks, the starlings or the anemones—the sharp nights and the warm glow of the noonday sun.

3

At Philippi, he found again the delightful, tactful, subtle young physician with the cultured tastes who had first led him from the Troad to Macedonia. The danger of Jews robbing them, or throwing Paul overboard, had been evaded at last, and they could await the aid of the wind. After celebrating the Resurrection, they prepared, therefore, to sail from Kavalla past Thasos and Samothrace down the coast of Asia Minor on their way to Jerusalem.

Since the physician was with them, we know what happened from day to day as they sailed on through the blue seas to the sun, and to the holy places of Jerusalem.

At first the wind was adverse, and it took them three or four days to reach the plains of Troy. Twice, we remember, Paul had been to Alexandria on his way to Macedonia: once after his long journey through the plateaux of Asia Minor, once after his long sojourn in Ephesus: and each time he had been able to spread his blessed message. There was plenty to occupy him for a week as he passed among the converts to build them up in that faith and charity and hope which mingled with one another in his contemplation of the perfect life. The festival of the Resurrection so joyfully celebrated at Philippi filled his mind with a sense of triumph even in the midst of trials. At Alexandria, on the eve of that Sunday which he was already keeping as a weekly festival, Paul met the Christians to partake with them of the mystery of Holy Communion in a room three stories above the street. He continued speaking for hours; as it struck midnight, he was still discoursing.

It is even now occasionally remarked that a long sermon can lull listeners to sleep. On this particular evening, one young Christian was so powerfully affected by this particular quality of the preaching that he fell through the window against which he had been leaning, crashed to the ground below, and was apparently killed. Paul went down to the body: taking a lesson from Elijah, and confident in the power with which the Christ had endowed him, he stretched his body, with its immense reserve of vital and healing power, over the body of the young man.

"Do not trouble," he said, arising, "for his life is in him." He then returned to the upper room, and found in the breaking of the bread the mysterious presence and power of the Christ.[9]

The elation of the company reached its height when, as dawn broke and Paul departed on the road to Assos, they found that the heavy sleeper had not closed his eyes for the last time. From the city where, a year or two before, he had undergone such torment of anxiety, Paul now set out in thankful joy.

His journey that Monday morning led him through delightful woods over hills from which he could see both Mount Ida and the Aegean. The oaks were now in full foliage, the hellebore spread its green, and the asphodel its pallid petals, above the grass. As they came down to Assos, they saw its granite citadel rise on a crest of rock.

It was here that Paul rejoined the companions who had sailed round Cape Lectum, and from here he could look along the coast to the sheltered harbour of Edremid and backwards to Mount Ida. As Assos and Ida faded from the view, Lesbos emerged to the South, and on Lesbos glittered the walls of Mitylene which were so finely placed against a mountain crest that it had struck both Cicero and Horace as singularly lovely. The island had nurtured the poet of passion: it was here that Sappho had loved and sung. But if the thought of Paul searched with eagerness so fine a sight, it was not for the songs of the Lesbians but their souls. It was to ask again if false worship had entrapped the inhabitants of this enchanting spot into depravity: yet it would be going too far to suggest that, either here or in the hardly less attractive prospects which opened on his eyes between Scio and the Asian hills, he was unthankful amidst such themes of praise. On the one side were the gigantic heights of the mainland: on the other the beautiful island with its white houses amidst green foliage of pine, ilex, citron, and the flowers of late spring. For at that season, those delightful scenes were as though newly created in all the freshness of the ripening summer. So on past Chios, Samos, past the hard fought ridge of Mycale they sailed to the mouth of the Cayster, and to Trogyllium where they anchored for the night.

The dawn rose over the heights of Messagio and Tmolus, which in his long sojourn in Ephesus he had come to know so well: but he did not put into the mouth of the Cayster to revisit Ephesus. It is conceivable that the voyage of the ship was determined before he boarded it: it is possible that he dared not return to a city where his presence had already proved so embarrassing to those responsible for maintaining order. It is certain that he was in haste to reach Jerusalem: but in any case he did not land before he reached the mouth of the Meander at Miletos.[10]

Thither he summoned his friends from Ephesus to tell all that filled his mind and heart. That danger and affliction were coming he knew, with that infallible intuition which was the gift of the Spirit; "but none of these things move me," he said, "nor do I attach any price to my life, if only I can accomplish my appointed course with joy, and the ministry which I received from the Lord Jesus to tell forth the blessed message of the grace of God. For indeed I know that all of you, among whom I have gone from city to city proclaiming the Kingdom of God, shall see my face no more."[11]

Temptation and difficulties would trouble the Church at Ephesus. Cruel wolves would harry the flock. Men teaching false doctrines would try to seduce the believers; so let them be vigilant, remembering that for three years Paul had ceased not night nor day to warn each of them—with tears.

"And now," he said, "at the last I commend you to God, and to the word of His grace—to Him who is able to build you up and give you a heritage with all who have been made holy. I have sought for the silver, the gold, the apparel of no man. You know yourselves that these hands have provided for my needs and for those who were with me. And I did this to give you an example—by toiling in that way to support the weak, and to recall the words of the Lord Jesus, how He said: 'It is more blessed to give than to receive'."[12]

The chronicler who reports this speech continues his story

with words as simple and touching: "After having spoken these words, he knelt down and prayed with them. They burst into tears, throwing themselves on his neck, and kissing him again and again, sorrowing above all that he had said, You shall see my face no more. And they followed him down to the very ship."[13]

5

His heart softened and consoled, he sailed down the smiling coast past the long island of Kos until he reached Rhodes with its view of the blue Taurus across the strait; its harbour, its citadel, its hills, its roses, its groves of olives, its orchards of fruit, were all glistening in the presence of the spring. Whether in this paradise he left the treasure of his message, the chronicler does not tell: his interest appears to be absorbed in the voyage, and he no more now than at other times wrote descriptions of places. It is only for us who know the singular charm of those islands and coasts to recall through what scenes Paul and his party moved, how, though their forebodings weighed against their consolations, all were ordered into peace: because in the predestined plan for each of them, every trial was an opportunity to come closer to the Lord they worshipped, that they might augment their weight and treasure of glory; they were persuaded that in their search for union with God all things were working together to perfect their eternal good, and that not the greatest cataclysms in heaven or earth could separate them from the love by which God had made them one with Himself in the Christ.

At Patara, over against Rhodes in Asia Minor, the party found a ship which was sailing direct for Phenicia. Taking a course to the south of Cyprus past that port of Baffa where he had had such interesting encounters with Sergius Paulus some nine or ten years before and sheltered by the heights of Troödos from the northern breeze, they sailed round past Larnaka and Famagusta and the sunny beaches of the Eastern end of the island; then, after a spell of the more open sea, they found themselves in the famous harbour of Tyre.

Paul had passed through it many times in his journeys to and from Cilicia on the Orontes and Jerusalem, and now he found disciples who welcomed him;[14] as at Alexandria Troas, he stayed with them a whole week. In all these visits, he felt a premonition of danger, which his friends shared. "Do not go", they pleaded, but he felt constrained to sail on; and, on the sands below the Lebanon, he faced a scene of devotion almost as touching as at the mouth of the Meander. Even the women and children came with him to the beach; and there they too knelt and prayed.

It was but a short sail down the coast from the harbour of Tyre to the even more picturesque port of Acre. Here too a little citadel was thrust into the sea to protect a tiny harbour. The last extensions of the Lebanon were changing into the hills of Galilee among which lay the village of Giscala[15] from which his family had come to Tarsus; among them also to the East was Nazareth. Across the long curve of the bay rose the beauty of Mount Carmel, in which sheltered the cave of Elijah. He was back at last in the sacred country of his people. But a short journey down the coast with its rock and its beaches and his ship had reached its destination at Caesarea.

6

The earlier journeys of Paul were ended. He had indeed taken his story on the wings of the morning; the scenes through which he had passed were not only singularly beautiful in outline and in verdure, but on them also the sun shone brilliantly. The theatre, the arch, the temple, and the statue had added to lands, already favoured by nature, the ennobling associations of classic taste. The finest thoughts of genius and citizenship had been nurtured amongst those monuments: there Plato had spoken and Aristotle: there Euripides had sung; there Alexander had dreamed of his civilizing conquests: there Homer had told of his heroes; and a line of philosophers had taught the nobleness of a life of restraint, while sport and ideals mingled with music to train a young man to strive eagerly in his love of the beautiful, the good and the true.

In all these scenes the Israelites had been told already of a purer religion: for their sublime literature rang with the worship of a God who loved them. It had been the privilege and drama of the life of Paul to tell alike to Israelite and Hellene, to Ionian and to Italian the blessed message that God's love reserved for them powers richer than any among them had dreamed.

Paul had, in the peace which passes all understanding, made known to them the secret of how to know God, how to live in Him, how God had made them citizens in the commonwealth of heaven; how He had not only looked after them with watchful care, but in the mysteries of grace had initiated them into the life of His Divine perfection; He had given them His Spirit to dwell in their own hearts; He had changed them from glory to glory by accepting them into His own holiness in the Christ and in His Church.

7

The height, the intensity, the marvel of this love, this faith, this hope, each merging into the other to attain its own perfection, were so rich that the finest records of genius, like the most beautiful combinations of sea and mountain, are hardly suggested in the narrative and letters of one who, though a greater and more impressive genius than any yet known in these glittering scenes, held genius as nothing unless it was consecrated by grace. Silver, said an old chronicler, was nothing accounted of in the days of King Solomon. Of so little account was a masterpiece of poetry, sculpture or philosophy against the novel riches of redemption. The new wealth, bountiful and enduring—even for the rudest—was the treasury of grace and peace, such as they found both in themselves and one another when they were accepted into that communion so hallowed that Paul knew it as the Christ.

8

The moon had waned and filled again as he sailed down from Kavalla to Caesarea: the spring had advanced to a glowing warmth in a region of flowers: the oak of the wood was exchanged for the palm. "He had sailed in the finest season on the brightest coast and in the fairest weather."[16] And we do well to recall all these, but only that we may the more enhance the personal interest of his story: that we may recall his personal apprehensions, and the assurance he owed to his faith: and that we may see and feel the closeness of affection which bound him as an Apostle to those who, through his voice, had been made the inheritors of splendour.

In all these things there is, even from the human point, a drama. He was a Jew, always in danger from the plots of the Jews. Everywhere he had had a premonition that he would be yet once more arrested, and when he finally landed in Judaea, this premonition was set before him and his Christians with a curious sense both of vividness and of mystery. At Caesarea they were the guests of one of the first adherents of Christianity, a certain Philip. All of his four daughters had kept from men, to live to Christ alone: and while he passed among them, the Agabus, who at Antioch some ten years before had prophesied the famine, arriving from Jerusalem, now approached him before them all; taking from Paul the belt he wore, Agabus had bound it round his own feet and hands. "Here", he said, "is what the Holy Spirit has pronounced. The man to whom this belt belongs will be bound at Jerusalem by the Jews and delivered over to the nations."[17] When they heard this impressive warning, so dramatically delivered, the friends of Paul begged him not to go to Jerusalem.

To a man, urging himself on against his natural inclinations and his fears, it is hard for him when friends support the blandishments of his own ease. "Ah!" he cried out. "What are you doing to weep like this and break my heart? As for me, I am ready not only to be fettered but even to die at Jerusalem for the sake of the Lord Jesus."[18] When a man insists that heroism is above comfort or safety: those who love him most are forced to add to his sacrifice the weight of their own sorrow. His friends at Caesarea could only say, "God's will be done!"[19]

CRAFT IN JERUSALEM

1

THE PILGRIM PARTY HAD MADE THEIR PREPARATIONS AND, making a numerous band, they climbed up through Kefr-Saba to Jerusalem. At last Paul could place his offering in the hands of the waiting doubters. The austere James was waiting for him with his robe of white linen, and his venerable beard. "They received us", says the chronicler, "with joy."[1] But what was the reason for that joy, and how far did it go? At this point, the brevity of the chronicler awakes in Renan the sharpest suspicion. Nothing is said of the money Paul had taken so much trouble to collect, and Renan even asks whether the insinuation was not made that Paul was trying to buy the Apostolic authority with money. What is certain is that among the most powerful Christians of Jerusalem the great missioner found none to take him in. His host was a man from Cyprus![2]

2

In the absence of Peter and Paul, had not the zealots in the Holy City been clinging to every Jewish observance in the most pharisaical way? Were they not bitterly opposed to the broad view that faith was superior to the Mosaic observance, that the nations were to inherit the promises made to Abraham, and that for those who were christened, even circumcision was unnecessary: they were unprepared for all that was universal and advanced in the ways and thoughts of Paul? To the magnificent story of his mission, even to the proof of his success offered in hard cash, they answered with words so cautious as to be churlish. The tactful ellipsis of Lucanus veils but cannot hide the irony.

They glorified God, he said, and said to Paul: "You see, brother, what thousands of Jews have the faith, and all of them insist upon the Jewish law. Now they have heard that you came here teaching to the Jews scattered among the nations that they should separate from Moses, telling them not to circumcise their sons and not to conform to the observances! Then what is to be done? Undoubtedly there will soon be a demonstration, for they will soon know that you are here. You must do what we now tell you"[3]—and with this they prescribed that he should join with four men who were taking that vow of the Nazarite he had taken at Cenchrea: shave his head —dress, in fact, as a penitent—make the appointed sacrifices of animal slaughtered, and also pay for theirs! By this means, so it was suggested, he would avert suspicion. He would certainly lose most of what slender resources he had reserved.[4]

But the story which follows is far from reassuring. Not a word is said of James, or of any support for Paul from any of that company. All that we hear is that, as at so many places before, the Jews now rose against him with accusations as noisy as they were unjust. They said that he had profaned the temple by entering with his Ephesian convert, Trophimos: they shouted that he had preached everywhere against the temple, against the Jewish Law and against the Jewish people. Suddenly the steps and dust of the narrow passages in the old walled city were in uproar. Surging, pushing, shouting, crowds started out among the booths of the bazaar. In the area of the temple, while the Levites blew their trumpets against the profanation, the crowd seized Paul, thrust him out, and locked the gates of the temple area. As Paul was dragged and pushed along, blows hailed on him.

The man then in charge of Jerusalem, as governor or tribune, was a certain Lysias, a Syrian, or Greco-Syrian, who for a substantial sum had been made a Roman citizen. On buying this honour he had taken the Emperor's own name of Claudius. To this Claudius Lysias Roman soldiers hastened to report that the city was in uproar. Assembling his centurions and his soldiers, the tribune hurried to the crowd which was ill-treating Paul. At the sight of the armed authority the crowd scattered. Paul was left alone to be arrested and fettered with two chains.

3

Who was he? What had he done? When the authorities asked these questions of the Jews, they raised a new tumult. Some answered one thing; others another. Not knowing what judgment to form, the tribune ordered Paul to be led to the fortress, the tower Antonia. The rabble surged after, shouting "Kill him! Kill him!"[5]

Nevertheless, Paul obtained permission to address the crowd. Those who arrested him were not a little astonished to find him not only speaking Greek, but explaining that both he himself was a Jew and that he had civic rights in a town as cultured as any in Asia. Raised above the crowd on a flight of steps and now speaking Hebrew, he soon had the hearing of the Jews and explained how zealous a Parush he had been, studying his rabbinism from a master no less than Gamaliel: he recapitulated the story of his conversion, not omitting to mention that he had been a leader in persecution, conniving at the death of Stephanos—until the Christ had said to him: "It is to nations afar that I wish to send thee."[6]

This sentence reminded the crowd of what had incited them to fury. "Away with such a fellow from the earth!" they cried in re-kindled frenzy. "It is not fit that he should live."[7] Once again a great wave of shouting burst from the throats of the rabble. They were in a mood of high excitement. If this was the result of Paul's speech, it did not commend him to the tribune, who gave orders that the offender should be again shut up in the tower to see what cruelty would persuade him to confess. He was rapidly stripped and tied down, and the torturing whip lay ready for its grim work on his worn flesh. Paul's presence of mind did not desert him: it was not until he was strapped down for the torture that he found an opportunity to impress the centurion in charge. Then: "Is it lawful", he asked, "for you to scourge a Roman citizen who has not even been found guilty in a court?"[8]

The words which had secured his freedom from the dungeon near the arch of Pompey at Philippi did not fail in the tower built at Jerusalem in honour of Mark Antony. "What are you about?" asked the Centurion of Claudius Lysias. "This man has the rights of Roman citizenship."[9] The tribune hurried back to Paul with the anxious question: "Are you really a Roman citizen?"[10]

The answer, and a nameless authority behind it in the personality and culture of the prisoner, startled the oriental mind of Lysias. "At a great price I obtained this citizenship," said Lysias,[11] for did it not assure the protection of the law wherever Rome ruled? Now, knowing its worth, had he impugned it? The next words of Paul impressed him still more: "I had it from my birth".[12]

The tribune reflected; the next morning, having freed Paul from his fetters, he convoked the Sanhedrin and sent Paul down to meet it.

The head of this Hebrew council was a rabbi whose name was Ananias ben Nedebaï. It would perhaps not be surprising, even to-day, that a man notorious both as a skinflint and a heavy eater was held in high esteem in Jerusalem;[13] and no sooner had Paul, with that piercing glance and that impassioned tone which had so often impressed both the learned and the poor, begun his speech by saying that he was acting in good faith, than Ananias, rising in the white robe which contrasted with his coarse Jewish features and his heavy figure, gave order to one of his satellites to strike the prisoner in the mouth.

It was an outrage that Paul resented with all the energy of his temperament. "God shall strike you, you wall of white-washed stone", he cried. "You claim to judge me according to the Torah, and in defiance of the Torah you give orders that I shall be struck."[14]

But proud words could not help him. "What!" cried the Jews, scandalized. "You are insulting the high priest of God!"[15]

Paul saw the need of calm and excused himself. "I did not know, brothers," he answered with well-veiled irony, "that *he* was the high priest. If I had known I would not have spoken so: for it is written: *Thou shalt not insult the leader of thy people.*"[16] This reference to a text in Exodus, with its discreet thrust at the personal weakness of a greedy man, produced a more favourable impression. Paul went on to explain that he was a Parush, the son of a Parush.

"Do you know why they accuse me?" he asked. "Because I hope for the resurrection of the dead."[17]

He had chosen from his faith a point on which all the Parushim would join battle at any moment with their rivals, the Sadducees, and immediately a furious discussion arose.

When the debate became noisier and noisier, Claudius Lysias intervened once more and had Paul brought back to his prison in the tower Antonia.

Meanwhile his thwarted enemies bound themselves under a curse that they would neither eat nor drink till they had his blood. The plot spread amongst the Parushim till it reached Paul's own relatives. Among these was a nephew, who managed to obtain access first to Paul himself and then to the tribune. Claudius Lysias, knowing that it might be long before he heard the end of such an outrage against a Roman citizen, decided to send Paul well guarded to Caesarea, where his case could be referred to the Roman Governor.

And so when Paul left for the last time the city of peace it was with a Roman escort of two hundred lancers, seventy other mounted soldiers and two hundred foot. Claudius Lysias, knowing his Jews, was determined to run no risks with his important captive, a Roman citizen, whom the Jews were determined to kill—and though the greater number had turned back at Kefr-Saba, when they believed the danger passed, it was still at the centre of a clattering cavalcade that Paul entered the port he had left a fortnight before.

5

The authority before whom Paul now appeared was one of those loose Roman *arrivistes* to whom the Emperor Claudius had handed over the administration of Judaea after the fall of the Herodian house. He was a political adventurer—of a type only too notorious in modern Paris—who had wormed his way to success through a succession of dirty intrigues both with women and local leaders. Beginning as a slave, he owed his first opportunities to Antonia, the daughter of Mark Antony and Octavia. His brother Pallas making her a fortune, she obtained freedom for them both. Felix had then made his way to Syria, and worked in the administration till he became a Procurator, or Governor, of the whole district.

His character was deformed by an ugly combination of cruelty and lust; he was, says Renan, not only disgraceful but disgusting. Even when he exercised the powers of a king, he retained the mind of a slave.

But he had a way with women: three separate queens had each been his paramour. Of these, the first was the grand-daughter of no less famous a pair than Antony and Cleopatra: she was therefore the niece of Antonia who had freed Felix from slavery. As a descendant of Cleopatra, she inherited talent and allurement; but this niece of Antonia, having married the man whom Antonia had freed, was only to be cast aside for another of whose story nothing remains, except that she too was abandoned for a young Jewish princess, a girl of seventeen, Drusilla, who had been married to Aziz, King of Homs. From him Felix seduced her with the help of the magician whom Paul had encountered in Cyprus.[18]

Such had been the life of the lurid personage before whom the Roman law now brought, among the marble courts and palaces of Caesarea, the genius divinely chosen for the embassy of Christ.

It says something for the traditions of Roman justice that Paul in no way suffered from this dubious official. The terms in which his case was reported by Lysias were fair, if not strictly accurate. He had been accused by the Jews not of any crime but in matters relating to their Torah, and was in danger of death when Lysias, having heard that he was a Roman citizen, tore him from their hands: hearing that the Jews were intending again to entrap him, Lysias had sent Paul under a strong guard to Caesarea where the Jews could state their charges.

It was five days before Ananias ben Nedebaï arrived, supported by certain of those ministers whom we know as priests or ancients; and—from this tactful chronicler—this may well mean ministers of the Christian Church. These had hired a pleader with the Roman name of Tertullus, who set out his case against Paul in the open court. "Here", the pleader said, "was a pestilential fellow, an agitator, a follower of the tiresome sect who had even tried to profane the temple, and whom they would have judged according to the Torah, had not Lysias torn him from their hands."[19]

It was for Paul to answer. In his defence he still thought it more discreet to say nothing of the Messiah. "I serve the God of our Fathers", he said, "according to the religion which they call a sect—believing all that is written in the Torah and the Prophets, but having this hope that there will be a resurrection, both of the righteous and of sinners. And that is why I make every effort to have a conscience clear before God and before men. What wrong have I done?"[20] he asked. He had brought an offering to the temple; he had raised no tumult; he had broken no law: the only noise he had occasioned was a debate over the resurrection of the dead!

Now Felix knew enough to understand what this reticent phrase meant: he was well aware that the Christians founded their hopes on the assurance that their Christ had risen from His sepulchre.

Some movements of a soul which, though leprous, was not dead gave Felix a deeper interest in the case before him. A man of passion may link even his scarlet sin with kindly impulse. Conscience awoke curiosity and a craving for redemption, while habit counselled corruption. Felix neither gave judgment nor dismissed the case. Sometimes he merely asked if his prisoner would bribe him: while sometimes he wondered if, at a price not too high, he might have a pledge for the future of his soul. Paul, remembering from the Proverbs that "the fear of God is the beginning of wisdom", spoke of justice, of self-control, of the need of a good conscience in view of the judgment after death. Such a teaching was anything but soothing to such a man as Felix; in fact he was terrified. Saying that this was enough for the present, he commanded Paul to leave him.[21]

With these intrigues and questions, two whole years went by, and still Paul was not freed. At the end of that time Felix was transferred: but since he calculated he would get more out of the Jews by keeping his prisoner under arrest, Paul was still a prisoner when a new and honest Governor, Porcius Festus, was installed at Caesarea in the year 60; Festus was to administer justice where Felix had indulged his vice.[22] What was he to do with the prisoner whom Felix had left in chains?

When he went up to Jerusalem Festus heard of fresh accusations brought against Paul: the Jews again demanded that the man they hated should be brought to Jerusalem; he was also given information of a fresh scheme to ambush the prisoner on his journey and despatch him. Festus decided that once again the accusers should come down to Caesarea.[23] Many and grave were the charges they brought, but nothing could be proved. Paul argued once more that he had done nothing reprehensible against the Jewish law, nor against the temple, nor against the Emperor. Festus, to please the Jews, suggested that Paul should once more go back to Jerusalem and once more face the Sanhedrin. "If there is nothing in their accusations", answered Paul, "no one has the right to hand me over to them. I appeal to Caesar."[24]

The natural disappointment of Paul over his apparent failure in Jerusalem; the ambushes and trickery of his own people; their virulent hatred; their obstinate will to do him to death: the failure of the men around James to support him: all had combined to weary and disgust him. On the other side, out of this disappointment came the opportunity he had so long cherished. He could, by appealing to the Emperor, ensure his way to Rome. He could carry the vast conceptions with which he had been inspired from the intrigue and fanaticism of Jewry to the great capital which was the centre of the system which had so often vindicated him, he could go to the meridian of the Empire's power and peace.

7

Before he reached Rome, however, he was to have many adventures. Not the least interesting of his encounters came to him immediately. One of the most remarkable women in the East was about to appear in Caesarea. Berenice, who was to be the subject of a famous play of Racine, was a daughter of Herod Agrippa I and of a sister of Philo of Alexandria.[25] She was to become the favourite, and almost the Queen, of the Emperor Titus. The Drusilla whom the reprobate Felix had seduced from the King of Homs was her younger sister. Wherever she went, she became the subject of scandal—even now when she was living with her step-brother, Agrippa II,[26] a young, good-looking, talented, versatile Jew who, having been brought up at Rome, had come back to reign as head of the house of Herod—that house of whom one member had become a Christian at Antioch. This Jewish prince arrived, with his striking sister, at Caesarea for a visit of ceremony to the new Roman governor. In the course of their visit, Festus spoke of the impressive prisoner who was awaiting an opportunity to sail to Rome and the Emperor.

Festus explained that Paul had committed no crime: it was simply a matter of Jewish controversy, and, added the sceptical Italian, of "a certain Jesus who had died, and who Paul insisted was alive".[27] "As it was embarrassing for me to conduct an enquiry on such subjects," concluded Festus to Agrippa, "I asked him if he was willing to go to Jerusalem to be tried there on these accusations. But Paul having appealed that his case might be brought before the Emperor, I have given orders to keep him under guard until I send him to Caesar."

"I, too," answered Agrippa, "would have liked to hear what the fellow has to say."

"To-morrow," answered Festus, "you shall hear him."[28]

8

The next morning the Prince and his sister came into the audience room in state, attended by an imposing retinue. The tribunes and the leading personages in the neighbourhood were summoned to do them honour. Festus invited Agrippa and Berenice to take their seats on a place of dignity. Before this assemblage Paul was ordered by Festus to appear. Festus then formally explained that Paul had done nothing worthy of death, but that he had appealed to the Emperor. If he was to appear before the Emperor, however, then the Governor must also send in a report, for how, he asked, can an official send a prisoner to higher authority unless he reports the accusation against him?

The King, turning to the prisoner, signified that he should now speak in his own defence, and as Paul raised his hand, the clang of his chain first broke the waiting silence.

It was in no unworthy scene that he spoke for the last time in his own country to tell the King the significance of his life.

It was before a Roman Governor, before a Prince of the House of Herod the Great who had treated with Antony and with Augustus; it was before the niece of Philo.

"I count myself fortunate, King Agrippa, to have to-day to plead my cause before Your Majesty of all the accusations brought against me by the Jews." So Paul began with that courteous tone which was the natural expression of his Jewish nationality, his sweeping projects, and the lofty tenor of his life. "For you know better than any their customs and their controversies. I ask you therefore to hear me patiently. My life from the early days of my youth has been passed in Jerusalem in the midst of my race: this all the Jews know, if they care to give evidence, having knowledge of me from the first that, according to the strictest party of our religion, I lived as a Parush. And now", he continued, "I am here on trial because I believe in the promises which God made to our fathers: this is the hope for which the Jews accuse me. Now does it seem impossible", he asked, "to a Jew to believe that God can raise the dead?"

He recapitulated his own story: how he had thought it his duty to oppose with all his strength the name of the Nazarene: how he had received authority from the high priests to persecute the Christians: how he had put them under arrest, and by persecution pressed them to abjure their faith, and how he had finally obtained permission to push his persecution beyond Palestine.

Then once more he told his experience in the sands near Damascus: how he had come face to face with Jesus in His dominion and power: how he had become a different man and preached a change of heart and mind. Everywhere he had gone with his message, both to small and great, saying nothing but what the prophets had said, that the Messiah must suffer, and that, being the first to rise from the grave, He should proclaim light to the Jewish race and to all nations.[29]

As the hall rang with the solemn asseverations of the inspired speaker in his proclamation of the fact on which his faith and his Church were built, Festus felt that, before the power of this man, his own control of the situation was slipping away.

"You are raving, Paul," he shouted; "your long studies have turned you mad."[30]

"I am not raving, Your Excellency," answered the speaker in a tone quieter, but not less firm. "I am speaking the language of truth and discretion. The King is informed about these things and to him I speak with confidence. I am convinced that none of these things is hidden to him: for these things have not been done in a corner out of the way."[31]

Then, turning to the Prince, he spoke with rising force. "Do you believe the prophets, King Agrippa? I know that you believe them."[32]

Agrippa strove, with wit and irony to wrap his feelings from Paul's gaze. "A little more and you would persuade me to be a Christian."

Paul's intense earnestness and warmth overwhelmed the assemblage as he answered: "I would to God, a little more, or much more, but that not only you, Lord King, but all those who hear me were such as I am myself—except for these chains."[33]

Agrippa had heard enough. He rose from his throne, and with him Berenice and Festus and their suite, and passed in procession from the hall. As people of power and cultivation do, after an encounter with a personality of unexpected force, and with issues which invite them to change the current of their lives, they tried to show good will, and yet not too much. "The fellow", they said, "has done nothing to deserve imprisonment, much less execution."[34]

Finally Agrippa, to dismiss the matter, spoke in the same tone to Festus. "This fellow might have been set free if he had not appealed to Caesar."[35]

NOTE.—Those who wish to concentrate on the personal narrative may omit the following chapter.

THE MEANING OF SACRIFICE

1

EW HAVE WRITTEN ON THE TOPOGRAPHY AND THE CHRON-
ology of St. Paul's life with more authority than Sir William
Ramsay. Sir William Ramsay has recorded that in his view
Paul, while still at Caesarea, was occupied with preparing a
case for his Church, its worship, its doctrine and its way against
the Jews who had always troubled him, and at whose instance
he had undergone the arrest which kept him at Caesarea. Here
we meet the question of a document of the early Church which
is of the highest interest. It has been adduced as evidence in
several lives of St. Paul, though it is ignored in others: it gives
in a style of remarkable power a statement of the Christian way
as against that of the temple and the unbelieving Jews, and it
reproduces many arguments and considerations on the central
problem of Paul's career. We find it in our Bibles as "the
Epistle of Paul the Apostle to the Hebrews".

"Are we therefore", asked Ramsay, "to disconnect it absolutely from the Apostle Paul?"[1] To this question he gives an
answer a biographer should not ignore:—

"If that were so, it is difficult to see how such a strong body
of early opinion should have regarded it as originating indirectly from Paul and as conveying his views about a great crisis
in the development of the Church. Clement of Alexandria and
Origen, while both recognising that the language is not that of
Paul, suggest different theories to account for what they recognise as assured facts—that the views and plans are those of
Paul. . . .

"This tradition of a Pauline connection was so strong as to persist even though there was already in the second century a clear perception that the style was not that of Paul. It was common in early manuscripts to place Hebrews in the middle of Paul's epistles, even between Galatians and Ephesians. Origen mentions that 'the primitive writers' were positive as to the connection of Paul with the Epistle. A very ancient tradition, therefore, of the strongest character, guaranteed that Paul stood in some relation to the Epistle."[2]

2

So much for Ramsay. An even greater authority is that of Westcott who says: "There is unquestionably a sense in which Origen is right in saying that the thoughts of the Epistle are the thoughts of St. Paul. The writer shows the same broad conception of the universality of the Gospel as the Apostle of the Gentiles, the same grasp of the age-long purpose of God wrought out through Israel, the same trust in the atoning work of Christ and in his present sovereignty. He speaks with the same conscious mastery of the Divine counsel. But he approaches each topic from a different side."[3]

Westcott died long since. In 1939 an exhaustive work appeared, which shows that Bleek, on whom Westcott based much of his work, had not seen all the authorities: in this new and exhaustive work, Professor Leonard supports with much erudition the unexpected proposal that this epistle may well show what Paul could do, if instead of dictating, he had set out to write his prose in an ordered treatise. Few may accept that; but, at the same time, Professor Leonard offers another proposal which accords with the contentions of Sir William Ramsay: that this epistle has St. Paul behind it, but was written by another. It may well have been worked out by several others; but this will not exclude his connection with it.

3

And at this point, one may well state three considerations which many theologians have omitted to discuss. The first is that of Ramsay, that if St. Paul's inspiration is denied, it has never been found that the Epistle could be satisfactorily attributed to any other author. The second arises out of this: the writings of St. Paul are the work of a literary genius of the highest order: Hebrews is also the work of a literary genius of the highest order, an order equal, if not superior, to that of St. Paul, as shown in work admittedly his. Which is easier to imagine? That a writer superior to St. Paul arose, wrote this epistle much along the lines of Paul's thought and using many expressions peculiar to him and then completely disappeared leaving no trace behind, or that St. Paul, as the most vigorous and inspiring writer of the time, conceived its broad lines and contributed some of its striking expressions, expressing it perhaps first in Hebrew, while leaving it to others, closer in touch with Alexandrian thought, and feeling the Hebrew view, to mould it into an ordered whole? A Bishop of to-day, if issuing a Pastoral, may give ideas to an able writer, ask the writer with others to compose the Pastoral; and then, with additions and corrections, the Bishop will send it out as his Pastoral. So an Anglican scholar of to-day, the Bishop of Oxford, thinks it may have been in this case. There remains a third question: from whom could the reference to "our brother, Timotheos" come if it were not from those in the immediate circle of Paul, and therefore under the influence of Paul?

It is such considerations as these, joined to a knowledge of the Italian traffic through Caesarea, which inclined Ramsay to accept Lewis's argument that in an account of Paul's imprisonment at Caesarea, this epistle should not be ignored.[4]

There was no reason why the gifted Apollos himself should not have come over to Caesarea from Ephesus or Corinth. Lucanus, who in such admirable prose gave a redaction of Paul's speeches at Lystra and Athens, was with him. So was Aristarchos. Marcus may well have returned to him. He was not far from Alexandria. A brilliant circle of friends might well have been with him in Caesarea.

Before leaving Judaea for the last time, it would have been natural to him first to plan an address to questioning Jewish Christians, whether at Jerusalem or elsewhere, and send it with a salutation from the Christians travelling to and from Italy. Here then is a reasonable occasion for the Epistle to the Hebrews to have been written. Here were several writers to round the style and order the composition.

This Epistle fully endorses that great cosmic view of redemption which it had been the peculiar vocation of Paul and of him alone to set out for that age: with him it develops in moving and eloquent iteration the power of faith. Like him, it shows a mind crowded with a wealth of life that gives rich and soaring ideas, original and poetic expressions: it shows also that acquaintance with the Book of Wisdom which Paul had shown in *Romans;* like him, it builds up an argument with quotations from impressive passages of Hebrew poetry: indeed, it quotes three particular psalms he had himself quoted elsewhere. In it there are no fewer than 46 words found nowhere but in epistles admittedly written by him.[5]

Like him, it builds up its argument on the grace of faith; it agrees with him in its view of justification, of the place of obedience and hope in relation to faith, and of the redeeming work of Christ. Like him, it treats the Old Testament allegorically: more remarkable than any of these, it shows resemblances to his speech to Agrippa and Festus.[6] It is, above all, because of those resemblances that it is discussed here rather than later.

4

It begins with the most majestic period in the New Testament, and continues its argument with a dignity only equalled by the wealth of expression. It begins with one theme: the pre-excellence of the Christos over the angels, and over Moses. It establishes each by a use of the psalms, which is at once impressive and mystical. It then proceeds to show the Christos pre-excellent over the Jewish priesthood: over the high priest who, in the temple at Jerusalem, made offerings and sacrifices first in the outer court and once a year in the Holy of Holies: for what was the meaning of those great words: "Thou art a priest for ever in the order of Melchizedech"?[7] Before Melchizedech even Abraham had bowed.

"For God, thinking to show more abundantly to the heirs of the promise the immutability of His counsel, introduced an oath that by two immutable things (and among these God could not deceive us) we, who have fled to take hold of the hope that is held out to us, might have strong encouragement: we have as an anchor of the soul, sure and firm, this hope which enters into that sanctuary beyond the veil, into which Jesus had entered for us as a forerunner, having become a high priest for ever in the order of Melchizedech."[8] This hieratic figure, kingly, mysterious, who long before the institution of the Levitical priesthood had come out of the unknown to offer sacrifice of bread and wine, and to whom Abraham had bowed, had haunted the Hebrew tradition till in a psalm his priestly order suggested both hieratic power and eternity.

"Thou art a priest for ever in the order of Melchizedech." Here was a type more prophetic of the Christos than any Levite. A priest inheriting his tradition from the dawn of time, a priest who was a king presiding more at the altar of mystery than at the throne of power, on this figure the insight of genius fixed with that happy interplay of logic with imagination which was typical of the writings of Paul: "Consider how great a man was he unto whom Abraham the patriarch gave a tenth out of the chief spoils . . . This Melchizedech, King of Salem, priest of God most high, who met Abraham returning from the slaughter of the Kings and blessed him, to whom also Abraham divided a tenth part of all (being first by interpretation King of righteousness, and then also by interpretation King of Salem, which is King of peace; without father, without mother, without degrees of ancestors, having neither beginning of days nor end of life, but made like unto the Son of God abideth a priest continually)."[9] After this great flight, the passage takes (as so often with Paul) a turn of intricate exposition to establish the superiority of the priesthood of Christ in this type above the Levites and the Law:[10] for after the likeness of Melchizedech arises another priest who is born not according to a commandment marred by human weakness but according to the power of a life never to be sundered. This new hieratic power, through His remaining for ever, has an inviolable sacredness of function so that He can save to the uttermost those who come through him to God; He lives for evermore to mediate for us —a high priest, holy, innocent, undefiled, separated from sinners and loftier than the heavens. Such was the figure of the kingly and mysterious hierophant who officiated for men among eternal things.

5

The order of Melchizedech did not exclude the more familiar idea of Levitical priesthood. For the Christ completed that also; just as He was more excellent than the angels, so He was more excellent than the house of Aaron; Aaron was the minister of an earthly sanctuary, he officiated in a tabernacle pitched not by the Lord but by man. The Levites ministered on earth from day to day. But the Christ, as He had obtained a name more excellent than the angels, had obtained also a ministry more excellent than the Levites; He was the mediator of a better contract established by law on better promises. Such a promise had been boldly pronounced by Jeremiah. "I will put my laws in their mind, and in their hearts will I write them, and they shall be my people and I shall be their God."[11]

6

The next points dealt with are those Mosaic sacrifices which had survived from tent to temple. "What was the mystery signified by the slaughter of animals, this shedding of blood, but that the Christ, having come as a high priest of good things to come, of a greater and more perfect tabernacle not made with hands, that is to say not of this creation, nor yet through the blood of goats and calves, but through His own blood, entered in once for all into the holy place, having obtained eternal redemption?"[12] The Jews had hoped for some real expiation from these crude slaughters. "How much more shall the blood of Christ who through the eternal Spirit offered Himself without blemish unto God cleanse your conscience from dead works to serve the living God?"[13]

That was the gist of it all: this ritual of blood meant the outpouring of the very principle of life that in it the death inherent in sin might be swallowed up in life. So was applied in the imagery of the temple the doctrine of a living sacrifice, the outpouring of life and blood that others might live; this doctrine, that the Christ, in His life and His blood, was the supreme example of love and giving, had already been set out at Corinth for the Romans. There the doctrine was stated: "while we were yet sinners, Christ died for us. Much more then—being now set right in the eyes of God in His blood—shall we be saved."[14] Now for the Jews particularly, the same idea was set in other terms: "Once in the final harmony of the ages, hath He been manifested to annul sin by the sacrifice of Himself."[15] In either case men were to attain to the saving goodness by receiving the selfless outpouring of a heart that loved them.

"The scriptural idea of blood", says Westcott, "is essentially an idea of life and not of death . . . the blood poured out is the energy of present human life made available for others."[16] By taking human flesh and blood to Himself, the Messiah made it possible to offer it as a perfect sacrifice of obedience; through His obedience, perfected even in death, the Christ could offer up humanity. His blood is the blood of sprinkling which quickens each believer, and it is also not only a means of consecration for each believer but for the race a new relation to God: "its hallowing, cleansing power reaching to all things with which man has contact".[17]

7

The idea of sacrifice was not merely Jewish, it was fixed in all the known religions—as the moon is fixed in the sky of night. It meant not merely an unselfish effort, not merely a duty and a service: it meant in all countries—and so it had meant for thousands of years—the idea of offering an outward and visible gift to the mysterious Power or Powers—which the Jews knew to be One—to attract His attention, to appeal to His mercy, to symbolise the veneration felt for His power, and finally as a means of sharing in His mystery. "Sacrifice is the navel of the world" said one of the Indian Vedas. It was the cord by which the life of the unseen power was conveyed to the feeble dependence of men. Such was the idea which in India inspired the Brahmins among the palms and cities of the Ganges: such among the plateaux and mountains of Persia was the worship associated with the contest between Ahuramazda and Ahriman and commemorated in the feats of Mithra, son of the morning and lord of hosts: such were the gifts presented in the book *Li-ki* among the yellow people of China to be offered on the altar of heaven in Pekin; such, where the Nile brought from Abyssinia to Egypt its wealth of silt and water, was the necessity which led the people who had built the pyramids to offer gifts to Ammon Ra; such among both subtle Greeks and powerful Romans was the idea which led them to offer to Zeus, to Pallas or to Aphrodite the libation of wine, and the perfume of incense from the altar in the marble temple, or the grove of ilex.

It was the idea of sacrifice which led the women of Argos to the wooded seclusion of Epidauros to make in the round temple of Asklepias their humble sacrifices of fowls or cakes as a sign of thanksgiving for a cure.[18] It was the idea of sacrifice which impelled a Hellene after an earthquake or a stormy voyage to offer the votive tablet which he called an anathema before the statue of Hermes or the Dioskuroi, or even to the "Divine Inspiration" and the "Eternal Time".[19]

Sacrifice was the idea which, in the crude rite of the taurobolium, led the devotees of Mithra and of Ma to lie naked under the scaffold where a steer was being slaughtered that they might be stained in its blood.[20]

Such among the Hebrews whom Paul knew was the impulse which moved men to offer their *minchah,* sometimes of wine or grain, but more often of bird or animal slain in the temple, because the life of the creature was symbolised in its blood. The word *blood* therefore to Paul had always the intense sense of the power and mystery by which men live. Was it not written in Leviticus: *The life is the blood.*

To the Hebrew the idea of sacrifice had been familiar from the time of Moses. When the Jews were a nomad tribe, to them as to the nomads of the desert a meat meal was a rare treat. But always they had been enjoined to abstain from eating the meat with the blood. The blood was sacred to the Lord!

The first Shaul had built an altar where the animals could be slaughtered and drained of the blood: the same Shaul at an earlier day had joined with the prophet Samuel to eat of the feast thus made. And so from the beginning the idea of sacrifice was associated with the idea of a feast which was a common feast of brotherhood among the feasters, and which implied a communion with the Almighty to whom the life—in the blood —had already been offered.[21]

The Hebrews had several kinds of offering: in the *peace offering,* the blood was thus offered, with certain portions of the fat which was burnt. But even before the Jews had gone into exile in Babylon, they had also offered up, in the burnt-offering, a whole animal to be burnt by fire—in what the Greeks called a holokaust. When they came back from Babylon and elaborated their worship, in their sense of penitence and humiliation, the Jews added to this a sin-offering and a trespass-offering. The trespass-offering, or guilt-offering, was a form of restitution for injuries done to another man. The sin-offering became the most general of the offerings. In this the flesh was burnt away from the altar, and what of it was consumed was eaten only by the priests. Yet none of them could atone for that sin which was a deliberate and conscious rebellion against God's law: "for the soul which doeth aught with a high hand, whether he be home born or a stranger, the same blasphemeth the Lord and that soul shall be cut off from among His people".[22] Rather was it the idea of sacrifice that he who through his defects, whether weakness, negligence or ignorance, had fallen short, should offer a gift that would make the life of the giver at one with the Giver of Life. Sacrifice is an outward and visible sign in which man, to pay his dues to God and attain his end, symbolises his renunciation of evil and seeks good with an offering which, if accepted and sanctified by God, will be a means of communion with God.

8

Joining, therefore, the crude drama of the slaughter-house with the idea of feasting and with that of the sacred law, which was the means of union with the Most High, the universal idea of sacrifice was established in Israel.

When Shaul, in the long travail of learning by heart, was learned in the piety and the wisdom of his people, he accepted it. It was the ritual which accompanied the poetry of Israel, and that too linked him with the traditions of ancient Asia, with the wisdom of the Egyptians, and at last with the metaphysical wisdom of Athens and the Hellenists. So the young Israelite of Tarsus was the heir not only of a literature at once personally and mysteriously sublime, but of a tradition both of worship and wisdom which had come from many centuries and many lands, a wisdom which gave the mind of man an opening into all wisdom and all knowledge, and took him up through many scales of being into the secrets of the Unseen and of the Divine.

And here, at last, in the death of Christ and in the sacrament which shows it forth, Paul read the story of all effort and all sacrifice. For we live only by life and ease being given up. The very meat of our festive banquets comes from the slaughter-house: the love in which life is generated is a drama of joy and pain: this age of machines does not provide apparent ease and regularity of life for the many without inflicting on others the sordid monotony of factory life. For all things a price is fixed: the finest treasures are never bought for nothing. In every life there is a pathos and a travail: and this is its song of honour.

The heart does not cease to feel, nor love to link with life, when man looks through life and death into eternal things. The gold with which we buy this communion with heaven is still sacrifice. Such was the background both of the writer's ritual life as an Israelite in the temple, and of his life as a minister and steward of the Church. "Almost all things", he wrote, "are by the law purged with blood: and without shedding of blood is no remission. It was therefore necessary that the symbols which suggest the reality in the heavens should be purified with these, but the heavenly things themselves with better sacrifices than these. For Christ entered not into holy places made with hands, the antitype of the true ones, but into heaven itself, now for our sakes to appear before the face of God.[23]

9

Such thoughts as these do much to harmonise the two phases of Paul's zeal: and they do so through the hallowed poetry Paul had learnt in youth. It had spoken of burnt-offerings and sin-offerings being less than unity with the will of God in that mysterious and intricate intermingling of sense and soul, a body, beating with its blood;[24] he found that body and that blood afresh in the communion of the new mysteries,[25] by which came the grace and peace of Christ's hallowing life within him: "having, therefore, brethren, boldness to use the entrance into the holy place in the blood of Jesus, the entrance which He inaugurated for us, as a fresh and living way through the veil—that is the way of His flesh; and having a great priest over the house of God, let us draw near with a true heart in fulness of faith, having sprinkled our hearts from an evil conscience and having laved our bodies in pure water":[26] so did the sacramental mysteries complete the explanation of the ritual act of the high priest.[27] So, therefore, the writer could say: "We have an altar at which they who serve the tent have no right to eat"[28]: for as Leo the Great was to say afterwards, "Christ was the high priest not of the temple but of the world to come".[29]

Writing to recalcitrant Corinthians, Paul had written: "he who drinks of that cup unworthily drinks to himself damnation being guilty of the Lord's blood".[30] So here it is asked: "to how much sorer punishment is he condemned who tramples under foot the Son of God and deems the blood of the testament in which he has been made holy a common thing, and pours scorn upon the Spirit of grace?"[31] Such sacrilege demands God's fiery vengeance. "It is a fearful thing to fall into the hands of the living God".[32]

The expressions are changed: but are we to think that the thought, the energy, the passion, the genius of Paul had nothing whatever to do with it?

10

The Epistle now hymns from the ancient story of Israel the triumphs of faith. Abel, Noah, Abraham, Isaac, Jacob, Joseph, Moses, Daniel, Samuel and the prophets, what was their valour but the record and pæan of faith? It was a story like Paul's own: mockings, scourgings, bonds, imprisonment, stonings, temptations: they were slain with the sword: they went about in sheepskins, in goatskins: being destitute, afflicted, ill-treated, wandering in deserts, and on mountains, and in dens and caves of the earth[33]—yet all this was not enough, their faith bore them witness of a promise yet to come, "God having foreseen some better thing concerning us, that apart from us they should not be made perfect".[34]

11

We have seen how again and again Paul had used the metaphor of sport. Now this epistle, in its insistence on the need of heroism, returns to the thought of the athlete stripping for the race, in the crowded arena, and with this thought of nakedness and effort subtly connects a reference occurring more than once to the Spartan discipline of endurance which Jew and Greek alike received from those who loved them. "For whom the Lord loveth He chastens, and uses the whip on every son whom He receives."[35] "Therefore let us also, having so great a cloud of witnesses hanging about us, lay aside every impediment and the sin which cloaks us round. Let us run with hard effort the race that is set before us, looking direct to the Jesus who, as captain of the games, the starter and prize-giver of the faith, who for the joy that was set before Him, endured the cross, despising its shame and has sat down at the right hand of the throne of God, lest you weary, slackening in your souls; for in your combat with sin, you have not yet fought till the blood flows—and remember the encouraging words—for I speak to you like boys with warmer encouragement—it is for mastery that you endure: for the father of our spirits chastens us for our profit, that we may be partakers of His holiness."[36] Moses had trembled on Mount Sinai: but you, says the writer, "are come to Mount Sion and the city of the living God, the heavenly Jerusalem, an innumerable host of angels in festive assembly, and to the Church of the firstborn enrolled in heaven and to God the judge of all, and to the spirits of righteous men made perfect, and to Jesus, the Mediator of the New Testament, and to the sprinkling of His blood which speaks better things than that of Abel."[37]

The combination of Hellenist and Hebrew which was the ripe fruit of the Alexandrian tradition could not have been expressed with a power, a fervour and poetry more typical of Paul than this passage, impassioned and sublime.

"Follow after holiness without which no man shall see the Lord."[38] That objurgation which was the theme of every epistle written by Paul was repeated here with those injunctions, those citations both so typical of his method till he summed up his message afresh in the moving words of the final adjuration:

"The God of peace who brought from the dead, our Lord Jesus, that great Shepherd of the sheep, through the blood of the everlasting covenant, make you perfect in every good thing to do his will, working in you that which is well-pleasing in His sight through Jesus Christ to whom be glory for ever and ever."[39]

Such then in a majesty of order which is unique, and a rounded splendour of style beyond what Paul alone attained even in those passages which show him a master, is the epistle which when first mentioned by Origen was connected with his name and which (not *entirely* without reason—as we have seen) remains in our Bible as *The Epistle of Paul the Apostle to the Hebrews*.

And surely it would have been strange if a mind to which symbolism and allegory were so congenial, which was at once so incisive and so mystical, had not reflected about the central rites of temple worship in Jerusalem in their relation to the sacrifice of Christ once and for all offered and yet remaining in undiminished fulness to be applied to the souls in Christ's body in those central and holy mysteries where bread and wine are offered on the Altar to set forth the Lord's death. For to that bread, changed because it was consecrated, Paul applied the words of the Christ: THIS IS MY BODY, and of that wine he asked "THE CHALICE OF BLESSING WHICH WE BLESS, IS NOT THIS THE COMMUNION OF THE BLOOD OF CHRIST?"

The Christ was his high priest over the house of God: a priest for ever in the order of Melchizedech.[40]

THROUGH WRECK TO ROME

1

WHEN HE LEFT CAESAREA THE LIFE OF CHRIST'S ENVOY
abruptly changed. From his great preoccupation with the relation of his Church to the Temple and the Law, from harrowing
by fanatical Jews, from the life of a man under guard in the
summers and winters of the coast of Palestine, from speaking
before a governor and a king, his drama now turns back to that
struggle with wind and waves which had so often endangered
him in the long years of his travel, and once drove him to
spend a night and a day in the deep. It is thus that he has an
opportunity to revisit at Sidon the adherents of the Church:
it is thus that at a far island he was to manifest his gifts in
relation to a serpent and a storm; but his story is now a sailor's
story; and yet another side of this remarkable man is seen
when he shows an instinct for the sea which far excelled that
of the captain of the ship in which he sailed.[1]

2

The story is one a seaman understands in his own language.[2]
They went on board a ship which had been sailing down from
Edremid; casting off from the wharf they made all sail, keeping in close to the Syrian shore, and after their day in Sidon,
got under weigh again, and beat up along the shore of Cyprus
with the wind dead ahead. They then got a fair slant over the
sea between Cyprus and Perga, and put into Myra, two miles

inland from the mouth of the Andraki, which was then a little port sheltered by hills.

At Myra the Roman Centurion in charge found an Egyptian ship which sailed from Alexandria over a halcyon sea and was now bound for Italy. This second ship, either because she was what sailors call "a slow old tub", or because they struck that season of dead calm common in those seas in late October, made many days of the passage to Crete so that as they fetched Crete there were signs of change in the sky and, as they could not weather Crete, they ran down to leeward of it till they reached Salmone; hauling upon a taut bowline, so that they first passed to windward of it, they ran into a little harbour called Fairhaven, not far from Lasea. They had by now made a long voyage of it, the season of calm had gone by, and Paul knew what squalls over a rising sea were only too likely to mean.

Calling all hands to the after part of the boat where the passengers—no less than 276—were gathered: "Gentlemen," he said, "I can see that if we sail on longer now, it will not be without damage and cost, not only to the freight and the ship, but to us and our lives".[3] A choice already of life and death on that waveless sea: such was the issue with which Paul faced them.

The Egyptian sailors, however, with the careless confidence of well-fed men, thought they knew more of the sea than a Jewish Rabbi travelling as a chained prisoner: and the centurion, not unnaturally, believed the craftsmen. Nevertheless, many had qualms; and after much discussion the majority, some because they were impressed by Paul, some because of reluctance for risks, decided that they had better try to fetch in to Phenice, a little Cretan port with two channels—one to the north-west, the other to the south-west of its little haven. When, therefore, a southerly breeze sprang up, they got under weigh and kept along the Cretan shore: but Paul's forebodings were about to be vindicated: before long the wind hauled round to the northward, and from thence, drawn by the heat of the Sahara, it began to blow with rising force. As soon as the hurricane struck the ship they found they could not lay up to the wind; they drew up the helm and scudded before it: getting under the lee of the islet called Clauda, they had hard work to haul up the boat they had been towing alongside. But finally they hoisted her up to the davits, and passed belly lashings around the ship to thrap her together: then, in fear they would be driven down on the Syrtis, towards the coast of Cyrene, they clewed up and furled everything and let the ship run before the storm, the decks cleared and the masts bare.

Each day Paul's prophecy was realised more clearly. Winds blew harder: and the tumult of the sea became a terror; the frightened crew pulled themselves together to heave overboard some of the cargo. The day after that, the wind increasing yet further, they flung overboard any gear they could spare. And still the gale blew under a sky so heavy that they could get neither a meridian altitude nor a lunar observation, nor track their way by the stars; as they scudded on beneath a wild, dark sky, the storm blew away their last hopes of life. A thousand billows heaped their menace over a bark driven unceasingly over the restless sea. The wind roared on under the vast night; and as the ship pitched on through the waves, the wretched travellers were battered by the roll and pitch of the ship. They lay inert, exhausted, chilled, in a horror of misery and uncleanness. If from time to time a sailor staggered to the deck, he saw a sight that appalled him. A myriad of surging movements, each part and portion of a vaster motion, actuated by the tyranny of the storm, gave in every direction an aspect of complex and overwhelming anger.

According to a common notion of the time, the elements

were the abode of powers of the air. The tumult of cloud and wind and water suggested to a terrified mind that these powers had burst into maniac fury. The whole surface of the sea had become one dizzy whirl of rushing, writhing, tortured rage: the bellying waves coiled, bounded and crashed in an anarchy of titanic but wanton convulsions. Paul was familiar with the terrors of the sea; but never had they borne on him so to appal, to buffet and to exhaust him. Panic was all around, mixed with bitterness and cursing: the terror of darkness was but increased when through the whistle and scream of the wind, the darkness was riven by impetuous lightning. Starving and exhausted by the effect of sickness, sickened by the panic and blasphemy around him, and completely ignorant of his whereabouts, the worn traveller was as exhausted and humiliated as by the torment of the scourge. His character and genius were utterly worn down.[4]

3

Then suddenly, out of the darkness of the night, there shone that lambent and piercing brilliance which more than once had visited him in distress, as it had changed long since in the sand above Damascus the current of his life. He felt himself again in the presence of a power he could no more question than withstand. Before it, the very torment of the sea seemed to lose its significance. And as he was aware of a presence, so he was aware of a voice which told him that over the wind and tempest his God was master, and would lead him to Rome and to the Emperor. Not a soul in that ship should drown.

This gave a new and supernatural strength to Paul. He waited through the night, invigorated and serene. In the morning, he was able to press on captain and crew the soundness of his judgment. They had learnt from the damage to the ship and the cost of cargo thrown overboard that his words were worth listening to: he told them now that they need not give up hope; if they kept up their courage they might count that, whatever happened to the boat, all on board would come safe to land.

"For in the night", he said, "the angel of the God whom I serve and who is my Master stood beside me saying: 'Have no fear, Paul, for you are to come before the Emperor: and God has given you as His gift all who travel with you.' So be of good heart, gentlemen, for I have faith in God that He will do as it has been declared to me: but the ship will come to ground on some island."[5]

4

For a fortnight more, they were knocked about in the gales in the sea at the mouth of the Adriatic. At last, one night just about the beginning of the first watch, the look-out on the forecastle saw that the water was shoaling. They took soundings and got twenty fathoms: at the next sounding they got fifteen. It was to keep the ship from foundering on the rocks they let down four anchors, and held on for daylight.

Some of the crew, when they had the boat down in the water, pretending to kedge anchor to midward, thought this would give them their chance to desert: but Paul pointed out to the Centurion and his soldiers that if the sailors left the ship no one could possibly be saved. Taking his advice, the soldiers cut the boat's painter and let her drop free.

At daybreak, Paul told them all to take a meal, pointing out that for a whole fortnight they had had no nourishment. "And so", he said, "I strongly advise you to take some food, for this is essential to your being saved: and not a hair of your heads shall be lost."

Then, before them all, he gave thanks as he had learnt to do and received the broken bread. And at this all took heart, and all refreshed themselves. And when they had eaten enough, they felt stronger and threw the cargo into the sea. It was daylight now, and they were near an island, what it was they knew not, but one little inlet gave them calm water for a landing. They hauled up the anchors, slacked the rudder braces, let fall the mainsail, and ran the ship head on for the inlet. At the mouth of it, however, there was a bar on which the bow of the ship ran aground while the stern was knocked to pieces by the breakers which writhed around and struck upon her failing timbers. While the morning air was whitened by the swirling spray that rose from the crest of the waves into the wind like shreds of torn sheets in the flight and fury of the wind, the breakers swirled around the wreck or crashed on the neighbouring rocks.

The Roman soldiers were not less brutal than the storm: their counsel was to kill the prisoners whom the angry weather had spared, lest any of them should swim ashore and escape. The Centurion, however, who had been well disposed to Paul from the beginning, having learnt to trust him entirely, gave other and better orders. The swimmers he said could strike out for the shore while the others held on to planks, ladders and broken pieces of the ship. And it was done accordingly. In the evening, as Paul had promised, every one of the 276 in the ship came safe to land.[6]

5

The mysterious source of fortitude which had enabled Paul to overcome seasickness, fear and exhaustion, and take a lead at a critical moment to give not only moral support but the counsels of common sense, and which had vindicated his earlier judgments, was the strength which had come to him from his vision in the night; nor could the mystery of sustaining power desert him when, safe from the threatening sea, he faced the islanders among whom he was cast. As rain poured down, to add its misery of wet to the chilly blast of the wind, he gathered brushwood and sticks to heap upon the fire which the inhabitants had kindled to comfort them against the bitter weather.

As he did so he was able, in a new drama of danger, to impress those around him. Hidden in one of the branches which he had picked up was a snake. As he brought the wood to the heat, the snake wriggled from it to coil round his hand, and hung from it with forked tongue and the threat of death.

In such signs, the naïf islanders saw the judgment of the eternal powers. Clearly, they said, this man is a murderer, for after he has been saved from the sea, justice forbids him to live. But Paul shook the serpent into the fire and showed no sign of hurt, while the islanders waited for him to swell up and die. Still they watched: and still finding him well, they changed their minds and said he was a god. Sir William Ramsay reminds us that the Maltese viper is not poisonous; but surely the islanders should have known the danger of their own snakes! [7]

Nor was this the only incident by which Paul impressed the hospitable inhabitants. At the house of a certain Publius, who took a lead both in government and in kindness, Paul healed his host's father of combined malaria and dysentery. This gave him a name which spread over the whole island so that all who were ailing came to him for cure. And they received it. Sir William Ramsay reminds us again that Paul had in his company a physician, and this modest physician tells the story; but it is the same physician who credits Paul with miracles several times.

6

Thus three months went by, and spring weather brought back sailing to the calmed waves: the sailors of a ship which had sailed direct from Alexandria under the sign of "The Great Twin Brethren" and which had sheltered in one of the Maltese harbours (for it was Malta on which the shipwrecked company had landed), saw that a favourable speed ruffled the mirrored masts. In the calm waters of the Maltese inlet the breeze blew warm from the south: to this ship the wrecked company were now transferred: sailing on through the Straits of Messina, past Syracuse and Reggio, past Scylla and Charybdis, they made a rapid voyage to that translucent water in the Bay of Naples, where Shelley later saw old palaces and towers

Quivering within the waves' intenser day.[8]

Virgil had related with what contentment Aeneas, after his long journey, touched the soil of Italy. Paul had come both from Troy and from Damascus to see more beauty than Aeneas could have surveyed; for to hill and plain, to tilth and woodland, to olive, aloe, maize and vine, was now added the marble palace, the brick viaduct and arch, the rounded splendour of building which the Romans had set up in the rich blue Italian day. Among these Paul brought what he himself called "the glorious evangel of the blessed God".[9]

How different was this smiling land—pearly already with the bloom of almonds — from the biscuit-coloured islet on which he had been cast up by the raging storm! Here earth in the mild harmonies of blue and rose held the beauty of Hellas without its austerity. Paul travelled on towards Rome by that Via Appia which Statius called the queen of the great imperial roads.[10] As he came near to his journey's end, he received a great consolation. The Saints of Rome (for thus he called those who had received the graces of the Holy Spirit) came out to meet him at the marbled courts of Appius and led him onwards with joy. Among enthusiastic Christians, he entered the imperial city with a forestaste of the veneration which his name was to receive through the ages. And here, after consoling and encouraging the Christians, he turned his mind to the two remaining problems: how to impress the Romans; how to reconcile the Jews.

The Roman scene is highly significant and singularly noble. It is a genial earth where Apollo's summer look comes early, through brilliant but delicate light: for the Roman air is as suave as it is transparent. Monte Mario direct above the Tiber, Soracte, gently rising in the distance, steep over the lakes of Nemi and Albano the Alban hills marked the skyline beyond the wide sweep of the Campagna: an everlasting wash of air played then, as it plays now, upon the walls of Rome. The Mediterranean umbrella pine, the olive, the cypress, the myrtle and the ilex spread their unwithering green over a light of laughing flowers as the anemone and the iris succeeded the jonquil and the violet; laburnum flowered after the peach tree and the pear; vines spread their tendrils along the trellised arbours: and as the sun warmed, the winding of the cicalas among the grass mingled with the murmur of innumerable bees, while lizards slept on the warm stone, before nightingales poured their clear notes to moon and stars.

Already at Rome, architecture recorded the sense of Empire; the long aqueduct, the triumphal arch, the rounded temple, the marble colonnade, prepared already for the towering brickwork of the baths of Caracalla and Diocletian to speak of the wide beneficence of the government of Augustus and his house. Sculpture already attested the strength and dignity of Roman character. Here everywhere was both expressed and felt the immense majesty of the Roman peace. Such was the Italy Paul had so long and eagerly planned to reach. Such was the civilisation to which he had become a debtor.[11]

7

The City of Rome meant more and showed more than any of her provinces. Whosoever aspired to play a part in great affairs was bound to come there, and that inspired instinct which led Paul to Rome meant for him, said Renan, an event almost as decisive as his conversion. It was indeed of pregnant significance that the Christ Himself had promised "As thou hast borne witness for Me in Jerusalem, so shalt thou bear witness for Me in Rome!"[12]

As they approached the walls of the eternal city, Julius the Centurion led his prisoner to the *Castra Praetoriana* which Sejanus had built near the Via Nomentana, and handed him over to the prefect of the praetorium.[13] Those who appealed to the Emperor were considered his personal prisoners, and kept in custody by the Imperial Guard. At this time, there was a single prefect of the guard, Afranius Burrhus, and he a man of unusually noble character. Paul was still chained—chained to a *frumentarius*[14]—but this did not prevent him moving about or speaking as he wished: and he was able before long to live in his own lodging.

How was he to proceed? The little body of enthusiasts who had welcomed him on the road from Naples had not been converted in the synagogue. They were rather traders from the

East, men who had come up to the imperial capital from Ostia or Pozzuoli and had little to do with the large colony of Jews: for these were more than 20,000, and had an important synagogue.[15] Yet before these Paul must proclaim his evangel. They were still the chosen people to whom were given the covenant, the promises, the prophets, the hope of salvation. He arranged that certain of the rabbis should come and see him. When they came he stated his case with his accustomed subtlety. He had come to Rome, he said, to appeal to the Emperor: not that he had profaned the Law, still less that he had any design of accusing the people: "but if I wish to see you or speak to you", he said, "it is for the reason that I wear a chain, because dear to me above all is the hope of Israel".[16] Thus did he introduce his theme: the Christos and the Resurrection.

So far his course was favourable enough. The Jews had heard nothing against him personally, and were curious to hear what a pupil of Gamaliel had to say about a movement which had aroused opposition in every quarter.[17]

On the day fixed for him to speak, a considerable number of Jews came to his lodging. He spoke for hour on hour, seeking to show both from Moses and the Prophets that the Messiah of which they spoke was no other than the Jesus whom he knew: that the kingdom they expected was no other than the Church. Some were persuaded: others incredulous: and so they left him.

8

At this new experience of suspicion and contrariety which he could not but contrast with the esteem in which he had been held by the Maltese, and the prestige he had gained among his company on the two ships on which he had sailed through such great dangers, he saw that it was not for nothing that he had been sent to preach Christ to the nations. Was it not already signified by his favourite Isaiah in the Septuagint he had read so long ago and all his life?

> This people's heart is waxed gross
> And their ears are dull of hearing,
> And their eyes they have closed,
> Lest haply they should perceive with their eyes,
> And hear with their ears,
> And understand with their heart,
> And should turn again,
> And I should heal them.[18]

He had written some of that already in his Epistle to the Romans, of which, of course, the unconverted Jews had heard nothing. He had learnt that those words were more than once on the lips of the Christ Himself: but this saving action of God is sent, so Paul warned them with angry emphasis, "as a message to the nations: and *they* will hear".[19]

Such were the last words we hear falling direct from the lips of Paul. They mark the fact that from henceforward his centre was in Rome, and not Jerusalem: among the nations, and not in his own tribe.

Meanwhile he had won the way to Rome: for two whole years he remained in a house which he rented, and none disturbed him as with confidence, under the Roman sun, he announced that Kingdom of God and that universality of the Church, which the triumph of Augustus had made easier to understand, but which were yet so much more potent than the Empire that they could transform it and shine beyond it to regions which no Caesar ever knew.

NEW PROBLEMS

1

FROM THIS TIME ON ALL DIRECT CHRONICLE OF PAUL'S LIFE ceases. The sources which remain have all been the subject of debate. Nevertheless, even if the evidence has been contested, certain statements remain, and furnish the best indication of how Paul lived his remaining years.

Apart from much in the field of archæology, a little of this evidence is in the record of others. Much also remains in epistles which bear the name of Paul, which were for centuries accepted by all as his work, and which no one has been able to prove were either written by him at an earlier date, or written later by another.[1] The majority of scholars agree with a tradition which they harmonise with a statement of Eusebius: that Paul was set free and travelled again.[2]

Nero, at the centre of an august system, owed his throne to crime, and grew to be a monster. But at the first he was more capricious than malign.[3] In dealing with Paul he endorsed the law which gave immunity to Jews. So Paul, secure because he was a Jew, was able to say once more that the Messiah of Israel was the hope of all men.

Freed at last, therefore, by the supreme authority of the Empire, the diplomatist of grace could now make freer plans than ever before. He had for years cherished the hope of preaching in Spain, and his disciple, Clement of Rome, tells us that he travelled to the limits of the West. It is true that no Church in the Western Mediterranean or in Spain has any tradition of a visit of Paul, but there is no other evidence against this assertion. It is therefore reasonable to think that the mission he had conducted on either side of the Aegean was now taken along the shores of Italy and Provence to the wilder lands of the Iberian peninsula, and that to suit their hardihood and independence Paul learnt new methods of approach.[4]

2

Did he also travel back to the Aegean? Before we can answer that, we must face those who deny that Paul wrote the letters which stand in his name in the Bible, two addressed to Timotheos, one to Titus. This denial was taken up first by Baur a hundred years ago, after that by Renan, and later still by Moffat. It was stated with fascinating and ingenious skill by Dr. Harrison in 1921, in a work which put that of his predecessors into the shade. Yet argument is another thing from proof. The fact remains that many scholars still accept Paul's authorship of these Epistles: nor, in spite of the valiant efforts of Dr. Harrison, have they found any suitable occasion for them in the narrative of St. Paul's life before his first arrival in Rome.

The argument that St. Paul wrote these epistles was best put by Dean Plummer. The difficulties involved in the assumption that the epistles are wholly or partly a forgery are not less serious than those which have been urged against the well-established tradition of their genuineness. The very strong evidence in their favour has to be accounted for. "It is already clear, full and decided as soon as we could expect to find it."[5]

The arguments against Paul's authorship come under two heads: first that they show a Church much more highly organised than Paul knew: but there is no proof that the Church was not organised under overseers before he died, and there were certainly deacons.[6] The statement therefore is arbitrary. It is no argument against these epistles that, written to particular friends of St. Paul, ministering in his absence, they contain evidence not found elsewhere: on the contrary, this is an argument that they were genuine. For a forger would not dare to be original. The second argument—advanced by Dr. Harrison with tireless industry—is that based on the number of expressions peculiar to them.[7] But though Dr. Harrison's contentions impressed Dr. Lock, this scholar—when later he wrote his commentary on these Epistles—still left the authorship of Paul uncontested.[8] And, remarkable as is the number of peculiar expressions, their number greatly declines when we see those already found in the Septuagint, or used in another grammatical form in the other epistles. "There is", says Dr. Lock, "no word impossible to St. Paul, no word not natural to him . . . much change of vocabulary, including even particles, is due to the kind of letter, not argumentative, not written to Churches nor to private friends but to close, intimate fellow-workers."[9] And something may be due to the amanuensis: for of the words not found in other epistles, 34 are in St. Luke.

But the method of assessment as chosen by Dr. Harrison, the argument from the use of unusual expressions, has lost its vogue among literary authorities. Scholars no longer apply to Homer or to Shakespeare the incredulities of fifty and a hundred years ago. It has been reserved for certain clergy to cling to a fashion of scepticism which laymen long since discarded. The scholars of to-day should no longer be mesmerised by the Teutonic methods which seemed impressive fifty years ago. Early in the century Sir William Ramsay issued a salutary warning:—"At present, as we are struggling to throw off the fetters which impeded thought in the nineteenth century, it is most important to free ourselves from its prejudices and its narrowness.

"The age and the people of whatever nationality whose most perfect expression and greatest hero was Bismarck, are a dangerous guide to the twentieth century. In no age and country has brute force and mere power to kill been so exclusively regarded as the one great aim of a nation, and the justification to a place in the Parliaments of Man, as in Europe during the latter part of the nineteenth century, and in no age and country has the outlook upon the world been so narrow and so rigid among the students of history and ancient letters."[10]

To put shortly the question of the Pastoral Epistles, we find that among the generation to whom they were given they were not questioned. The case against them was at no time taken as proved. The majority of scholars have rejected it through the centuries, and reject it still.[11] The common sense which scouts the notion that books so deeply venerated and so generally admired for the soundness and goodness of their teaching, were the work of impostors is vindicated by the scrutiny of specialists, and receives a further endorsement when we apply the tests of a biographer. We may take it safely, then, that after his first imprisonment in Rome, Paul returned to the Aegean.

3

Apart from these letters to Timotheos and to Titus, there are two Epistles which by their personal references fit closely together, which were written from prison—there is no mention in either of them of Rome. In one of them Paul spoke of being in chains, and being an old man. It has been argued most ably that, like the *Letter to the Philippians*, they were written from Ephesus during St. Paul's first long stay there, while he was in difficulty with the Corinthians. Scholars as a whole have not accepted this argument either; but neither have they disproved

(Victoria and Albert Museum)

ST. PAUL AND THE VIPER

From a mural of the XII Century in Canterbury Cathedral.
Drawing reproduction by kind permission of Professor E. W. Tristram

(Lubinski)

VIA APPIA—"QUEEN OF THE IMPERIAL ROADS" TO ROME

it: nor can they undermine the conjecture that if, after his first visit to Rome, Paul was again in Asia Minor, he might again have been arrested there and written these two Epistles then.[12]

But why suppose this? The reason is that the writer is asking a friend in Chonas to prepare him a lodging, for he hoped shortly to arrive. It seems unlikely that he should hope shortly to arrive in the depths of Asia Minor if he were a prisoner in Rome. And why should Timotheos, the Bishop of Ephesus, be with him in Rome? Had Marcus with Cephas also found his way there? To these questions no answer has been returned.

Nevertheless, we must admit that the weight of opinion still, as in the past, inclines to the idea that both these letters were written from Rome. In support of this is the fact that both Lucanus and Aristarchos were with Paul. And there are so many of the same people mentioned in both of them, that it seems they were written much at the same time. But if we cannot picture precisely how or where Paul wrote these letters, their object and their views are not the less clear. One of them is a personal letter to a particular man, Philemon, of whom Paul heard great things. His faith and love had a power to attract and work on others: they refreshed men of holiness: they were to Paul a well of joy and consolation.[13]

Yet into the friendship of Paul with this admirable convert, a dramatic episode had entered. Paul had converted a slave who, after robbing Philemon, had run away from him. This slave, by a curious irony, bore the name of Onesimos which, being translated, means profitable.[14]

Now Paul was determined not to keep the runaway with him lest a good Christian should be outraged: he must treat the robbed master as one gentleman would treat another: so he sent the slave back—converted, "not now as a servant but as much more than a servant, a brother, dear especially to me, but how much more unto thee, brother in the flesh and in the

Lord"[15]—both, that is to say as one you have long known, and now greet in the fellowship of the faith. "If you count me as a partner, receive him as myself. If he has done you any wrong, or is in debt to you, put that to my account. I, Paul, write with my own hand I will repay it: though I need not add what you owe to me, the soul which is your inmost self. Relying on your obedience I write, knowing that you will do all I say, and more."[16] Here, in its warmth, its tact and its sense of Christians being one in their oneness in Christ and His Holiness, is a picture of the courtesy of the aged saint toward one of those friends to whom he wrote as a sharer in their joy.

4

Yet from Philemon and the volcanic valley of the Lycus, disquieting reports had reached him. It was a wild region often shaken by earthquakes: geysers strengthened the people's belief in demons and mysterious powers. The nearness of Ionia linked them with old philosophy, that of Phrygia with extravagant speculations. The Christians there had been converted by Epaphras. It had been hard for them, as it has since been hard for many, to understand the uniqueness of Christ, and to engage on that quest of faith, hope and love which combined to make a man blameless and holy in the life of grace. The mysteries of the Christian life interested the converts of Chonas (then called Kolossai) less than rules of diet, and of discipline of the body, to which they joined an excessive interest in those ministering spirits and angels, some of whom governed the planets, but who, though they complete the scheme of salvation, are not its centre and secret; some of them believed that when they said Christ Himself was the chief of these angels, they claimed enough for Him.

In Philo, the attempt to combine Platonism with the Old Testament had produced an interesting, if confused, philosophy. But in the regions of Asia Minor there was already a tendency towards other novelties, a tendency which afterwards developed into the heresy called Montanism.[17] Like the adherents of the mystery-religions, the converts at Chonas looked for salvation: like them they welcomed baptism: but they combined a belief in planetary influence with the Jewish teaching about angels, so as to regard the angels as rulers of the stars in their courses. Into this system they fitted both baptism, the Eucharist, and the Messiah of Paul. They could admit that the Christos was the master of angels and ruler of spirits. They could admit that He was the power by which the material universe had been created: they could admit that He had appeared to the patriarchs. But they trusted also to subsidiary angels for whose influence they prepared by fasting and other ascetic exercises in an elaborately tuned system of discipline, till they should attain to the fulness of the hidden mysteries attained by philosophy: for this completion of the system implied to them something more than Christ.[18] Converts of Epaphras, they had never known the dynamic power with which Paul preached his Redeemer as all in all.[19]

For the secret of Paul's religion was an experience ascending in climax beyond climax past the subtlest speculations of men. It was a doctrine built on another order of life, a mystical and supernatural experience. And since this was given in the Church from the Christ, it was given for the life of the Church as a whole.

From it, then, should overflow some conviction, some gift of faith, some diffusion of grace that would confirm those to whom belief was an experience less intense, and life a more normal struggle for a kindly and unselfish life.[20] This interplay of advanced mysticism with good and gracious manners was not least in the realities of the faith: it was very different from that combination of asceticism with intellectualism which made the innovators at Chonas proud and superior to common men.[21]

Such was the Gnostic heresy—in certain particulars curiously like contemporary theosophy—of which he had already had an inkling some years before at Corinth. It was the idea of an esoteric knowledge, introducing a scheme of life which, though not without its attraction and elevation, was at once too close to hygiene, to magnetism, and to human schemes or fancy, and too far from the true mystery of the indwelling Christ. *He* through grace changed character and soul, and knit men and things together to take their place in a perfect order, sustained by His Spirit.

These men were also less often to perceive what Paul offered because they were fascinated by certain powers in nature: the curious radiance of the moon, which could turn fish rotten and had a strong effect even on human minds if they were unbalanced: the attraction of magic and the influence of the stars: rules about not touching or approaching certain impure things: above all strict rules about the taking of food and drink: particular attention to certain seasons and festivals as exclusive opportunities: these ideas were current at the time, not only among Ionians but among Jews; they have often attracted people since. Paul had issued warnings and directions about them more than once. He repeated them now with some precision, fully admitting the advantage of keeping rules to put the body in due subjection, but insisting that the highest success in an hygienic or ascetic scheme of living, and the power to associate it with a theory of the spiritual life were very far from that mystical transformation which made men perfect in the Church, living as cells and members of the Body of the Christ with His own life. The former, however attractive, was a human scheme. It was not a revelation from God of how to live in and with the holiness of faith.

5

Faith in the Kingly Redeemer, love for all living a redeemed life, a hope laid up in Heaven, all coming in the truth of the evangel to give knowledge of the grace of God: such, said Paul, were the qualities, such the conceptions which will lead Christians with joy even in their sufferings to thankfulness to the Father who had made them fit and worthy to be partakers of the inheritance of the saints in light.[22] . . . "Therefore," he wrote, "I do not cease to pray for you and long that you might be filled with the knowledge of His Will in all wisdom and spiritual understanding, that you might walk worthy of the Lord towards all giving of pleasure, being fruitful in every work of good, and increasing in the knowledge of God, strengthened with all might according to His glorious power."[23]

Such was the triumph which he pictured for those whom Christ, the dear Son of the Father, having redeemed them through His blood, forgiving their sins, had brought from the powers of darkness into the kingdom of His light.[24]

6

Christ, as Paul proclaimed, is not merely the master of the planets and their rulers, He is in Himself the sum and picture of all perfection.

1. He is the image of the invisible God.

2. He is the "first-born", that is the primal type, of every creature.
3. All things, both visible and invisible, both men and angels, are created by Him and for Him.
4. In Him all things attain to their perfect relation to one another.
5. Therefore He is pre-eminent above all things.
6. Pre-eminent also in the hierarchy of grace, He is the head of the Church.
7. In Him therefore is the completion and perfection of every being, both singly and together.[25]

As the Wisdom of the Universe, He offered to all things that consummation which they have in the completeness and the fulness of the All which is God:[26] in dying, He had died not only for all men but for all things. He, in one word, had reconciled to Himself in one harmony of peace the existence of visible things and the hierarchies of the unseen: and He, who above all ranks of creatures reigned in the central height, reigned there as taking thither in Himself the nature of the created world and the life of the redeemed. This mystic vision of the scheme of things was a mystery hidden from ages and generations of men: but in all the riches of its mystery it was given to all who, by faith in the Christ, accepted it. Their hearts were knit together in love to attain all the wealth of the full assurance of understanding that they might acknowledge the mystery of God—both of the Father and of the Christ in whom are hidden all the treasures of wisdom and knowledge.[27]

7

All philosophy and science, both natural and occult, are out-done in this sweep and flash of mystic vision in which the

Christian consummated his faith in the act of adoring the Christ: "For in Him dwells all the fulness of the Godhead bodily. And you are complete in Him who is the head of all the angelic hierarchies—thrones, dominations, virtues, princedoms, powers."[28]

This theme was one with the perfection of the Mosaic law and the sacred tradition of Israel. Let him therefore put it again in the form of words so sacred to the Israelites:

"In Him also you are circumcised with the circumcision made without hands, in putting off the body of the sins of the flesh by the circumcision of Christ, buried with Him in baptism, in which also you are risen with Him through faith in the working of God who raised Him from the dead. . . .

"If you then be risen with Christ, seek those things which are above, where Christ sits enthroned at the right hand of God. Set your affection on things above, not on things of the earth. For you are dead, and your life is hidden with Christ—in God."[29]

Such was the great vision of mystical theology in which Christ's envoy frames his portrait of a Christian. He sees the simple believer set high in the heavenly places. "Man with God is on the throne."[30] By the burial and resurrection in which the believer rose from the christening in which he was born again, he had passed beyond all ranks of things, seen and unseen, to the central height. For, when the eternal doors had lifted up their doors for the King of Glory to come in, He had brought with Him all who put their trust in Him, in the solidarity of the human nature He had exalted.

> He had raised our human nature
>   On the clouds to God's right hand,
> There we sit in heavenly places,
>   There with Him in glory stand.

Jesus reigns adored by angels,
    Man with God is on the throne.
Mighty Lord in Thine ascension
    We by faith behold our own.

So did a nephew of Wordsworth a hundred years ago write as a hymn the doctrine which St. Paul gave to the Colossians. This sublime doctrine was restated for the whole realm of nature in the words of the most philosophical of mystics, St. John of the Cross, Doctor of the Universal Church:—

"In the lifting up by the Incarnation of His Son, and in the glory of His resurrection according to the flesh, not only did the Father beautify His creatures in part, but we can say that He left them all clothed with beauty and dignity. . . . They are all clothed with marvellous natural virtue and beauty, wondrously derived from and consummated by that infinite supernatural beauty of the image of God whose beholding of them clothes the world and all the heavens with beauty and joy just as does also the opening of His hand. . . ."[31]

"God nurtures and gives being to all creatures which have their root and life in Him. And thus in grace and wisdom, the contemplative admires their beauty which not only each of the creatures—both celestial and terrestrial—has from God, but which they make among themselves in the wise, ordered, gracious and loving mutual correspondence, both of the lower creatures among themselves, and of the higher likewise among themselves, and between the higher and the lower—a thing of which the knowledge gives the soul great beauty and delight."[32]

8

So does St. John of the Cross explain what St. Paul hinted of the music which the universe makes in Christ: of the beauty with which Christ's splendour invests it. Against his golden splendour St. Paul sets his scheme of moral renewal—that even the most ordinary should practise decent, honest, peaceable behaviour. The corollary of his mystical theology was to exchange lying, blasphemy, filthy talk, bad temper, spite and vindictiveness for a heart of compassion, kindness, gentleness, patience and forgiveness: for love and charity which are the bond of perfectness."[33] "Let the peace of God rule in your hearts," said the Apostle, "and be thankful."[34] "Let the word of Christ dwell in you richly in all wisdom."[35]

And how would this mystery of grace be made manifest? By a happy life in the home, with wives not overruling their husbands nor husbands bullying their wives: the children obedient, the parents encouraging and gentle with their children, the servants working cheerfully, the employers considerate and just,[36] the talk tactfully and courteously suited to whoever was to hear it, and seasoned with the salt which would give it the right flavour;[37] the believers buying up in the market-place of time every opportunity of either making a good impression, or explaining a difficulty.

The brilliance with which Paul in one short letter set out the cosmic grandeur of the Christ, and connected it with the daily rub of life and temptations, showed that he knew what saints and churchmen have experienced from age to age. Neither philosophy nor mysticism frees a man from the cross of living in the common world of things and men with the imperfections both of others and of himself.

9

Paul now turned his eyes to the most important of the Isles of Greece. He had established in Crete Titus, the companion of many of his adventures, who was having to deal not with highly intellectual rivals to the mystery but just the daily faults of ordinary people. Paul now wrote to his follower to warn him in familiar words of the simple duties and standards of a Christian life; the need to avoid brawling, avarice, violence, the need to practise self-restraint, discretion, justice.[38] Paul had no high idea of the Crete of the time; he fully recognised the fussiness of the Jews there. Yet still he intermingled with his warning counsels to an old friend in need of guidance that central doctrine of a glorious redemption which he mentioned in one form or another in every epistle he wrote: "not through the works of right living which we did but according to His mercy did He save us—through the laver of a second birth and the renewing of the Holy Spirit which He poured upon us richly through Jesus Christ our Saviour: that, set right by His grace, we should be inheritors, according to the hope of everlasting life."[39]

1 0

Paul had left Titus behind him to set in order the things left undone, and to ordain "ancients" or "priests" and "bishops" in every centre. With the example of Corinth before him, Paul's care was to establish order: to be sure that those who were in charge of the community as ministers should inspire confidence. Not excitable, not hot-tempered, not avaricious, not arousing comment on account of riotous children, but living exemplary lives of kindness, moderation, good sense, prayer and finally holiness. Such must be those who were ordained as ministers for the fellowship of Christ's religion.[40]

When Paul himself was present, he could speak with the tongues of men and of angels; he could show wit, charm, irony,

magnetism, intense thought and the power of religious exaltation: but he knew that he must not expect each of his representatives to be either genius or saint: and with the good sense
which gave his passion and piety their hold over the common
men, he could speak in words that came more easily to the lips
of the physician, Lucanus, than to himself, words borrowed
perhaps from a general formula of directions sent round to the
Churches, words like wholesome, sound, devout, sensible, which
would appeal to ordinary men and women of the world who
do not quite understand the mystery of grace. For them he
must issue his plain guidance: servants must not pilfer, nor be
disrespectful; young men must not be roysterers, or loose in
conduct. The practical missioner speaks from a common knowledge of the ways of ordinary men and women. For "Christ
Jesus", as he was to tell Timotheos, "came into the world to
save *sinners*".[41] And so—though he might speak of a changed
life, and the Divine Spirit, and the high prerogative of the
Church—he kept his mind on the combination of regular worship with right conduct, and both with self-control: that men
might live in this present world not only a godly but a right
and a discreet life.

These, after all, are the common cares of the average life of
those who mean to live as Christians: and though there were
no doubt some lives where the dyes of sin were crimson, there
were others beguiled by nothing other than bad temper, or
spite, or gossip, or envy, or argument and controversy over
trifles. He had his word for each of them.

11

If he must write to Titus in Crete as to how to choose well
and keep in order the men on whom hands had been laid, so

he must leave a document of guidance for Timotheos in Ephesus. He must write in words that could be quoted to those in Ephesus who had worked against him, to warn Timotheos against the pedants or precisians, who—like the Parushim of Jerusalem—preferred controversy over minute points of learning or ritual to that Christian life which was love out of a pure heart, a good conscience and faith unfeigned. Why waste energy over all this haggling about the meaning of the Jewish law? Breakers of all the commandments: crimes of the worst order: murder, indecency, perjury, and outrages against the lower classes were common enough. Against them shone in its brilliance the glorious evangel of the blessed God.

And to Paul's trust, even though at one time he had sworn and worked violently against it, that message was committed. It could save him, it could save others: and now, in turn, Timotheos must guard it.

How? The Church was a universal benefaction. Intercessions must be made for all sorts and conditions of men, and thanksgivings should be general too. First of all let the Church give its support to rulers and men in authority that order may safeguard a peaceable life pursued in fervour and determination.[42]

To pray properly, men must give up their quarrels and arguments: to pray properly, women, when they go to church, should not think first of how to make an impression on the men who were to see them there![43]

Still more important were those who ministered in the churches: whether of the class of superiors: or ministrants. Take first the former: the "bishops". Had they the gifts of sobriety, self-control, dignity? Could they manage their own families? Were they generous and tactful with others? Had they a good reputation outside the Church so as not to cause scandal, and its inevitable reactions?[44]

If so much is required for Bishops and priests, there are

demands also to be made of deacons. They must not be the sort that says one thing to one man, another to another: they must be trustworthy, self-restrained, and above a passion for making profits on their transactions: one ought to remember that, as deacons, they are undergoing a test for preferment.[45] Deaconesses, too, should be self-restrained and reliable, not gossips.[46] By such should be governed the Church of the living God: it is the pillar and the foundation of an eternal truth: of the mystery of holiness which worships—and by worshipping grows towards—the Christ.

1 2

At this point, the question of gnostic, or as we might call it, theosophical teaching arose in Ephesus, as it had done in Chonas: there too were people who put a false emphasis on celibacy or the choice of food. But the real question, said Paul, is less of the food than of the mood. Eaten with thanks, what food is bad?[47] Physical training has some value: but how much more has the training of the soul, which wins life from the God of Life.

So Timotheos, if he still seemed a slight and youthful figure, must exercise a constant eagerness for perfection, remembering that he had received the gifts of an ordained minister.

1 3

But no sooner had the discreet writer given his personal warning than he thought of another administrative problem: the widows who demanded support, or who wanted to help.[48] They should be women for whom their own families could not provide and they should be at least sixty years old; women younger than sixty with nothing to do easily become gossips and busybodies, and some of them are followers of Satan.

Yet another difficulty: suppose any should attack the reputation of "a priest" or "ancient". It must be proved by more than one witness and must be scrupulously analysed: but if a priest is proved wrong, let the reproof be salutary.[49] Do not mix with people whose name is tarnished; but keep yourself rather far above reproach and gossip.

At this point, Paul was reminded of the delicate constitution of Timotheos: who was ever too abstemious, whose digestion was weak, and who was often ill. Well, ill-health does not help a man to either sound judgment or administration, so let him not hesitate to take wine.[50]

Generally, Paul said, both vices and virtues are plain enough to see: but there are some involved cases where one has to discriminate most carefully.[51]

14

Yet another question remained: to keep servants up to a standard. Even if a Christian servant has a pagan and inconsiderate master, the servant must not be disrespectful: nor must he claim the ground of Christian brotherhood for ceasing to be respectful.[52]

Paul's letter had begun with a warning against hair-splitting arguments from religious intellectuals, whose skill in learned controversy may even lead them to well-paid posts.[53] He came back to that point, and points out how hopeless it is when the hope of preferment begins to control a man's actions.[54] Timotheos must avoid all that; he must set his aim on loyalty, love, endurance, on upright dealings in the world, and fervour in the love of God which would lead upwards above all thrones and dominions to Him who reigned in the mystery of inaccessible light.[55]

Ah, yes: and if theology might lead to preferment, so for business men money can be an end in itself. But the true riches is a beneficent and social life among all the good things which God gives us to enjoy with one another.[56]

"And yet again", Paul wrote, "avoid controversy which so easily becomes mere talk: in such an atmosphere, who can realize the *mystery* of the faith?"

1 5

Such in all its homeliness, all its sense, is Paul's direction to the young friend he trusted: it shows how shrewd was his solicitude, and how, as the years went on and he saw how the Christians were being organised, he met this difficulty—as he had met earlier ones—with the skill of an elastic mind made to sway and rule men. In this essay on the choice of clergy and the government of men, eternal life and the mystery of Christ are mentioned little: his favourite expression "in Christ" occurs less often. There is no word of living among the heavenly realities. What is shown is that acumen which is the counterpart and proof of spirituality. Dante breaks in upon the raptures of the *Paradiso* for invective against corrupt clergy.[57] Bunyan, at the very gate of the heavenly city, gives an incisive account of how men slide from religion to worldliness.[58] Sir Thomas Browne, who in his youth had written his romance of *Religio Medici*, in his old age wrote homely letters, and *"Christian Morals"*. Paul too leaves his flights of mysticism to give again, as he had given to Titus, the advice clergy need when they are dealing with very ordinary people. For Paul was not merely a visionary. Like most Saints he was a shrewd leader of men.[59]

AN ESSAY ON UNITY

1

WHEN PAUL FIRST WROTE TO TIMOTHEOS, HE WAS IN MACE-
donia. When he wrote to Philemon, he spoke of being in
chains. As the same name occurs in *Philemon* as in *Colossians*,
the two letters were written at the same time and from the
same place; since Timotheos was with him, the most natural
place for him to be was Ephesus. If this is so, the conclusion is
that Paul, now an old man, was again under arrest—in Ephesus
—and what is more likely, if as the religion of the Christians
became better known to be something other than Judaism, both
Romans and Jews organised against it, while Nero, as he
became more and more debased, came into sharper and sharper
conflict with the things, and with the men, of God?

The general tradition and the statements of Eusebius agree
that Paul was arrested a second time. But where was he
arrested? On the strength of a later reference Troas[1] had been
suggested, and a transference to Ephesus would best explain
the references in *Philemon* and *Colossians*. If so, and as tradition so constantly affirms, Paul ended his life in Rome, the
only conclusion is that he was taken back there as a prisoner.

2

From Rome then we must date the last and greatest of his
essays, the *Epistle to the Ephesians*, the epitome of his teaching on the divine plan, and on the completion of the work of

the Christ in His body the Church, to consummate the unity of truth in the truth of unity.[2]

After opening with the habitual greetings of grace and peace, it bursts into an enthusiastic mystical celebration of the divine design of saving men by bringing them through grace to the spiritual blessings which made them live as one body with one another in the life and realities of heaven—in the Christ.

"He chose us in Him before the creation of the world that we should be holy and immaculate in His sight in love, fore-ordaining that we should be adopted as sons into Himself through Jesus Christ, according to the good pleasure of His will, to the praise of the glory of His grace, in which He made us gracious in the Beloved.

"Through His blood (which is His life), in Him we have redemption, the forgiveness of sins, according to the riches of His grace.

"In all wisdom and knowledge He lavished it upon us, making known to us the mystery of His will, according to the good pleasure which He purposed to accomplish in Him."[3]

This was the stewardship and dispensation of the fulness and passage of time: to incorporate all things, both those in heaven and those on earth, under one head, the Christ.

"In Him", said Paul, "we Jews were also foreordained according to the purpose of Him who orders all things according to His will, we who have beforehand hoped in the Christ, are assigned to God, as His children, to be to the praise of His glory, and you men also of other nations, hearing that Word of truth which was the evangel of His salvation, and believing in Him, are marked with a visible sign of the Holy Spirit of promise, who is the pledge and first installment of our own share in Him, so that God's own possession might be redeemed, and His grace made triumphant in glory."[4]

Here in all its riches and its splendour was the final evan-
gelical statement in one hymn of praise of the design of God in
Christ and in His Church. Here in fact was Paul's inspired
vision of the order of the universe. It was a mystery which
only an inspired intuition can accept, and to receive it was the
very essence of the faith. Paul—in an irradiating intercession
which made his soul a window for less profound believers and
less advanced mystics—prayed that the Father of glory would
so enlighten the hearts of His children that, by the lightning
of revelation, their minds might understand, firstly, the hope
to which they were chosen and called; secondly, what was the
riches of their glorious lot as saints and men of the spirit; and,
thirdly, the transcendent greatness of Christ's power for all
those who had the faith: for all this energy, this strength, this
might, were displayed in the Christ, the Christ who had been
raised from the dead to be set above all the unseen powers—the
thrones and dominations, and every name that is named, not
only in this phase of existence but in that which is to come, at
the right hand of God.[5]

Christ's ascension was no mere personal triumph. It was the
consummation of a great process. He did not triumph alone.
He triumphed containing in Himself the Church, as head of
it, His body, "the fulness that filleth all in all".[6]

What is the meaning of this high poetic phrase? Its meaning
is inexhaustible. But the sense is that all creation, which had
been straining and longing for perfection, attains it when it is
arrayed in harmonious order for the service of men and of
angels, and they in relation to it; all things are constituted,
both severally and together, in this hierarchical order. This is
the design for those who understand and share the power and
the mystery of Christ. When they are all under the direction
of Christ, and inspired by His power within them, His plan
and part in creation is completed in each separate life and

existence; and creation is completed in Him in one fulness of order and harmony: all this is attained through direct relation to Him, through sharing His comprehensive purpose, in the energy in which He worked to attain it, and in the triumph and glory of His own perfectness as the head of the Church. The Church sums up His purpose in creation, both in heaven and on earth, for it is the fulness that completes each thing in the harmony of all things—through, with, and in Himself.

3

According to an ancient office of the Church, God is both power unchangeable and light eternal: by the tranquil operation of His perpetual providence. He is carrying out the work of man's salvation.[7] But man's salvation was not the mere safeguarding of certain elect souls. It was part of the Divine means to restore to the perfection of God the original Divine design, all things, not only men, but nature, air, electricity and the stars. And thus in the whole mystery of Christ, it may be felt and seen that the things which had grown old are being made new, and that the things which had been cast down are being raised up, and that all things are returning to perfection through Him from whom they took their origin.

4

No sooner had St. Paul in his hymn of praise recapitulated the essentials of his inspired scheme of the universe than he turned to the contrast between it and the Roman Empire through which he had travelled. He had seen men dead in their sins, and disobedient, acting, under the power of evil spirits, as they felt inclined by their lower nature. But on them God had poured out the riches of His mercy—the grace which made them whole: He had incorporated them into the Christ, and raised them up in Him and with Him to the heavenly state: so had He shown to the age to come the transcendent riches of His grace. If they could, through faith, see what this scheme was (faith itself was a divine gift) and then through grace perform the works set to their hands, they had completed what God had ordained.

Before, the non-Jews had been cut off from the singular privileges of Israel, its law, its confidence and trust, its hope, its bond with the one true God. But now they were brought near by sharing in the life of Christ: for it was He who had broken down the barricade that cut them off from the holy of holies: it is He who is our peace. What had divided them? It was the Jewish code. But now that was abolished: the Christ, in the mystery of His death, had killed the enmity between Jew and non-Jew. He had opened the gate of heaven for all mankind: He had in His own infinity completed the law of sacrifice: He had created in Himself one new being, and so made peace. "Through Him we both have access in one spirit to the Father."[8]

The idea of a body was transformed into that not merely of a great crowd in a temple, but of the temple itself, "You are no more strangers and sojourners but you are fellow-citizens with the saints, and in the household of God, being built upon the foundation of the Apostles and prophets, Jesus Christ Himself being the chief corner stone".[9] Dante was to picture the Church triumphant as a rose of living petals:[10] St. Paul saw the Church—whether militant, expectant or triumphant—as a cathedral of living stones in which each chapel and constituent part, fitly framed together as a thing admirable in itself, helped to complete the range and majesty of the whole building for the home and house of God in His creation.[11]

O that we could share his triumphant vision, this mystery that he knew by revelation, in which Jew and non-Jew were sharers and fellows in an unsearchable wealth, in an eternal purpose, in a complex wisdom which would delight the thoughts not only of men, but of the highest angels!

5

All that remained was to pray and to pray again that what had been given to him as a mystic revelation might shine on the inward eye of others: it was a wealth of glory almost beyond the strongest grasp of the loftiest mind: for when Christ dwelt in the heart His power transcended every thought and every desire, and filled men with the fulness of God: at this thought again the worshipper was lost in adoring wonder.

And so Paul went on to write that since this transcendent order of grace and glory was the inheritance of all who had the faith, let them keep with one another in gentleness and patience the unity of the spirit in the bond of peace. They were all *one*. They were called to one faith in one hope; they were received in one baptism to be one body and one spirit in one Lord. One God and Father of all was above all, through all, and in them all.[12] Through all ranks of creatures, from the central height, the Christ poured out His wondrous diversity of gifts and operations that each, performing his own proper part on his own proper instrument, should combine the one orchestral music of creation. As the perfectly co-ordinated body lives, fitly framed and knit together, from that which each cell provides, each, in the due measure of its special function, contributes to the increase of the whole for the purpose of the head: thus all believers come to fulfil the mystery of a perfect Christ: they attain the measure of His stature as they complete His life in mutual love, and thus are made perfect in *one*.[13]

6

Such was the mystery and secret of God's purpose and design as Paul had received it by revelation. His thankfulness irradiated into intercession; for how could he wish other than to share this abounding wealth of knowledge? But it was not enough merely to tell of it what the words of genius and holiness could tell: he must face the contrast which heathen humanity presented, he must survey the common tendencies and temptations of the men he would convert, or had converted, and warn them against hardness of heart, and the greed associated with sensuality. "Put away the former manner of life: change the old man for a new man: change what had been corrupted to the pattern of its deceitful passions to be renewed in the spirit of the mind. Put on the new man created in the righteousness and holiness of the truth. The truth is in the Christ. Learn it in Him."[14]

Let anger, clamour, bitterness and abuse be changed to forgiveness and tenderness of heart. Let him that stole steal no more. Let a man's speech be uncorrupt, helpful, courteous. Offer your lives as not merely a sacrifice to God, but as Christ did, as a sacrifice made attractive by the incense burnt with it to make the air sweet with its perfume.[15] Walk as the children of light, where the sunshine plays. Let your gaiety not be that of carousals, but the joy of noble music and of song. Let the home be arranged unselfishly to make all in it happy: no rudeness and hectoring from masters to servants, and from servants a single-hearted and devoted service.[16]

Give all thou canst: high heaven rejects the lore
Of nicely calculated less and more.[17]

7

Yet it was not in these moral directions that Paul's final encyclical ends. Between the daily duties, and the charm of a happy home, there was a warfare of unseen and mighty powers. Paul's mind went back to the Roman soldiers: he had known them all his life: they moved sacrosanct to maintain order and were admired for their prowess; as he wrote there may have been one beside him keeping guard with sword, breastplate and helmet gleaming together.

Such must be the armour of the soul. To withstand the strategy of Satan faith must put on the panoply of God. "For our wrestle is not against flesh and blood, not against mere human men and women, but against demoniacal powers, against thrones and dominations, against those who are despots over the dark powers of the world,[18] against those forces which are the essence and spirit of evil in the heavenly order itself. Such powers must be fought with agencies and weapons which are themselves not of this world. Therefore it is that men must arm themselves from head to foot with Divine weapons so that, no matter how dire and fierce the strife, they should stand undismayed, having accomplished all their duty. Their loins must be girt up with the belt of truth, their breastplate must be rightness of life, on their feet the preparation of the evangel of peace, their shield the faith which can shield them from the darts of the malignant enemy, even if those darts are tipped with fire, their helmet salvation, their sword that cutting edge of the spirit which is the word of God."[19]

Thus, in worship, petition, intercession and persevering in

the work of the saints, they could make Paul himself, an ambassador in fetters, bold to deliver his supreme despatch. Peace, love and faith as gifts from the Father and the Christ, and grace for those that love with the immortal and uncorrupt love of those already raised to the heavenly order, such was the final combination of gift with ideals with which Paul closed that last encyclical to Asia which was a compendium of all he had come to see in his Christ.

8

Still thinking as a Jew, but a Jew who was a member of a universal Church in which the non-Jew was called to the same blessedness, still arguing the necessity of faith in what was heard, still visiting the temple at Jerusalem where he had worshipped as an eager Jew from Tarsus, still hymning the power of divine grace, still combining charity and love with faith and hope, still convinced of the offices of angels, but upborne more than ever by a wide-reaching inward vision of the universality of the design of the Father of glory in the Christ, through the Holy Spirit, so as to emphasise words such as riches, energy, wealth, mystery, design[20]—all combining with glory—Paul was absorbed in the faith which made his many congregations into a Church which was one: of this Church combining the visible with the invisible, things present with things to come, the complement and fulfilment of the Christ, incorporated with Him to share in His majesty in the heavenly order in the blessed Trinity, he could have said already what Dante was to write of the Trinity in Unity:

> I saw in its abysmal deep immersed,
> Together in one volume bound with love,
> What is throughout the universe dispersed.[21]

HENCEFORTH THE CROWN

1

THE LAST WORD OF DIRECTION TO THE CHURCH HAD BEEN spoken—spoken triumphantly. There remains from the hand of Paul only one more document to consider. In it the clarion tone of cosmic triumph on sovereign beneficence dies away: it is the message of an old man to a young friend, a record of solicitude for a follower and helper—it is written to that dear friend—half Jew, half Greek, slight, delicate, diffident— whom he had circumcised some fifteen years before, and left in charge at Ephesus—Timotheos. And because this letter is more familiar, mentions more personal details, and at times rambles a little, it has been argued that Paul did not write it; others with far more reason contend that it represents notes written at various times to Timotheos and combined by him into one treasury of varieties of messages. But this suggestion, ingenious and attractive as it is, remains a conjecture. It is safer —as well as more suggestive and inspiring—to agree with the great majority of commentators through the ages up to the present day and treat the whole letter as Paul's testament and farewell.[1]

It is not a mere record of a spiritual friendship: it is also the message and direction of an Apostle to his successor in responsibility.

2

What was Paul? One who was chosen because he was needed to tell forth the promised life and salvation; he was now writing to a son dear to his heart to wish him grace and encouragement and inward peace.[2]

The friendship between them had been so blessed that it filled the old man's heart with love and gratitude, mingling with all his intercessions. "Day and night", wrote Paul, "I yearn to see you again, especially as I remember the tears you shed at our parting: if you could only come, my joy would be complete."[3]

Then the Apostle speaks to stir up in his disciple the gift within him, the gift of strength and self-discipline together with love. Timotheos should not be taken aback to see Paul arrested, but lean on the strength of grace: that grace had shone with radiant light in the appearance of Christ our Redeemer, who had shown that life was immortal. Paul had been appointed to proclaim with authority the teaching which Timotheos must hold fast in faith and love with the help of the Holy Spirit indwelling.

3

Cowardice and courage: Paul had seen instances of both: all his followers in Asia had run away from him: but Onesiphorus had sought him out even in Rome itself, and every visit was like a breath of fresh air.[4] Timotheos must come too, come and share the sufferings of the campaigning soldier, the effort of the athlete, the toil of the man working with his crop. What was the central truth of the evangel? The Resurrection. And as Paul thought of his evangel, he remembered that it was for it he was once more in chains like a criminal; and yet, even so, spreading the message of salvation which nothing could enchain.

Yet he must think of young Timotheos and his difficulties.

4

He must warn him to avoid wrangling controversy that eats out the life of the spirit like a cancer. There are varieties of minds and thoughts in the Church, just as there are all sorts of vessels in a great house. If one avoids these arguments, one may be a golden goblet: but in order to be this, Timotheos must flee the raw impulses of youth and seek loyalty, love, and peace—be courteous, tactful, gentle, discreet.

The aged man went on to prophesy trouble among Christians who would be thinking of self, money or pleasure: hard, conceited, proud, worldly, gossips. "Avoid these," wrote Paul to Timotheos. "You know how different my own life was, how I bore myself when persecuted in Antioch, in Konieh, in Lystra: persecution is the inevitable lot of those who have decided to live a fervent life in the Church of the Christ. But you have learnt his religion from those who knew what it was in its truth, as you have known the true significance of the Septuagint, and all its inner wisdom leading to the Christ and His salvation."[5]

5

"I charge you," continued Paul, "preach the evangel. Face your task with courage, in season and out of season, whether you are welcome or unwelcome, refute false teaching, rebuke those who have done wrong, be firm with those who refuse to obey, encourage those that do obey, always keeping patient, and elastic in your teaching. Keep calm: be ready to face suffering: your work is to preach the evangel, preach it to the full: your task is to be steward of the mysteries: minister them too.

"For I shall have to leave you: the time is short till my blood is poured out like a sacrifice to God; till I must strike my tent and be gone. I have fought the good fight: I have run my course to the end: I have kept the faith. Henceforth there is laid up for me the crown of right living which the Lord, the just judge of the race, will give me on that day, and not to me only but to all those whose hearts are set on His presence. For we shall be together with Him in love."[6]

6

It is that simple, personal speech of the heart which most fitly combines with the great vision of universal order he had pictured in his general letter. The majestic array was one with the sense of intimate communion, of personal reward: and speaking to his young friend and follower it was as natural for him to speak of this one side, and to speak again in his favourite language of the athlete, as in a general message on the unity of the Church it was right to speak of the noble promise of that.

But when human strength fails the faculties, and life ebbs away in the valley of the shadow, it is just the clinging of heart to the heart that loves them that is left to the weakness of the dying. "Thou", they say, "art with me: thy rod and thy staff comfort me."[7]

For the heroic old man was worn out now with the effort to convey his strength. He was aware that he was cold and weak and dying, and his heart ached with longing for his young friend. "Make every effort to come quickly," he dictated feebly. "I am very lonely. Demas has left me, having loved this present world. Crescens has gone to Galatia, Titus to Dalmatia. Only Lucanus is with me. Pick up Marcus and bring him with you: for he is always a useful helper. As for Tychicos, I sent him to Ephesus."[8] And then the dying man in his damp prison shivered: if only he had the cloak that he left at Troas when he was arrested: and then he thought of the rolls and parchments that had been with it:[9] but ah, then and again he had been betrayed, how few had supported him; all had fled! But yet again the Lord had delivered him, and He would lead him safe into His heavenly kingdom. To Him be glory for ever and ever!

His words seem to be echoing the psalm of dereliction which Jesus had quoted on the Cross. They mingle with the names of his closest friends, Priscilla, Aquila, Onesiphoros, Trophimos, and those new friends around him, Eubolos, Pudens, Linus, Claudia. For he was not alone, after all.[10] There was not only Lucanus, but new friends who were to uphold in Rome the glory of the Church and raise Romans also to heavenly places in the Christ. Thus His tireless Envoy came to his last greeting: *"The Lord be with thy spirit, and with thee GRACE."*[11]

7

To the eyes of Paul, the Roman scene, significant as it was, had displayed and with more striking clearness those contrasts between the world and Grace which he had seen so clear at Jerusalem, at Antioch, at Ephesus, at Salonica and at Corinth. Along the imposing Roman ways rushed the chariots of tyrants. From her marble palaces wretched slaves brought the tale of tyranny, of scandal, of crime: and in the meaner streets were smells, and dirt, and misery, and evil; at the head of society, master of the wide system of law and government, the judge to whom he had appealed, was a young man of twenty-four whose passion for effect became a horror.

Nero, as we saw, was the stepson of Claudius. He owed his throne to the fact that his mother plotted before he poisoned Britannicus. By this butchery he was raised to a position venerated as Divine; the irony was diabolical: and by it Nero's mind was unhinged. His soft and vain character sought the distraction on the one side of indulgence, and on the other of applause: and above all applause for his indulgences. The desperate way he drove in races, the frenzy of his music and his mimes, these were the exordium to vices and cruelties which were monstrous. Such was the result of committing to a comedian the government of the world.[12]

Seneca, and his brother Gallio, were degraded from the rank of counsellors, criminals such as Tigellinus took their place: outrages followed: and Rome was depraved. When the Emperor had condemned to horrible deaths the best around him, he took as counsellors the furies.

The whole system of law did not at once crack: and when the case of Paul at last had been brought before him, he had allowed justice to take its course. The New Movement was not yet persecuted; in the consolation given by a pure life, and the hope of heaven, and, mysterious above all, the presence of the Christ in the power of His Spirit—the Christians were filled with the peace and joy of their faith. When the Jews could feel lofty and unsullied in the practice of the Law, and the worship of the Unnameable, how high was the recompense of finding its promises fulfilled in the new and heavenly Kingdom, where the foretaste of eternity was already on their lips; where the Church was present in the power of the Holy Spirit.

For Paul, the contrast between a depraved court and the secret growth in obscure places of the new community was accentuated by his dealings with two men. On the one side he had appealed to Nero: on the other, he met in Rome the very man who had told him in Jerusalem what the Christ Himself had been seen to do, and what words He was heard to speak. For a period, Protestant scholars doubted if the Peter whom Paul had called Cephas had reached Rome: but (though there are none so deaf as those who won't hear) the voice of history has spoken. In his monumental work on St. Peter, the Dean of Winchester echoes it: not only is there a lack of evidence against the statements of Clement and Eusebius: not only is the tradition of Peter's presence in Rome widespread and undisturbed: but the evidence which in recent ages has faced the archæologists has convinced them absolutely.

"For the archæologist the presence and execution of SS. Peter and Paul in Rome are facts established beyond a shadow of doubt by purely monumental evidence. There was a time when persons belonging to different creeds made it almost a case of conscience to affirm, or deny, *a priori*, those facts according to their acceptance or rejection of the tradition of any particular church. This state of feeling is matter of the past at least for those who have followed the progress of recent discoveries."[13] Such is the evidence of Rome's foremost archæologist.

Archæology, as a science, has been born again. Piecing together, one by one, inscriptions, stories and statutes, the archæologists of to-day have learnt in Crete, in Egypt, in Syria, at Ur, to build up the record of two to three thousand years ago. In Christian Rome, which is but a corner of their recent diggings, they find evidence which only the most obstinate could persist in denying.

The denial was based on two hypotheses: first that the Christians of Rome were overcome by an absurd delusion about their immediate predecessors: but this can no more be sustained than the other hypothesis that in scattered and obscure corners they prepared for posterities centuries distant a complex hoax. Only one conclusion remains: and that is that with St. Paul in

Rome was also present St. Peter, whom the Church has hailed as Cephas, the rock.[14]

8

Turning his disgusted eyes from the dissolute farceur who reigned absolute above the Forum and the Tiber, Paul saw, passing through humble streets among the slaves and the Jews, the honest and humble radiance of the man whom the Christ had called from fishing to be a magnet for men: the man whom He had chosen to be—as receiver of the gift of faith—the Rock, the Cephas, on which to build a Church against which the gates of hell should not prevail.

What was the relation between the two men? History has linked their names together with that of their church in Rome. If they were not martyred together, their martyrdoms are commemorated in a single feast-day. Dean Selwyn, like Renan, points to the reasons for believing that they still exchanged much, as they had done when they first met in Jerusalem. He points out that in the first Epistle, attributed almost universally to St. Peter, there are many phrases shared with St. Paul. It almost looks as though Peter had turned to Paul for counsel: another index is that Paul henceforward refers with cordiality to Marcus who came with Peter, as he had travelled in earlier days with Barnabas. They had common helpers; Silvanus, Marcus.

When two men are joined by a common memory and enthusiasm, when they have leagued with one another against the same enemies, when they have travelled through dangers with one purpose, when they are united in love for the same leader, they are allies; but friendship gives a sympathy other than all these.

(Exclusive)

ROME——THE BASILICA OF ST. PAUL BEYOND THE WALLS,
BUILT OVER ST. PAUL'S TOMB

And beyond friendship there is that deeper intuition and unity which is supernatural. These two men were drawn together by one spirit to live in the one Body of Christ, knowing that the one God and Father of both was above both, through both and in them both; deep therefore was the love that, in the last days, drew together in Rome those two immortal names, and made one speak in the accents of the other.[15]

Their friendship was an alliance against death. In a few years Nero had surpassed his own excesses. Obsessed with the idea of impressing the people, and finding he could best do so by amusing them, his passion was to provide them with startling sensations: and what excitement so thrilling as horror?

Rome's austere tastes were changed for those of luxury.

The mind of the citizens was melodrama. Petronius came forward to rule as master over the arts of pleasure. A swollen and ornate architecture housed a people whose passion for sensations and sights carried them from excess to excess, such was the mood of the mob in the reign of a Caesar whose instinct was to govern by gratification.

Then in the July heat of the year 64, a more acute sensation broke in upon the carousals of the new Babylon. Its streets flamed into the purple night in a widespread conflagration.[16] There is in the heat and roar of a great fire something which stirs our nature to the depths. When it moves over the prairie, or the forest, with its lightning rush: as it scorches away the life of leafy trees, to leave charred stumps above a blackened earth, it comes as peril and bequeaths hideousness: in a great city, however, the drama is yet more moving. At every turn of its career, it throws an unpredictable menace at the homes and lives of men. With a roar and a crash, it tears down the work and destroys the treasures heaped up by years: in the movement of the flames, in the columns and clouds of smoke which darkens the sky, in the impetuous energy and power with

which it subdues to its voracity materials strong and precious:
it challenges the fierce effort of men to call to their aid the
force of water: yet even while it devastates, it calls forth a
thrill of admiration at its gorgeousness, and men are as fascinated by it as by the intrigue of a crime.

9

When the conflagration burst out in Rome, Nero was bath-
ing at Anzio: when he returned he realised that this was the
most dazzling and impressive horror of his life: wild memories
of the burning of Troy mingled with his delirious excitement,
and it was said that he turned to music to sense more completely the excitement the flames evoked. Mad for sensation,
he ordered them, when dying away, to be rekindled.[17]

On the excitement of the spectacle followed the realization
of the resultant ruin. Smouldering heaps of rags told the story
of the cost. And then arose a cry of vengeance. A diabolical
fury demanded that expiation should be made by the new
religion which ignored the conventions of Rome and detested
its scandals. Had its adherents not foreseen for the new
Babylon just such a ruin as had engulfed it? Most of them
were slaves of a low degree. Yet a final sensation could be
obtained by one of those executions which were the supreme
drama of Roman life: while among a vast crowd, the obese
young Emperor raised to his eye an emerald magnifier to
enjoy to the full the gestures with which a naked virgin sought
to guard her modesty while she faced the lion: further, to
indulge his sensations and their amusement, it was sought to
include the two leaders from Syria in the general accusation.
It is more likely than not that Peter and Paul met their deaths
on the same day.

Details are lacking: a tradition remains. It is that the impetuous old man who had so nobly struggled against his faults was crucified like his Master; but at his own request with his head downwards; it was not forgotten, however, that Paul was a Roman citizen: and, though condemned to death, he died by the sword. On a summer morning he was led out past the cypresses and the pyramid of Caius Cestius which rises above that "slope of green access" where the body of Keats and the ashes of Shelley were to be laid. Through the Ostian gate he passed over the campagna to a lonely fold of the hills.

There a Roman sword swept asunder head and body, and Paul passed to a double immortality: in heaven the unfading crown of grace, on earth a power ever renewed; for his words remain insistent, significant, mysterious from age to age: they speak from heart to heart. With Peter, he is himself central, not only in the history of Rome, but also in the veneration of the Church.

10

Among Rome's majestic monuments, the basilica which is built above his tomb has a singular grace and beauty. Alone in the campagna, far from the dust and rumbling, its charm and dignity are exempt from question. The cool, still spaciousness, the polished marbles, the quiet, sunny cloister, the perfection of a taste sublimed to majesty, suggest what Paul, even in his impetuousness, diffused: the peace of God which passes all understanding, the peace which keeps men's hearts and minds in the knowledge and love of God.

It is in the serenity of that victorious peace that Rome recalls to her people and her pilgrims the Jew who with devouring fury first gave himself to the zeal of Israel, who in doing so found his desired Messiah coming in a life so lowly to a triumph so transcendent that he was paralysed by his surprise: and who from that moment lived a life transformed, even while he developed to the full the peculiarities of his impulsive temperament and his elastic genius.

We see him adhere enthusiastically to the new movement. We see him seeking in solitude to reintegrate his inner life. He had received a direct knowledge of the Christ through his inner faculties of contemplation. With the inner eye he had seen: with the inner ear he had heard: by an experience that was supernatural, he had come face to face with Him by whom the worlds were made.

To be not disobedient to the heavenly vision, he must move from men to be alone with the Alone: he sought to be detached from all things: he passed by the bareness of faith and direct communion to mystical union with God. And so he remained for months, perhaps years, alone in the desert, putting away the things of the natural mind, and learning the art of contemplation. This is that "mystical theology which signifies the secret or hidden wisdom of God, wherein without the use of words and without the aid of any bodily or spiritual sense, as if in silence and quiet, hidden by darkness from all that is in the senses and of nature, God teaches the soul after a most hidden and secret manner, without her knowing how. This is that which some spiritual men call 'understanding yet understanding not'. This is not done by the understanding which the philosophers call active, the work of which is in the forms and fancies, and apprehensions of the bodily faculties: but it is done in the understanding as much as this is receptive and passive: without receiving such forms, it passively receives substantial knowledge, stripped of all images, which is given to it, without any work or action offered of its own".[18]

So it was that Paul developed into a habit of the soul what before had come in gleams and flashes. Yet this habit of divine communion showed that his Christ was truly Man, and had left His secret as something to be shared among the men He had chosen. For even in receiving revelations, Paul knew that his course might be vain if he did not compare it with the words of Peter. His conversation with Peter led, however, to yet another revelation when he heard the inward voice which from time to time returned to him. And this time it warned him that the Christ would send him far among the nations.

For some years we lose track of him. All that remains is a hint of ecstasies, and a rising reputation which brings him first to Antioch, and then takes him on a journey in which he displays his range of gifts before a Roman proconsul, before a Lycaonian crowd, and among those who frequent a Jewish kenishta. He then comes forward as an apostle of a Church emancipated from circumcision and built on the rock of faith in the Christ and His evangel.

Adroit one moment, enraged the next, he is the master already of a powerful individual style.[19] His career develops with impressive swiftness. He thinks in Roman provinces, he passes through them like a meteor, he leaves in them a new way of life, a way which joined sweet charity and kindling ardour like the morning. A Jew concentrating on Jews, he easily shows that he was not only conversant with the Jewish lore of his time—itself affected by Greek and Roman ideas—but with the philosophy and mysteries of the Hellenistic world. His voracious mind strikes at his quarry from vast and soaring sweeps. He learns from the subtle and the simple, and with extraordinary versatility suits himself to each. His wide travels leave their impress on his malleable genius. He is ready for every adventure, yet he consumes his hours as a craftsman. He keeps in touch with Jerusalem, yet he impresses others by occult powers and miracles. His very garments have the magnetic quality which he irradiates.

The same man shows himself intense, adventurous, courageous, sympathetic, gentle; he insists on the values of all nobleness, culture and good taste. At times incisive, at others mystical, he passes from adventure to adventure, and from uproar to uproar. Yet shrewdly he keeps his practical ends in view. At one time he compels admiration for his statesmanship, at another he captivates by his charm, at another he manages the situation by a stroke of diplomacy. Tactful, courteous, cosmopolitan, a man of the world, yet he is conscientious, zealous, fervent, intense while he preaches mostly to men who are strangers to privilege. Elastic in his approaches, he retains a fiery individuality: mildness, sympathy and tenderness to his friends, he is swift to resent a wrong. His heart glows with affection, he leans on companionship; yet he cultivates solitude. Equally impressive in the tribunal of a prince as in a bark driven to wreck by storm, he showed at every turn qualities of character which mark both the governor of men and the exquisite friend.

12

At the same time he becomes the master of a highly wrought Hellenic style; riding the deluge and the storm, his art strikes and rests on the loftiest summits of a new literature. He writes passages which echo down the ages with the resonance of their sublimity. Trained to learn by heart and store his memory with the grandeurs of the Septuagint, and above all of its poetry, his speech varies between a resonant grandeur and conversational acumen. His power is overwhelming. On the ears of St. Jerome his words fall as a thunder roll. "They seem at first like those of a rustic innocent who can neither lay a trap nor avoid one; but wherever you look, they flash lightnings. He winds into his subject; he seizes all he has touched: he turns his back only to conquer: and feigns flight only to down his enemies".[20] Erasmus, too, heard thunder in his words,[21] yet thought that, like Cleopatra, "he was cunning past men's thought".[22] Yet his writing, even when most intimate, or most consummate, gives the effect of a mind so absorbed in his subject as to be oblivious of both the rules and the stratagems of a writer. He has less the genius of style than the style of genius.[23]

At times he is careless: often disjointed: at times he makes a swift thrust into crudity: but, when he soars to the heights, neither orator nor poet can rival him in art, power, or mystery.

With a power of condensation and a novelty kindred to that of Shakespeare, he gives language a new range of meaning and shows that in his personality there was a force that was new. No style, said Renan, was ever so personal.[24]

It was a temperament which produced strong reactions: on the one hand riot and opposition, on the other a loyalty and ardour kindred to his own. This force of heart and temper makes itself felt in all he thought. "Style," said a great Italian critic, "is the life which your concept takes within you, and which you communicate to others in expressing it."[25]

And what above all marks the life of this envoy of grace is that which Meredith called the core of style—fervour. His soul, says St. Chrysostom, comprised the whole world and carried all men in itself, so near was it to God. "And he loved them so as if he had begotten them all, or rather showed them a greater warmth of affection than a father: for such is the grace of the Spirit, it exceeds the yearnings of the heart of flesh, and is moved by more ardent longings than theirs. And this one may especially see in the soul of Paul, who with the aid of love, rose up as it were with wings."[26]

13

Both as a man and as a writer, he was indeed the most remarkable of his time. But if in genius and in force of style he had no contemporary rival, he is remembered not for those but for something else. The sphere in which he conquers is that of heavenly grace. His special appeal is that he was *inspired*. His power is that which he shares with other writers of the New Testament: "their lofty spirituality, their unexhaustible capacities for instruction and consolation; their boundless adaptability to all ages and circumstances; above all their ceaseless power of satisfying the noblest cravings and aspirations of the human heart. Other writings are profitable for knowledge, for advancement, for amusement, for delight, for wealth. But these 'make wise unto salvation'."[27]

His career of adventures in beautiful and historic scenes fades before his vocation as an apostle. Again and again people have forgotten the Jew wandering in sun and wind through the Levant. They ignore everything but the core of his teaching. The sphere in which he displayed his power is that of holiness— a holiness attained through sharing in the redemption, through the life, the death and the resurrection of his Saviour. Paul's triumph was a mystic paradox: on the one side a personal faith in the Blood of Jesus: on the other, devotion to a Church which completed creation from the fulness which leads all things to all their perfections. For "God thinks an infinite good in infinite ways."

Both of these themes have shown a perennial power. An erring world may ignore them, to writhe in strange convulsions. It may allow the inventions of science and art to be swept into maniac schemes: it may see the resources of civilization gathered for tournaments of ruin. It may see man attain vast powers over nature to use them only for the waste and mania of strife. But even in these furies of agitation, there is, for those who accept the faith of Paul, a central peace; his adherents—stretching now from Jerusalem and Corinth, past Naples and the Tiber to every remoteness of the earth—find that in each they are assured of the peace and triumph which possessed him as he passed, obscure among yet obscurer converts—sharing with them the words and mysteries of grace.

In a pagan world they lived not merely untroubled. They cherished a hope which was a fixed assurance of eternal glory. While a world still demanded their allegiance and while it appeared to offer them justice and security, it faced them now with vice and scandal, and now with famine and dismay; but their real lives were in another region where a peace passing understanding kept their minds in the knowledge and love of God; where, filled with joy and peace in believing, they could, like Paul himself, abound in hope and in the power of the Holy Ghost.[28]

GENERAL AUTHORITIES

1.—ON ST. PAUL

ENGLAND produced two classical lives of St. Paul: Lewin, 1851 (the edition quoted here is the 3rd, 1875), 2 vols.; Conybeare and Howson, 1864, 2 vols. (referred to in notes as C. & H.), 1869. These were succeeded by that of Renan who wrote also: *Les Apôtres*, 1866, *L'Antéchrist*, 1872. Advantage of these was taken by F. W. Farrar, whose *St. Paul*, 1880, though written in an emotional style, is also a monument of learning. Many of the conclusions of these books were, however, shaken by Sir William Ramsay, whose books: *St. Paul the Traveller and the Roman Citizen*, 1895 (referred to as *S.P.T.*), *Cities of St. Paul*, 1907; *Pauline Studies*, 1906; *Historical Commentary on Galatians*, 1896; and *Luke the Physician*, 1902, established many new facts about the meaning of the term Galatia, and bearing on the date of the Epistle to the Galatians. There has been little to add to these works, though Stalker, *St. Paul*; T. R. Glover, *Paul of Tarsus*, 1925; A. D. Nock, *St. Paul*, 1938, are deservedly well known as studies. Frequently referred to is the I.C.C. commentary on *Romans* by Sanday and Headlam (referred to as S. & H.).

Meanwhile Fouard has produced his *St. Pierre*, and *St. Paul*, incorporating much of the scholarship of Renan while counterbalancing his scepticism. *La Théologie de St. Paul* (2 vols.), Paris, 1929, by F. Prat, S.J., is a work of the highest order.

In German we have: Harnack, *Die Mission und Ausbreitung des Christentums*, 1924; Schweitzer, *Die Mystik des Apostel Paulus*, 1930; Clement, *Paulus*, Giersen, 1904; Deissmann, *Paulus*, Tubingen, 1925; S. Wartz, *Paulus*, 5 Bande, Innsbrück, 1931; L. Schneller, *Paulus*, Leipzig, 1935; Josef

Holzner, *Paulus,* Freiburg, 1937; Kittel, *Theologischer Wörterbuch zum Neuen Testament,* 1932, in addition to Strack-Billerbeck's *Kommentarium zum Neuen Testament aus Talmud und Midrasch,* 5 vols., 1922-1928. See also Paley, *Horae Paulinae,* 1795; F. A. Spencer, *Beyond Damascus,* 1934; L. Tondelli, *Il Pensiere di San Paolo,* Milan, 1922; A. Vitti, *Vita S. Pauli, Exordia,* Rome, 1932.

Foakes-Jackson and Kirsopp Lake cover much ground in *The Beginnings of Christianity,* 5 vols., 1920-1935. Two general books of reference are: Smith, *Dictionary of the Bible,* 5 vols. (referred to as Smith, *D.B.*); Hastings, *Encyclopaedia of Religion and Ethics* (referred to as *E.R.E.*).

For use of words see Hope-Milligan, *Vocabulary to the New Testament;* Kittel, *op. cit.*

2.—ON THE GRECO-ROMAN WORLD

Cambridge Ancient History, vols. x, xi; Rostovtzeff, *Social and Economic History of the Roman Empire,* 1926, *Social and Economic Hellenistic World,* 1941; A. Fabre and A. S. Festugière, *Le Monde Gréco-Romain dans le temps de Jésus Christ,* 1935; Festugière, *L'Idéal Religieux des Grecs, Contemplation et la Vie Contemplative selon Platon;* Wendland, *Hellenistische-Römische Kultur,* 1912; E. Stemplinger, *Die Unbekannte Antike,* Leipzig, 1926; Fustel de Coulanges, *Der Antike Staat;* S. L. Caiger, *Archaeology and the New Testament.*

Classic Sources: Appian, *Civil Wars;* Suetonius, *Roman Emperors;* Pliny, *Natural History;* Plutarch, *Lives;* Tacitus, *Annals, History;* Flavius Josephus, *Antiquities, Jewish Wars.*

3.—ON JEWISH THINGS

Renan, *Les Apôtres*, 1866; Arendzen, *Men and Manners in the Days of Christ*, 1936; Jean Juster, *Les Juifs dans l'Empire Romain*, 2 vols., 1914; Bonsirven, *Le Judaisme Palestinien*, 2 vols., 1936; Baeck, *Das Wesen des Judenthums*, 2nd edn., 1922; A. Causse, *Les Dispersés d'Israël*, 1932; E. Schurer, *Geschichte des Jüdischen Volks*, 3 vols., 1911; Eichrodt, *Theologie des Alten Testament*, 3 vols., 1935; P. Riessler, *Alt-Judisches Schriften*, 1928; Deissmann, *Die Hellenisierung des Semitischen Monotheismus*, 1920; Ruppin, *Soziologie der Juden*, 1934; Paul Wendland, *Hellenistische-Römische Kultur*, 1912; Edwyn Bevan, *The Legacy of Israel*, 1927; R. T. Herford, *The Pharisees*, 1924; G. F. Moore, *Judaism*, 3 vols., 1929; E. C. Montefiore, *Judaism and St. Paul*, 1917; H. Wheeler Robinson, *Religious Ideas in the Old Testament*, 1913; Oesterly, *A History of Israel*, 1932; *Books of the Apocrypha*, 1935; W. Knox, *St. Paul on the Church in Jerusalem*, 1925.

NOTES

CHAPTER I

[1]Cochrane: *Christianity and Classical Culture*, 9. [2]Appian: *Civil Wars*, V; Plutarch: *Mark Antony*. [3]Suetonius: *Augustus*, 22. Cf. S. L. Caiger: *Archaeology and the New Testament*, 171. [4]Pliny, *N.H.*, XXVII. [5]Fabre-Festugière: *Le Monde Greco-Romain*, ch. V. [6]Velleius, II, 9. [7]Pliny, *N.H.*, XV, 105 and XIV, 5. [8]Wendland: *Kultur*, 187, 192-196. [9]Rostovtzeff: *Ancient World*, II, 291. [10]*Op. cit.*, II, 292. [11]Fabre-Festugière, *op. cit.*, I, 55-6, 124. [12]Plutarch: *De Alexandro*, I, 6, 8. [13]Maurice Jones: "The Hellenistic World" in *Expositor*, 1921, Vol. XXI, 350-4. [14]Cf. Plato: *Laws*, II, 673e; *Phil.*, 26b. [15]Festugière: *Contemplation*, 432-3. [16]Festugière: *Contemplation*, 423, 426. [17]Fabre-Festugière, *op. cit.*, 92-3; L. Homo: *Les Institutions Politiques*. [18]See L. Grasberger: *Erziehung und Unterricht in klassischen Alterthum*, Wurzburg, 1864-1881, Vol. III, 384-398; W. W. Capes: *University Life in Ancient Athens*. Cf. E. Stemplinger: *Die Unbekannte Antike*, Leipzig, 1936; Fustel de Coulanges: *Der Antike Staat*, Berlin, 1907; F. A. Spencer: *Beyond Damascus*; *Darstellungen aus der Sittengeschichte*, 4 Bände, Leipzig, 1921-22. [19]H. A. L. Fisher: *History of Europe*. [20]Macaulay: *Miscellaneous Writings* (1860) on Mitford's History of Greece. [21]Festugière: *Contemplation*, 210-251, 322-358. [22]Festugière: *L'Idéal Religieux des Grecs*, 19-20. [23]Rostovtzeff: *History of the Ancient World*, II, 291-2. [24]Rostovtzeff: *Social and Economic History of the Roman Empire*, Ch. III, especially p. 756. [25]Rostovtzeff, *op. cit.*, 83.

CHAPTER II

[1]Suetonius: *Augustus*, 76. [2]Renan: *Les Apôtres*. Cf. Tacitus: *History*, V, 4; Cicero: *Pro Flacco*, 28; Philo: *In Flaccum*, 37; *Legatio ad Carnim*, 36; Acts ii. 5, vi. 9. [3]Bonsirven: *Le Judaisme*, I, 4; Arendzen: *Men and Manners in the Days of Christ*, 98-102. [4]Martial, IV, 4; Ammianus Marcellinus, XXII, 5. [5]Martial: *Epigrammata*, VII, 57. [6]Tacitus: *History*, V, 5, 9; Dion Cassius: LXVIII, 32. [7]Josephus: *Antiquities*, XVIII, 3, 5; XX, 2, 4; *Bell. Jud.*, II, xx, 2; Acts xiii. 50, xvi. 14. [8]Tacitus: *Annals*, II, 5; *History*, V, 5; Juvenal, XIV; Ss. Dion Cassius, XXVI, 7, LXVIII, 14; Fl. Josephus: *Contra Apionem*, II, 39. [9]Tacitus: *History*, V, 5; Josephus, *loc. cit.* [10]Renan, *op. cit.* [11]For Diaspora: Causse: *Les Dispersés d'Israël.* [12]Ruppin: *Soziologie der Juden*, 68 ff. [13]Strabo: *Antiquities*, IV, vii. 2. [14]Ruppin, *op. cit.*, 68. [15]Jean Juster: *Les Juifs dans l'Empire Romain*, 116 ff.; Flavius Josephus, LXIV, x. [16]*Pro Flacco*, 28. [17]See E. G. Hardy: *Monumentum Ancyranum.* [18]Josephus: *Antiquities*, XV, x. [19]Bonsirven: *Judaisme Palestinien*, I, 5, 9, 12; Fouard: *St. Pierre*, Ch. III. [20]Bonsirven, *op. cit.*, I, 6, n.4; Reinach: *Textes*, 255, 290; Strabo: *Antiquities*, XIV, vii. 2. [21]Bonsirven: *op. cit.*, 1, 7. [22]Is. xxxiv. 8. [23]For Jewish religion, see Eichrodt: *Theologie des Alten Testament*, 3 vols. [24]Wheeler Robinson: *Religious Ideas in the Old Testament*; E. Schurer: *Geschichte des Jüdischen Volks*; Edwyn Bevan: *The House of Seleucus*, 2 vols. [25]See Ezra vii. 10. [26]R. T. Herford: *The Pharisees*, 58. [27]See Lauterbach: *Sadducees and Pharisees*, 186, 186a. [28]Ps. cxix. 7 A.V. [29]Ps. cxix. 1. [30]Herford: *The Pharisees*, 54. [31]G. F. Moore: *Judaism*, I, 163. [32]See *Pirqé Aboth*, VI. [33]M. de Grandmaison: *Jesus Christ*, Eng. trans., 273-4. [34]Montefiore: *Judaism and St. Paul*, 109. [35]H. Wheeler Robinson, *op. cit.* [36]Ps. xl. 6. [37]Ps. li. 18 A.V. [38]Is. lvii. 15; cf. P. Riessler: *Alt Jüdisches Schrifttum*, Augsburg, 1928. [39]Cruden's Concordance has 50 references to trust in God. [40]Jer. xxxi. 3. [41]Job xiii. 15; Job xlii. 50. [42]Numbers vi.

24. [43]Zech. viii. 5. [44]Is. lx. 11. [45]Wheeler Robinson, *op. cit.*
[46]Is. lxi. 1. [47]Mal. iv. 2. [48]For Greek influence on the Jews, see
Knox: *St. Paul and Jerusalem;* Oesterley: *A History of Israel,*
II, 175 ff., 217 ff.; Deissmann: *Die Hellenisierung des
Semitischen Monotheismus,* 11-14; Bonsirven, *op. cit.,* I, 37 ff.;
Eichrodt: *Theologie des Alten Testament,* Vol. III. [49]Luke vii.
5; Acts xvii. 4, 17. [50]Acts xviii. 7; Lagrange: *Le Messie,* 207-
209. [51]Philo: *De Circoncisione.* [52]Renan: *Les Apôtres.* [53]Tacitus:
Hist., V, 4. [54]Aristeas quoted in Oesterley: *Books of the Apocrypha,* 56, syncretizing in Wendland, *op. cit.,* 195-210. [55]G. F.
Moore: *Judaism,* I, 285. [56]Wisdom vii. 22-24. [57]Philo: *Leg.
Alleg.,* I, 13. [58]*Die Bibel deren Gott Jahweh heisst ist die Bibel
eines Volkes: die Bibel deren Gott* Κύριος *heisst ist die Welt-
bibel;* cf. Angus: *Environment of Early Christianity.* [59]Ps.
cxix. 1. [60]I Sam. ii. 10. [61]Is. ix. 7. [62]Micah v. 4; Is. xi. 2.
[63]II Macc. vii. 37; see Lagrange: *Le Messie,* 237, 248.
[64]Daniel vii. 13-14. [65]Guignebert: *The Jewish World in the
Time of Jesus.* [66]Ramsay: *Pauline and other Studies,* 69.
[67]Josephus: *Bell. Jud.,* II, xiii, 4; vii, 12; *Antiq.,* XX, viii, 6.

CHAPTER III

[1]Excellent accounts of Tarsus in *Dictionary of the Bible,* 5
vols., 1900; Ramsay: *Cities of St. Paul;* Deissmann: *St. Paul;*
Prat: *Theology of St. Paul;* Glover: *Paul of Tarsus,* Ch. I;
F. A. Spencer: *Beyond Damascus;* H. V. Morton: *In the Steps
of St. Paul.* [2]See R. Bultmann: *Der Stil der Paulinischen
Predigt,* 1911. [3]Prat, *op. cit.,* I, 14; cf. Pliny: *N.H.,* V, 52.
[4]Deissmann asserts that Shaul did not belong to the educated
class (*St. Paul,* 50-53). This is refuted by E. L. Hicks: *St.
Paul and Hellenism,* 7 ff. [5]Ramsay: *Pauline and other Studies,*
65. [6]F. A. Spencer, *op. cit.;* Horace's *Satires,* I, ix. 90. [7]Renan:
Les Apôtres, 291; Juvenal: *Satires,* XIV, 99 ff.; Martial:
Epigrams, VII, 29, 34, 54. [8]Ps. lxix. 9. [9]Strabo, XIV, 5, 13;
Zosimus: *History,* I, 6; Dion Cassius, LII, 36. [10]Prat: *The-*

ology, I. [11]Lagrange: *Le Messianisme*, 141. [12]Deissmann: *St. Paul*, 101; Prat: *Theology*, I, 18; Nock: *St. Paul*, 236-7. [13]Deissmann: *Die Hellenisierung des Semitischen Monotheismus*. [14]Prat (*Theology*, I, 17) says Shaul was in Tarsus till 13; Ramsay (*Pauline and other Studies*, 67) till he was 20; Canon Deane (*St. Paul and his Letters*, 29) quoting Edersheim (*Jesus the Messiah*) till he was 15. In spite of these, Canon Knox denies St. Paul was educated in Tarsus at all (*St. Paul and the Church at Jerusalem*, 94, 126). Cf. *Theology*, Dec. 1942. The texts he cites do not prove his assertion. [15]Ps. lxxxvii. 2. [16]For Gamaliel, see Fouard: *St. Pierre*, quoting *Pirqé Aboth*, I, 11. [17]Ecclus. xxxix. 1-3. [18]Acts xxiii. 3; Acts xxvi. 5; II Cor. xi. [19]Gal. i. 14. [20]Strack-Billerbeck: *Kommentar. aus Talmud und Midrasch*, II, 763. [21]Ps. lxiii. 2. [22]Is. v. 16; cf. Wheeler Robinson, *op. cit.* [23]Wisdom xviii. 1. [24]Cf. Glover: *Paul of Tarsus*, "reeking with blood and dung". [25]Exodus xx. 3. [26]See Hastings: *E.R.E.* [27]Ps. lxxiii. 23-26. [28]Ramsay: *Pauline and other Studies*, 69. [29]John iv. 24. [30]John iv. 29. [31]Matt. xxviii. 13. [32]Acts i. 9.

CHAPTER IV

[1]Ps. cxix. 165. [2]Cf. Romans vii. [3]Marlowe: *Faustus*. [4]John viii. 58. [5]John ix. 35-37. [6]For Stephanos, see Smith: *D.B.* Hastings: *E.R.E.*; Acts vi. 5-15. [7]Is. lxii. 1. [8]Acts vii. 52. [9]Acts vii. 53. For a valuable analysis of this speech, see Phythian-Adams: *The People and the Presence*. [10]Browning: *Easter Day*. [11]Acts ix. 4; xxii. 7; xxvi. 14. For comparison of the three accounts, see Glover: *Paul of Tarsus*, 62-4.

CHAPTER V

[1]R. T. Herford: *The Pharisees*, 163; cf. Montefiore: *Judaism and St. Paul*, 128-9. [2]Ps. ciii. 12. [3]Acts xxvi. 19. [4]For relations of visions to mystical life, cf. St. John of the Cross: *Ascent of Mount Carmel*, Book II, Ch. XXII. [5]Acts ix. 17; xxii. 13. [6]For

teaching of formulas, see A. M. Hunter: *Paul and his Pred-ecessors*, 14-40. [7]Binyon: *Augustine and Monica*. [8]For Arabia see Farrar: *St. Paul*; Lightfoot: *Galatians*, 87-90.

CHAPTER VI

[1]Acts ii. 36. [2]A. M. Hunter, *loc. cit.* [3]Acts iii. 19. [4]Matt. xviii. 20. [5]Acts ix. 23-4. [6]The basis of the narrative is Acts ix. 26-29; Galatians i. 18-24. For an alleged discrepancy between these, see Kirsopp Lake: *Beginnings of Christianity*, II, 269-270, 318-9; Ramsay: *Galatians*, 283-285. I owe to Bishop O'Rorke the following explanation of how the two accounts tally.

Paul essayed to join himself to the disciples, meaning the believers in general (Acts ix. 26) and they were all afraid of him. But Barnabas took him and brought him to the Apostles (27). His main object was to make a pilgrimage to Peter (Cf. Lightfoot: *Galatians*, 91-2) and he saw no other except James (Gal. i. 19). "The Apostles" therefore means Peter and James only. They hear of Paul's conversion. He was with these two Apostles, going in and out: when he preached boldly in the name of the Lord, it was only to Hellenist Jews unconverted. But so wrathful did these finally become that they sought to kill him (Acts ix. 29); he did not appear before the *Churches* in Judaea. These only heard the story of his conversion, and some were friendly enough to help him against the Hellenist Jews (Acts ix. 30). He then went on to Syria and Cilicia (Gal. i. 21) meaning Tarsus (Acts ix. 30) and Antioch (Acts xi. 23).

[7]For Barnabas, see Hastings: *E.R.E.*; Smith: *D.B.* [8]Acts xxii. 18. [9]C. & H., II, 21. [10]C. H. Dodd: *Apostolic Preach-ing*, 96.

CHAPTER VII.

[1]I Cor. ix. 22. [2]Cf. J. Schneider: *Die Vorkundigung des Paulus*. [3]Cf. H. A. A. Kennedy: *St. Paul and the Mystery Religions*,

280-1. [4]Romans v. 5. [5]For divinities of Egypt and of Persia, see Macgregor and Purdy: *Jew and Greek Tutors unto Christ*, 274. For aims of mysteries, see Angus: *Religious Quests of the Greco-Roman World*, 76; Cumont: *Les Religions orientales*, Paris, 1909. [6]Keats: *Ode to Psyche*. [7]Cumont: *The Mysteries of Mithra*, 149. [8]Wisdom xvii. 18, 19. [9]Ecclus. xliii. 9, 10. [10]Cumont: *The Mysteries of Mithra*, 190-1. [11]Prat: *Theology*, II, 385-90; J. Gresham Machen: *The Origin of Paul's Religion*. For a study of pagan religion in Tarsus, see H. Böhlig: *Die Geistes-Kultur von Tarsus mit Berücksichtigung der Paulinischen Schriften*, Göttingen, 1913. [12]L. Patterson: *Mithraism and Christianity*, 177. [13]H. A. A. Kennedy: *St. Paul and the Mystery Religions*, 228. [14]Reitzenstein: *Die Hellenistischen Mysterien Religionen*, 209. [15]Prat, Gresham Machen, *loc. cit.* Cf. V. D. Macchioro: *From Orpheus to Paul*, New York, 1930, Ch. ix, on the close connection between the Orphic Zagreus and the Pauline Christ. [16]Philo: *Quis Rerum Divinarum Heres*, xxiii; the expression was σπερματικὸς λόγος; see Drummond: *Philo*, 102, 125; Kennedy: *Philo's Contribution to Religion*, 158. [17]Philo: *Leg. Alleg.*, iii, 215; *Quis Rerum Div.*, 31; *De Spec. Leg.*, I, 43, f. [18]Kennedy, *op. cit.*, 145-150. [19]Ps. lxxxiv. 12. [20]Zech. iv. 10. [21]Armitage Robinson in *Ephesians* has an excursus on Χάρις but in the N.T. only. Burton in *Galatians* (I.C.C.) is more general. Cf. Gfrörer: *Philo* (1835), I, 128 ff.; Siegfried: *Philo v. Alex. als Ansleger des A.T.* (1875), 307; Drummond: *Philo Judaeus* (1888), II, 309-24. [22]Brehier: *Idées de Philon*, 222; Kennedy, *op. cit.*, 133-5. [23]Philo: *Quis Rerum Div.*, 190. [24]Jowett: *Commentary on Galatians*, 373. "To thread the maze of Philo's inconsequent and self-contradictory language is the work of a life-time, and students, admittedly of the first rank, come to diametrically opposite conclusions." K. E. Kirk, D.D.: *Essays on the Trinity and the Incarnation* (edited by Rawlinson), 190-1. [25]Ps. xlvi. 10. [26]Ps. cxix. 18. [27]Sencourt: *Carmelite and Poet;* cf. St. John of the Cross: *Cántico Espiritual*, xxxix, 12.

[28]II Cor. xii. 1-5. [29]St. John of the Cross: *Ascent of Mount Carmel*, Book II, ch. xxiv, xxv; *op. cit.*, xxiv, 3. [30]II Cor. xii, 8. Full discussions of this in Lightfoot: *Galatians*, 186-191; Ramsay: *S.P.T.*, 96-98; *Galatians*, 422-8; Goudge: *II Corinthians*, 121; Farrar: *St. Paul*, Vol. I, excursus x. [31]Chrysostom: *Romans*, Hom. xiii. [32]Acts xi. 25.

CHAPTER VIII.

[1]For description see Renan: *Les Apôtres*, 215, 223. He quotes Dion Chrysostom, Libanius, Pausanias, John Chrysostom, Juvenal, Tacitus, Philostratos and Josephus. Cf. Smith: *D.B.* [2]Ps. xxiv. 3. [3]Ps. xxiv. 4. [4]Acts xiii. 1-3. [5]Acts xiii. 4-7. For Sergius Paulus, see Ramsay: *S.P.T.*, 73 ff. [6]Acts xiii. 8-12. For Magus, see Kirsopp Lake: *The Beginnings of Christianity*; G. Rackham: *Acts*, 200-1. [7]For change of name, see Strack-Billerbeck: *Kommentar.*; Saulos, see F. A. Spencer: *Beyond Damascus*; Liddell and Scott, *ad loc.* [8]Acts xiii. 13. [9]For account of journey, see Ramsay: *S.P.T.*, Ch. V, and *Cities of St. Paul.* [10]Acts xiii. 14-44; G. Rackham: *Acts*, 207-217; Louis Robert: *Etudes Anatoliens.* [11]Acts xiv. 1-28. See Holzhey: *Die Theckla Akten*, especially for Onesiphorus.

CHAPTER IX.

[1]Gal. ii. 10. [2]See Lightfoot: *Galatians*, 128-132; Möhler: *Gesammelte Schriften*, 1-18; the view taken by author is Jerome: *Epistolae*, CXII. [3]Much learning is imbedded in Lightfoot's *Galatians*. Some of it is superseded by Ramsay's *Historical Commentary on Galatians*. Burton's *Galatians* (1920) is less valuable than others in the I.C.C., but contains a good bibliography up to 1920. The classical German commentary *Sieppert* (Meyer's, 1899) is superseded by Lagrange: *Epître aux Gal.*, 1927. Paul's claim for direct authority for his gospel: Gal. i. 8, 9, 11-12, 20. [4]Gal. ii. 19. [5]Gal. ii. 16-21.

[6]See Gal. iii. with Gal. iv. 5-6. [7]Gal. iv. 10, v. 5-7, vi. 16.
[8]Gal. iii. 7, 22, 26, 27. [9]Lagrange: *Epître*, LXIX. [10]Lagrange,
op. cit., LXX. [11]Gal. v. 16-25. [12]Gal. vi. 14. [13]Gal. iii. 2-4.
[14]Gal. ii. 19-21. [15]Lagrange, *op. cit.*, p. lxxviii.

CHAPTER X.

[1]Acts xv. 1-5; Rackham: *Acts*, 243-250. [2]Acts xv. 6-29. For
Council, see Appendix I. [3]For authority of Peter, see Renan:
Les Apôtres; F. Underhill: *St. Peter.* [4]Acts xv. 29. [5]Acts xi. 20.
[6]Acts xv. 36-40. [7]See Renan: *St. Paul.* [8]Smith: *D.B.*, IV, 768.
[9]Lewin: *St. Paul*, 188-9; Holzner: *Paulus*, 140. [10]E. F.
Brown: *Pastoral Epistles*, pp. xiii, xxiii. [11]Lewin: *St. Paul*, I
193-203. [12]Held back from Mysia, see Ramsay, *S.P.T.*, 196.
[13]Rhyndacos, see Ramsay: *S.P.T.*, 197. See journey to Edremid
in Clement's *Paulus*, 147. [14]Account of Asia Minor, Renan: *St.
Paul*, 129-30. [15]Homer: *Iliad*, II, 821 ff.

CHAPTER XI.

[1]For Luke, see Smith: *D.B.;* Ramsay: *S.P.T.*, 202-3; Ramsay:
Luke the Physician; also E. F. Brown: *Pastoral Epistles*, p. xix.
[2]*H.E.*, iii, 4. [3]Acts xvi. 9. For dreams, see Holzner: *Paulus*,
149. [4]For Philippi, see Collart: *Philippes.* [5]See Pliny: *N.H.*,
ix, 124-141; cf. Spencer: *Beyond Damascus*, 229. [6]Rackham:
Acts, 287. [7]If the prison were like some modern Turkish cave
prisons in Macedonia, such as Ramsay saw, an earthquake might
well displace both bars of doors and fixings of stocks. Ramsay:
S.P.T., 221. [8]Cicero: *In Verrem.* [9]Acts xvi. 25-37. [10]Latin:
dynarchus dasephus illeger. [11]Cicero: *De Prov. cons.*, 2.
[12]Strabo, 33; Lucian: *Asin. Aur.*, 46. [13]Gibbon: *Decline and
Fall*, Ch. XVII. [14]For Salonika, see G. Milligan: *Thessalonians.* [15]I Thess. ii. 9. [16]I Thess. ii. 2. [17]Acts xvii. 1-9.

[18]Suetonius: *Claudius*, 25. [19]Acts xvii. 10-12. [20]I Thess. ii. 8, 10-11. [21]Thess. iii. 12, 13. [22]See Prat: *Theology*, II, 7. For Paul's eschatology, see Prat: *Theology;* cf. I Thess. iv. 14-17. [23]I Thess. ii. 7. [24]I Thess. iv. 3, 4. [25]I Thess. v. 8; cf. A. M. Hunter: *Paul and His Predecessors.* [26]Acts xvii. 13-14. [27]S. H. Butcher: *Harvard Lectures,* 42.

CHAPTER XII.

[1]Wordsworth: *Evening Voluntary.* [2]Clement: *Paulus*, I, 370-1; Smith: *D.B.*, "Greece" (by H.F.T.). [3]Newman: *Historical Sketches* (1875), Vol. I, 20. [4]C. & H., I, 371-380; see Acts xvii. 22, 31; Prat: *Theology*, I, 59-61; Norden: *Agnostos Theos.*, 31-83, 113-124. [5]For Corinth, see F. S. de Waele: *Korinthos* (Stuttgart, 1934. Reprint from Pauly-Wissowa). Johannes Weiss: *I Korintherbrief*, ix, "Griechenland in der apostolischer Zeit." Cf. I Cor. i, Schaff-Herzog's *R. E.*, VII, 160-168.

CHAPTER XIII.

[1]Aquila already a Christian, because not baptized with the others, see I Cor. i. 14. Cf. Holzner: *Paulus*, 206. [2]See I Cor. i. 11, 14-15, xvi. 17. [3]I owe this passage, with other courtesies, to Canon Anthony Deane; cf. *St. Paul and His Letters*, 77. [4]I Thess. i. 1. [5]I Thess. ii. 5. [6]I Thess. ii. 19-20. [7]I Thess. iii. 12-13. [8]I Thess. v. 16-28. [9]See Renan: *St. Paul*, 231-2. Cf. Seneca: *Quaest. nat.*, IV, 2; V, 11; Statius: *Silv.*, II, vii, 32; Tacitus: *Annals*, VI, 3; XV, 73; XVI, 17. [10]Acts xviii. 14-15. [11]Acts xvii. 18. [12]II Thess. i. 11. [13]II Thess. ii. 13-14; cf. Chap. II, notes 55, 56. [14]Prat: *Theology*, II, 356-364. [15]These paragraphs follow Prat closely in his discussion of Eschatology. [16]For grace and glory, see Terrier: *La Grace et la Gloire.* Cf. Watkin: *The Philosophy of Mysticism.* [17]Rom. ix. 11. [18]Cf. Ps. cvii.

CHAPTER XIV.

[1]II Cor. xi. 24-26; F. A. Spencer: *Beyond Damascus*, 198. [2]Homer: *Iliad*, II, 459-463. [3]See C. & H., *op. cit.*; Renan, *op. cit.* [4]Suetonius: *Nero*, 36; Strabo, XIV, i, 20, 21. [5]Flavius Josephus: *Antiq.*, XIV, x, 11-15; Philo: *Leg.*, 40. [6]See Hastings: *E.R.E.*; Acts xviii. 24-28. [7]For occult phenomena, see Deissmann: *Light from the Ancient East*; E. E. Burrows: *Taboo, Magic and Spirits*, New York, 1931; E. Legge: *Forerunners and Rivals of Christianity* (2 Vols.), 1915; L. Thorndike: *History of Magic and Experimental Science*, 1923; Acts xix. 11, 12. [8]Tacitus: *Annals*, XIII, 1. [9]For murder of Aelius and Celer, see Tacitus, *op. cit.*, XIII, 4, 5; Dion Cassius, LXI, 6. Cf. Lewin: *St. Paul*, I, 337-8; Duncan: *St. Paul's Ephesian Ministry*, 101-3. [10]II Cor. xi. 23. [11]I Cor. xv. 30. [12]I Cor. xv. 32. [13]I Cor. i. 8. [14]Rom. xvi. 7. Cf. however S. & H., *ad. loc.* But Professor Duncan is wrong in translating Rom. xvi. 4 "who risked their necks to save me"; the real meaning has been shown by recent research to be "who were devoted to me". S. L. Caiger: *Archaeology and the New Testament* (1939), 144. [15]St. Clement in his *Corinthians*, V. See Duncan, *op. cit.*, 69-70, 131-6. Professor Manson disputes several of these points: *Rylands Bulletin* (1939). He cannot dispose of all. [16]Maurice Jones: *Philippians*; Duncan, *op. cit.*; Manson: "St. Paul in Ephesus", in *Rylands Bulletin* (1939), 5-6. [17]For *Praetorium*, see Mark xv. 16; Acts xxiii. 35. Cf. Matthew xxvii. 27. Cf. Duncan, *op. cit.*, 110; Kittell: *Wörterbuch*. [18]Phil. i. 26. [19]Phil. i. 21. [20]Phil. i. 29-30. [21]Phil. ii. 1-11. [22]W. Walsham How. [23]Phil. iii. 9-11, 20, 21; iv. 4-7. [24]Phil. iv. 8. [25]Phil. iv. 11-13.

CHAPTER XV.

[1]For glossolalia in pagan rites, see Eddison Mosiman: *Das Zungenreden*; Manson: "St. Paul in Ephesus", in *Rylands*

Bulletin (1939), 16-18. [2]K. Lake: *Beginnings of Christianity*, V, 17; cf. Eusebius: *H. E.*, V, 16, 7, 9. [3]Poulain: *Graces of Interior Prayer.* [4]Greville: *Memoirs*, Book II, Ch. xxii.; cf. J. Weiss: *Der Erste Korintherbrief* (Meyer), 335-339. [5]H. L. Goudge: *I Corinthians*, 133-5. [6]For whole subject, see Eddison Mosiman: *Das Zungenreden;* Origen: *Contra Celsum*, VII, 9; cf. Irenæus, V, 61; Farrar: *St. Paul*, 71. [7]See J. Weiss, *op. cit.*, 300-1. [8]Holzner: *Paulus*, 214. [9]Reference to veiling of women, Schweitzer: *Mysticism of Paul*, 10. That the word ἀγγέλοι refers to deacons is suggested by Canon G. C. Richards, D.D., who found it so used by Tertullian, *De Baptismo*, 4: *medicalibus quodammodo aquis per angeli interventum;* and 6, *in aqua emundati sub angelo Spiritui Sancto preparamini.* This, however, appears to be of doubtful application. For in a direct reference to this passage Tertullian speaks of unveiled women arousing the lust of the angels. Tertullian: *De Virginibus velandis.* [10]For points now involved, see T. W. Manson: "St. Paul in Ephesus", in *Rylands Bulletin* (1939). [11]I Cor. i. 12-13. [12]I Cor. i. 18-31. [13]Blass: *Grammar of New Testament Greek*, 300-301. [14]Browning: *Prince Hohenstiel-Schwangau.* [15]Acts xix. 9. [16]I Cor. ii. 1. [17]I Cor. ii. 6-9; cf. Is. xliv. 4. [18]I Cor. ii. 10-16; cf. Wisdom ix. 13; Is. xl. 13. [19]I Cor. iii. 7. [20]I Cor. iii. 16-23. [21]I Cor. iv. 4-5. [22]I Cor. iv. 11-13. [23]I Cor. v. 7-8. [24]For Paul on sex morality, see I Cor. vi. 15-20; vii. 1-11, 27-28. [25]I Cor. viii. 1-13; x. 19-20. [26]I Cor. xi. 5-6, 10. [27]I Cor. xi. 6, 14-15. [28]See I Cor. ix. 1. [29]I Cor. ix. 9; cf. Deut. xxv. 4. [30]I Cor. ix. 22-23. [31]I Cor. ix. 26-27. [32]I Cor. x. 19, 22-26, 28-33. [33]I Cor. xi. 26. [34]I Cor. xi. 20-34; x. 16-18 [35]I Cor. x. 16. [36]I Cor. xii. 1-31. [37]For definitions of love, see these: "For those who listen aright to the Divine, the word loving-kindness is used by the sacred writers and the Divine revelation with the same meaning as the word 'love'. It means a power of making one and binding together, and a peculiar commingling in the beautiful and the good" (Dionysius: *De Divinis Nominibus*, IV, 12). "The peculiar quality of love is to desire to be united and bound together with the beloved object to attain to perfection in the blessing of love" (Crisogono: *San Juan de la Cruz*, I, 336). [38]For a learned analysis of this chapter, see Ramsay: *The Teaching of Paul*, Ch. XLIX. For final passage on Paul's efforts, see Acts xx. 18-35; Holzner: *Paulus*, 260; Harnack: "Paul's Hymn of Love" in *Expositor*, May, June, 1912; Johann Weiss: *I Korintherbrief*, 313 ff. [39]For gnosis, see *The Trinity and the Incarnation*, edited A. E. J. Rawlinson; *Early Gentile Christianity* by A. D. Nock, p. 67, where it is maintained that gnosis is not merely a secret knowledge, but a means of power or regeneration. [40]Shakespeare: "Sonnet". [41]Gregory of Nyssa, *Opera*, Migne, II, 1303. [42]Johann Weiss: *Beiträge zur Paulinischen Rhetorik*, 200. Cf. E. Norden: *Die Antike Kunstprosa*, II, 509: "Together with the elevation of the thought, these assonances and cadences combine to give back to Greek prose something it has lost for centuries, the inwardness, the enthusiasm of a soul at one with God as in the hymns of Cleanthes and certain passages of Plato." [43]Longinus: *De sublimitate*. [44]Wilamowitz-Moellendorff: *Die Futur der Gegenwart*, I, 159. [45]St. Augustine: *De Doctrina Christiana*, IV, 7: *Sicut ergo apostolum praecepta eloquentiae secutum fuisse non dicimus, ita quod ejus sapientiam secuta sit eloquentia non negamus.* Cf. his notes on Romans v. 3-5. [46]Lagrange: *Epître aux Romans*, Introduction, xlvi. [47]For further references to Paul's style, see Nageli: *Das Wortschatz des Apostel Paulus*; Paul Wendland: *Hellenistische-Römische Kultur*, 341-360; Norden: *Die Antike Kunstprosa*, I, 129ss. [48]I Cor. xiv. 8. [49]I Cor. xiv. 9-19; cf. Farrar: *St. Paul*. Few support Blass in his original theory about Paul's artificial rhythms in *Rhythmen des asiatischen und romischen Kunstprosa*. Indeed he himself abandoned it in his *Grammatik des Neutestamentischen Griechisch*, 1913. For influence of the diatribe, see R. Bultmann: *Der Stil der Paulinischen Predigt*, Göttingen, 1910. [50]I Cor. xv. 10-12; cf. I.C.C., I Cor., *ad loc.* [51]I Cor. xv. 12-13. [52]*Ib.* xv. 16-18. [53]*Ib.*

xv. 12, 19. ⁵⁴*Ib.* xv. 20-28. ⁵⁵*Ib.* xv. 29-32. ⁵⁶*Ib.* xv. 33-34.
⁵⁷*Ib.* xv. 36-39. ⁵⁸*Ib.* xv. 39-57. ⁵⁹*De fide et symbolo.* ⁶⁰I Cor.
xv. 22. ⁶¹*Ib.* xvi. 24.

CHAPTER XVI.

¹Acts xix. 25-27. ²Acts xix. 28. ³Acts xix. 29-34. ⁴Acts xix. 36-
40. ⁵For Paul's subsequent actions, see Canon W. Knox: *St.
Paul and the Church of the Gentiles,* 144; Hastings' extra vol.,
376; Ramsay on Roads and Travel. See also, P. M. Harrison:
Problem of the Pastoral Epistles, 119, 120; T. W. Manson:
"St. Paul in Ephesus," Part III, in *Rylands Bulletin,* 1941.
⁶See II Cor. vii. 5-7. ⁷II Cor. ii. 13. ⁸II Cor. ii. 4. ⁹II Cor. ii. 14.
Knox: *op. cit.,* 129; cf. Appian: *Punica,* 60. ¹⁰II Cor. ii. 17.
¹¹*Ib.* iii. 2-3. ¹²*Ib.* iii. 16, Περιαιρετῖαι τὸ κάλομμα . ¹³*Ib.* iii.
16-18. ¹⁴*Ib.* iv. 7. ¹⁵*Ib.* iv. 8, 9; Plummer: *II Corinthians,* 123,
in I.C.C. ¹⁶II Cor. iv. 13, quoting Ps. cvxi. 10. ¹⁷II Cor. iv. 14.
¹⁸*Ib.* iv. 16-18. ¹⁹*Ib.* v. 1-3, 4-6. ²⁰*Ib.* v. 8-9. ²¹*Ib.* v. 14.
²²*Ib.* v. 17. ²³The new word is καταλλάγή , *Ib.* v. 20. ²⁴The
words πρεσβεύω and πρεσβύτης in the Greek East for the
Emperor's Legate; Deissmann: *Light from the Ancient East,*
379. ²⁵II Cor. v. 20; cf. Plummer: *II Cor.,* 185. ²⁶*Ib.* v. 21.
²⁷*Ib.* vi. 1. ²⁸Athanasius: *De Incarnatione Verbi,* 54. ²⁹II Cor.
v. 19. For a full discussion of the theories of atonement, see
Prat: *Theology,* II, 193-205; cf. H. N. Oxenham: *The Catholic Doctrine of the Atonement* (1881); Westcott: *The Victory
of the Cross* (1889); R. C. Moberley: *Atonement and Personality* (1907). ³⁰II Cor. vi. 3. ³¹II Cor. vi. 4-10. ³²Plummer: *II
Corinthians,* p. 193. "After the clauses we have a series of
severe contrasts, ending with a characteristic three-fold alliteration and an equally characteristic play upon the words". It was
praised also by Erasmus and Augustine. See also Chrysostom:
Homily 47. ³³For interpretation, see Plummer: *II Corinthians,*
I.C.C., p. 202 ff. ³⁴II Cor. vi. 16; vii. 1. ³⁵*Ib.* vi. 13; vii. 2, 4,

16; cf., however, Plummer, *op. cit.*, 204. [36]The plea for contribution, viii. 1; ix. 16; cf. Paley: *Horae Paulinae*, II, 1. [37]II Cor. x. 1-6. [38]The majority of scholars at the present day are inclined to think the chapters which follow were written before these which have preceded. Although this would make the argument of the Apostle more logical, there is no internal evidence to support such a conjecture. And St. Paul was not always logical. It is just as reasonable to conjecture that at this point Paul received news which excited him; in any case, the impassioned chapters which follow are typical of the impetuous reaction of his temperament. Plummer, *op. cit.*, xxv; Lake: *Earlier Epistles*, 123, 162. Or one may suppose different chapters to be written with different groups in mind. Holzner: *Paulus*, 317-8. [39]II Cor. x. 18. [40]*Ib.* xi. 2-6. [41]*Ib.* xi. 19-31. [42]*Ib.* xiii. 4-5. [43]*Ib.* xiii. 11-13.

CHAPTER XVII

[1]Almost every point in this chapter is compassed in the classic commentary on *Romans* by Sanday and Headlam, I.C.C. That of Meyer is also good. Much praise has been given to those of Professor C. H. Dodd, 1929, and that of Karl Barth (Eng. trans. by Hoskyns). To these the author prefers Lagrange. [2]Rom. xv. 19. [3]With *Wisdom* is mentioned the opening of *Second Esdras* by H. N. Bate: *A Guide to the Epistles*, 134-5; but parallels are not convincing. [4]Ramsay: *Pauline Studies*, 78. [5]Rom. i. 11. [6]Wisdom xiii. 5-9. [7]*Ib.* xiv. 27. For the influence of *Wisdom* on St. Paul see E. Grope: *Theol. abb. Weizsacker*, 251 ff. [8]Rom. ii. 29. [9]S. & H., 64, 68. [10]Gal. iii. 24-28. [11]For conjecture that Paul prepared part of his Roman Epistle at Jerusalem, see A. M. Pope: *Genesis of the Roman Epistle*, in the *Expositor*, Vol. XI (1921), 361. He quotes Kirsopp Lake and McGiffert. [12]Rom. iii. 28; cf. S. & H., 28-34. [13]Rom. iv. 20. [14]Faith is enthusiastic personal adherence; cf. Newman: *Lec-*

tures on Justification (1838), 308; S. & H., 34. [15]Rom. v. 1-2.
[16]*Ib.* v. 2-5. [17]*Ib.* v. 7-11, 17-21; cf. S. & H., 91-4. [18]Newman:
Lectures on Justification (1838), 184. [19]Rom. vi. 3-4. [20]*Ib.* vi.
5-13; cf. S. & H., 154-5 ff. [21]For definition of grace, see ante,
Ch. VII, notes 19 ff. [22]Rom. vi. 15-23. [23]Following first vii. 1-6,
then vii. 7-25. [24]Rom. vii. 1-3. [25]*Ib.* vii. 24; cf. earlier Chapter
IV, Section 1. [26]Newman: *The Dream of Gerontius.* [27]Rom.
vii. 1-11. [28]*Ib.* viii. 14. [29]*Ib.* viii. 11-17. [30]*Ib.* viii. 20. For further elucidation of this, see Dom Bruno Webb: *Why did God
permit evil?* Dodd in *Romans* gives a short and clear explanation of this passage. Barth, *Romans,* 305-317, gives another,
not clear and not short. [31]Tennyson: *The Dream of Fair
Women.* [32]*Op. cit.;* cf. Rom. viii. 22. [33]Rom. viii. 28-30.
[34]*Ib.* viii. 31-39. [35]*Ib.* ix. 3-5. [36]The reference to grafting has
been supposed to show that St. Paul did not understand grafting. The passage does not prove it. [37]Rom. xi. 33-36. [38]The
general argument covers the intervening chapters relating to
the peace of the Jews. Again this is a parallel with *Wisdom;*
cf. S. & H., 267-9. For reference to Jews and O.T., see S. & H.,
261-7, 341-350. [39]Rom. xii. 1-2. [40]*Ib.* xii. 9-21. [41]*Ib.* xiii. 11,
14. [42]*Ib.* xiv. 1-3. [43]*Ib.* xiii. 1-7. [44]*Ib.* xv. 12-13. [45]It is believed
by many that Chapter XVI was addressed to Ephesus; cf.
G. S. Duncan: *St. Paul's Ephesian Ministry,* 207-8. This suggestion, though valuable, received no support from S. & H.

CHAPTER XVIII

[1]For murder plan see Rackham: *Acts,* 375; Holzner: *Paulus,*
337. [2]Newman: *Historical Sketches* (1865), Vol. I, 21.
[3]*Ibidem.* [4]I Cor. v. 7. [5]Phil. i. 8. [6]*Ib.* iv. 7. [7]*Ib.* iv. 8. [8]II Cor.
iii. 18. [9]Following Acts xx. 4-6. Cf. Rackham: *Acts,* 375-380;
C. & H., II, 203-210. [10]Cf. C. & H., II, 214-234. [11]Acts xx.
19-26. [12]*Ib.* xx. 32-35. [13]*Ib.* xx. 36-38. [14]*Ib.* xxi. 3-6. [15]For
Giscala, see Jerome: *De Viris Illustribus,* V. [16]C. & H., Ch.
XX, 242. [17]Acts xxi. 11. [18]*Ib.* xxi. 13. [19]*Ib.* xxi. 14.

CHAPTER XIX

[1]Acts xxi. 17. Cf. Renan: *St. Paul*, 509-12; Farrar: *St. Paul*.
[2]Holzner: *Paulus*, 342: *"Die offizielle Kirche von Jerusalem hatte für den grössten Apostel kein Quartier"*. [3]Acts xxi. 20.
[4]The narrative which tempts Renan, Professor Holzner, and the present writer to suspect that the proposal was disingenuous convinces Rackham that Paul had been welcomed sincerely (Renan: *St. Paul*, 514-7; Rackham: *Acts*, 414-5). [5]Acts xxi. 31.
[6]*Ib*. xxii. 21. [7]*Ib*. xxii. 22. [8]*Ib*. xxii. 25. [9]*Ib*. xxii. 26. [10]*Ib*. xxii. 27. [11]*Ib*. xxii. 28. [12]This short phrase tells all there is to know about Paul's Roman citizenship and γεχεύνημαι can mean "become" as well as "be born". [13]For Ananias ben Nebedaï, see Renan: *St. Paul*, 528-9; Derenbourg: *La Palestine d'après les Thalmuds*, I, 230 ff. [14]Smith: *D.B.*; Acts xxiii. 3. [15]Acts xxiii. 4. [16]*Ib*. xxiii. 5. [17]*Ib*. xxiii. 6. [18]The story of Felix and Drusilla is based on Tacitus: *Annals*, V. Cf. *History*, XII, 54; Suetonius: *Claudius*, 28, 16, and Josephus: *Antiquities*, XX, vii, 1; XX, viii, 5; *Bell. Jud.*, II, xii, 8; Renan: *St. Paul*, 534-5; Holzner: *Paulus*, 358; Lewin: *St. Paul*. Drusilla was the 17-year-old sister of the Agrippa and Berenice before whom Paul later appeared. The terms of Lysias' report are in Acts xxiii. 26-30. [19]Acts xxiv. 2-8. [20]*Ib*. xxiv. 10-21. [21]*Ib*. xxiv. 24-26; cf. Renan: *St. Paul*, 535. [22]Acts xxiv. 27. [23]*Ib*. xxv. 1-10. [24]*Ib*. xxv. 11. [25]Berenice, a niece of Philo. Dr. Edwyn Bevan attracted the author's attention to this interesting detail. Tiberius Alexander was a nephew of Philo (see Farrar: *St. Paul*, II, 303. Cf. Flavius Josephus: *Antiq.*, XVIII, viii). So therefore also was his brother Archelaus to whom Agrippa I gave as wife Mariamne. Of this marriage was born Berenice (Josephus, *loc. cit.*). [26]For her relations with her brother Agrippa II, see Flavius Josephus: *Antiquities*, XX, vii, 1-3. Cf. Renan: *St. Paul*, 535, 543; Holzner: *Paulus*, 358-359. [27]Acts xxv. 19. [28]*Ib*. xxv. 21, 22. [29]*Ib*. xxvi. 2-23. [30]*Ib*. xxvi. 24. [31]*Ib*. xxvi. 26. [32]*Ib*. xxvi. 27. [33]Had Agrippa spoken in the Latin he learned

at Rome, the expression here translated "a little more" would have been Paullo: a play on the former speaker's name: Acts xxvi. 28. [34]Acts xxvi. 3. For contemptuous sense in ἄνθρωπος, see Moulton and Milligan: *Vocabulary*, Vol. I, 44. [35]Acts xxvi. 32.

CHAPTER XX

[1]Ramsay: *Luke the Physician*, 310. [2]*Ib.*, 310-311. [3]Smith: *D.B.* (1893), Vol. I, 1314. [4]See Appendix II for further notes on authorship. [5]Leonard: *Authorship of Hebrews*, 114. [6]Ramsay: *Luke the Physician*, 327. [7]Ps. cx. 4; cf. Hebrews v. 6-26. [8]Heb. vi. 17-20. [9]*Ib.* vii. 1-3. [10]*Ib.* xiii. 1, 2, 6. [11]Jer. xxxi. 33; Cf. Masure: *Le Sacrifice du Chef*, Conclusion of Book. [12]Heb. ix. 11-13. [13]*Ib.* ix. 14-15. [14]Rom. v. 8-9. [15]Heb. ix. 26. [16]Westcott: 293-4. [17]Westcott: 294. [18]Herond IV, quoted in Festugière: *Le Monde Greco-Romain*, 87-92. [19]Festugière, *op. cit.*, 108-9. [20]Cumont: *The Mysteries of Mithra*, 179-180. [21]Wheeler Robinson: *Religious Ideas of the Jews*. [22]Robertson-Smith: *Religion of the Semites*, 350. [23]Heb. ix. 22-24. [24]Ps. xl. [25]I Cor. xi. 25. [26]Heb. x. 19-20. [27]The sacramental mysteries explain the ritual act of the high priests; Westcott: *Hebrews*, 323, citing Leviticus xvi. 4. Cf. Masure: *Le Sacrifice du Chef*. [28]Heb. xiii. 10. [29]Leo: *Sermons*, LX, 5. [30]I Cor. xi. 27. [31]Heb. x. 29-30. [32]*Ib.* x. 31. [33]*Ib.* xi. [34]*Ib.* xi. 40. [35]Heb. xii. 6; cf. Proverbs xiii. 24. [36]Heb. xii. 10. [37]*Ib.* xii. 21-25. [38]*Ib.* xii. 14. For holiness, see S. & H.: *Romans*. [39]Heb. xiii. 20-21. [40]The references in this section are to I Cor. xi. and Heb. vii.

CHAPTER XXI

[1]Acts xxvii. 1-8. [2]The classic authority on St. Paul's Voyage is H. Smith, 1867. The present exposition also owes much to Captain Codman of Massachusetts, who made a nautical trans-

lation of this chapter. His translation has been published by the author's old friend, Professor S. E. Morrison of Harvard University, who kindly sent him a copy. [3]Acts xxvii. 9-10. For ἄνδρες see Kittel: *Wörterbuch*, I, 363. [4]Acts xxvii. [5]*Ib*. xxvii. 23-26. [6]*Ib*. xxviii. 1-10. [7]The Maltese snake *Coronella austriaca* has, it is true, no poison fangs; but though ignorant people imagine all snakes to be poisonous, the Maltese may then have had a poisonous snake. Ramsay: *Luke the Physician*, 64, 65. The question of Luke's skill having something to do with the cure is brought up also by Ramsay. [8]Shelley: *Ode to the West Wind*. [9]I Tim. i. 11. [10]*Appia longarum regina viarum* (Statius: *Silv.*, 2-12). [11]For Paul's debt to Roman civilisation, see T. W. Manson: *Presidential Address*, Oxford Society of Historical Theology, 1941, p. 74. [12]Acts xxiii. 11; cf. *Ib*. xix. 21; xxvii. 24. [13]*Ib*. xxviii. 16; Suetonius: *Tiberius*, 37; Pliny: *Epistles*, X, 65; Josephus: *Antiquities*, XVIII, vi, 7. [14]For *frumentarius*, see Josephus, *loc. cit.*; Seneca: *De tranquilitate animae*, 10. [15]Josephus: *Antiq.*, XVIII, iii, 5 and XII; Tacitus: *Annals*, II, 83; cf. Renan: *St. Paul*, 536. [16]Acts xxvii. [17]For the reaction, see Renan: *L'Antéchrist*, 6. [18]Acts xxviii. 27. [19]*Ib*. xxviii. 28.

CHAPTER XXII

[1]See Appendix III. Cf. Eusebius: *H.E.*, II, xxii, 2. [2]Renan: *L'Antéchrist*. [3]Momigliano: *Nero*, in C.A.H., Vol. X, 704. [4]For Paul's journey westwards, see C. & H., II. Cf. Rackham: *Acts*, 510-1; Clement: *Epistle to the Corinthians*, V; Prat: *St. Paul*, 188-9. See Appendix III. [5]Plummer: *The Pastoral Epistles*, 10. [6]See Lightfoot: *Dissertation on the Apostolic Age*, 144-155. [7]Dr. Harrison: *Pastoral Epistles*. [8]Lock: *The Pastoral Epistles*, xxii-xxxv. [9]Lock, *op. cit.*, xxix. [10]Ramsay: *Luke the Physician*, 9. [11]See Appendix III. [12]See Appendix III. Lucanus and Aristarchus with Paul, Philemon, 2-4. [13]Philemon, 5-8. [14]For further discussions on Onesimos see Duncan: *St. Paul's*

Ephesian Ministry, 72 ff. Opinions in favour of these epistles being written in Rome were of course general till attention was drawn to the use of πραιτώριον for the establishment of a *proconsul.* [15]Philemon, 16. [16]*Ib.* 17-21. Cf. Paley: *Horae Paulinae* (1825 edn.), 217-236. [17]For a further knowledge of Montanism I am indebted to Mr. G. A. P. Freeman, B.Litt., and his unpublished thesis on the subject. [18]The general attitude of Kolossai is best described by Canon W. Knox: *St. Paul and the Church of the Gentiles*, 149-156. [19]Knox, *op. cit.*, 149, 151. Cf. Duncan, *op. cit.*, 76; Col. i. 16-18, 21-22. [20]Col. i. 19. [21]Knox, *op. cit.*, 149, 156. [22]Col. i. 4-6, 12. [23]*Ib.* i. 9-11. [24]*Ib.* i. 13-14. Cf. C. F. Burney: *Journal of Theological Studies*, Jan., 1926. [25]Col. iii. 15-19. [26]Knox, *op. cit.*, 164-5. [27]Col. ii. 26-28. [28]*Ib.* ii. 9-10. [29]*Ib.* ii. 11-12. [30]C. Wordsworth: "See the Conqueror mounts in triumph". [31]St. John of the Cross: *Cántico Espiritual* (2nd redaction), V, 45. [32]St. John of the Cross: *Cánt. Esp.*, XXXIX, 11; Peers, II, 410. [33]Col. iii. 5-14. [34]*Ib.* iii. 15. [35]*Ib.* iii. 16. [36]*Ib.* iii. 17, iv. 1. [37]*Ib.* iv. 6; cf. Ramsay: *S.P.T.*, 148-9. [38]Titus i. 7. [39]*Ib.* iii. 4-7. [40]This exposition closely follows Lock: *Pastoral Epistles.* [41]I Tim. i. 15. [42]*Ib.* ii. 1-3. [43]*Ib.* ii. 9-10. [44]*Ib.* iii. 1-7. [45]*Ib.* iii. 8-13. [46]*Ib.* iii. 11. [47]*Ib.* iv. 4-5. [48]*Ib.* v. 3-12. [49]*Ib.* v. 19-20; Lock, *op. cit.*, 62-3. [50]*Ib.* v. 23. [51]*Ib.* v. 24-5; Lock, *op. cit.*, 62-3. [52]*Ib.* vi. 1-2; Lock, *op. cit.*, 64-5. [53]*Ib.* i. 5-6. [54]*Ib.* vi. 3-5; Lock, *op. cit.* [55]*Ib.* vi. 11-16. [56]*Ib.* vi. 7-10; Lock, *op. cit.*, 67-70. [57]Dante: *Paradiso.* [58]*Pilgrim's Progress* (orig. edn.), p. 152. [59]"St. Paul's epistles are connected with the history by their particularity and by the numerous circumstances which are found in them. When we descend to an examination and comparison of these circumstances we not only observe the history and the epistle to be independent documents unknown to, or at least unconsulted by each other, but we find the substance and often many minute articles of the history recognised in the epistles by allusions and references which can neither be imputed to *design*, nor, without a foundation in truth, be accounted for by accident, by hints and expressions and single words dropping as it were fortuitously from the pen of the writer, or drawn forth, each by some occasion proper to the place in which it occurs but widely removed from a view to consistency or agreement. These we know are effects which reality naturally produces, but which without reality at the bottom can hardly be conceived to exist." Paley: *Horae Paulinae* (1825), 265-266.

CHAPTER XXIII

[1]The suggestion here made that Paul was arrested in Troas depends on the reference to parchments and cloak left there (II Tim. iv. 13). But it receives support from Lewin, who, however, thinks that the arrest took place at Troas, and that is why cloak and parchments were left behind (*St. Paul*, II, 370). [2]The best commentary on this Epistle to the Ephesians is that of Armitage Robinson. Another excellent one is that of Westcott; nor should that of Hitchcock (1913) be ignored. [3]Eph. i. 4-10. [4]*Ib*. i. 11-12. [5]*Ib*. i. 19-22. [6]*Ib*. i. 23. [7]Prophecies for Easter eve in *Roman Missal*, 2nd collect. [8]Eph. ii. 18. [9]*Ib*. ii. 19-20. [10]Dante: *Paradiso*. [11]Eph. ii. 21-22. [12]*Ib*. iv. 3-6. [13]*Ib*. iv. 12-16. [14]*Ib*. iv. 17-24. [15]*Ib*. iv. 31, v. 3. [16]*Ib*. vi. 1-9. [17]Wordsworth: "King's College Chapel". [18]Eph. vi. 12. W. Knox, *op. cit.*, 202, takes this expression in an astrological sense but κοσμοκράτωρ also meant an Emperor, the head of a dynasty. Cf. Kittel: *Wörterbuch*, III, 913. [19]Eph. vi. 13-17. [20]See Westcott, *Ephesians*, XXXVIII. [21]Dante: *Paradiso*, XXXIII, 85-88.

CHAPTER XXIV

[1]See Appendix III. Cf. Canon A. Deane: *St. Paul and his Letters*, 252-8. [2]The narrative follows Lock's exposition in I.C.C., *Pastorals*. [3]Lock, *op. cit.*, 82-3. [4]Lock, *op. cit.*, 89. [5]II Tim. iii. [6]*Ib*. iv. 6-8; cf. Lock, III. [7]Ps. xxiii. 4. [8]II Tim. iv.

9-12. Peter spoke in the accents of Paul in I Peter. Cf. E. G. Selwyn, *op. cit.* [9]II Tim. iv. 13. [10]*Ib.* iv. 21. [11]*Ib.* iv. 22. [12]For Nero see Renan: *L'Antéchrist*, 124. A. Momigliano: *Nero*, in C.A.H., X, 717-721. Cf. Suetonius, 20, 23, 24, 29, 39; Josephus: *Antiquities*, XX, viii, 3. [13]Lanciani: *Pagan and Christian Rome*, 1892; cf. A. G. Mackinnon: *The Rome of St. Paul.* [14]For St. Peter in Rome see Lanciani, *op. cit.;* Marucchi: *Christian Epigraphy;* Underhill: *St. Peter;* Renan: *St. Paul;* Rackham: *Acts*, 510-1; E. G. Selwyn: *First Epistle of St. Peter.* [15]For Nero, see further, Renan, *op. cit.*, and Momigliano, *op. cit.* [16]A. Profumo: *Le Fonti e i tempi dell' Incendio Neroniano* (1905). [17]*Ibidem.* [18]St. John of the Cross: *Cántico Espiritual*, 2nd red., XXXIX, 12; Peers, II, 401. Cf. *Mount Carmel*, II, xxii, 12; Peers, II, 180. [19]See further references to his style in Plummer, Maurice Jones, Bossuet: *Panégyrique de St. Paul.* [20]Jerome: *Ad Pammachum*, 62, 13. [21]*Ad. Col.* iv. 16. [22]"Cunning . . . . thought": *Tanta vafrities est non credes eundem* (*Monumentum loqui*, Erasmus, Id. Dedication). [23]Grimm: *Letters* (1788). [24]Renan: *St. Paul*, 232: "*A la fois vif, rude, poli, malin, sarcastique, puis tout à coup tendre, délicat, presque mièvre et câlin, avant l'impression heureux et fine au plus haut degré, habile à semer son style de réticences, de réserves, de précautions infinies, de malignes allusions, d'ironies dissimulées, il devait exulter dans un genre qui exige avant tout du premier mouvement.*" [25]Bonghi: *Lettere Critiche*, 82. [26]Chrysostom: Proem to *Romans.* [27]Plummer, *op. cit.*, 396. [28]Rom. xv. 13.

APPENDIX I*

THE DATE OF *GALATIANS*

1

AT CHAPTER IX THE NARRATIVE HAS TO THREAD ITS WAY through acute controversy. The famine had been mentioned in Acts xi. 28-30 before the journey to Cyprus and South Galatia. But a discrepancy is suspected between the narrative in Acts xv. and that in Galatians i. This discrepancy, closely connected with the date of *Galatians,* has been dealt with at length by Lightfoot, *Galatians,* 123-128; Ramsay, *Historical Commentary on Galatians;* Kirsopp Lake, *Earlier Epistles of St. Paul;* C. W. Emmet in *The Beginnings of Christianity;* and discussed once more by Professor T. W. Manson, *Rylands Bulletin,* Vol. 24, 1940, pp. 69-80. None of these arguments is conclusive.

The writer offers a new suggestion: it is that, when, after the famine had been prophesied, a difficulty arose whether converts to Christianity must accept the Torah and circumcision, Paul and Barnabas found in their contributions during the famine a means to commend their case against the stricter Jews. Following Ramsay, he takes the view that Paul and Barnabas first went to Jerusalem with a contribution and that Peter came back with them, agreeing at first with their broader example, but afterwards—to avoid trouble—appearing to give way to the rigorist Jews who arrived from Jerusalem.

As this question involves the reliability of the *Acts,* and that in turn the date of the Epistle to the Galatians, it is better to discuss that question at once.

On the authority of Lightfoot, the Epistle was for many

---

*As explained in the Preface, these appendices are inserted to explain how the biographer threads his way around obstacles, and not to settle controversies between learned authorities who may each claim a right to his opinion, and allow a similar right to another.

years supposed to have been written in Corinth in the seventh year of St. Paul's great journeys, and immediately before *Romans*. As Lightfoot knew of Galatia only as the Angora region, colonised by Gauls, he could not place *Galatians* early, and on account of its resemblance to *Romans* it was taken that it must have been written at the same time, to deal with the same problem.

The difficulty about this acceptance was that there is in *Galatians* no mention of the Council at Jerusalem in Acts xv. Lightfoot therefore puts forward a very able and ingenious case that the Council took place on the occasion of St. Paul's second visit to Jerusalem, as related in Galatians i. 18. This contention followed the line taken by earlier biographers of St. Paul and has been accepted by conservative scholars, Prat and Lagrange, in the course of the last twenty years.

The trouble is, however, that this theory is *too* ingenious. This was shown by Ramsay who, as the result of archaeological researches on the spot, saw that St. Paul always referred to districts by the names by which they were known to the Roman administration. This brings two districts, Phrygia and Lycaonia, visited by St. Paul in his first recorded journey, into what he called *Galatia* (Cf. Rackham: *Acts*, 195-6).

Ramsay worked out this theory in his *Historical Commentary on the Galatians*, and also in *The Teaching of Paul*. He reminds us that this Epistle was sent from "Paul and all the brethren who were with him". It came with the authority of a Church which the recipients respected. There could be only two such churches, Jerusalem and Antioch. But no one pretends that the Epistle was written from Jerusalem (Cf. Gal. i. 18). Therefore, Ramsay concludes, it *was* written from Antioch.

2

This is also the argument of Douglass Round in *The Date of Galatians*, as also that of Kirsopp Lake in *Earlier Epistles*

of St. Paul, and C. W. Emmet in *The Beginnings of Christianity,* II, 282 ff. Renan (pp. 313-4) and F. A. Spencer (pp.
297-8) take it that it was written at Antioch after the second
recorded journey: but they do not argue this. Ramsay, on the
other hand, produces cogent reasons why it was written before
that journey (*Historical Commentary,* Chaps. XIX, XX).
The main reason is a perfectly simple one. It is that St. Paul
does not mention the Council at Jerusalem, which took place
on his third visit (Acts xv.).

Now it is perfectly true that Paul does not mention this
Council in *Romans* or in any other Epistle: but the Epistle is
not biographical like that of *Galatians,* where he is emphasiz-
ing each occurrence that led to his position.

Ramsay's contention is furthermore supported by the words:
"I marvel that ye have so soon turned back", with which the
letter opens. They suggest that the letter was written just after
he had been with them for the first time.

3

The early date for *Galatians* is accepted not only by the
Jesuits, Cornely and Crampon, but by the Anglicans, Dean
Bate and Canon Deane, and the Munich professor, Josef
Holzner. It has, however, been contested by the Dean of
Christ Church (in an unpublished paper, courteously placed at
the disposal of the writer), who follows Professor Manson's
address to the Oxford Society of Historical Theology (also
courteously placed at the writer's disposal). Furthermore, it
has been ignored by both Prat and Lagrange; nevertheless, it
appears to the present writer the only satisfactory solution of
a long controversy. He thinks that neither Prat nor Lagrange,
nor the Dean of Christ Church, nor Professor Manson does
full justice to Ramsay, nor yet to Kirsopp Lake.

Placed in this position, the letter which was read at Antioch
before it was sent (see Ramsay, *Historical Commentary on*

Galatians) would pursue a double purpose. It would settle the question for those among whom it was written, as it settled the question for those to whom it was addressed. When Paul passed later on his journey through these districts there is no mention of further difficulty.

4

How then are we to account for the marked resemblances not only in thought but in actual expression between *Romans* and *Galatians* if they were written at an interval of some seven years?

This is not difficult. As Paul found the same problem constantly recurring, as it was the main problem of his career, it must always have been at his fingers' ends. And his memory was excellent. But A. M. Pope, in the *Expositor* (Vol. XXI, 1920, p. 363), furnishes the further suggestion that the first eleven chapters of *Romans* were a recapitulation of the case Paul had laid before the council at Jerusalem.

In any case, to argue that a man with so elastic a genius as that of Paul could not recall for a similar purpose the argument he had used several years before is arbitrary. There is therefore no solid case against the early date for this Epistle: but to place it in this early date harmonises both with every word in the Epistle, every sentence in *Acts*, and the general development of Paul's life.

5

It has been common among German critics to consider Luke's narrative unreliable: but to this the answer of Ramsay is sufficient. "This is not the case of two commonplace, imperfectly educated and not very observant witnesses who give divergent accounts of certain incidents which they saw without paying much attention to them. We have here two men of high education, one writing a formal history, the other speaking under every obligation of honour and conscience to be careful in his words: the subjects they speak of were of the most overpowering interest to both: their points of view must be very similar, for they were personal friends, and one was the teacher of the other and, naturally, had moulded his mind during long companionship. If ever there was a case in which striking agreement was demanded by historical criticism between two classes of documents, it is between the writings of Paul and Luke" (*St. Paul the Traveller*, 15).

6

In 1941, Professor Manson restated some of the difficulties which Baur brought up a hundred years ago: (1) At no point does Paul refer to the authority of the Council. (2) During his stay in Ephesus, Paul is still fighting for his status: a party at Corinth invokes Peter against him, and Paul does not quote any authority in reply. (3) In fact, after the Council, Paul's letters show no sign that the tension was resolved: after the Council, Paul circumcised Timothy. (4) In Galatians ii. 7 ff., Peter is entrusted with the gospel of the Circumcision and an apostolate of the Circumcision. In Acts xv. Peter presents himself as an apostle of the heathen. (Manson's *Presidential Address to Oxford Society of Historical Theology*, 1941, pp. 9-10). Baur therefore concluded that *Acts* was a picture of the 2nd century, written to reconcile Peter and Paul. This no scholar now accepts, but Professor Manson thinks that *Acts* was written after the Jewish revolt of 66-70, when the Christians wished to place themselves on the Roman side against the Jews (Manson, *op. cit.*, p. 12).

Professor Manson is perfectly right in seeing with Baur that the chief difficulty of Paul's whole career—at least till he came in conflict with the Gnostic heresy at Colossæ—was the desire of the Jewish Christians to keep the Church a department of

Judaism: but the real question which Professor Manson at that time passed over is the fact that Peter, in spite of what was said in Galatians ii. does also become an apostle to the Gentiles (Acts xv. 7).

That Paul was never a *persona grata* at Jerusalem is, of course, true. But this is no reason to read into the factiousness of Corinth, and the arrival there of Jews hostile to Paul, a deliberate personal war between Paul and Peter; the conjecture of one man, even though he is a German, is not enough to undermine a tradition existing from the earliest times. Let us turn from Baur to Renan: Renan sees the signs of sharp disputes, but with them of deep underlying agreement. *"Il faut aussi dans l'appréciation de ces débats tenir grand compte du caractère juif, vif et susceptible, porté aux violences de langage. Dans ces petites coteries pieuses on se brouillait, on se raccommodait sans cesse; on avait des mots aigres et néanmoins on s'aimait"* (*L'Antéchrist*, p. 33).

It is easy to explain why St. Paul does not refer again to the council at Jerusalem. It was convoked to settle a dispute at Antioch. It did not leave in Paul's mind the idea of a dogmatic and fixed pronouncement. His mind and moods were constantly adjusting themselves to new conditions: he became more and more cognisant of the Greco-Roman world. So also did St. Peter, who was also a traveller. But the more conservative and pharisaical Jewish Christians never reconciled themselves entirely either to Paul or to his policy. Both were the objects of their constant suspicion: if they came among his missions, it was to criticise; the criticism would take any form that appealed to the ingenuity of Jewish malignance: to depreciate Paul himself, to question the effect he produced, to assert that he was a departure from the true religion, the religion of Christ and of Peter.

So in all times and in all places do the narrow and bigoted attack the more subtle and exalted spirits: so do the conservative and sluggish impede reform. But there is no reason to identify Peter with this attitude. Affected by it from time to time he might be, but he too was the object of its hostility, and not the less because he worked chiefly among the Jews. The Roman tradition which names Peter and Paul together is supported by the obvious influence of Paul on Peter's first epistle (see Renan: *L'Antéchrist*, pp. 32-34; E. G. Selwyn: *Peter*). No idea of a fixed enmity is mentioned by Foakes Jackson in his *Peter, Prince of Apostles*, or Bishop Francis Underhill in his *St. Peter*. The mere existence of a Peter faction at Corinth coincided with that of an Apollos faction: but no one has suggested that there was a permanent conflict between Paul and Apollos: nor is there ground for thinking of it, in the case of Paul and Peter—even if Augustine's interpretation of the incident at Antioch should be preferred to that of Jerome and Origen.

APPENDIX II

THE AUTHORSHIP OF *HEBREWS*

THE ARGUMENT OF LEWIS WAS STATED FIRST IN "THE THINKER," Oct. and Nov., 1893, and afterwards in the *Biblical World*, Aug., 1898 and April, 1899. Resemblances to Paul's speech to Festus and Agrippa in Acts xxvi. 2-23 were noted by Ramsay in *Luke the Physician*, 327 (cf. Lewis, *supra*). Lewin believes that St. Paul was actually the author (*St. Paul*, II, 302). So also does Bishop Wordsworth: as Paley and Lardner before him. For the 46 words, see Leonard: *The Authorship of the Epistle to the Hebrews*, p. 113.

Although the writer, on the recommendation of Sir William Ramsay, places the epistle in connection with St. Paul's imprisonment at Cæsarea, he was first inclined to conceive it being composed at Pozzuoli or some other Italian port after St. Paul's release from his first imprisonment. It was so that the phrase, "They of Italy salute you" (xiii. 24) seemed most apposite, as "They of Asia salute you" comes from Ephesus in I Cor. xvi. 9. But this phrase could be applied to a port where many Romans came. The suggestion which recommended itself to the present writer received powerful support from one of the most learned theologians of the 18th Century: see Nathaniel Lardner: *Works*, 1831, Vol. VI, 110. All the facts now available had already been taken into consideration by Lardner.

He is followed by Lewin: *St. Paul*, Vol. II, ch. vii.

It is not uncommon for men talking about *Hebrews* to quote from the saying of Origen, "Who wrote it, God knows": these words taken by themselves are misleading. What Origen wrote was this: "If I were setting forth my own judgment, I should say that the thoughts are the Apostle's, but the diction and composition are due to some one who has taken notes of the master's teaching. If, then, any Church holds this epistle as Paul's it may be left happily in its belief: for it was not at random that the ancient tradition attributed it to him: but who it was who wrote it down, God knows. Some say that Clement, who became Bishop of the Romans, wrote the Epistle, others that Luke wrote it".[1] This is powerful evidence. Writing less than a hundred years after the death of St. Paul, Origen says that a powerful tradition not without reason attributed the Epistle to him.

This statement was nevertheless contravened by Tertullian;[2] it was implicitly denied in the Muratorian Canon,[3] but it receives again strong support from Clement of Alexandria, who wrote, "that the epistle is Paul's, and it was written to the Hebrews in the Hebrew language, and that Luke translated it with zealous care and published it to the Greeks, whence it is that the same complexion of style is found in the translation of this Epistle and of the Acts: that the phrase, Paul the Apostle, was not placed at the head of the Epistle for good reason; for, he says, in writing to the Hebrews who had formed a prejudice against him and viewed him with suspicion, he was wise not to put his own name there."[4]

That Clement of Rome himself knew the Epistle is proved in his *Epistle to the Corinthians*, Ch. XXXVI, written some thirty years after Paul's death, but he says nothing about its authorship. It was not until later centuries that the Western Church agreed with Clement of Alexandria, and with Origen.

When witness fails, scholars have turned to internal evidence. On the strength of style, the opinion of the last fifty years has not stopped at the judicious position taken by Westcott: but in 1939 the whole matter was reviewed in a learned work of Dr. Leonard who found strong internal reasons against the statements first made by Bleek and Windisch, and afterwards widely accepted. Leonard admitted that τελείωσις,

---

[1] Eusebius: *H. E.*, VI, 25. [2] Leonard: *The Authorship of the Epistle to the Hebrews*, 6. [3] *Ibid.*, 5. [4] Eusebius: *H. E.*, VI, 14. Translation by Westcott.

not δικαιοσύνη, was the author's ideal: that the power of the Resurrection is replaced by Christ's entry through the blood of His sacrifice into the sanctuary of heaven: that Mosaism is viewed not as a moral but a sacerdotal code, and that the word faith has changed its connotation to something more intellectual.

But still stronger are the arguments of style. The abrupt edges, the impetuous rush, the incisive personal argument of Paul are changed for a calm artistic regularity. The colour is Levitical, the rhythm has a rhetorical perfection, the sentences are knit together in calm artistry, periods are balanced and rounded, transitions are skilful, exhortation intermingles with the whole argument instead of being reserved to the end. The imagery changes—the human body is regarded as a veil; the expressions "in Christ" and "in the Lord" disappear; and the movement is regular, not impassioned and impulsive. Such are the objections with which Professor Leonard deals in his imposing book of research.

He notes that the mention of Timotheos comes from no one so well as from Paul.[5] That the formal salutations are typical of Paul;[6] that the last words occur something like thirty times;[7] that the theology of angels is St. Paul's;[8] that the view of human sinfulness is St. Paul's;[9] that the view of the Torah as a preparation is St. Paul's;[10] that the view of Christ is St. Paul's;[11] that, though the soteriology of *Hebrews* has a liturgical and sacerdotal colour, the view of redemption is the same;[12] that the doctrine of faith and justification is that of *Romans;*[13] that faith here is linked, as elsewhere in St. Paul, with both obedience and hope;[14] that the doctrine of the Holy Spirit is that of St. Paul;[15] that though the words are changed, the idea of a Church remains as citizenship, a participation in Christ and His Spirit;[16] that this Epistle has similar ideas of death and judgment;[17] that it teaches that Christ is a cosmic mediator to whom all things are put in subjection.[18]

[5] 41. [6] 42. [7] 42. [8] 47-49. [9] 49-51. [10] 51-53. [11] 53-66. [12] 66-75. [13] 75-82. [14] 82-90. [15] 90-92. [16] 95. [17] 91-103. [18] 102-106.

But the question of *Hebrews* being in agreement with Paul's doctrine has never been seriously in question. It has been agreed that it was written by someone who was at least fully cognisant of the lines of his teaching. The real question is how far the book shows such marks of diction and style that would justify one in thinking that Paul gave more than the basic ideas to the book. In this field Professor Leonard's research has reached some surprising results.

He deals first with the question of those unique words and expressions known to New Testament scholars as ἅπαξ λεγόμενα. Taking the original number of these to be after careful scrutiny 150, he points out that those in the Pastoral Epistles are 170. Now the Pastoral Epistles are not themselves universally accepted, but since the argument for a forgery is not accepted either, the more favoured notion is that, though they may not all have been written as printed, yet they were St. Paul's work (see Appendix III).

But apart from this, of the 150 words in *Hebrews*, 20 were taken direct from the Septuagint. Of these, no less than another 76 occur in the *Wisdom* literature. This leaves only 54 words. Of these 8 are adjectives or privatives. Of the residue of 46 words, most fit into the scheme of Paul's thought and imagery.[19]

But there is a yet more remarkable observation. It is that there are common, both to *Hebrews* and other Epistles which have been attributed to St. Paul, 56 words: if we take from these the words peculiar to the Pastorals, there are still 46 common expressions. In *Hebrews* there are 13 *chapters*. This means that on an average there are more than three words in each chapter which *Hebrews* shares and shares alone with Epistles certainly written by Paul. "No other personal vocabulary that is known to us, not only in Christian literature but in the whole range of Hellenistic literature", says Dr. Leonard, "coincides so much with the vocabulary of St. Paul as the 990

[19] Leonard, *op. cit.*, pp. 113-115.

words which make up the lexicon of the Epistle to the Hebrews".[20]

A whole series of particles ἐάν, εἰ οὐ, εἰ μή, εἰ καί, ὅταν ὅτε, ὥστε, μηδείς, μηδε, ἄρα, πάντοτε and the yet more frequent εἴ τις, εἴτε, εἰ πώς ποτε, εἰ δὲ καί, εἴπερ, ἐκτός, εἰ μή, εἰ γε, μή πῶς, μηκέτι, μεν οὖν γε all disappear: but none of these occur with exclusive frequency in other Epistles: and all might be corrected or eliminated by a skilful redactor, who apparently also had a taste for hyperbaton and the genitive absolute.[21]

The Epistle shares with St. Paul's admitted Epistles both antithesis and chiasmus, the oratorical imperative and the oratorical question, paronomasia, alliteration and assonance, the rhetorical repetition of a certain word, the triplets of adjectives, and the amphora.[22] What of imagery? In *Hebrews* there are nine different ranges of imagery: (1) the house and family; (2) the body; (3) nature; (4) religion; (5) agriculture; (6) soldiers; (7) sailing; (8) movement; (9) games. All of these can be paralleled in other Epistles, and where a new image comes in, such as *sabbath*, or *city*, or *anchor*, it can be explained either by the object of the Epistle, or by Paul's widening experience.[23] So experienced a sailor as Paul was familiar with the use of the anchor, though the word may have been suggested by Lucanus, who was still more interested in nautical things. With further thoughts of Rome, and of Jerusalem, it is natural to bring in the word city. The more closely one examines the imagery, the more one notices echoes of that used by Paul.

It is, of course, true that there is in this Epistle a sense of ordered construction lacking in all other Epistles: *sic non est aliqua scriptura quae ordinate procedat in ordine verborum et sentantiis sicut ista"*, said St. Thomas. "Each element", said Westcott, "which seems at first sight to offer itself spontane-

---

[20] Leonard, *op. cit.*, pp. 118-119. [21] Leonard, *op. cit.*, pp. 121-125. [22] Leonard, *op. cit.*, pp. 130-138. [23] Leonard, *op. cit.*, pp. 138-145.

ously, will be found to have been carefully adjusted to its place, and to offer in subtle details results of deep thoughts so expressed as to leave the simplicity and greatness of the whole perfectly unimpaired".[24] But though themes once touched are here taken up again till the whole is of such a unity as cannot be paralleled in St. Paul, yet there are many examples of this mode of argument.[25]

Blass, in his earlier work on Asiatic prose rhythms, believed that he detected in *Hebrews* the same rhythms as in the Epistles which are generally ascribed to Paul, but few believe there are such rhythms.

And, finally, while *Hebrews* xii. 3 recalls from *Wisdom* that argument of God's grandeur from creation which had already been quoted, as we have seen, in the first chapter of *Romans*, the hieratic tone in the Epistle finds its parallel in other Epistles of Paul.[26] (See Leonard, *op. cit.*, p. 44.)

---

[24] Westcott: *Hebrews*, XLVI-XLVII. See Romans v. 1-11, vi. 12-14, vi. 19-25; Gal. iii. 1-29, iv. 12-20.

[25] Blass: *Die rhythmische Komposition des Hebraen Brief* (Theol. und Kritik, 1902).

[26] Cf. Romans xv. 15-20; II Cor. ii. 15; Phil. ii. 17, iv. 18, and even II Thess. ii. 13, as well as Eph. v. 2.

APPENDIX III

THE PASTORAL EPISTLES

HORT, IN HIS "JUDAISTIC CHRISTIANITY" (pp. 130-131), disposed of the general arguments then current against the Pastoral Epistles: "To the best of my belief they are genuine and that not merely in parts. (1) It is true that the Pastoral Epistles imply a period of activity in St. Paul's life of which we have no further evidence; but neither is there any evidence against it. (2) The ecclesiastical arrangements are said to be a fiction of a later time: but this is mainly owing to misunderstanding of the ecclesiastical arrangements already implied; partly also to arbitrary assumptions as to the date of institutions. (3) The doctrines condemned are said to belong to no earlier time than the 2nd Century; but this, as we shall see, is due to a misunderstanding of what the doctrines really are". (He deals with this on pp. 143-6.)

The real difficulties, said Hort, lie in the field of language, and for this he refers to Bernhard Weiss's introduction to his Meyer Commentary. Meyer, however, does not attack the Pauline authorship. On the contrary he suggests that those who doubt it have raised unnecessary difficulties: *Alle solche Hypothesen gänzlich in der Luft schweben und sich kaum irgend eine klare Vorstellung von Zweck und Art solcher Billette gewinnen lässt, wie sie hier vorausgesetzt werden, erschwert diese ganze Annahme das Problem, statt es zu erleichtern* (p. 68).

The genuineness of the Pastorals was strongly supported by Vernon Bartlet in the *Expositor*, Jan.-May, 1913. He insisted that if we want to consider Paul, as he was, not a formal writer of theology but a missionary, then we must accept these Epistles.

Such was the dominant conviction of British scholars till Dr.

Harrison produced his book in 1921. But though he establishes the fact that there are 306 words which occur in these three Epistles, and no others, the number of words per page rising on an average to 33, whereas the highest in any other Epistle was 17, the force of his contention disappears when we see that the highest proportion elsewhere is in *I Corinthians*, then in *II Corinthians*. For in these Paul was dealing with peculiar difficulties. In *Colossians* the figure is 10, in *Ephesians* 12.

The industry and ingenuity of Dr. Harrison have, it is true, left an impression on Professor Nock (*St. Paul,* 231) and Canon Knox (*St. Paul and the Church of the Gentiles*), but they are discounted by Lock, who repeats what Vernon Bartlet had already insisted, that the words were such as one would expect from Paul (see Lock: *Pastoral Epistles,* p. xxix). Among later scholars, this view is taken by Dean Bate, by Canon Deane, by Prat.

But since Dr. Harrison's argument is thoroughly ingenious, it deserves a little more consideration. This has been given in an unpublished paper by the Revd. John Coutts, who points out that the number of words shared by the Pastoral Epistles with those of Paul is 542.

Mr. Coutts points out that Dr. Harrison's graphs are misleading in that Harrison arranges the order of the Epistles to force the graph into an ascending line. The Epistles are arranged differently in each graph. And if drawn in the order suggested as chronological in the biography, the graphs would show a steep *fall* before the Pastorals. They would become so erratic as to prove nothing.

Showing in II and III a preliminary variation of 75 per cent, it would prepare us for another sharp jump.

But if "stylometric analysis" of this kind is to be applied to Paul, it should be controlled by other examples. What does this control prove? Lutoslawski in his *Origin and Growth of Plato's Logic,* arrived at an absolutely different conclusion from A. E.

Taylor when he was employing similar methods in *Plato, the Man and His Work*. The results, in other words, depend on the man who is working.

When we examine the actual words more closely, we are led to the conclusion that most of the 306 words adduced by Harrison are wholly different words: this is not the case. Many are such words as ἄλλως, διώκτης which are words already used by St. Paul as another part of speech, or are compounds, such as δίλογος, ματαιολογία, of words he had already used. This is the reason why Lock, after seeing Harrison's case, rejects the argument of peculiar words—as Bartlet and Ramsay had done before seeing it. In fact the Pastoral Epistles have only 175 words not found elsewhere in the New Testament, and of these many are found as other parts of speech in St. Paul himself. On closer scrutiny, the linguistic argument is really much weaker than Dr. Harrison would allow.

Dr. Harrison's argument depends on the idea that Paul never escaped from his first imprisonment. But against this we have the testimony of Clement and Eusebius, of the Muratorian Fragment, and indirectly of *Romans*.

There remains the final argument: does the situation suggested by the Pastorals differ from that of St. Paul's lifetime? Bartlet and Ramsay have already said *No*. To this one may add a quotation from the final pages of Mr. Coutts's MS.

"There remains the argument that the circumstances implied by the Epistles fit in remarkably well with various different points in the narrative of Luke in *Acts*. Goudge's criticism in G.G.G. seems to lessen the force of this already trivial argument.

"There remain the arguments based on ecclesiastical organization, situation, and the prevalence of false doctrine. Far from finding this to be so, we find, on a casual reading, numerous echoes of the state which we find elsewhere. There are men who teach a different doctrine, as there are in Galatians. These men seem (I Tim. iii. and sq.) to be Jews or Judaizers, for the mention of the law follows soon, and for the preoccupation with genealogies we are referred to the Book of Tabilus. (It seems these enquiries after genealogies were such as resulted in the genealogies of Matthew and Luke. We can imagine St. Paul's contempt for those who thus seek to know Christ after the flesh.) Men exalt themselves as teachers of the law. The law is good, but not made for the just, i.e., the justified. Cf. Romans vii. 12: 'So that, the law is holy, and the commandment holy, righteous and good'. But 'before faith came' (and with it justification) 'we were kept in ward under the law'— Gal. iii. 23. Paul recounts his past life. Hymenæus and Alexander are delivered to Satan for a reformative purpose, that they may be taught not to blaspheme. Cf. I Cor. ii. 3: 'to deliver such a one unto Satan for the destruction of the flesh, that the spirit may be saved in the day of the Lord Jesus'.

"There follows on this a series of passages which bear remarkable parallels to I Corinthians.

"(1) The position of women: 'But I permit not a woman to teach . . . for Adam was first formed, then Eve' (ii. and sq.). 'Let the women keep silence in the Churches' (I Cor. xiv. 34).

"(2) In *Corinthians*, St. Paul gives a series of rulings. He refuses to forbid idol meats. Yet he advises against them for the sake of the weaker brother. He will not forbid marriage, but says the unmarried state is better. He advises unmarried and widows to remain so, if they safely can. Out of this we expect extremists to arise, and, in fact, St. Paul's words in *I Corinthians* are probably elicited by extremists. Thus in *I Timothy* he inveighs against teachers 'forbidding to marry and commanding to abstain from meats which God created to be received with thanksgiving.' This is a possible reference to unclean beasts. Further, he has to regulate the status of those widows who accepted his challenge to remain unmarried. They are to be honoured, but not to neglect their children. They are not to be recognised under the age of sixty in view of scandals which have arisen.

"The attitude to slavery is exactly that found in Philemon.

"These form the obvious parallels. Let us consider the passages we have omitted. Timothy is clearly given directions to appoint presbyters (I Tim. v. 2) and given directions concerning their characters (evidently very necessary, since the Corinthian elders had tolerated incest in their priests). [The notice seems to contemplate a ministry of Presbyter-Bishops and deacons.] Now, in St. Paul's final speech to the Ephesian church, we find Presbyter-Bishops (Acts xx. 17, 28); Timothy is told to appoint Presbyters. Paul appointed such himself in the Churches of S. Galatia, and it seems natural that he should delegate this work to his trusted disciple if he were absent and need for new appointments arose.

"The prayers for the kings are in undoubted line with St. Paul's thought (Romans xiii. 1-3).

"Thus the hasty examination of *I Timothy* shows nothing contrary either in situation, church government or organisation to what we should expect.

"To sum up. The linguistic evidence is nothing like so strong as Harrison makes out. The historical arguments are worthless. There is no sufficient ground for denying the Pauline authorship of the Pastorals as they stand, considering the external evidence. (Echoes in Ep. Barn., Clem. Rom., Ignatius, Polycarp, admitted by Clem. A., Tertullian, Irenæus.)

"Further, if, as we may reasonably assume, there was by this time a body of directions used by the other apostles and missionaries for the direction of the churches, and nothing seems more likely, then it is surely more likely, if we have to admit non-Pauline matter, that St. Paul included part of these directions in his own letter, than that a second-century writer included scattered fragments of St. Paul in a composition of his own". It might be remarked in conclusion that the arguments in Paley's *Horae Paulinae* (1790) summed up the scholarship of preceding centuries and continued to be respected for over a hundred years by eminent scholars. Paley's animadversions and sinewy arguments on the Pastorals are in his chapters XI-XIII.

As for the recent suggestion that Paul's name was used as a literary convention not intended to deceive, Paley's word also carries weight: "Until the conclusion of the fourth century, no intimation appears of any attempt whatever being made to counterfeit these writings" (Paley: *Horae Paulinae* (1825), 263-4).

APPENDIX IV

THE AUTHORSHIP OF *EPHESIANS* AND *COLOSSIANS*

THAT ST. PAUL WROTE EITHER "COLOSSIANS" OR "EPHESIANS" was denied by almost every liberal Lutheran writer of the nineteenth century. It will be sufficient to cite the names of Holtzmann, author of an *Einleitung in das Neue Testament*, 1892; Pfleiderer, author of *Der Paulinismus*, 1890; Weiss; Soden; Klöpper and, later, Wendland, author of *Hellenistische-Römische Kultur*, 1912. But ingenious and painstaking as their work was, it has proved nothing. It was very thoroughly dealt with by Hort in his famous *Prolegomena* to *Romans and Ephesians*. He there examines with the utmost care the external evidence (111-118). This leads him to the following conclusion: "In the authorities certainly belonging to the first century, Clement of Rome, and The Two Ways, we have highly probable, though not absolutely certain, evidence. Of Hermas, a writer who also may belong to any time early in the second century, much the same may be said, though here the probability almost reaches certainty. In Ignatius, probably about ten years from the beginning of the century, we find absolute certainty, in one case (ὡς ὁ κύριος τὴν ἐκκλησίαν) as well as high probability in others. Lastly, in Polycarp, there are two clear quotations which do not admit of doubt. From Barnabas and from the Didache—except The Two Ways —we obtain no evidence. Thus it is all but certain on this evidence that the Epistle to the Ephesians was in existence by about 95 A.D.; quite certain that it was in existence by about fifteen years later, or conceivably a little more" (p. 118).

With regard to internal evidence, Hort made an exhaustive study of the German critics already mentioned, as well as of the text itself of both *Ephesians* and *Colossians*. His conclusion is as follows: "The more closely we scrutinise those parts of both Epistles which most nearly resemble each other—scrutinise them comparatively and scrutinise them in their respective contexts—the less possible it becomes to find traces of a second-hand, imitative character about the language of either. The stamp of freshness and originality is on both; and thus the subtle intricacies of likeness and unlikeness are a peculiarly strong kind of evidence for identical authorship, whether the author is St. Paul or another. Whatever, therefore, supports the genuineness or the lateness of either Epistle, does the same for the other. In both we have not merely the *prima facie* evidence of his name both in the text and in the unanimous ancient tradition, but close, and yet for the most part not superficial, connections in language with his other Epistles, and that not such a connection as can with any reasonable probability be explained by the supposition of borrowing. Above all, we find in both the impress of that wondrous heart and mind" (*Prolegomena*, p. 168).

So exhaustive was Hort's scrutiny of the evidence, and so definite his conclusions, that Armitage Robinson, in his critical edition, 1903, stated that there was nothing more to say. Westcott, in 1906, set out verbatim (pp. xxv to xxxii) the external evidence on which Hort had based his conclusions. He then proceeds to examine *Ephesians* in relation to the other Epistles of St. Paul (pp. xxxvii-liii). His conclusion he sets down in the words of Llewelyn Davies (p. xxxvi): "Those who cannot read the Epistle to the *Ephesians* without being awed by the peculiar loftiness, by the grandeur of conception, by the profound insight and by the eucharistic inspiration which they recognise in it, will require strong evidence to persuade them it was written by some other man who wished it to pass as St. Paul's. Apart from the question of the morality of the act, imitators do not pour out their thoughts in the free and fervid style of this Epistle. Nor can we easily imagine how such an imitation could have been successful either near the time of

St. Paul or at any subsequent period. It is not conceivable that it should have made its appearance without exciting wonder and enquiry. In the lifetime of St. Paul the pious fraud would not have been attempted. Within a few years of his death, the difficulty of deceiving his friends and the Church in such a matter must have been very great. At a later time the estimation in which St. Paul's writings were held would have ensured the careful scrutiny of any previously unknown work put forward in his name" (Llewelyn Davies: *Introduction to Ephesians*, p. 9).

We may put this contention more tersely. It is that we must suppose a literary inventor—if not an actual forger—to have had a genius greater than that of St. Paul, to have been able to put the stamp of genius on his counterfeit till his gift of trickery became sublimity. We must then imagine him to have brought out his forgery so adroitly as to impose on Paul's closest friends—if he were already dead; to have evaded Paul himself if he were living. We cannot be surprised that both Abbott before Westcott and Gore after him refused to entertain such an hypothesis—especially as it was unsupported by evidence. One would have thought that only German credulity was equal to so bold an acceptance of the idea of clever invention—if not imposture—in a book venerated as sacred through the ages. But it is not so. Both Professor Nock and Canon Knox have hammered at this door, while an American, Professor Goodspeed, has hastened past them. While accepting *Colossians* for St. Paul they deny him *Ephesians* (see Nock: *St. Paul*, 231; Knox: *St. Paul and the Gentiles*, 182-5). But they produce no new evidence; and, to ring the changes on their ingenuity, the latest to produce a book on the subject, Mr. Synge, pursues with equal enterprise, and certainly far more plausibility, the hypothesis that Paul wrote *Ephesians* but not *Colossians* (F. C. Synge: *Ephesians*, 69-76).

Such are but a few of the variations of conjecture which persuade a biographer that he is safer to follow the historic documents rather than the most novel or audacious flights of supposition issuing from Lutheran Germany where, since these lucubrations were indulged, religion has practically broken down, and where Ramsay's warning of forty years before has been vindicated in two successive wars.

For further considerations on this subject one might prudently retrace one's steps to Paley's *Horae Paulinae,* which, even if it was published in 1790, set down evidence which should not be ignored.

APPENDIX V

ST. PAUL'S ESSENTIALS

FROM THE BEGINNING TO THE END PAUL HAD CONSISTENTLY proclaimed that the Divine purpose was to incorporate men into Christ that they might share through grace in His goodness and in that awful and immaculate purity which is holiness.

(1) "God sent His Son", he wrote in *Galatians*, "that we might receive the adoption of sons, and because we are sons, God has sent forth the Spirit of His Son into our hearts.[1] . . . If we live in the Spirit let us also walk in the Spirit.[2] For the fruits of the Spirit are love, joy, peace."[3]

(2) Writing first to the Thessalonians he said: "This is the will of God—your sanctification; for God has called us not to uncleanness but to holiness."[4]

(3) Writing to them a second time he said: "God has from the beginning chosen you to salvation through sanctification of the Spirit and belief of the truth to which He called you through our evangel to the obtaining of the glory of our Lord Jesus Christ."[5]

(4) Writing first to the Corinthians he wrote: "Christ Jesus is from God made unto us wisdom and righteousness and sanctification and redemption: he also will confirm you to the end that you may be blameless."[6]

(5) Writing to the Philippians he wrote: "God works within you both to will and to act of His good pleasure . . . that ye might be blameless and innocent, the sons of God . . . filled with the fruits of righteousness, which are by Jesus Christ, unto the glory and praise of God."[7]

(6) Writing to the Corinthians again he wrote: "I will be a Father unto you and you shall be my sons and daughters, saith the Lord Almighty. Having therefore these promises, dearly

[1]Gal. iv. 5.　　[2]Gal. iv. 6.　　[3]Gal. v. 25.　　[4]I Thess. iv. 3, 7.　　[5]II Thess. ii. 12-13.
[6]I Cor. i. 30, 8.　　　　[7]Phil. ii. 13, 15; i. 11.

beloved, let us cleanse ourselves from all defilements of flesh and spirit, perfecting holiness in the fear of God: for God who commanded the light to shine out of darkness has shone in our hearts to give the light of the knowledge of the glory of God in the face of Jesus Christ."[8]

(7) Writing to the Romans he wrote: "The Spirit beareth witness with our spirit that we are children of God, and if children then heirs—heirs of God and joint heirs with Christ. For whom He foreknew, He also ordained to be conformed to the image of His Son."[9]

(8) In *Hebrews,* through the analogies of the sacrifices in the temple, the doctrine is the same: We are sanctified through the offering of the body of Jesus Christ once for all . . . for by one offering has He perfected for ever those who are sanctified —of which the Holy Ghost also is a witness.[10]

(9) To Timothy he wrote from Macedonia: "God our Saviour will have all men to be saved and come to a knowledge of the truth, and the grace of our Lord Jesus Christ was exceeding abundant with faith and love which is in Christ Jesus."[11]

(10) To Titus he wrote: "The kindness and love of God our Saviour toward man appeared not by works of righteousness which we have done, but according to His mercy has He saved us by the washing of regeneration and renewing of the Holy Ghost, which He shed on us abundantly through Jesus Christ our Saviour that being set right in His eyes by grace we should be made heirs according to the hope of eternal life."[12]

(11) The same doctrine is put clearly in *Colossians:* "The Father hath made us meet to be partakers of the inheritance of the saints in light. God would make known what is the riches of the glory of the mystery among the Gentiles; which is Christ in you, the hope of glory, whom we preach, warning every man and teaching every man in all wisdom that we may present every man perfect in Christ Jesus."[13]

---

[8] II Cor. vi. 18; vii. 1; iv. 6.   [9] Rom. viii. 16, 17, 29.   [10] Heb. x. 10, 14-15.
[11] I Tim. ii. 4; i. 14. [12] Titus iii. 4-7. [13] Col. i. 12, 27-28.

Such then had been the undeviating view of the purpose and design of God for the Christian. He was to state it most clearly of all in the final epistle he wrote for his converts: Eph. i. 3-12.

(12) "Blessed be the God and Father of our Lord Jesus Christ, who hath blessed us with all spiritual blessings in the heavenly things in the Christ, just as He has chosen us in Him before the foundation of the world that we should be holy and immaculate in His sight in love, having predestined us for the adoption of children through Jesus Christ for Himself according to the good pleasure of His will to the praise of the glory of His grace by which He made us gracious in the beloved. In whom we have redemption through His blood, the forgiveness of sins, according to the riches of His grace in which He has been plentifully generous to us in all wisdom and prudence, having made known to us the mystery of His will, according to the good pleasure which He purposed in Himself, that in the dispensation of the fulness of times He might gather together all things both those of heaven, and those of earth, in one in Christ, in whom also we have obtained an inheritance, being predestined according to the purpose of Him who worketh all things after the counsel of His own will that we should be to the praise of His glory."

(13) Writing to Timothy at the very last he said: "God has saved us with a holy calling, not according to our works, but according to His own purpose and grace which was given us in Christ Jesus."[14]

(14) He associated salvation with delightful courtesy. "Let every one of us please his neighbour for his good to edification",[15] he said. "I please all men in all things, not seeking my own advantage but the advantage of many",[16] he claimed. "Walk worthy of the Lord unto all pleasing." Such was his ideal for the Lycus valley.[17] This courtesy was to be consummated in taste for pure, beautiful, and honourable things.[18]

[14] II Tim. i. 9.　　[15] Rom. xv. 2.　　[16] I Cor. x. 33.　　[17] Col. i. 10.　　[18] Col. iv. 6.

APPENDIX VI

ST. PAUL'S EVANGEL

WHAT THEN WAS THE MYSTERY HIDDEN FROM THE BEGIN-ning of the world which Paul set out to announce as his evangel? It was a scheme of God in relation not only to the souls of men but to all He had created: to lead each and all to their consummation in Himself.

But God Himself was a mystery dwelling in inaccessible light as Three Persons: a Father of glory, realising His perfection in the Eternal Generation of His Son, a generation which was completed in the meeting of these two perfections in a third and mysterious person, a Spirit of Love.

From His eternal existence in the heavenly order, God had seen the falling away of both angel and man: men could be restored only when the Divine, having mingled with them in all the travail and sorrow that had come with evil into creation, had raised them up with and into Himself.

What then was to be the mode of restoration? It was first the choice of a peculiar people who were to be prepared for it by the gift of faith, by promises, by a covenant, by an august Law, and by prophecies and revelations pointing to a kingly redeemer, the Christ. And this Christ was no other than the very Son of God, begotten before the day star in the womb of the morning, and by whom the mystery of the Divine had given to void and nothingness the form of creation. The hope of Israel was to be fulfilled in nothing less than in being taken into God through the Son.

He, emptying Himself of His splendour in the heavens, took the nature of man (and indeed of creation) into Himself. That He should ratify, perfect and fulfil the Law already given, that He should relate it to all law and all life, that He should manifest in its fulness the significance of sacrifice by coming under the judgment passed on man's disobedience to law, by taking the curse on Himself, He was one not only with man but with his sin; He died the death that the Law, not unjustly, passed on the worst of men. Here God reached out to men at their most miserable and made atonement to the uttermost. Christ died. But this was the supreme proof that God, as love, sought for unity with man. So much did He love the world.

But Christ having died to meet sin, yet lived to raise creation to God. Having overcome the sharpness of death, He rose again with the essence and nature of created things, with the soul and body of man. Thus He glorified them; He raised them above the thrones and dominations of the unseen to the majesty on high and He endowed them with His Spirit.

Just as He had made faith the preparation for His promises, so He gave faith as the means of partaking in His life. Faith was a supernatural power and strength which made first the mind, then the heart, then the life of believers one with Him in His whole work of redemption. It thus set them right in His eyes. It operated on them through mysteries which established them in Himself, and made them sharers in His death and resurrection. Essential to these mysteries was still faith; the faithful were made cells of Christ's tissue, in His Church which was the fulfilment of Himself in His relation to the world, and which, in one assembly of the living and the dead, rose with Him to glory in the heavenly order. The life of the Church was a transforming life, not only changing men to saints, not only giving men holiness, but providing the means by which creation, as a whole, is prepared to meet the Christ in His transforming splendour, as He makes a new heaven and a new earth. It was a life transformed by the Holy Spirit indwelling. It was a new creation, nourished by holy mysteries.

Here then is the theme which Paul called now his announcement, now his evangel, now his mystery. It was a transforming light which vibrated through the heart and will, to irradiate life with flashes of discovery, and then with powers which were divine. It was not merely a faith, but it was a hope of proceeding from gift to gift towards wealth immeasurable; thirdly, it made men sharers in the magnetic system which drew men and things together in order as it drew all together to the perfect centre. When hope and faith have met their consummation, love will still remain.

There was one word for this gift which came into the souls of men to make them perfect in the Church. This word was grace. As it was given to men to share with one another, it was peace. It led them onwards and inwards, through hopes ever richer, to mysteries more and more brilliant till the children of faith became like to that for which they hoped. It changed them from glory to glory as by the Spirit of the Lord. It united them with Him and with one another in one Body in the fulness of love.

This then is the true light: this is the abundant life. Of this theme Paul never wearies: it meets us at every turn of his writings. He keeps telling us—in compound words he created to express the newness of his idea—that we are to be of one body with the Christ, to suffer with Him, to be crucified with Him, to rise again with Him, to be made alive with Him, to continue in life with Him, to be of one form with Him, to be glorified with Him, to be enthroned with Him, and to reign with Him. We do this by living in holiness in His Church. On these interlocking ideas of grace, of holiness, and of the Church—through grace—Paul insists with the iteration of a tireless confidence.

In his Epistles alone, excluding the less direct evidence of both *Acts* and *Hebrews*, he uses the words "holy" and "holiness" 95 times; the word "grace" 90 times; the word "Church" 60 times; he uses the expression "in the Lord" 50 times; "in Christ" or "in the Christ" 34 times; "in Christ Jesus" 48 times, and returns to the thought saying "in whom" or "in Him" another 29 times: the sum is 164. And his references to the "Spirit" are 72.

Take the average of his 80 chapters, then the idea of the Church occurs in three-quarters of the chapters, the idea of holiness or sanctification in every one, that of grace in every one, that of the Spirit in almost every one—and the idea of being *in the Christ* twice in *each*.

Well might Paul say that "through Him, and in Him and for Him are all things". He was the original cause of their existence: He was the power sustaining them in His existence: He was the purpose to which all grow and move by grace which is itself the gift of His Spirit.

Such in its simplest outlines was the combination of metaphysics, mysticism and theology which, uniting the Word and the Sacrament, was the embassy of grace.

INDEX

Aaron, 251.

Abel, 258.

Abelard, 190.

Abraham, 15, 31, 43, 46, 88, 97ff., 204, 231, 249f., 258.

Achaia, 81, 136, 138, 141, 219.

Acre, 34, 103, 227.

Acro-Corinth, 128.

Acropolis, 125, 128ff.

Adana, 107.

Adonis, 69.

Adramyttium, *see* Edremid.

Aelius, 149.

Aegina, 123.

Aeneas, 111, 268.

Aeschylus, 19, 20, 132.

Afranius Burrhus, 270.

Agabus, 230.

Agrippa, Herod, 240.

Agrippa II, 240-244, 248.

Agrippina, 148f., 306.

Ahriman, 253.

Ahuramazda, 253.

Ajax, 10.

Alexander the Great, 4, 6, 14, 107, 108, 135, 198, 228

Alexandretta, 34.

Alexandria, Egypt, 3, 23f., 71, 142, 200.

Alexandria, Troas, 112, 222f., 227, 248.

Allah, 80.

Am-ha-aretz, 17.

Amphibolis, 117.

Ammon Ra, 14, 253.

Ananias of Damascus, 56.

Ananias ben Nedebaï, 235, 238.

Andraki, 262.

Andronicus, 150.

Angites, 114.

Annaeus Novatus, *see* Gallio.

Anselm, 190.

Antioch on the Orontes, 13, 16, 66, 80ff., 103, 105, 144, 240.

Antioch in Pisidia, 88, 91, 93ff., 203, 303, 306.

Antiochus Epiphanes, 4, 88.

Antiochus IV, 16.

Antipatris, *see* Kefr Saba.

Antonia, 236f.

Antonia (Fortress), 233f., 236.

Antony, Mark, 3f., 16, 28, 32, 234, 236f., 242.

Aphrodite, 86, 111, 132, 159, 253.

Apollo, 5, 6, 26, 70, 80, 269.

Apollonia, 117, 221.

Apollos, 147, 156, 161, 174, 181, 200, 201, 248.

Appian Way, 269.

Aquila, 133, 147, 305.

Arabia, 58.

Arcadia, 126.

Archeology, 307.

Argos, 126, 137.

Aretas, 63.

Arethusa, 117.

Aristarchos, 184, 248, 277.

Aristides, 8.

Aristotle, 6, 9, 122, 228.

Artemis, 146, 183ff.

Asia, province of, 109, 144ff.

Asiarchs, 184.

Asklepias, 253.

Assos, 223f.

Assur-bani-pal, 32.

Athanasius, 190.

Athenodorus, 32; University of, 31.

Athens, 3, 9, 32, 119, 125-131, 137, 142, 157, 181, 218ff., 255.

Athos, Mt., 113, 117, 123, 141.

Atonement, 75.

Attica, 122, 126f., 133.

Augustine, 95, 173, 180.

Aziz, 237.

Baal, 69.

Baffa, 64, 83, 115, 226.

5022

MEASUREMENT AND STATISTICS

MEASUREMENT

A Basic Tex

VIRGINIA L. SENDERS DEPARTMENT OF PSYCHOLOG

New Yor

STATISTICS

and

mphasizing Behavioral Science Applications

IIVERSITY OF MINNESOTA

XFORD UNIVERSITY PRESS 1958

© 1958 BY OXFORD UNIVERSITY PRESS, INC.

Library of Congress Catalogue Card Number: 58:5040

PRINTED IN THE UNITED STATES OF AMERICA

150.13
Se5
m

PREFACE

This book is written for students taking their first course in statistics. To them I have addressed a special word about how the book is written and how it should be used to meet their needs most efficiently. Instructors using the book for classroom teaching will find that section helpful also. To the instructor, as well as to others browsing in these pages for special purposes—advanced students reviewing elementary material or research workers looking up a particular topic—I should say a few additional words. The organization of the book is unusual. The various statistical measures are not taken up in the conventional order but in an order determined by the scale of measurement with which their use first becomes appropriate. The casual browser may be startled, for example, to find the information, or uncertainty, measures treated before such basic statistical tools as the mean and standard deviation have even been introduced. The logic which makes this order necessary can be understood from a preliminary study of the table of contents, of section 2.5, and of the summary tables in Chapters 9 and 16. I would commend these pages to the attention of even the most casual reader.

I have assumed no mathematical training on the part of the student beyond partially forgotten high-school algebra. Throughout the text I have attempted to steer a safe course between the Scylla of frightening mathematical rigor and the infinitely more dangerous Charybdis of sloppy thinking. One way of doing this is to substitute words and examples for formal mathematical expressions, and the inevitable redundancy which results may prove irritating to advanced readers. I risk their irritation willingly if it means that students can understand a little better the *why* of the manipulations they carry out.

A full academic year will probably be necessary to cover all of the material presented here. However, the book can readily be adapted for use in a shorter course. For this purpose I would recommend an

72897

emphasis on perspective, with the design of acquainting the student
with the over-all purposes of statistics, with the underlying inter-
relationship of measurement and statistics, and with the principles
of probability and statistical inference. Within this framework,
individual statistical techniques can be used as typical illustrations.
This approach should leave the student with a knowledge of exactly
what he does not know, as well as of what he does. For such a course,
Chapters 1, 2, 9, 10, 11, and 16 must be read in their entirety. From
Chapters 3 to 7 enough material should be selected to satisfy the
student's immediate practical needs and to provide the foundation
for later reading on statistical inference. From Chapters 12 to 14,
typical inferential statistics may be selected freely for intensive
study. Chapter 8, on descriptive statistics for the ratio scale, and
Chapter 15, which introduces the analysis of variance, can well be
omitted in a minimum course. Chapter 0 helps the student to review
his basic mathematics and introduces the techniques for handling
significant digits and the summation sign; it should be referred to
as needed throughout the course.

Many people have helped to put the book together. Two classes
of students at Antioch College learned their statistics from a preliminary draft, and their patience with its defects, their enthusiasm,
and their suggestions contributed immeasurably to the present
improved version. To many people at Antioch I owe a special debt
of gratitude. I should like to mention particularly Miss Joyce
Ellmer, Mrs. Constance Norris, and Mr. Ronald Wallis, who contributed significantly to the production of the preliminary edition
or helped in the transition from first to final form. The co-operation
of the Mathematics Department, under the chairmanship of Dr.
Julian Blau, made the first trial-runs possible.

Mr. James V. Bradley of the Aero Medical Laboratory at Wright
Air Development Center gave me many helpful suggestions for
Chapter 13, on inferential statistics for the ordinal scale. Mr. Gary
Yonemura of Columbia University, and Mr. Donald Gene Daven-
port of the University of Minnesota checked answers to the computational problems. Mrs. Sylvia Rosen has prepared an index which
should vastly increase the book's usefulness.

Perhaps my greatest indebtedness is to Dr. William J. McGill
of Columbia University, and Dr. Philburn Ratoosh of the Ohio
State University, both of whom read prepublication drafts of the

manuscript with unstinting attention to detail. Besides making many suggestions that have improved the clarity and readability of the book, they have taught me much about statistics and saved me from breaking into print with errors of which I had been unaware.

In spite of the efforts of all of these people, some errors and obscurities probably remain, and for these I must take full responsibility. My final debt of gratitude is expressed in advance to those readers—students, instructors, statisticians, or others—who will take the trouble to tell me about them so that they may be corrected in the future.

I should like, in closing, to express my thanks to the many authors and publishers who graciously permitted me to reproduce material from their works. These are generally acknowledged where the material appears. I am indebted to Professor Sir Ronald A. Fisher, Cambridge, to Dr. Frank Yates, Rothamstead, and to Messrs. Oliver and Boyd Ltd., Edinburgh, for permission to reprint Table N from *Statistical Tables for Biological, Agricultural and Medical Research.*

V.L.S.

Minneapolis, Minnesota
February, 1958

This book has been written for you. In fact, I might almost say that it has been written *to* you. It has not been written for statisticians, for research workers in other fields, or even for your instructor. The 'you' that I have in mind is a person who is taking a first course in statistics, majoring in some area of the behavioral sciences, convinced of the need for studying statistics but not entirely sure why it is necessary, a little rusty on his high-school mathematics, intelligent, serious, moderately willing to work—and just a little apprehensive. I have written to meet your needs, and I should like to say a few preliminary words about how I have written and how you can make best use of this book.

First of all, the book is slanted toward the behavioral sciences, and particularly toward psychology. That is because I am myself a psychologist and not a statistician. If you are majoring in some other field, however, you can still use it easily by supplying some of your own examples and applications, and by watching in your reading for situations where the statistics you are studying would be appropriate.

How much of your high-school algebra do you remember? Chapter 0 will help you to diagnose your difficulties and to review forgotten material. It also introduces the concept of significant digits and presents rules for their treatment; in this chapter, too, you will find an explanation of the meaning and use of the summation sign. By putting this material in a separate chapter, I have been able to present the subject matter of statistics in an organized manner and without interruption for preliminary matters of technique. The book really begins, therefore, with Chapter 1.

In section 2.5 you will find an outline of the organization of the book. It is there so that you may view the whole before you start learning details about the parts. Chapters 9 and 16 contain summary tables to which you should refer frequently as you progress through the book. They will help you to integrate new material, see where it fits with the old, and avoid getting lost in a mass of details.

There are many problems and questions interspersed throughout the text. For the most part these have been designed to further your understanding rather than your arithmetic. The more you answer, especially those of the 'thought problem' type, the better will be your understanding of the material. Answers to the computational problems are given at the ends of the chapters. Very slight differences between your answers and those in the text may be due to differences in the number of figures carried throughout the computations, so use common sense in interpreting them. Several people have now checked these answers for accuracy, but a few mistakes may nevertheless have slipped through. I know what agony this can cause, and you have my sincere apologies for any occasions where it has happened. I should be most appreciative if you would drop me a postcard telling me of any errors you find so that I can correct them for the benefit of future readers.

I think that if you read the book slowly and carefully, actually studying it rather than reading through for sense as you might a psychology book, you will find Chapters 1–10 understandable even without the help of an instructor. Beginning with Chapter 11 you will notice a change in difficulty level which may make you feel that you have lost your grip on the subject matter. There are two reasons for this. First, beginning with this chapter and continuing through the rest of the book, the mathematical derivations are much too complicated to explain in an elementary book, so you will be asked to take a lot on faith. This in turn may lead you to feel that there is much that you don't understand that you ought to understand. Actually, at this time you're not supposed to grasp the *why* of many of the things you learn in these chapters, so don't be distressed if you can't. A second reason for the increased difficulty level is that I have had to assume in writing the later chapters that you have mastered the preceding ones. New ideas and new words are introduced in the first half of the book; they are *used* in the second half. This means that you'll be reading material written in a language you mastered only a few weeks ago, and this is bound to give some difficulty. I hope these words of warning will help you to avoid feeling lost and discouraged when you encounter this harder material.

Here it is then. I've honestly had a lot of fun writing it. Sharpen your pencil, buy a new notebook, and study actively. I hope you learn some statistics and even have some fun learning.

Sincerely,

Virginia L. Senders

p. 30, par. 2, line 1: change 13 to 12
p. 63, last par., line 1: change 2.3 to 2.2
p. 68, par. 2, line 7: change 2.2 to 2.3
p. 91, computations: change .2941 to .2914
p. 94, computations: change .4641 to .4644
p. 121, Fig. 4.9: line for 91st percentile is misplaced
    last par., line 3: change 140–149 to 150–159
    correct subsequent claculations. $S = 151.17$
p. 122, lines 1 and 3: change 141.17 to 151.17
    par. 3: change 4.8 to 4.9
. p. 132, par. 1, lines 9 and 10: change .43 to .47
p. 133, par. 2, line 1: change 4.2.1 to 4.3.1
p. 207, table, last col.: change 5.7 to 5.8; 58.9 to 59.0; 91.8 to 91.7;
    99.2 to 99.4; 99.9 to 99.7

p. 229: Formula 7.1.1 should read $E^2 = 1 - \dfrac{\text{within groups variance}}{\text{total variance}}$

p. 237, Formula: change *between group variance* to *total variance*
p. 277, par. 2, line 8: change y to x
p. 289, Fig. 8.7, title: change $y = ax + b$ to $y = a + bx$
p. 303, next to last line: change 8.4 to 8.3
p. 304, par. 2, line 1: change 8.27 to 8.22
p. 372, Fig. 11.5, title: change $\leq$ to $=$
p. 375, par. 1: change 7 and 8 to 6 and 7, and 6 to 5
p. 376, Fig. 11.9: change $\frac{1}{16}$ to $\frac{1}{64}$
p. 385: omit question 3b and answer on p. 388
p. 391, par. 2, lines 8 and 9: interchange words "upper" and "lower"
p. 404, line 8: change 47.725 to 47.72
p. 407, 3×4 table: change 25* to 30* and 70* to 80*
p. 417, computations, last col.: change 72.2 to 69.4; 32.2 to 32.1; 7.1
    to 71.1; 35.6 to 35.7; 222.3 to 283.5
    $\chi^2 = 283.5$

p. 421, tables: change 244 to 256 and 256 to 244

p. 443: omit par. 5

p. 447, computations at bottom of page, last col.: correct values are
1.00, 1.00, .07, .07, .06, .06, 1.00, 1.00, 4.26

p. 448, line 1: change 4.28 to 4.26

p. 466, par. 4: interchange values for $\chi^2_{.025}$ and $\chi^2_{.975}$; change 20.8 to 18.5

p. 483, computations: change 16.4 to 15.8; $F = 1.22$

Corrected answers to questions

QUESTION	ON PAGE	CORRECTED ANSWER
5	Self-test	189.8 (approx)
7	Self-test	3789.6
31	Self-test	$\dfrac{1}{2\sqrt{2}}$
2c	30	200–600
6d	30	13.036
2b	84	Men as % of arts and letters majors $= 38.9$
4	139	$r_0 = +.077$ or $-.054$
4b	190	3rd, 175/419, 904
4e	198	.9772
2	201	.2119
6	201	.1492
8	201	.0075
6	236	$\bar{X} = 245.5$
2	242	$E^2_{xy} = .597$
3a	257	2.5, .4
4	266	$\tilde{Y} = .296X - 9.6$
4h	354	not hungry, or not college food, or both
9a	354	$5!/(52 \times 51 \times 50 \times 49 \times 48)$
2	395	.37–.89
7	395	.4784
5	411	.50, .025, etc. as given
1e	478	$-.53$ to .67, etc.
1g	478	$-.82$ to $-.20$, etc.
1	492	$t = 3.71$

TABLE OF CONTENTS

Chapter 6. Interval and ratio scales, II. Theoretical distributions and measures of individual position, 180

Chapter 7. Interval and ratio scales, III. Measures of correlation, 227

29.* $y = x^{-3}$
30. $y = x^{\frac{1}{2}}$
31.* $y = x^{-\frac{3}{2}}$

32.* Solve for x:

$$\sqrt{16 + x} = 8 - \sqrt{x}$$

In questions 33–6, find log x.

33. $x = ab$
34. $x = a^3$
35. $x = \dfrac{1}{a}$
36. $x = a + b$
37. What is $\log_b b$?
38. What is $\log_b b^2$?
39. $b^{\log_b x} =$
40. What is: antilog $(\log x + \log y)$?
41. What is: antilog $3(\log y)$?
42. What is: antilog $2(\log y - \log x)$?

What are the *characteristics* of the logarithms of the numbers in problems 43–5?

43. .003
44. 2459.6
45. .49
46. What is the slope of the line whose equation is $2y = 4x + 3$?
47. What is the intercept of the line in problem 46?
48.* What is the equation of the straight line going through the points $(0, -3)$ and $(2, -5)$?
49.* Solve for x and y:

$$3x - 2y = 3$$
$$4x + 2y - 32 = 0$$

50.* Draw a graph to present the following data:

A rat is run on a maze for seven successive days. The number of errors is determined for each day. Records for the sixth day are accidentally lost, but the other results are:

Day	1	2	3	4	5	7
Errors	21	12	14	8	2	4

* * *

Now check your answers from the key on p. 33. Make a list of the questions you missed, and compare them with the list below to see what subjects you need to review and where to find the review material.

IF YOU MISSED ANY OF THESE QUESTIONS	YOU SHOULD REVIEW	IN
1, 2, 3	Rounding	Section 0.2.1
4, 5	Approximation	Section 0.2.2
6, 7, 8	Square root	Section 0.2.3 and a mathematics review book
9, 10, 11	Reading a table	A mathematics review book
12–16	Fractions	Section 0.2.4
17	Algebraic manipulation	A high-school algebra book or mathematics review book
18, 23–31	Exponents	Section 0.2.6
19–22	Ratios, proportions, percentages	Section 0.2.5 and a mathematics review book
33–45	Logarithms	Section 0.2.6
46–48	The straight line	A high school algebra book or a mathematics review book
49	Solving simultaneous equations	A high-school algebra book
50	Graphs	Section 0.2.8 or a book on graphic methods

0.2 Review of Selected Topics

The following pages provide only a brief review of certain selected topics. More extended treatments can be found in high-school or college algebra books, or in mathematics 'refresher' books. An excellent one for this purpose is H. M. Walker, *Mathematics Essential for Elementary Statistics*, New York, Holt, 1951.

0.2.1 Rounding:[1]

RULE 1: When the first (left hand) digit of those to be dropped is less than 5, the last digit to be retained is left unchanged.

[1] See section 0.3.2 for treatment of significant digits.

Example: Round 78.14 to the nearest unit.
Process: The first digit to be dropped is 1, which is less than 5. The last digit to be retained, 8, is therefore left unchanged.
Answer: 78

RULE 2: When the first digit to be dropped is more than 5, or is 5 followed by anything except a succession of zeros, the last digit to be retained is increased by 1.

Example 1: Round 89.6 to the nearest unit.
Process: The first digit to be dropped is 6, which is more than 5. The last digit to be retained, 9, is therefore increased by 1.
Answer: 90
Example 2: Round 865.00034 to the nearest multiple of 10.
Process: The first digit to be dropped is 5 followed by .00034. .00034 is something other than a succession of zeros, and the last digit to be retained, 6, is therefore increased by 1.
Answer: 870

RULE 3: When the first digit to be dropped is 5, or is 5 followed only by a succession of zeros, the last digit to be retained is increased by 1 if it is odd and left unchanged if it is even.

An easy way to remember rule 3 is to recall that numbers ending in 5, or in 5 followed only by zeros, are always rounded to even numbers.

Example 1: Round 845.75 to the nearest tenth.
Process: The first digit to be dropped is 5. The last digit to be retained is 7, an odd number. It is increased by 1.
Answer: 845.8
Example 2: Round 9.08500 to the nearest hundredth.
Process: The first digit to be dropped is 5 followed only by zeros. The last digit to be retained is 8, an even number. It is therefore left unchanged.
Answer: 9.08

Error may be introduced by the too-mechanical application of rule 3 when successive roundings are to be carried out. For example, if 749 is rounded to the nearest multiple of 10, it becomes 750. If 750 is then rounded, by the application of rule 3, to the nearest hundred, it becomes 800. But 749 is closer to 700 than to 800.

The best way to avoid this difficulty is not to do successive roundings. If they are to be done, a small $+$ or $-$ after the number obtained on the first rounding will indicate that it is actually slightly more or slightly less than the rounded number. Thus:

749 would be written 750$^-$, and later rounded to 700.
853 would be written 850$^+$, and later rounded to 900.

This treatment is necessary only when the first digit to be eliminated on later roundings is a 5 or a 5 followed by nothing but zeros.

Rule 3 can also lead to error if there is a great preponderance of odd over even or even over odd last-digits-to-be-retained. If the following numbers were to be rounded to the nearest unit and then added, the application of rule 3 would lead to an answer that is considerably too large:

745.5	rounds to		746
757.5	"	"	758
949.5	"	"	950
621.5	"	"	622
443.5	"	"	444
3517.5			3520

This difficulty can be avoided by ignoring rule 3 and using, instead, any other rule that will raise about half the numbers to the next digit and leave the other half unchanged. Deciding which to do on the basis of the fall of a coin is a clumsy but satisfactory method. Or the rounding can be postponed until the sum has been obtained (or other computations carried out); the final answer, rather than the component figures, is rounded.

Questions

1. Round to the nearest tenth: 2.19, 2.13, 2.15, 2.25.
2. Round to the nearest unit: 459.885, 555.000, 774.2, 6.00135, .4981, 4.5, 16.50005, 29.50, 50.05.

3. Round to the nearest unit. You will later be asked to round to the nearest multiple of 10: 274.9, 154.5, 345.1, 225.3, 194.6, 865.2.
4. Round the results of the roundings in problem 3 to the nearest multiples of 10.

0.2.2 Approximation: In practical statistical work, the ability to do rough mental calculations serves three functions:

1. It may eliminate the need for further, accurate computation by showing that an answer is much higher or much lower than some requirement.
2. It provides a quick check on the approximate accuracy of involved pencil-and-paper calculations.
3. It may help in the placing of decimal points, particularly in machine computations.

There is no set of mechanical rules for finding approximate answers. Practice with many different kinds of problems is the only way of obtaining the necessary skill. *Whenever* you have a problem requiring extensive calculation, start by getting a rough approximation of the answer. Your own calculations will provide the necessary check on your approximation. The following suggestions are only hints, not hard and fast rules:

1. Memorize the squares of numbers from 10 to 20.

$$11^2 = 121 \qquad 16^2 = 256$$
$$12^2 = 144 \qquad 17^2 = 289$$
$$13^2 = 169 \qquad 18^2 = 324$$
$$14^2 = 196 \qquad 19^2 = 361$$
$$15^2 = 225 \qquad 20^2 = 400$$

Example: What is 13×14?
Answer: Between 13^2 and 14^2, hence between 169 and 196.
Example 2: What is $\sqrt{305}$?
Process: $17^2 = 289$, and $18^2 = 324$.
Answer: Between 17 and 18.

2. In doing mental multiplication:

   a. Round the numbers off. Usually only the left-hand digit should be accurate.
   b. Factor, and work with the factors, then multiply back.

Example: What is 4920 × 224?

Process: Approximately 5000 × 200, or 5000 × 2 × 100. 5000 ×
           2 = 10,000. 10,000 × 100 = 1,000,000.

Answer: Approximately 1,000,000.

3. In doing mental divisions:

   a. Round the numbers off.
   b. Cancel zeros in the dividend.
   c. Complete the problem by doing a mental division of the re-
      maining numbers.

Example: What is 6,124,291 ÷ 2382?

Process: Approximately 6,000,000 ÷ 2000. 6,000,000 ÷ 2000 =
           6000 ÷ 2.

Answer: Approximately 3000.

4. In doing mental additions:

   a. Where there are only two addends, round and add mentally.
   b. When there are many addends, ignore all digits except the
      one or two on the extreme left and add those, *or*
   c. If the many addends are very similar, get a rough idea of the
      size of a typical addend and multiply by the number of
      addends.

Example 1: What is 17,866,244 + 419,911,004?

Process: 18 million plus 420 million. 20 plus 18 is 38.

Answer: Approximately 438 million.

Example 2: What is the sum of the numbers below:

7619
8244
2091   Process: Ignore the three right-hand digits. Add the two
3999   left-hand columns. Their sum is 59.
24625   Answer: Approximately 59,000.
15155

Example 3: What is the sum of the numbers below:

3.111
2.904
3.162
3.274
2.818
3.222
2.911
3.000

Process: All the numbers are very close to 3. There are 8 numbers. $3 \times 8 = 24$.

Answer: Approximately 24.

5. In doing mental square root:

 a. Round the number off.
 b. Try successive approximations.
 c. Remember that $\sqrt{100}$ is 10, and $\sqrt{10}$ is 3.2, and factor.

Example: What is $\sqrt{38,449}$?

Process: 38,449 is approximately 40,000. Try 20×20. The answer is 400—too low. Try 200×200. The answer is 40,000.

Answer: Approximately 200, but somewhat less.

Example 2: What is $\sqrt{35,221}$?

Process: 35,221 is approximately 35,000. Since 36 is a perfect square, call it 36,000. Try 60×60. Answer: 3600. Too low. Try 600×600. Answer: 360,000. Too high. Then the answer must be $\sqrt{60 \times 60 \times 10}$ or $60\sqrt{10}$ or 60×3.2.

Answer: Slightly less than 190.

6. To place decimal points:

 a. Round off every number until it has only one digit that is not a zero.
 b. Carry out the calculation, using pencil and paper if necessary.

Example: What is $24.639 \times .000968$?

Process: $20 \times .001 = .020$.

Answer: Somewhat more than .02.

7. Look for your own short cuts. Anything that works easily (and correctly) for you is a good technique.

0.2.3 Square Root: The long hand-computation method of finding a square root should be used only as a last resort, unless you are especially adept at it. There are many easier ways, such as using a table or factoring out perfect squares or a combination of these two.

Example: What is $\sqrt{34{,}193{,}247.3}$?

Process: 1. Start with the decimal point and mark off by two's.

2. Find $\sqrt{34}$ or the square root of the next lowest perfect square: 5.

3. Put 5 in the answer, and also put it down as a divisor. Proceed as in long division. $5 \times 5 = 25$, which is subtracted from 34.

4. Bring down the next pair of figures. The new dividend is 919.

5. Add the last figure in the answer, 5, to the last divisor, 5. $5 + 5 = 10$. These are the first two digits of the new divisor.

```
                 5   8   4   7. 5
        5 |34 19 32 47. 30
          25
      108 |9 19
          8 64
     1164 |55 32
          46 56
    11687 |8 76 47
          8 17 99
   116945 |58 48 30
          58 47 25
             1 05
```

6. Try 9 for the third digit. $9 \times 109 = 981$, which is larger than 919. Try 8 for the third digit. $8 \times 108 = 864$. 8 is the second digit in the answer. 864 is subtracted from 919 and the next two digits are brought down.

7. Add 8 to the old divisor. The new divisor will be one thousand one hundred and sixty something.

8. Repeat the steps above until the problem is completed.

Answer: 5847.5.
Check: $6000 \times 6000 = 36{,}000{,}000$.

0.2.4 Fractions:

1. Rules for multiplication:

$$\frac{a}{b} \cdot \frac{c}{d} = \frac{ac}{bd} \qquad\qquad \text{Example: } \frac{1}{2} \cdot \frac{3}{5} = \frac{3}{10}$$

$$\frac{a}{b} \cdot \frac{c}{a} = \frac{ac}{ab} = \frac{c}{b} \qquad\qquad \frac{2}{3} \cdot \frac{1}{2} = \frac{2}{6} = \frac{1}{3}$$

$$\frac{a}{bc} \cdot \frac{d}{ae} = \frac{ad}{abce} = \frac{d}{bce} \qquad\qquad \frac{3}{7} \cdot \frac{5}{6} = \frac{15}{42} = \frac{5}{14}$$

2. Rule for division: Invert divisor and multiply.

$$\frac{a}{b} \div \frac{c}{d} = \frac{a}{b} \cdot \frac{d}{c} = \frac{ad}{bc} \qquad \frac{1}{2} \div \frac{3}{5} = \frac{1}{2} \cdot \frac{5}{3} = \frac{5}{6}$$

$$\frac{a/b}{c} = \frac{a}{b} \div \frac{c}{1} = \frac{a}{b} \cdot \frac{1}{c} = \frac{a}{bc} \qquad \frac{\frac{1}{2}}{3} = \frac{1}{2} \cdot \frac{1}{3} = \frac{1}{6}$$

$$\frac{a}{b/c} = \frac{a}{1} \div \frac{b}{c} = \frac{a}{1} \cdot \frac{c}{b} = \frac{ac}{b} \qquad \frac{1}{\frac{2}{3}} = \frac{1}{1} \cdot \frac{3}{2} = \frac{3}{2}$$

3. Rules for addition: Find a common denominator. Convert all fractions to this denominator and add numerators. Reduce if possible.

$$\frac{a}{b} + \frac{c}{d} = \frac{ad + bc}{bd} \qquad \frac{1}{2} + \frac{2}{3} = \frac{3 + 4}{6} = \frac{7}{6} = 1\frac{1}{6}$$

$$\frac{a}{be} + \frac{c}{de} = \frac{ad + bc}{bde} \qquad \frac{1}{6} + \frac{2}{15} = \frac{5 + 4}{30} = \frac{9}{30} = \frac{3}{10}$$

0.2.5 Ratios, Proportions, and Percentages: Ratios, proportions, and percentages are all fractions.

To say that the ratio of spades to all cards in the deck is 1 to 4 (often written 1:4) is to say that if we divide the number of cards that are spades by the total number of cards, the resulting fraction is $\frac{1}{4}$.

Proportions are fractions in which the denominator is 1.000. What is the proportion of spades in the deck?

$$\frac{1}{4} = \frac{x}{1.000} \qquad x = \frac{1}{4} = .250 \qquad \frac{1}{4} = \frac{.25}{1.00}$$

Percentages are fractions in which the denominator is 100. What per cent of the cards are spades?

$$\frac{1}{4} = \frac{x}{100} \qquad x = \frac{100}{4} = 25$$

A proportion is converted to a percentage by multiplying by 100.

$$.25 \times 100 = 25.0$$

0.2.6 Exponents and Logarithms:

A. EXPONENTS:

Definitions:

$x^n = x$ multiplied by itself n times. $x^3 = x \cdot x \cdot x$
$$a^5 = a \cdot a \cdot a \cdot a \cdot a$$

Definition		Examples	
$x^{-n} = \dfrac{1}{x^n}$	$x^{-2} = \dfrac{1}{x^2}$	$a^{-3} = \dfrac{1}{a^3}$	
$x^{1/n} = \sqrt[n]{x}$	$x^{\frac{1}{2}} = \sqrt[2]{x}$	$a^{\frac{1}{5}} = \sqrt[5]{a}$	
$x^{-1/n} = \dfrac{1}{\sqrt[n]{x}}$	$x^{-\frac{1}{2}} = \dfrac{1}{\sqrt{x}}$	$a^{-\frac{1}{5}} = \dfrac{1}{\sqrt[5]{a}}$	$8^{-\frac{1}{3}} = \dfrac{1}{2}$
$x^{m/n} = \sqrt[n]{x^m}$	$x^{\frac{2}{3}} = \sqrt[3]{x^2}$	$a^{\frac{3}{5}} = \sqrt[5]{a^3}$	$3^{\frac{3}{2}} = \sqrt{27}$
$x^{-m/n} = \dfrac{1}{\sqrt[n]{x^m}}$	$x^{-\frac{2}{3}} = \dfrac{1}{\sqrt[3]{x^2}}$	$a^{-\frac{3}{5}} = \dfrac{1}{\sqrt[5]{a^3}}$	$3^{-\frac{3}{2}} = \dfrac{1}{\sqrt{27}}$
$x^0 = 1$	$3^0 = 1$	$(27y)^0 = 1$	$(-4)^0 = 1$

Laws of exponents:

Laws		Examples	
$x^m \cdot x^n = x^{m+n}$	$(x^3)(x^5) = x^8$	$(x^{\frac{1}{2}})(x^{\frac{1}{2}}) = x$	$(x^5)(x^{-\frac{3}{8}}) = x^{\frac{37}{8}}$
$x^m \div x^n = x^{m-n}$	$\dfrac{(x^3)}{(x^5)} = x^{-2}$	$a^5 \div a^{\frac{1}{2}} = a^{\frac{9}{2}}$	
$(x^m)^n = x^{mn}$	$(x^2)^3 = x^6$	$(a^4)^{\frac{1}{2}} = a^2$	

B. LOGARITHMS:

Logarithms are seldom used for calculation in statistical work—computing machines are faster and better for most purposes. But they are frequently employed to describe data or to manipulate exponents. It is important that you understand what logarithms are and why they work as they do.

Definitions:

The logarithm of x to the base b is the power to which b must be raised to make it equal x.

$$b^{\log_b x} = x$$

The most common value for b, the base, is 10. Logarithms to the base 10 are called **common logarithms.** To find a common logarithm, the question to ask yourself is, 'To what power must 10 be raised to make it equal this number?'

$.0001 = 10^{-4}$	The logarithm of	.0001 is -4, which is written '$\bar{4}$'
$.001 = 10^{-3}$	"	"	"	.001 " -3	"	"	"	'$\bar{3}$'
$.01 = 10^{-2}$	"	"	"	.01 " -2	"	"	"	'$\bar{2}$'
$.1 = 10^{-1}$	"	"	"	.1 " -1	"	"	"	'$\bar{1}$'
$1 = 10^{0}$	"	"	"	1 " 0
$10 = 10^{1}$	"	"	"	10 " 1
$100 = 10^{2}$	"	"	"	100 " 2
$1000 = 10^{3}$	"	"	"	1000 " 3

and so on.

Finding the logarithm of a number that is not an integral power of 10 takes two steps. The first is to find the logarithm of the next-lowest power of ten. The second is to find out how much greater than that power the exponent of ten must be to make it equal the number. For instance, if we seek the logarithm of 20, we first determine that 20 is greater than 10^1 though less than 10^2. The logarithm of 20 will therefore be 1 point something-or-other. By referring to a table, we find that the something-or-other is .30103. So the logarithm of 20 is 1.30103.

The logarithm of the next lowest integral power of 10 is called the **characteristic.** The characteristic of 20 is 1. The characteristic of .004 is -3. The characteristic of 2435 is 3.

The characteristic of any number equal to or greater than 1 is one less than the number of digits to the left of the decimal place.

The characteristic of a number between 0 and 1 is negative and greater than 1 by the number of zeros that follow the decimal.

The **mantissa** is the second part of the logarithm. It tells how much greater than the characteristic is the power to which 10 must be raised to make it equal the number. The mantissa of the logarithm of 20 is .30103. The mantissa of a logarithm is always positive. It is found by reference to a table of logarithms.

Because the characteristic of a logarithm can be negative but the mantissa must be positive, it is well to think of negative logarithms this way: the logarithm is *minus* the characteristic *plus* the mantissa. Thus the logarithm $\bar{1}.9999$ is minus 1 plus .9999. That logarithm is almost zero. (*Not:* almost minus 2.)

Change of base of logarithms: While 10 is the most common base for logarithms, other bases are sometimes used. In this book we shall frequently use logarithms to the base 2. Since no tables are published for logarithms to the base 2, we shall have to find these logarithms by using a conversion formula. The general formula is:

$$\log_b x = \frac{\log_c x}{\log_c b}.$$

In the particular case of converting from the base 10 to the base 2, this formula becomes:

$$\log_2 x = \frac{\log_{10} x}{\log_{10} 2} = \frac{\log_{10} x}{.30103}.$$

For example, what is $\log_2 10$?

$$\log_2 10 = \frac{\log_{10} 10}{.30103} = \frac{1}{.30103} = 3.3219$$

When the logarithm is negative the procedure is a little more complicated. Suppose we want to find the logarithm to the base 2 of .25. Log_{10} .25 is $\bar{1}.39794$. We cannot substitute that number directly in the formula, but must ask ourselves: how much below zero is that logarithm? If you remember that the mantissa is always positive, you will see that we have gone *down* one whole unit, then *up* about four-tenths of a unit. That leaves us about six-tenths of a unit below zero. By exact subtraction, we find that we are actually *down* by .60206. The number that we substitute in our conversion formula is $-.60206$.

$$\log_2 .25 = \frac{-.60206}{.30103} = -2 = \bar{2}$$
$$\log_2 .25 = \bar{2}$$

We can check that finding directly, for $.25 = \frac{1}{4}$, and $\frac{1}{4} = 2^{-2}$. By the definition of logarithms, then, $\log_2 .25$ must be $\bar{2}$.

When the answer fails to 'come out even,' we must convert it back from a negative to a positive mantissa, as in the following example:

$$\log_2 .47 = ?$$
$$\log_2 .47 = \frac{\bar{1}.67210}{.30103} = \frac{-.32790}{.30103} = -1.08926$$
$$-1.08926 = -2 + ?$$
$$= -2 + .91074$$
$$\log_2 .47 = \bar{2}.91074$$

LAWS OF LOGARITHMS:

$\log ab = \log a + \log b$ Examples: $\log 3x = \log 3 + \log x$

$\log a^b = b \log a$ $\log m^{-4} = -4 \log m$

$\log \dfrac{a}{b} = \log a - \log b$ $\log \dfrac{125}{37} = \log 125 - \log 37$

$\log \dfrac{1}{a} = - \log a$ $\log \dfrac{1}{100} = - \log 100 = \overline{2}$

Questions

Find the numerical value of:

1. $2^5 \cdot 2^2$

2. $\dfrac{3^4}{3^2}$

3. 7^0

4. $4^{\frac{1}{2}}$

5. $27^{\frac{1}{3}}$

6. 6^{-2}

7. $4^{\frac{3}{2}}$

8. $49^{-\frac{1}{2}}$

9. $(\frac{1}{4})^{-\frac{1}{2}}$

10. $8^{-\frac{2}{3}}$

11. $\dfrac{3^3}{7^0}$

12. $(\frac{1}{8})^{-\frac{1}{3}} + (\frac{1}{9})^{-\frac{1}{2}}$

13. 572×10^6

14. 2.36×10^{-8}

15. $8^{-\frac{2}{3}} + 225^{\frac{1}{2}} - 3^2$

Convert radicals to exponents and solve for y in terms of x:

16. $y = \sqrt{x} \cdot \dfrac{1}{\sqrt[3]{x}}$

17. $y = \left(\dfrac{1}{x^4}\right) \sqrt[5]{x}$

18. $y = (\sqrt[2]{x^3})(x^4) \left(\dfrac{1}{\sqrt[9]{x^7}}\right) \left(\dfrac{\sqrt[6]{x}}{\sqrt[3]{x^2}}\right)$

What is:

19. $\log_{10} 10$

20. $\log_2 2$

21. $\log_{67} 67$

22. $\log_e e$

23. $\log_b b$

What is:

24. $\log_{10} 10^2$

25. $\log_{10} 100$

26. $\log_2 4$

27. $\log_3 9$

28. $\log_4 16$

29. $\log_{12} 144$

30. $\log_e e^2$

31. $\log_b b^2$

What is:

32. $\log_{10} 10^9$

33. $\log_2 2^{27}$

34. $\log_{34} 34^{-16}$

35. $\log_e e^{-1}$

36. $\log_b b^x$

What is:

37. $\log \frac{1}{100}$

38. $\log_2 .50$

39. $\frac{1}{2} \log_2 \frac{1}{2}$

40. $\log_3 \frac{1}{27}$

41. $\log_6 \frac{1}{36}$

42. $\log_b \dfrac{1}{b}$

43. $\log_b \dfrac{1}{b^n}$

What is:

44. $\log_{10} \left(\dfrac{100}{3x} \right)$

45. $\log 6ab$

46. $\log (9x)^3$

47. $\log 9x^3$

48. $\log (3x + 4y)$

Find $\log_2$ of:

49. $\frac{1}{16}, \frac{1}{32}, \frac{1}{2}, 8, 64, 256$ (All are integral powers of 2)

50. 13, 29, 244, .47, .03 (None is an integral power of 2. Use conversion formula)

0.2.7 Graphic Presentation of Data: A graph is a device for presenting visually the relationship between two (or more) variables. Since there are many different kinds of graphs, no single set of fixed rules for their construction can be formulated.

A good graph should be *clear, complete*, and *correct*. It should *not be misleading*, and it should *not be aesthetically offensive*. If you keep these principles in mind and make sure your graphs follow them, you will do better than if you try to follow rules mechanically. The rules below admit of many exceptions. However, they are ordinarily the best techniques for making a graph that follows the principles given above.

1. **The independent variable,** which is the one the experimenter controls, manipulates, or chooses, *should be plotted on the x-axis, and the* **dependent variable,** which is the one the experimenter measures, *should be plotted on the y-axis.*

Examples: An experimenter determines the number of errors made by a rat running a maze on each of 10 learning trials. *Trials* is the independent variable and is plotted on the x-axis; *errors depends* upon trials. *Errors* is the dependent variable and is plotted on the y-axis.

A research worker determines how many families receive incomes of $0 − $2000, $2001 − $4000, and so on. Income is the independent variable; number of families is the dependent variable.

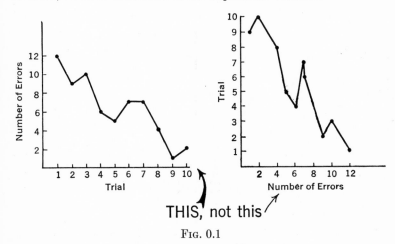

THIS, not this

FIG. 0.1

2. *Low numerical values are plotted at the bottom of the y-axis and at the left side of the x-axis. High numerical values are plotted at the top of the y-axis and the right of the x-axis.*

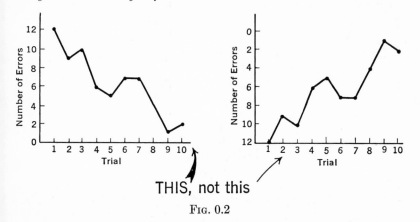

THIS, not this

FIG. 0.2

3. *Axes should be clearly and completely labeled. Units of measurement, if there are any, should be specified.*

Example: An experimenter determines the time required by a rat to run a maze on each of ten successive learning trials. The *x*-axis should be labeled *Trials*, and the *y*-axis, *Time* (*sec.*). Numerical values of both variables should be indicated.

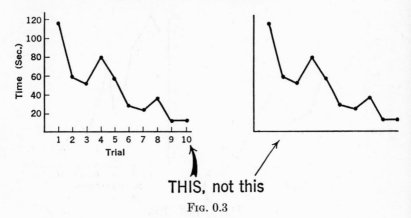

FIG. 0.3

4. *If two or more lines or curves are plotted on one graph, they should be clearly distinguishable, and a key should be provided for identification.*

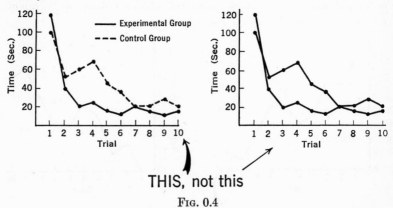

FIG. 0.4

5. *A graph should have a title* which, along with information in the graph itself, provides the reader with everything he needs to interpret the relationship presented.

6. *Horizontal and vertical dimensions should be in reasonable relationship to each other.* What is a 'reasonable relationship' will depend, of course, upon the data to be presented. If, however, there is no

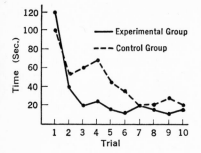

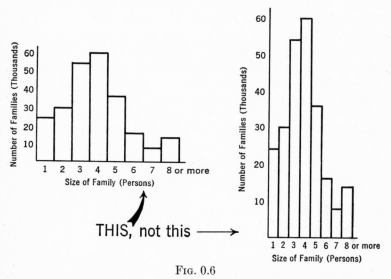

FIG. 0.5 Learning curves for control and experimental animals. Experimental animals received 1cc. of drug X per day, while control animals were injected with 1cc. of saline solution. Each point is an average time for 8 rats.

THIS, not this ⟶

FIG. 0.6

reason to do otherwise, it is a good idea to make the graph about three-fourths as high as it is long.

Some practical suggestions:

Buy your graph paper with care. For most general purposes the best paper is that ruled with 10 lines to the inch, with heavier rulings on every tenth line. Paper that has eight lines to the inch with heavier rulings every eighth line is likely to be confusing unless measurements are recorded in halves, quarters, eighths, and so on.

Think before you make a mark! How many squares on the graph paper do you have available, and what range of values do you want to represent on the graph? Make sure your graph, with the units you have chosen, will fit on the paper you have available.

One consideration when you select graph paper is the relation between your unit of measurement and the number of squares on the paper used to represent each unit. If one square on the graph paper can represent one unit of measurement, the graph will be easy to plot and to read. Unfortunately this is not always possible. Suppose, for example, you have 40 squares available to represent a range of 90 units of your variable. You decide, therefore, to use 30 of the squares and to let one square stand for 3 units. How, then, do you plot a point for 23 units? It will be represented by $7\frac{2}{3}$ squares on the paper, and thirds of a square are both hard to measure and hard to read. In such a case, you might do better to let 4 squares stand for one unit, or, better still, try to find more suitable paper. If you can, visit a store that specializes in engineering supplies and look at the different kinds of graph paper and at the special drawing equipment that is available for various purposes.

Ordinarily a lead pencil of medium hardness (2.5 or 3) is the best for classroom work on graphs. Colored pencils are tempting, but since it is seldom practical to *publish* a graph in color, it will be worth while to learn other techniques for differentiating different lines instead of depending on color. There are many varieties of dotted and dashed lines and of crosshatching. Some students prefer to use ink. Ink makes a fine looking graph, and its use is highly commendable provided there aren't too many false starts. Your instructor will inform you of any special requirements he wishes to impose.

There are two kinds of rulers that are worth owning. First, buy a transparent ruler, preferably one that is ruled in both inches and millimeters and that has solid lines drawn along its length. With this you will be able to draw parallel lines without measurement, get a quick idea of whether a set of points falls along a straight line, and estimate the best fitting straight line for any set of points. Second, buy a ruler with a thin metal strip inserted in one edge. When you rule an ink line with this, you can move the ruler away from the line immediately without danger of blotting.

Above all, remember that a graph is primarily a way of conveying information, not an artistic production. If you can make it clear, complete, and accurate, you can usually count on the aesthetic factors to take care of themselves.

0.3 Two New Techniques

0.3.1 The Summation Sign: A mathematical symbol that tells the reader to perform a particular operation is called an *operator*. Symbols like $+$, $-$, $\times$, $\div$, and $\sqrt{\ }$ are operators with which you are familiar. These symbols can be translated into words such as 'add the symbols on either side of the sign,' 'subtract the second figure from the first,' and so on. The summation sign, Σ, is also an operator, and is translated, 'obtain the sum of...' or simply 'summation' or 'sum.'[2]

Suppose you go into a store and price three articles. You decide to buy all of them and want to know what your total bill will be. Let us call the first price X_1, (read: 'ex sub one'), the second, X_2, and the third, X_3. Then your total bill, T, will, of course, be $X_1 + X_2 + X_3$. If we let X_i stand for the price of any individual item, then we can also write:

$$T = \Sigma X_i$$

This is read: 'T equals summation X sub i,' and it means: the total bill is the sum of the prices of the individual items.

There are two other, more complete, ways of writing the same thing:

$T = \sum^{i} X_i$, which is read: 'T equals the summation over i of X sub i,' and means that the total is the sum, for all the individual items of the individual prices; or

$$T = \sum_{i=1}^{i=N} X_i \qquad \left(\text{usually abbreviated to} \qquad \sum_{1}^{N} X_i \text{ or } \sum^{N} X_i\right)$$

which is read: 'T equals the summation from i equal to 1 to i equal to N of X sub i.' That notation means that if there are N items, the total is the sum of the prices of all the items from the first to the Nth. In our example $N = 3$, and the notation above would mean we obtained the sum of the prices of all articles from the first through the third. When a simple summation sign with no limits of summation is given, it is assumed to mean the summation from $i = 1$ to $i = N$.

[2] The symbol Σ is actually the Greek letter sigma, but it should never be called that in statistical work, because the word 'sigma,' to a statistician, means the symbol σ, the small letter.

Questions

1. Write the following as summations:

    a. $x_1 + x_2 + x_3 + x_4$
    b. $y_1 + y_2 + \ldots + y_{37}$
    c. $x_1^2 + x_2^2 + \ldots + x_n^2$

2. Write out the following summations in full:

    a. $\displaystyle\sum_1^5 x_i$
                  b. $\displaystyle\sum_1^n y_i^2$

3. Find the numerical values of the summations below, taking the following values for the various X_i and Y_i: $X_1 = 3$; $X_2 = 5$; $X_3 = 4$; $X_4 = 2$; $Y_1 = 8$; $Y_2 = 6$; $Y_3 = 9$; $Y_4 = 7$.

    a. ΣX_i e. ΣY_i^2
    b. ΣY_i f. $(\Sigma X_i)^2$
    c. $\Sigma X_i Y_i$ g. $(\Sigma Y_i)^2$
    d. ΣX_i^2

4. Is it true that $(a + b)^2 = a^2 + b^2$?

5. Is it true that $(\Sigma x_i)^2 = \Sigma x_i^2$? Explain.

There are three important rules about the use of the summation sign.

1. The summation of the sum of two or more terms is equal to the sum of their separate summations.

$$\Sigma(X_i + Y_i + Z_i) = \Sigma X_i + \Sigma Y_i + \Sigma Z_i$$

This theorem can be proved by writing out the summations in full:

$$\begin{aligned} \Sigma(X_i + Y_i + Z_i) &= X_1 + Y_1 + Z_1 + X_2 + Y_2 + Z_2 \\ &\qquad + \ldots + X_n + Y_n + Z_n \\ &= X_1 + X_2 + \ldots + X_n + Y_1 + Y_2 \\ &\qquad + \ldots + Y_n + Z_1 + Z_2 + \ldots + Z_n \\ &= \Sigma X_i + \Sigma Y_i + \Sigma Z_i \end{aligned}$$

2. The summation of a constant times a variable is equal to the constant times the summation of the variable.

$$\Sigma k X_i = k \Sigma X_i$$

The proof of the theorem is simple:

$$\Sigma k X_i = k X_1 + k X_2 + \ldots + k X_n$$
$$= k(X_1 + X_2 + \ldots + X_n)$$
$$= k\Sigma X_i$$

If you consider the example of the three prices, you will see how this theorem works out in practice. Suppose each of the three prices is doubled. Then the total amount you will have to pay is also doubled. You do not have to double each price and get the sum of the doubled prices.

3. The summation of a constant from 1 to N equals N times the constant.

$$\sum_1^N k = Nk$$

For example, if N were 4 and the constant, k, were 3, we should have:

$$\sum_1^4 3 = 3 + 3 + 3 + 3 = 4 \times 3 = 12$$

This theorem is really just a way of saying that multiplication is a short method of doing addition.

If you are given a problem involving a summation sign, you may have to use all three of these rules in combination, plus a little algebra. Let us consider a problem and see what the technique is for working it out:

What is $\displaystyle\sum_{i=1}^{i=N} (X_i - \mu)^2$? ($\mu$ is the Greek letter mu.)

The first step is to carry out all the operations to the right of the summation sign. In this case, that means that we must square $(X_i - \mu)$.

$$(X_i - \mu)^2 = (X_i^2 - 2\mu X_i + \mu^2)$$

Next, we identify the variables and constants. In this case that is easy, for X_i has a subscript, while μ does not, so X_i is a variable and μ a constant. In practical statistical work it may take a little thought to decide which is which.

Once the constants and variables have been identified, the summation sign is applied according to rules 1, 2, and 3. Each term is considered separately.

$$\sum_{i=1}^{i=N} (X_i^2) = \Sigma X_i^2$$

$$\sum_{i=1}^{i=N} (-2\mu X_i) = -2\mu \sum_{i=1}^{i=N} X_i \quad \text{(by rule 2)}$$

$$\sum_{i=1}^{i=N} (\mu^2) = N\mu^2 \quad \text{(by rule 3)}$$

So, finally:

$$\sum_{i=1}^{i=N} (X_i - \mu)^2 = \sum_{i=1}^{i=N} X_i^2 - 2\mu \sum_{i=1}^{i=N} X_i + N\mu^2 \quad \text{(by rule 1)}$$

Questions

1. Write the following as summations:

    a. $x_1 - 8 + x_2 - 8 + x_3 - 8 + x_4 - 8$
    b. $4y_1 + 4y_2 + 4y_3 + \ldots + 4y_n$
    c. $x_1y_1 + x_2y_2 + \ldots + x_ny_n$

2. Write out the following summations in full:

    a. $\displaystyle\sum_{1}^{n} (x_i - y_i)$ c. $6\displaystyle\sum_{1}^{n} y_i^2$

    b. $\displaystyle\sum_{1}^{n} (x_i + 5)$ d. $\displaystyle\sum_{1}^{n} (x_iy_i - 2)$

3. Find the numerical values of the summations below, taking the following values for the various x_i and y_i: $x_1 = 3$; $x_2 = 5$; $x_3 = 4$; $x_4 = 2$; $y_1 = 8$; $y_2 = 6$; $y_3 = 9$; $y_4 = 7$.

    a. $\Sigma(x_i + 4)$ c. $\Sigma 3(x_i + y_i)^2$
    b. $\Sigma 2y_i^2$ d. $\Sigma(x_iy_i - 1)$

4. By the application of rules 1, 2, and 3, write each of the following as a series of separate summations:

Example: $\displaystyle\sum_{i=1}^{i=N} (X_i - \mu)^2 = \sum_{i=1}^{i=N} X_i^2 - 2\mu \sum_{i=1}^{i=N} X_i + N\mu^2$ (Proof given in text.)

a. $\displaystyle\sum_{i=1}^{i=N} 4X_i^2$ c. $\displaystyle\sum_{i=1}^{i=N} (x_i + c)(y_i + c)$

b. $\displaystyle\sum_{i=1}^{i=N} a(x_i + 2)^2$ d. $\displaystyle\sum_{i=1}^{i=N} k \log X_i$

0.3.2 The Accuracy of an Answer: Numbers can be divided into two classes: exact and approximate. Ordinarily exact numbers are those obtained by counting, and approximate numbers are those obtained by measurement, though there are exceptions to this generalization. If you say that there are 16 people in the room you usually mean that there are exactly 16, but if you say that the length of a line is 100 cm., you do not mean that it is *exactly* that. If you are reporting to the nearest centimeter the line may be 100.3 cm. or 99.8 cm. and you will still call it 100 cm. You might even have rounded your results off to the nearest multiple of 10 or of 100. Your report of 100 cm. as the length of the line is an approximate number.

An approximate number carries with it the possibility of an error. If our measurements are accurate to centimeters, then the report of 100 cm. carries with it the possibility of an error of half a centimeter in either direction, which we might write:

$$100 \text{ cm.} \pm .5 \text{ cm.}$$

If our measurements were accurate only to the nearest multiple of 10, then we could write:

$$100 \text{ cm.} \pm 5 \text{ cm.}$$

indicating that there was a possibility of an error of 5 cm. in either direction.

Suppose, now, that we have two lines, each 100 cm. long and each measured to the nearest centimeter. We wish to find the sum of their lengths:

$$100 \pm .5 \text{ cm.}$$
$$+100 \pm .5 \text{ cm.}$$
$$\overline{}$$
$$200 \pm 1 \text{ cm.}$$

The sum carries with it the possibility of an error of a centimeter. The total length might be as little as 199 cm. or as much as 201 cm.

If we wanted to find the total length of sixteen 100 cm. lines, we should have:

$$16(100 \pm .5) = 1600 \pm 8 \text{ cm.} \quad 1600 - 8$$
$$= 1592. \quad 1600 + 8 = 1608.$$

The true sum might be as low as 1592 or as high as 1608. When we report the sum to be 1600, we certainly cannot guarantee the last zero, and even the zero before that may be in error.

Or suppose we have a rectangle whose sides are 10 cm. and 12 cm., both measurements good to the nearest centimeter. What is the area of the rectangle? We can write:

$$(10 \pm .5)(12 \pm .5) = ?$$

By multiplication we find that the area may be as large as 131.25 sq. cm., or as small as 109.25 sq. cm. When we say that the area is 120 sq. cm. we cannot guarantee the last digit, and even the second digit may be in error.

Calculations made from approximate numbers may carry with them considerable possibility of error, and it is well to recognize that possibility in advance and report results to no greater accuracy than they can be guaranteed. The size of a possible error can be determined by the methods we have just demonstrated, and, indeed, these remain the most fundamental methods whenever shortcuts and mechanical rules leave any doubt. But there are more efficient and more mechanical methods of dealing with the problem. The first step is to determine the number of **significant digits** in the figures with which we are working.

Digits are used for two purposes: to tell the *size of the unit* in which we are making our measurements, and to tell *how many units* there are. If, for example, we say that there are 161,000,000 people in the United States, we probably mean that our unit of measurement is millions of persons, and there are 161 such units. The zeros in the figure are there to tell us the size of the measuring unit. The digits 1, 6, and 1 are there to tell us how many such units there are. These three digits are called **significant digits.** The number of significant digits in a figure is the number of digits whose purpose is to tell 'how many.' The zeros in the figure 161,000,000 are not significant, because they are there not to tell how many but only to identify unit size.

Let us consider another example. If we say that the size of something is .0056, how many significant digits are there in that figure? We first ask, 'What is the unit of measurement?' The answer is one ten-thousandth, or .0001. How many of these units are there? Fifty-six. Two of the four digits are there to answer the question, 'how many?' There are two significant digits in the figure .0056. How many significant digits are there in the figure 113.0? Here the unit of measurement is .1, there are 1130 such units, and hence four significant digits.

A figure such as 5000 is ambiguous. The zeros may be there to identify the unit of measurement or they may be there to tell how many units there are. The unit of measurement may be 1, in which case all four of the digits tell how many and are significant, or it may be 10, or 100, or even 1000. If the unit of measurement is 1000, then only one digit, 5, is there to tell how many, and only the 5 is significant. To avoid this ambiguity we place a bar or a dot over the last digit that is there to tell how many. So $500\overline{0}$ means that the unit of measurement is 1 and there are 5000 such units. In that figure there are four significant digits. Or we might have $50\overline{0}0$, which means 500 units of 10 and has three significant digits, or $5\overline{0}00$, which means 50 units of 100 and has two significant digits, or even $\overline{5}000$, which means five units of 1000 and has only one significant digit.

Once the number of significant digits in a figure has been determined, a single simple principle will tell us how accurate our answer can be. A chain can be no stronger than its weakest link. In multiplication, division, and the extraction of square roots, the answer cannot be accurate to more significant digits than any of the component numbers, and even the last of these digits may not be accurate. We found, for example, that the sum of sixteen 100 cm. lines, each measured to the nearest centimeter, could be as low as 1592 or as high as 1608. The sum, however, would reach one of those extremes only if all the measurements were 'off' the maximum amount in the same direction, an unlikely sort of happening. Probably the sum will be someplace between 1595 and 1605, and the answer, 1600, will be accurate to the nearest multiple of 10: $160\overline{0}$.

Even here, though, the third digit, while probably accurate, is not guaranteed. In this problem 16 is an exact number, having as many significant digits as we might wish, but the 100 is only an approximate number. It has three significant digits. The answer, therefore, cannot have more than three significant digits, and only two are guaranteed to be accurate.

When we multiplied 10 × 13, we were multiplying two figures each with two significant digits. The answer, therefore, can contain only two significant digits, and only the first of these is guaranteed. We can say for sure that the product will be closer to 100 than to 0 or 200, and we can say with a fair degree of confidence that the answer will be closer to 120 than to 110 or 130. We cannot feel any assurance at all that the answer will be closer to 120 than to 119 or 121.

In addition and subtraction the problem is different. Suppose we wish to add 14,671 and 2. Each of these figures is accurate to the nearest unit, so we can write: $(14,671 \pm .5) + (2 \pm .5) = (14,673 \pm 1.0)$. The answer is guaranteed accurate to four significant figures and is probably accurate to five, even though one of the addends has only one significant digit. When we add, therefore, we are concerned not with the *number* of significant digits but with *how far to the right* the digits are significant. The sum (or difference) cannot be accurate farther to the right than any of the addends. The procedure for adding approximate numbers is to round all figures until they are accurate one more place to the right than the least accurate addend (the one with its last significant digit occurring farthest to the left). Then add, and then round the sum one more place. For example:

1$\bar{6}$000	is rounded to	1$\bar{6}$000
2121		2100
69		100
2		0
		18200 which is rounded to 1$\bar{8}$000

Questions

1. Write the margin of error after each of the following figures. The first two have been done for you.

a. 13$\bar{1}$ Ans.: 131 $\pm$ .5   f. 16,$\bar{5}$00
b. 12$\bar{0}$0   Ans.: 1200 $\pm$ 5   g. 1$\bar{5}$,000,000
c. .004   h. .00210
d. 14   i. 15,000,$\bar{0}$00
e. 247.3   j. .032

2. In each of the following multiplications the first number is exact, the second approximate. Write the margins of error after the second number, then multiply and find the lowest and highest possible answers. The first problem has been done for you.

a. 5 $\times$ 16   Ans.: 5(16 $\pm$ .5) = 80 $\pm$ 2.5   80 $-$ 2.5 = 77.5;
    80 + 2.5 = 82.5.
b. 10 $\times$ .24
c. 4 $\times$ $\bar{1}$00
d. 100 $\times$ .006
e. 12 $\times$ 12
f. 1000 $\times$ .00241

3. In each of the following multiplications, both numbers are approximate. Write the margins of error after both numbers, multiply, then find the lowest and highest possible answers. The first problem has been done for you.

a. $\bar{2}$00 $\times$ 12   Ans.: (200 $\pm$ 50)(12 $\pm$ .5)

$$200 + 50 \qquad\qquad 200 - 50$$
$$12 + \quad .5 \qquad\qquad 12 - \quad .5$$

$$100 + \ 25 \qquad\qquad -100 + \quad 25$$
$$2400 + 600 \qquad\qquad 2400 - 600$$

$$2400 + 700 + \ 25 \quad 2400 - 700 + \quad 25$$

Limits: 1725 to 3125

b. 6 $\times$ 7
c. 14 $\times$ 6
d. 140 $\times$ 14
e. .0031 $\times$ 9.5
f. .0211 $\times$ 3
g. 2$\bar{1}$,000,000 $\times$ 2

4. For each of the figures below, determine three things: (1) the size of the unit of measurement; (2) how many units there are; and (3)

the number of significant digits. The first problem has been done for you.

a. $16\overline{7}00$ Ans.: (1) 100; (2) 167; (3) 3
b. $167\overline{0}0$ g. 15,789,022.00
c. $1670\overline{0}$ h. 1.0004
d. 16700.0   i. .00240
e. 16700.00   j. 0.05
f. 15,789,022   k. 121

5. In the following computations the number in italics is an exact number, while the other is approximate. Round the answers off to the appropriate number of significant digits.

a. *8* × .04 = .32   Ans.: .3
b. *100* × 4444 = 444,400   f. *.24* ÷ 6 = .04000
c. 100 × *4444* = 444,400   g. .24 ÷ *6* = .04000
d. $\overline{2}000 ÷ 9 = 222.2$ h. *.2323* × $\overline{1}000$ = 232.3000
e. *2000* ÷ 9 = 222.2   i. .2323 × *1000* = 232.3000

6. In the following computations both numbers are approximate. Round the answers off to the appropriate number of significant digits.

a. 291 × .042 = 12.222
b. 4976 × $\overline{2}000$ = 9,952,000
c. 5784 ÷ 7.2 = 803.3333
d. $\sqrt{169.94}$ = 13.0361
e. $(77)^2$ = 5929
f. 144.39
   37
    .65
    9
   $\overline{1}0$
_____

g. $4\overline{5}, 000$
   221
     .68
   453.4
   12
   8
_____

References

1. Arkin, H. and Colton, R. R. *Graphs, How to Make and Use Them*, New York, Harper, 1936.
2. Arkin, H. and Colton, R. R. *Tables for Statisticians*, College Outline Series, No. 75, New York, Barnes & Noble, 1950.
3. Barlow, P. *Barlow's Tables of Squares, Cubes, Square Roots, Cube Roots and Reciprocals of all Integer Numbers up to 12,500*. L. J. Comrie (ed.) 4th ed., Brooklyn, N. Y., Chem. Pub. Co., 1941.
4. Brinton, W. C. *Graphic Presentation*, New York, Brinton Associates, 1939.
5. Freund, J. *A Modern Introduction to Mathematics*, Englewood Cliffs, N. J., Prentice-Hall, 1956.
6. Lutz, R. R. *Graphic Presentation Simplified*, New York, Funk & Wagnalls in association with Modern Industry Mag., 1949.
7. Richardson, M. *Fundamentals of Mathematics*, New York, Macmillan, 1946.
8. Spear, Mary Eleanor, *Charting Statistics*, New York, McGraw-Hill, 1952.
9. Walker, Helen M. *Mathematics Essential for Elementary Statistics*, New York, Holt, 1951.

Answers

Self-test, Page 3

1. 770
2. 760
3. 760
4. 1,040,078 (approx.)
5. 1,898 (approx.)
6. 75
7. 1198.3
8. 60.332
9. 0.47900
10. 500.5
11. 94.32
12. $\frac{22}{39}$
13. $\frac{2}{33}$
14. $\frac{4}{11}$
15. $\frac{4}{69}$
16. $\frac{2b}{a}$
17. $4a - 7$

18. $\sqrt{a}$
19. .25
20. 25%
21. $33\frac{1}{3}\%$
22. less
23. 1
24. 32
25. 2
26. 576
27. 4
28. $\frac{1}{2}$
29. $\frac{1}{8}$
30. $\sqrt{2}$
31. $\frac{1}{2}\sqrt{2}$
32. 9
33. $\log a + \log b$
34. $3 \log a$
35. $- \log a$

36. $\log (a + b)$
37. 1
38. 2
39. x
40. xy
41. y^3
42. $\dfrac{y^2}{x^2}$
43. $\bar{3}$
44. 3
45. $\bar{1}$
46. 2
47. $\frac{3}{2}$
48. $y = -x - 3$
49. $x = 5, y = 6$
50. See fig. 0.7 (page 35)

Page 8

1. 2.2, 2.1, 2.2, 2.2

2. 460, 555, 774, 6, 0, 4, 17, 30, 50

3. 275^-, 154, 345^+, 225^+, 195^-, 865^+

4. 270, 150, 350, 230, 190, 870

Page 17

1. 128
2. 9
3. 1
4. 2
5. 3
6. $\frac{1}{36}$
7. $2\sqrt[3]{2}$
8. $\frac{1}{7}$
9. 2
10. $\frac{1}{4}$
11. 27
12. 5
13. 572,000,000
14. .0000000236

15. 6.25
16. $x^{\frac{1}{6}}$
17. $x^{-\frac{19}{5}}$
18. $x^{\frac{38}{9}}$
19–23. 1
24–31. 2
32. 9
33. 27
34. $\overline{16}$
35. $\overline{1}$
36. x
37. $\overline{2}$
38. $\overline{1}$
39. $-.5$ or $\overline{1}.5$

40. $\overline{3}$
41. $\overline{2}$
42. $\overline{1}$
43. $\overline{n}$
44. $2 - \log 3 - \log x$
45. $\log 6 + \log a + \log b$
46. $3(\log 9 + \log x)$
47. $\log 9 + 3 \log x$
48. $\log (3x + 4y)$
49. $\overline{4}, \overline{5}, \overline{1}, 3, 6, 8$
50. 3.700, 4.858, 7.931, $\overline{2}.911$, $\overline{6}.941$

Page 24

1. a. $\displaystyle\sum_1^4 x_i$; b. $\displaystyle\sum_1^{37} y_i$; c. $\displaystyle\sum_1^n x_i^2$

2. a. $x_1 + x_2 + x_3 + x_4 + x_5$; b. $y_1^2 + y_2^2 + \ldots + y_n^2$

3. a. 14; b. 30; c. 104; d. 54; e. 230; f. 196; g. 900

4. No.   5. No.

Page 26

1. a. $\displaystyle\sum_1^4 x_i - 32$; b. $4\displaystyle\sum_1^n y_i$; c. $\displaystyle\sum_1^n x_i y_i$

2. a. $(x_1 - y_1) + (x_2 - y_2) + \ldots + (x_n - y_n)$
   b. $(x_1 + 5) + (x_2 + 5) + \ldots + (x_n + 5)$
   c. $6y_1^2 + 6y_2^2 + \ldots + 6y_n^2$
   d. $(x_1 y_1 - 2) + (x_2 y_2 - 2) + \ldots + (x_n y_n - 2)$

3. a. 30; b. 460; c. 1476; d. 100

4. a. $4\displaystyle\sum_1^N x_i^2$; b. $a\displaystyle\sum_1^N x_i^2 + 4a\displaystyle\sum_1^N x_i + 4aN$; c. $\displaystyle\sum_1^N x_i y_i + c\displaystyle\sum_1^N x_i + c\displaystyle\sum_1^N y_i$

$+ Nc^2$; d. $k\displaystyle\sum_1^N \log x_i$

Page 30

1. c. .004 ± .0005; d. 14 ± .5; e. 247.3 ± .05; f. 16,500 ± 50;
   g. 15,000,000 ± 500,000; h. .00210 ± .000005; i. 15,000,000 ± 50;
   j. .032 ± .0005
2. b. 2.35–2.45; c. 200–607; d. .55–.65; e. 138–150; f. 2.405–2.415
3. b. 35.75–48.75; c. 74.25–94.25; d. 1883.25–2037.25; e. .0288225–
   .0300825; f. .052625–.074025; g. 30,750,000–53,750,000
4. b. 10, 1670, 4; c. 1, 16700, 5; d. 0.1, 167,000, 6; e. 0.01, 1,670,000,
   7;
   f. 1, 15,789,022, 8; g. 0.01, 1,578,902,200, 10; h. 0.0001, 10,004, 5;
   i. 0.00001, 240, 3; j. 0.01, 5, 1; k. 1, 121, 3
5. b. 444,$\bar{4}$00; c. 44$\bar{4}$,000; d. $\bar{2}$00; e. $\bar{2}$00; f. .04; g. .040; h. $\bar{2}$00;
   i. 232.3
6. a. 12; b. $\bar{1}$0,000,000; c. 8$\bar{0}$0; d. 13,036; e. 5$\bar{9}$00; f. 2$\bar{0}$0; g. 4$\bar{6}$,000

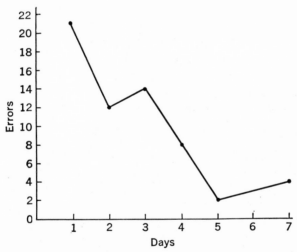

FIG. 0.7   Number of errors made by a single rat in a maze. Data for
day 6 were not available.

1. Were 'errors' plotted on y-axis and 'days' on x-axis?
2. Is the horizontal spacing of the points, including that for days 5 and 7,
   correct?
3. Is the vertical spacing of the points correct?
4. Are both axes correctly labeled?
5. Are the horizontal and vertical dimensions of the graph in reasonable
   proportion to each other?
6. Does the graph have a title?

THE WHY AND THE WHAT OF STATISTICS

Our world is really a very confusing place.

Of course, it doesn't seem confusing to you—but then you've lived here all your life. Other people have already made order out of the chaos (or found order existing in the chaos, depending upon your philosophy of science) and have passed their findings on to you. You *know* what a man is—how big and how heavy he is likely to be. You *know* that men are stronger than women and humans are more intelligent than snails. You know that a body dropped from a point above the earth's surface will fall to earth; you know that people with a lot of money usually wear finer clothes than those with little money. You know all these things, partly because you've observed them for yourself and partly because other people have told you. It's pretty hard to imagine what life would be like if you did not know these and millions of other facts.

Yet there are things you do not know, there is order you do not recognize. There is a frontier of knowledge beyond which you have not gone. There are, for example, forms of life you could not identify or classify, regularities in the social behavior of men and of animals that are unknown to you.

There is a further frontier beyond which no one has penetrated. In the physical world there is consistency and lawfulness that has never been described. In the world of plants and animals there is sense and organization where even the eye of the most erudite scientist perceives only chaos and confusion. The little that is known, the few laws that have been formulated about the behavior of human beings are only narrow trails into a vast area as yet almost completely uncharted. To pass beyond the frontier of knowledge and to map the unexplored realm is the work of the scientist.

It is not an easy job. For nature has a gigantic practical joke to spring upon the mapmaker: *variability*. Would you describe a maple

leaf exactly? Then every maple leaf that grows upon a tree will con-
found your efforts and make a lie of your careful description. And if
you cannot give a precise description of a maple leaf, how much
harder to describe a man. Abstract we can and do, seeking to include
in our description only those characteristics that apply to all maple
leaves or all men, yet the abstract picture that applies to all is an
impoverished portrait of any one.

From man's point of view, variability is nature's practical joke,
but from nature's own point of view, variability is the most fundamental regularity. No two leaves, no two fingerprints, no two personalities, no two rivets, though manufactured under the most controlled conditions, are exactly alike. That simple fact might well be
called the first law of nature. It applies not only to objects but to
relationships between objects. Men are stronger than women? Yet
who would deny that some women can outlift, outwrestle, outgrip
some men? Humans, surely, are more intelligent than snails? Perhaps, but a bright and well-educated snail can gather his own food,
produce young, protect himself against external dangers, while a
human idiot cannot. Adults are taller than children? For the most
part, yes, but there are tall children and short adults, youthful
giants and aged midgets. Yet these examples of relationships come
from the charted and familiar territory of everyday life. They are
relationships so strong and so dependable that all of us take them for
granted. Who is to say that there are not other relationships, un-
recognized or unformulated, obscured by the variability of nature
and challenged by the striking exceptions?

The regular irregularity of nature makes cautious men of scientists. The story is told of a scientist and his friend who observed a
field of sheep.

'Look,' said the friend, 'those sheep have been sheared.'

'Yes,' replied the scientist, 'on *this* side, anyway.'

The words 'in general,' 'a trend toward,' 'a tendency for,' 'in all
probability,' 'under the conditions of this experiment' are the scientist's defensive weapons against nature's joke.

But science has a great offensive weapon, too. If variability is the
first and most dependable law of nature, then science will turn
nature's joke back upon her and study the variability. The business
of science is prediction, but variability makes prediction hazardous.
Very well. Science will not only predict—it will describe in advance

the error of its own predictions. The tool that is used to do this is statistics.

Were it not for variability there would be no need for statistics. If all men were exactly the same height, for example, we would name that height and that would be an end to the matter. But variability there is, and so we name not *the* height but the average height, not *the* hair color but the most typical hair color; and when we have described the typical we go on to describe and delimit the variability, saying, for example, that the shortest man is so tall, and the tallest man is of such a height.

The first important use of statistics is to give a complete description of a group. A group, as we use the term here, is an aggregate of individuals. By 'individual' we do not necessarily mean a person. An individual is a single entity—perhaps a person, perhaps a rat, perhaps a day, an electric-light bulb, a blood cell, or a housing development. When we set out to describe a group we must renounce immediately the idea of doing a complete job. Since we cannot even give a complete description of a single individual—say a rat, for example—we abstract those aspects that are of concern to us. We may describe the rat's color or his weight, his performance on a maze or his basal metabolic rate. These aspects of the individual that we abstract for measurement and description are called **variables.** When we speak of describing a group, what we really mean is that we shall describe some aspect of the group, some variable.

Groups—aggregates of individuals—are of two kinds: complete and incomplete. A complete group is one that includes all the individuals of the specified kind. If we bleed John Jones dry and spill not a drop, then the red cells in the blood we have collected are the complete group of John Jones's red blood cells. A complete group is technically called a **population.** If we merely extracted a pint of blood from Mr. Jones, or if we spilled a few drops during the blood-letting process, the red cells available for our inspection would be an incomplete group, since not *all* of them would be included. An incomplete group is called a **sample.** In a sense, though, a sample is itself a kind of population, for while we may not have all of Jones's blood, we have all that we have, and we can speak of the population of cells-extracted-and-available-for-analysis.

Whether we choose to think of a given group as a sample or as a population depends upon our purposes in studying it. Though the

150.13
Se5
m

pupils in a classroom are only a sample of the pupils in the school, and those, in turn, a sample of the pupils in the country, the teacher who has that classroom under her supervision is interested in the pupils as a complete group, a population. The educational research worker, on the other hand, when he uses these pupils as subjects in a test of educational theory, cares little about the particular class he studies if he cannot generalize from that class to others. He studies the class as a sample, and his aim is to generalize to the population from which the sample came.

Statistics that describe a group are called **descriptive statistics.** That is true whether the group is a sample or a population. But if we wish to generalize from our knowledge of a sample to the population of which the sample is only a fraction, mere description is not enough. We must make inferences on the basis of our partial knowledge, and statistics is a tool for making those inferences well and wisely. The techniques that enable us to draw inferences about populations from our knowledge of samples are called **inferential statistics.**

1.1 Statistics as a Tool for Description

When a group has been selected for study and measurements of some variable have been made and recorded, the data, at this time a long list of words or numbers, are ready to be organized and described. There are many ways they could be organized and an almost infinite number of generalizations that could be made about them, but not all of these would be very useful. There are five questions we commonly ask of the data.

1. What general picture emerges?
2. If an individual is a member of the group, what is our best prediction about him in terms of the variable under investigation?
3. How bad is that prediction? What is our margin of error?
4. If measurements of two variables have been made on the same individuals, how much will knowledge of one variable improve our prediction of the other?
5. How does a single individual compare with the rest of the group?

Let us consider these questions in more detail.

1.1.1 What General Picture Do the Data Convey? No general picture emerges from a long list of numbers. If our group consists of

72897

100 men whose heights we have measured, the list of 100 heights, in random order, tells us little or nothing. Our first step toward bringing order out of the chaos is to organize our measurements. The way to do this is to tabulate the number of men having each measured height. When this chore is finished we shall be able to say that so many men were 5'4", so many 5'5", and so on. This count of the number of individuals falling into each class of the measured variable is called a **frequency distribution.** It is really just an ordered rearrangement of the original data.

Since our interest is in getting an over-all view of the data, we often plot frequency distributions as graphs. This visual presentation conveys a general impression to most people more readily than does any list of numbers.

1.1.2 If an Individual Is a Member of the Group, What Is Our Best Prediction about Him in Terms of the Variable under Investigation? We have a general picture of our data, and we can observe from the frequency distribution that, though the shortest man in the group is 5'2" and the tallest man is 6'4", most of the men are of middling height—say 5'9" or 5'10". If we know that an individual is in this group and must guess or predict his height, we shall not hypothesize that he is 5'2" or 6'4", but rather suppose that he is fairly typical and guess him to be 5'9" or 5'10". Exactly what we guess depends upon the definition of the word 'best.' If a miss is as bad as a mile, a small error as bad as a large one, then the best prediction is the one that has the greatest chance of being absolutely right. In that case, we shall guess our individual to be of the most common height. Perhaps the best prediction is the one that will make the average error of prediction the smallest, or perhaps it is the one that is just as likely to be too high as to be too low. The exact figure we give as our prediction will depend upon our definition of the term 'best.'

Nevertheless, any prediction will be of a measure that is, in some sense, typical or average. Those words are as vague as the word 'best,' and we shall see in the chapters to follow that there are many measures of the typical, many kinds of averages. The statistics that answer the question about what to predict are the various kinds of averages.

Though we phrase the question in terms of 'best prediction,' this does not mean that in practice we shall actually be making predictions or guesses. When we are describing a group we already know all about it, and guessing would be sheer foolishness. However, the structure of statistics and the relations of averages to measures of variability and to measures of relationship are easier to grasp and understand if we speak of prediction rather than of averages. In other texts you may encounter other terms that refer to averages: 'measures of central tendency' and 'measures of location' are terms that are frequently employed.

1.1.3 How Bad Is That Prediction? That we must ask this question is an acknowledgment of the fact that nature has us licked. We cannot make a perfect prediction because variability is the most fundamental fact of nature. Answering the question and describing accurately the size of a possible or probable error in prediction is the turning back of nature's joke upon herself.

Whatever we predict about the height of an individual in our group, we know that we cannot be off by more than 14 inches. If we made the foolish prediction of 5′2″, the height of the shortest man, and the individual in question actually turned out to be the tallest man, who is 6′4″, our error of prediction is 14 inches, and that is as bad as it could be.

Just as the words 'best prediction' could have many meanings, so can the words 'how bad?' A prediction can be bad because it is very unlikely to be absolutely right, or it can be bad because it is likely to be in error by a large amount. There are many ways of describing the badness of a prediction, depending upon how we define 'badness.' These many measures of badness are all ways of describing the variability of our group. They are sometimes called 'measures of variability,' and we shall frequently refer to them also as 'measures of unpredictability.'

1.1.4 If Measurements of Two Variables Have Been Made on the Same Individuals, How Much Will Knowledge of One Variable Improve Our Prediction of the Other? Let us suppose that we have measured not only the heights but also the weights of the 100 men in our group. We have already seen that when we predict a man's height our error can be as large as 14 inches. But suppose that we know that the man weighs 95 pounds. Common sense suggests that any man as light as that will not be very tall. In fact, he probably will not be as tall as average, and we might do well to predict him to be 5′2″ or 5′3″. We find from an examination of our data that the shortest man with a weight of less than 100 pounds is 5'2'', and the tallest man with such a weight is 5'4''. If we make use of our knowledge of these facts, and of the man's weight, in making our prediction, we cannot be in error by more than 2 inches, whereas without knowledge of weight we might have been in error by 14. Unpredictability has been reduced from 14 to 2, a reduction of $\frac{6}{7}$.

When knowledge of one variable improves predictions of another, the two variables are said to be **correlated.** Height and weight are correlated, though not perfectly. If they were perfectly correlated, there would be no error left in our predictions of weight once we knew height and vice versa. The greater the improvement in prediction, the more strongly are the variables related.

1.1.5 How Does a Single Individual Compare with the Rest of the Group? If Arnold Smithers, a member of our group, is 6'1'' in height, what more can we say about him? If the average height of the group is 5'9'', then we can say that Mr. Smithers is taller than average—4 inches taller, in fact. We can also examine our frequency distribution and report that there are so many men shorter than Smithers, so many of the same height, and so many who are taller. All of these are ways of specifying Smithers' relationship to the group of which he is a member, and there are other ways that we shall discuss in later chapters.

We have left this question until the last because we cannot describe an individual in relation to the group until we have described the group. When we have organized our data, found an average, and determined the variability, then we are ready to compare an individual with his fellows.

Those are the questions. When they have been answered the group has been described as completely as statistics can describe it. The whole study of descriptive statistics is the study of the answers to those five questions.

1.2 Statistical Inference

Description is enough when the group is complete. When the group is a sample drawn from a larger population, description is an important first step, but it is not enough by itself. In that case our interest is not in the particular group we have measured but in the larger whole of which it is only a part, and conclusions about the larger whole must be inferences drawn from our partial knowledge. Some inferences are very safe and others are very tenuous. Inferential statistics is a body of techniques that will tell us what inferences we can draw and how safe we are in drawing them.

Inferential statistics fall into two main categories: those that tell us our margin or error when we predict some population measure such as an average, and those that enable us to test hypotheses about populations. Let us consider an example of each of these.

1.2.1 The Margin of Error in Predicting a Population Measure:

We have pricked Mr. Jones's finger, extracted a drop of blood, and found that 50 of the 100 white blood cells in that drop are diseased. Clearly our interest is not in the drop of blood we have extracted but in the blood remaining in Jones's body, which we cannot study *in toto* for obvious reasons. In the drop available for our inspection, 50 per cent of the cells are diseased, but it does not follow from this that *exactly* 50 per cent of the remaining cells are also diseased. The percentage might be 45 or 55, and our finding of 50 would still be quite reasonable. Our best prediction is 50 per cent, true, but there is room for error in that prediction. The question is, how much error? Would we be likely to draw a drop in which 50 per cent of the cells were diseased if only 5 per cent of the cells in Jones's body were diseased? It could happen, but it would be unlikely. There's a good chance, then, that only 45 per cent of Jones's white blood cells are diseased, but practically no chance that only 5 per cent are diseased. What about 20 per cent? 60 per cent? When does an estimate stop being reasonable? Statistics can tell us.

If a statistician were called in and asked to work on this problem, he would first demand a more precise definition of 'reasonable.' We should tell him something like this: we want two numbers, a low estimate and a high estimate of the percentage of diseased cells in Mr. Jones. And we want to be able to say that we have 19 chances out of 20 of being right if we say that Jones has no fewer diseased cells than the lower estimate and no more diseased cells than the higher estimate.

The statistician would get out a pencil and paper. He would make mysterious scratches and set the wheels of a calculating machine whirring. He would look sober and consult a table in the back of the book. He would stroke his beard, and then say:

'Your best guess is that 50 per cent of the cells in Jones's body are diseased. But you have 19 chances out of 20 of being right if you say that not less than 40.20 per cent or more than 59.80 per cent of the cells are diseased.'

Those limits, found by the techniques of inferential statistics, represent the margin of error in our prediction of 50 per cent.

1.2.2 **Hypothesis Testing:** Suppose a subject walks up to you and says, 'I can tell the suit of a playing card just by looking at the back of it. Test me.' You say to yourself, 'Well, either he can or he can't. Hypothesis one is: "his identification will be no better than pure chance"; hypothesis two is: "his identification *is* better than chance." Which of these hypotheses is true?' You set up a simple experiment. You select four playing cards of different suits and ask your subject to arrange them in the order: spades, hearts, diamonds, clubs. To your amazement, the subject does so with perfect accuracy.

You say to yourself, 'Yes, yes, but it could have been an accident. How likely is it that, if the subject's claim were totally false, he would have been so lucky?' You sit down with pencil, paper, and a statistics book and determine that there are exactly 24 ways those four cards could have been arranged. (Try it!) If the subject's arrangement was pure luck, then he was a mighty lucky man. He was a winner on a one in 24 chance. That challenges your credulity, and you reluctantly conclude that you must reject the hypothesis that his judgment is no better than pure chance. Of course, you may be wrong. Maybe he did pull that one lucky shot. Nature being what she is, you can never be absolutely sure, but in this case you can feel twenty-three twenty-fourths sure, which is good enough for most people.

In practice, inferential statistics is much more important, particularly to psychologists, biologists, and social scientists, than descriptive statistics. The reason is not hard to find: these scientists try to make generalizations that will apply universally, yet many practical considerations—lack of time, lack of money, lack of available subjects, or the unfortunate necessity of killing every subject studied—prevent them from making measurements of populations. They must study samples, but are seldom interested in the samples themselves. Inferential statistics permits them to go beyond their data and tells them how much risk they take in doing so.

1.3 Statistics as an Approach to Life

The person who takes his study of statistics seriously will learn from it more than a collection of techniques. He will learn to see the world about him *probabilistically*.

Nature's great caprice, variability, makes our world a world of uncertainty, a world where there is no absolute surety, but only varying degrees of probability. Some things are highly probable, some highly improbable, some are quite probable, and others about as probable as a coin is to fall heads. What the man on the street regards as impossible, the person who thinks statistically knows is merely highly improbable.[1]

The person who recognizes the probabilistic nature of the universe does not ask questions that demand absolute answers. He does not say to his doctor, 'Will I get well?' but, 'What are my chances of getting well?' He does not ask his broker whether a stock will increase in value but for the probability that it will increase. He knows that the improbable event is not an impossible event—in fact, he knows that the improbable event must eventually happen if it is given enough opportunity. But he devotes no undue worry to the danger of being struck by lightning while lying in bed because he knows that, while this *will*, someday, happen to somebody, it is very unlikely to happen to him.[2]

You think, perhaps, that if you hold a book in mid air and then let go, the book is *certain* to fall to the floor, but you are wrong. Between the book and the floor are molecules of air. These are in constant movement, and the directions of their movement are random. At any given moment, some are moving up, some down, some sideways. It is *highly improbable* that all the molecules should be moving up at the particular moment that you release the book, but it is not impossible, and if it should happen, the book would not fall but float gracefully to the ceiling. Few of us lose our libraries in this manner, but consider how very unlikely it is that all the billions of

[1] This statement is not meant to deny that some things are logically inconsistent, and in that sense impossible. It is impossible to have a square circle because the definitions of square and circle make such a thing logically inconsistent.

[2] The story is told of the British statistician who never sought a bomb shelter during the London blitz. He had figured the probabilities and decided that his chances of being hit were too low to warrant the effort. He changed his mind, however, when the elephant in the London Zoo was killed by a bomb. All we can say is that in changing his mind he was behaving irrationally.

air molecules should, just by chance, move in exactly the same upward direction all at once.

In the physical world probabilities are usually very very high or very very low. That is so because they result from the interaction of an almost infinite number of particles, any one of which may behave erratically, but all of which are very unlikely to go berserk at the same instant. Most of the physical laws of the universe are laws not about individual particles but about enormous numbers of particles. And in numbers there is relative certainty.

It is sometimes said that the physical sciences are exact sciences, while the life and social sciences are statistical, but that is a very misleading statement. If the universe is probabilistic, if variability is the basic fact of nature, then all sciences must be statistical. There are, however, two differences between the physical sciences and social and life sciences that are worth examining.

The more important difference between the two is that variability, in the physical world, is usually small enough so that it does not obscure the effects under investigation. Variability in living organisms, on the other hand, may be so great that finding the regularities is difficult. Those are very abstract statements; let us illustrate them with an analogy.

The marksmanship of two men is to be compared. Actually A is a very much better shot than B, but that fact is not known at the start of the contest.

At first each man is equipped with a nineteenth-century gun known as a King's Musket, a gun which was described as follows in 1814, by Colonel Hanger of the British army:

> The soldier's musket, if not exceedingly ill-bored (as many are), will strike the figure of a man at 80 yards; it may even at 100; but a soldier must be very unfortunate indeed who shall be wounded by a common musket at 150 yards, provided his antagonist aims at him; and as to firing at a man at 200 yards with a common musket, you may must as well fire at the moon and have the same hopes of hitting your object. I do maintain and will prove, whenever called on, that no man was ever killed at 200 yards, by a common soldier's musket, by the person who aimed at him.

and by the Board of Royal Engineers, in 1841, as follows:

> At a distance of 150 yards, a target, about twice as high and twice as broad as a man, could, with very careful shooting, be hit three times out of

four; beyond that distance, notwithstanding that the musket was fired from a stand and every precaution employed to ensure steadiness and success, the result was nil. Nothing could be learnt at all, except that the target was never hit and the balls could never be found. The mark was made twice as wide as before, but of ten shots at 250 yards not one struck.[3]

Obviously A's superior marksmanship will have a difficult time in manifesting itself when the men are equpped with such guns, though if many thousands of rounds were fired, A's superiority would eventually become apparent. *The variability of the gun is so great that it obscures the real difference in ability between A and B.*

The King's Muskets are then abandoned and each man is equipped with a precise target rifle. Only a few shots are required to show that A is overwhelmingly better than B.

The social scientist's search for the regularities of human behavior can be compared to the rifle match with the King's Muskets. The regularities are there, but they are often obscured by the tremendous variability that is so characteristic of life and living things. Physical science is more like the second match, where regularities are easy to see because there is little variability to overshadow them. But both kinds of science study real effects, and both must acknowledge and deal with variability. The difference is one of amount rather than of kind.

The other difference between physical sciences on the one hand and life and social sciences on the other is that the social or life scientist is often asked to make predictions about the functioning or behavior of a single individual, while the physical scientist is seldom asked to make predictions about a single molecule or atom. When social scientists make predictions about people en masse they do very well indeed, as indicated by the success of the Gallup and other polls, and by the accuracy with which the National Safety Council regularly predicts holiday traffic deaths. Prediction for the individual is a good deal poorer. The pollster can tell you how many people will vote Democratic, but he cannot tell you whether you will do so. Similarly, the physicist can predict with extreme accuracy what fraction of a gram of radium will disintegrate in a ten-year period; he would be much less successful if he tried to predict which particular atoms would disintegrate. If the social scientist's results

[3] *Shotguns and Shotgun Shooting*, The Sportsman's Bookshelf, Vol. I, New York, Stackpole and Heck, 1950, p. 5.

sometimes seem vague or inaccurate, it is not because he can do so little, but because he sometimes tries to do so much.

A statistical approach to life and a probabilistic view of the universe are not things that can be taught. No course in statistics can change an absolutistic outlook to a probabilistic one. But the student who thinks seriously about the reasons behind the techniques he learns may find that he comes out of a statistics course with a radically revised philosophy of life. One who does that, though he cannot compute a standard deviation or derive the formula for a correlation coefficient, has learned a great deal.

Review Questions

1. Explain what is meant by each of the expressions below. Don't try to give formal definitions—just explain in your own words.

    a. variability
    b. individual
    c. variable
    d. population
    e. sample
    f. correlated
    g. perfectly correlated
    h. descriptive statistics
    i. inferential statistics
    j. probabilistic universe

2. What questions does descriptive statistics answer?
3. What are the two principal functions of inferential statistics?

If you like to ponder deep philosophical questions, you might give some thought to this one:

We have said repeatedly in this chapter that variability is a fact of *nature*, that uncertainty and unpredictability are inevitable results of the kind of universe we live in. Many reputable thinkers maintain that variability is a fact of *human knowledge*, that uncertainty and unpredictability are inevitable limitations imposed upon us by the *nature of man* rather than by the *nature of the universe*. Which point of view is more defensible?

You might come back and think some more about this question

when you have finished your statistics course and know more about unpredictability.

References

Almost every general psychology text has a chapter on statistics. Skimming over one of these will give you a specific idea of the kinds of problems with which statistics deals and the kinds of tools it uses.

1. Kline, M. *Mathematics and Western Culture*, New York, Oxford Univ. Press, 1953, pp. 322–94. An elementary, non-mathematical discussion of the statistical view of the universe.
2. Wallis, W. A. and Roberts, H. V. *Statistics, A New Approach*, Glencoe: The Free Press, 1956, pp. 3–99. A discussion of the purposes, uses, and misuses of statistics, with many provocative examples.

NUMBERS, THINGS, AND MEASUREMENT

Statistics, we have said, is a way of describing the world around us. That means that when we use statistics, even though we work with numbers, we are not interested in the numbers themselves but in the things they stand for. If there were 25 people in a group, and we wanted to describe the typical height of the group, we *could* line the *people* up from shortest to tallest, then point to the man in the middle and say, 'He is of typical height.' But that would be cumbersome. If we know each man's height in inches, we find it more convenient to line up these *numbers* and point to the middle number. And so it is with many statistics. We push numbers around instead of people, or fish, or sacks of potatoes, because it's a lot more convenient. But we must make sure that we get the same results when we manipulate the numbers that we would if we manipulated the objects for which those numbers stand.

Measurement is the process of assigning numerals to objects according to rules.[1] Notice that we say 'numerals,' rather than 'numbers.' By a 'numeral' we mean a symbol: for example 'A' or 'VII' or '26,' whereas by the word 'number' we mean a symbol that has certain fixed relationships to other symbols. That is, the *numbers* 3 and 2, when operated on by a process we call addition, always yield another specified number, 5. But the *numerals* 3 and 2 may be nothing but names, and it may be as meaningless to talk about adding them as to talk about adding C and B. The rules by which we assign numerals to objects tell us how many of the formal properties of numbers (arithmetic) are also properties of the numerals. That, in turn, will depend upon how many properties of numbers are also properties of the objects to which we assign the numerals. It may or may not be

[1] Stevens, S. S., Mathematics, Measurement, and Psychophysics, Chap. I in *Handbook of Experimental Psychology*, S. S. Stevens (ed.), New York, Wiley, 1951, p. 1. The whole treatment of measurement and scaling presented here is an adaptation of Stevens' treatment as covered in his handbook chapter and other papers.

true that when we add the *objects* identified by the numerals 3 and 2 the result will be equivalent to another object which carries the numeral 5. That depends upon the rules by which the numerals 3, 2, and 5 have been assigned. There are at least four different sets of rules by which numerals are assigned to objects. The most lenient set requires merely that different numerals be assigned to different objects, and the numerals are nothing except identifying tags; when we have used this set of rules and then want to push the numerals around instead of the objects, we cannot assume that the numerals behave like numbers in any respect except that of being different from each other. We can't add the numerals, for example, because we haven't shown that we'd get the same result by adding the numerals that we'd get by adding the objects. At the other extreme is a very strict set of rules which requires that the objects to which we assign numerals have all the properties of real numbers. When we have used these rules, we can treat the numerals assigned to the objects just as if they were numbers and apply all the techniques of arithmetic and mathematics. These four sets of rules result in four different kinds of measuring instrument, or scale: the nominal, ordinal, interval, and ratio scales. By oversimplifying a bit, we can summarize the differences among these four scales as follows:

If all you can say is that one object is *different* from another, you have a **nominal scale.**

If you can say that one object is bigger or better or *more* of anything than another, you have an **ordinal scale.**

If you can say that one object is so many *units* (inches, degrees, etc.) more than another, you have an **interval scale.**

If you can say that one object is so many *times* as big or bright or tall or heavy as another, you have a **ratio scale.**

The nominal scale is the weakest measuring instrument, and the ratio scale, because it permits us to treat numerals just like numbers, is the strongest. The rest of this chapter will be concerned with the rules for the construction of each of these four scales.

2.1 The Nominal Scale

The most basic operation involved in any kind of measurement is the operation of differentiating, or 'telling apart.' We can differentiate people according to sex, for example, and then we can call all those of one kind 'men,' and those of the other kind 'women.' We can, with more difficulty, classify mental patients according to their psychiatric diagnoses, making up rules for the borderline cases, and then call the resulting classes 'paranoid schizophrenic,' 'manic-depressive,' and so on.

If we have a clear and unambiguous way of categorizing objects or people, we have the simplest scale of measurement, the nominal scale. It now remains only to assign symbols or numerals to the categories or classes we have set up. As the word 'nominal' implies, the 'numerals' used for this kind of scale are simply names. Any names at all will do. The names may be words such as 'schizophrenic,' 'manic-depressive,' 'involutional melancholic'; or they may be nonsense syllables, or letters of the alphabet, or numbers. The basic rule by which numerals (or names) are assigned to objects on the nominal scale is this:

Two classes which are different with respect to the variable or quality being 'measured' shall not bear the same name; two individual objects which are the same with respect to this quality shall not be placed in classes bearing different names.

If one set of numerals has been assigned to the classes of a nominal scale, any other set of numerals may be substituted for it, provided only that the new set does not violate the basic rule above. If we have decided to classify people according to sex, and have called the sexes male and female, we are at liberty to substitute the symbols M and F, or A and B, or 2 and 1 for male and female, for such substitutions will not violate our basic rule of numeral assignment. If we let the symbol N stand for one of our original numerals, and the symbol N' for a numeral to be substituted for the original one, we may formulate the rule by which numerals may be substituted as follows:

$$N' = s(N)$$

which is to be read: 'N' equals s of N.' In this equation, the letter s stands for the words 'any direct substitution for.' The equation therefore reads: 'The new numeral may be any direct substitution for the old one.'

If we have chosen numbers for our numerals, we must remember that the formal rules of arithmetic which apply to numbers do not apply to the objects that are identified by the numbers. Suppose, for example we have administered a set of questions to which the answers 'yes,' 'no,' and 'uncertain' are permitted. We decide to call a 'yes' answer '1,' a 'no' answer '2,' and an answer of 'uncertain' '3.' It turns out that the three answers are chosen equally often by the respondents. Suppose, now, that we unthinkingly decide to find out what the 'average' answer is. Averaging the numbers assigned to the classes gives us the number '2' as an answer. Are we to conclude, therefore, that the 'average' response to the questionnaire was 'no'? Such a conclusion would make very little sense. The *numbers* can be added and subtracted, but the categories of response cannot. In obtaining an average we have ignored the fact that the rules of arithmetic which apply to numbers do not apply to the classes for which those numbers stand.

Although the formal rules that apply to numbers do not apply in any way to the numerals used to identify the classes of a nominal scale, such a scale is not, as it might at first seem, utterly useless. If we can do no more than differentiate between the objects to be measured and give names to the classes obtained from the differentiation, we still have several measures available to describe the characteristics of the whole group and its relationship to other groups. All these measures are based on a *count* of the objects to which each numeral has been assigned. They will be discussed in Chapter 3.

2.2 The Ordinal Scale

Often we can decide not only that two things are *different* but also that one of them has more or less of some quality than the other. Our language is rich in comparative words—richer, smarter, better, taller, hotter, and so on. It is because we can make comparative judgments that these words are useful.

If, after we have classified our objects on a nominal scale, we can then *order* the classes in such a way that each class has more of the quality upon which the classification is based than has any one of the preceding classes, we have an *ordinal* scale. We can be sure that our ordering is complete and self-consistent if and only if we can show that three relationships exist among the classes.

Let the letters A, B, and C be the names of any three different classes of objects. Let the symbol

$>$ mean 'is greater than' or, more generally, 'has more of the quality than';

< mean 'is less than' or, more generally, 'has less of the quality than';

≯ mean 'is not greater than'; ≮ 'is not less than,' and the symbol ≠ mean 'does not equal.' Unless the three relationships below can be shown to hold, we do not have an ordinal scale:

1. If $A \neq B$, then either $A > B$ or $A < B$. This is known as the property of **connectedness.** It states that if A is different from B, then either A has more of the quality than B, or A has less of the quality than B.

2. If $A > B$, then $B \ngtr A$. This is the property of **asymmetry.** It states that if A has more of the quality than B, then B does not have more of the quality than A.

3. If $A > B$, and $B > C$, then $A > C$. This is the property of **transitivity.** If A has more of the quality than B, and B has more than C, then A has more of the quality than C.

Once we have established a basis for differentiation between classes, and have shown that the relationships of connectedness, asymmetry, and transitivity hold among the classes, we have an ordinal scale.

An example of an ordinal scale in fairly common use is the scale of hardness of minerals established by the operation of scratching. Take any ten minerals and attempt to scratch each mineral with every other. It quickly becomes apparent that a diamond (if we have one) will scratch every other mineral but can be scratched by none. Sandstone, on the other hand, can be scratched by every other mineral and will scratch none. The rest of the ten quickly fall into place. Each will scratch every mineral in the series between itself and sandstone, will not scratch any mineral between itself and diamond, and can be scratched by all the latter. If hardness is defined as the quality of being able to scratch, then we have an ordinal scale of hardness. The symbol $>$ now means 'scratches,' which is the same thing as 'has more hardness than.'

Now that we have established an order for our classes, we are ready to assign numerals to them. The basic rule by which numerals are assigned to classes on an ordinal scale is this:

The order inherent in the formal system of the numerals shall correspond to the order empirically established among the classes.

Numbers have a conventional order: 1, 2, 3 . . . etc.; letters have a conventional order: $A, B, C \ldots Z$. If we use numbers or letters to identify our minerals, the conventional order of the letters or numbers must correspond to the order in which the minerals have been placed by the operation of scratching. Starting with sandstone, we may assign the numerals

$$1, 2, 3, 4, 5, 6, 7, 8, 9, 10$$

or just as logically

$$37, 38, 149, 742, 743, 744, 1189, 2340, 10001, 243968$$

or

$$A, B, C, D, E, F, G, H, I, J$$

or

$$B, D, E, G, L, S, U, V, W, Z$$

In all of these examples, the order of the numerals is preserved. But we cannot use the following set of numerals:

$$13, 8, 14, 7, 21, 2, 1, 9, 10$$

because these numerals do not fall in their conventional order, while the objects to which they have been assigned do have an ordered relationship.

If one set of numerals has been assigned to the classes of an ordinal scale, a new set may be substituted if the numerals of the new set follow the same order as those in the original. This fact may be expressed symbolically in the following way:

$$N' = o(N)$$

where N' stands, as before, for a numeral of the new set; N stands for a numeral in the original set, and o means 'any substitution that preserves the original order.' This equation is read: 'A new numeral may be any substitution for the old, as long as the original order is preserved.' The first four sets of numerals given above may be substituted for each other, because all obey this rule. The fifth set does not obey the rule, and therefore it may not legitimately be substituted for any of the first four.

The numerals assigned to the classes of an ordinal scale behave like numbers only in so far as they have the conventional order of numbers. *Numbers* can be added and subtracted, but what happens if we try to add and subtract the numerals of an ordinal scale? To answer this question let us consider an ordinal scale of tennis-playing ability. We have four men, each of whom plays a game of tennis with every other man. Jones beats all the other men and is beaten by none of them. Smith is beaten by Jones but beats the other two consistently. Brown is beaten by Smith and Jones but consistently beats the fourth man, while Whifflebottom is always beaten by the other three. To Jones, then, the numeral '4' is assigned, to Smith the numeral '3,' to Brown, '2,' and to Whifflebottom the numeral '1.' The men have been ordered in tennis-playing ability; the order of the numerals corresponds to the order of ability and is therefore logical and appropriate.

Now it is agreed that the men shall play a game of doubles. Since $4 + 1 = 2 + 3$, it seems to everyone that a team consisting of Jones and Whifflebottom should have an equal chance against Smith and Brown. The match is so arranged, with the audience placing even-money bets. The result is that Smith and Brown do not allow Jones and Whifflebottom to score a single point. Since the 'average' or 'total' abilities of the teams were, at least numerically, equal, how does this strange result come about?

Easy. Smith, Jones, and Brown are all, it turns out, Olympic champions. There are differences among them, but all are very, very good tennis players. Whifflebottom stumbled onto the court while looking for the men's room and has never seen a racket before. Relative to Whifflebottom's '1.' the other men all deserve numerals in the thousands.

The moral of the story is that when numerals are assigned to classes on an ordinal scale, the ordered relation of the numerals is important, but their absolute values—the differences between the numerals assigned to adjacent classes—are not. The only measures that can appropriately be used with an ordinal scale are measures that do not depend upon the absolute values of numerals or numbers. There are many such measures, and they will be discussed in Chapter 4.

Questions

1. Below is a list of foods. Select a classifying principle and divide the foods into four or five classes on the basis of it. Now assign names (numerals) to those classes.

a. Do you have a scale? What kind?

b. Can you substitute the numerals 1, 2, 3 . . . etc. for the names you have previously assigned? What properties of numbers do these new numerals have?

c. Is there any way in which you can order the classes into which you have divided the foods?

FOODS

Roast beef	Leg of lamb	Veal chops
Tomato soup	Broccoli	T-bone steak
Coffee	Potatoes	Wax beans
Melba toast	Consommé	Stew
Lamb chops	Milk	Ice cream
Spinach	Relish	Stewed tomatoes
Chocolate pudding	Chicken	Tea
Rice	Blueberry pie	Butter
Oranges	Stew	Caviar
Bread	Watermelon	Pancakes
Ketchup	Spaghetti	Root beer

2. How would you go about constructing an ordinal scale for the measurement of sympathy in a group of kindergarten children? How would you define the relationship $<$? How would you test for the criteria of connectedness? Asymmetry? Transitivity?

3. Do the same for the measurement of intelligence in a group of school children of different ages.

4. Below is a list of occupations. Rank them from highest to lowest according to what you believe the typical incomes for these occupations to be. Now rank the occupations according to your opinion of the 'social status' of the people in them.

a. Can you combine the two sets of ranks in any way to give a scale of socio-economic status? Test the new scale to see if it meets the criteria of connectedness, asymmetry, and transitivity. (Pay particular attention to connectedness.)

b. Divide the occupations into the four income groups: high income, above-average income, below-average income, and low income. Assign four numerals (other than the names just given) to the categories. Give two other sets of numerals which can be substituted for those you have just assigned. List four other numerals which cannot be legitimately substituted, and explain why the substitution is improper.

c. If a man of 'high income' and a man of 'low income' pool their earnings, will they have the same amount of money between them as a man of 'above-average income' and a man of 'below-average income' who pool *their* earnings? Explain.

OCCUPATIONS

Barber's apprentice	Sales manager
Superintendent of nurses	Construction foreman
High-school principal	Long-distance truck driver
Lathe operator	Stenographer
Air Force colonel	Private secretary
Senior transport pilot	Movie star
Poet	Associate professor
Assistant minister	Dietician
Funeral director	Psychiatrist
Railroad porter	Circuit-court judge

5. If your grade in a course is to be based on the results of two equally weighted quizzes, and you get an A on one and a C on the other, does it immediately and automatically follow that you should get a B for the course? Discuss.

2.3 Interval and Ratio Scales

In addition to making comparisons, we may be able to quantify those comparisons. Sometimes we can say not only that John is older than Mary but also that John is three years older. This room is not only warmer than that—it is five degrees warmer. To make such quantitative comparisons we must have a *unit of measurement*. A scale for which a unit of measurement has been established is called an **interval scale.**

If, in addition to a unit of measurement, we also have an absolute zero point, we have what is known as a **ratio scale.** When our classes have been measured on a ratio scale, we can say not only that A is so many units greater than B, but also that A is so many *times* as great as B. The scale of calendar time is an example of an interval scale that is *not* a ratio scale. A year is a year is a year, and the time interval between the years A.D. 100 and A.D. 200 is the same as the interval between the years A.D. 1800 and A.D. 1900. But the year 200 is not *twice as late in time* as the year 100, even though it is twice as late after the birth of Christ. We do not know when time 'began' so we have chosen the birth of Christ as an arbitrary starting point or zero. We could have chosen some other starting point—the estimated date of the first written record, for example, and then our years would have different numerals, and different relationships would exist among the numerals.

The interval scale and the ratio scale are discussed together here because the operations necessary to establish them, and the rules by which numerals are assigned, are identical for the two with one exception. For a ratio scale we apply our operations and our numerals to the *total amount* of the quantity or quality being measured, while for an interval scale we apply the operations to differences from some arbitrary zero point.

Once an ordinal scale has been established a new relationship must be defined and a new operation developed before we can progress to either an interval or a ratio scale. The relationship to be defined is that of *equality;* the operation to be developed is *addition.*

Equality is defined in the following way: A and B are equal if and only if

$A \not> B$ and $A \not< B$. (A does not have more of the quality being measured than B, and A does not have less of the quality than B.)

If $A > C$ then $B > C$. (If A has more of the quality than C, then B also has more than C.)

If $A \not> C$ then $B \not> C$. (If A does not have more of the quality than C, then B doesn't either.)

The relationship of equality is transitive, symmetrical, and reflexive. What this means formally is that

If $A = B$ and $B = C$ then $A = C$ (transitivity);

If $A = B$ then $B = A$ (symmetry);

$A = A$ (reflexivity).

In the formal system of mathematics two things that are equal are identical. There is no difference between them. When we apply the term 'equal' to two objects of the physical world, however, we usually mean that we cannot find any difference between them—which is not the same thing as saying that there is no difference. Finer measuring instruments make equals unequal. The boys whose weights are identical on the bathroom scale may have different weights when measured on the better instrument in the doctor's office. In the *logical* system equality means 'no difference'; in the empirical system of everyday life it means 'no difference that can be detected by a particular measuring instrument.'

Having defined equality we are now ready to consider the operation of addition. What do we mean when we say that two things are added? That depends upon the things. For example, if we want to add the lengths of two sticks, we lay the sticks end to end. The new length, extending from the left end of the left stick to the right end of the right stick, is the sum of the lengths. If we wish to add weights we put both weights in the same pan of a balance. Two electrical resistances are added by putting them in series in a circuit.

But how do we add the abilities of our tennis-playing friends of the previous section? Put two men on the same team? Everyone who has ever played a game of doubles knows that, though two players are equally good at singles, one of them may be piggish or overgenerous when playing with a partner. Two excellent singles players may make a poor doubles team. Adding tennis-playing abilities would seem to be a good deal harder than adding lengths.

The way to know whether a particular operation for addition is satisfactory or not is to apply it and then see if the following requirements are met:

1. If $A + B = C$, then $B + A = C$. This statement says that the order in which the things are added shall not affect the result. It is known as the **commutative property.**

2. If $A = A'$ and $B > O$, then $A + B > A'$. To say that $B > O$ means that B is discriminably different either from the arbitrary zero which we have chosen as the starting point of our interval scale or from a known absolute zero. The difference must be in the direction of having more of the quality than none at all. This statement then says that an object which, by itself, has some positive amount of the quality being measured must also have a positive effect when added to another object.

3. If $A = A'$ and $B = B'$ then $A + B = A' + B'$. This statement is known as the **axiom of equals.** It says that if equals are added to equals, the results are equal.

4. $A + (B + C) = (A + B) + C$. This is known as the **associative property.** Requirement 1 told us that the order in which the objects were added must not affect the result. This requirement tells us that the order in which the operations of addition take place must likewise have no effect on the results.

We have stated that lengths can be added by laying end to end the objects whose lengths we wish to add. If we start our measurement with a collection of straight sticks labeled A, A', B, B', and so on, we may actually make physical tests of all the criteria above.

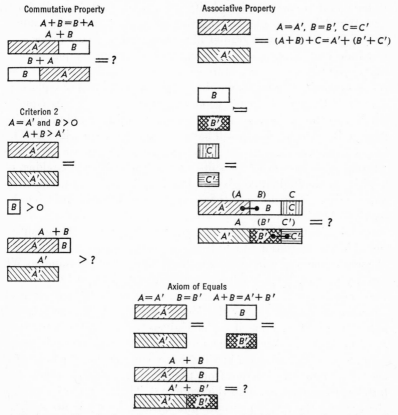

FIG. 2.1   Can the lengths of the sticks be added by laying the sticks end to end? Only if the four criteria of additivity are satisfied. In this figure the criteria are tested and found to hold.

Figure 2.1 shows exactly how these tests would be made. Since every one of the four criteria is satisfied by the physical tests, we conclude that the laying of sticks end to end is a good operation for adding their lengths.

But consider the ill-fated attempt to add tennis-playing abilities by putting players on the same team. Let us think for the moment about the second and third requirements listed above. Jones and Brown may be equally matched in tennis-playing ability, and Whifflebottom (who has been practicing since we last met him) may occasionally return a ball that is sent to him and hence may be said to have more tennis-playing ability than none at all. But will Jones and Whifflebottom, playing together, beat Brown playing alone? Probably not. On that ground alone we should therefore have to conclude that playing abilities could not be added by putting the players on the same team. Moreover, we can also show that the proposed operation for addition fails to satisfy the axiom of equals. If Jones and Brown are equally good, and Smith and Black are equally good, we cannot be sure that Jones and Smith, playing doubles against Brown and Black, will have a 50-50 chance of winning. The interactions among styles of play may give one team a great advantage over the other in spite of the preliminary matching of abilities of the individual players. Putting two players on a doubles team is definitely not a satisfactory way of adding their tennis-playing abilities.

Social scientists are frequently interested in measuring qualities for which no operation of addition is possible and for which no unit of measurement can be developed. Attitudes are one example. We can say that one man is more favorably inclined toward the church than another man, but we cannot add different degrees of pro-churchness, nor can we say that one man is six 'churs' more favorable than another. Thus, if we have given three men the Thurstone Scale of Attitude Toward the Church, and we find that their scores are 6, 8, and 10, we are *not* justified in concluding that the man with the score of 10 is as different from the man with the score of 8 as the latter is from the man with the score of 6. These numerals describe the *order* of the men's attitudes and nothing more. Traits such as ascendance-submission and introversion-extroversion, when they are measured, yield ordinal scales only. They cannot be added, and units of measurement cannot be established, so we cannot construct interval or ratio scales for these variables.

Questions

1. Consider the scales of sympathy, intelligence, and socio-economic status which you have established. What tests would you apply to show that two people were equal in each of these variables?

2. For which of the qualities below do you think a satisfactory operation for addition exists? What is it?

Length of lines	Depth of the ocean
Weight (or mass)	Teaching ability
Periods of time	Area of squares
Intelligence	Area of rectangles
Sympathy	Apparent brightness of white lights
Heights of buildings	Apparent brightness of lights of different colors

3. A subject adjusts the brightness of a green light until it is just as bright (that is, it looks as bright to him) as a standard red light. The green light is then taken away and a blue light substituted. He adjusts the blue light until it looks as bright as the red one. When you now show the subject the blue light and the green light together, they do *not* look equally bright. What criterion does this measurement of apparent brightness fail to satisfy?

4. Design an experiment to measure subjective weight (that is, how heavy things *feel* to people, rather than how heavy they are on a scale). Hypothesize any kind of results you like, and then decide what kind of a scale you will end up with.

Once we have established an ordered relation among classes and have then gone on to develop a satisfactory operation for addition, we are ready to assign numerals to our classes to form an interval scale. The basic rule by which numerals are assigned to classes on an interval scale is:

If the difference between two classes of objects, A and B, is equal to the difference between any two other classes of objects, C and D, then the difference between the numerals assigned to classes A and B must be the same as the difference between the numerals assigned to classes C and D. This rule may be generalized to state that *the differences between numerals assigned to pairs of classes must be proportional to the differences between the pairs of classes.*

The application of this principle is illustrated in Fig. 2.3. We start with four lines, A, B, C, and D. We shall call the difference between lines B and A one *unit* of length and represent it by the letter u. $B - A = u$. We may assign any numeral at all to A, but since B is one unit longer than A, the numeral assigned to B must be one larger than the numeral assigned to A. Let us call A '350'; then B must be called '351.' Now we compare lengths B and C. We find that $u + u = C - B$. Length C is two units longer than length B.

Therefore the numeral assigned to C must be two units larger than the numeral assigned to B. C must receive the numeral '353.' Finally we compare C to D. We find that D is longer than C, but the difference is only half as great as the difference between A and B. Thus D is one half a unit longer than C and must receive the numeral '$353\frac{1}{2}$.'

Two things about this procedure are noteworthy. First, we chose our starting point arbitrarily. We decided to call length A '350,' but we might have called it anything at all—for example, '127.' Had we

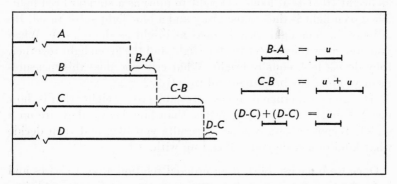

Fig. 2.2   Comparison of lengths of lines A, B, C, and D preparatory to the assignment of numerals. The breaks in the lines indicate that parts of the lines have been omitted. We do not know how much has been omitted, but we assume that the amount is the same for all the lines. For an explanation of the way in which numerals are assigned, see the text.

called it 127, then B would have been 128, C 130, and D $130\frac{1}{2}$. The *differences* between pairs of numerals are all that matter, and they are left unchanged by a change of the arbitrary starting point. The second thing to notice is that, although we decided to call the difference between A and B one unit, this decision, too, was arbitrary. We might, for example, have called the difference between C and D one unit. In that case the difference between A and B would have been two units, and the difference between B and C, four units. With our original starting point of 350, the numerals assigned to A, B, C, and D would then have been 350, 352, 356, and 357. But the differences between pairs of numerals would still be proportional to the differences between the pairs of lengths.

Once a set of numerals has been assigned to the classes of an interval scale, another set may be substituted if the numerals of the new set also follow the basic principle explained above. The rule for substituting numerals is:

$$N' = CN + K \quad \text{where } C > 0,$$

where N' is a numeral of the new set, N is a numeral of the original set, and C and K are constants. The constant C must be positive if the relationships among the old numerals are to be maintained in the new. If we change the starting point, or arbitrary zero of our scale, but leave the size of the unit of measurement unchanged, we simply make C in the equation equal to 1.

$$N' = N + K$$

If we leave the starting point unchanged, but change the unit of measurement, we make K equal to zero.

$$N' = CN$$

If we change both starting point and size of unit, both C and K must be specified in the equation.

The conversion of temperatures from the Fahrenheit to the centigrade temperature scales (or vice versa) is an example of the substitution of numerals on an interval scale. Both scales have arbitrary zero points. 0° Fahrenheit represented the coldest temperature Mr. Fahrenheit could produce—the temperature of a mixture of snow and common salt; while 0° centigrade is the temperature of the freezing point of water. The units of measurement are also different on the two scales. On the Fahrenheit scale, one degree is $\frac{1}{180}$ of the difference between the freezing and boiling points of water, while on the centigrade scale one degree is $\frac{1}{100}$ of that difference. To convert from Fahrenheit to centigrade temperatures, therefore, we must take account of both the difference in size of unit and the difference in starting point. The equation is:

$$C = \frac{100}{180}(F - 32) \quad \text{or} \quad \frac{5}{9}(F - 32)$$

Whichever scale we measure temperature on, however, the differences between numerals corresponding to different temperatures are proportional to the differences between the temperatures.

Questions

1. Three airplanes are flying at 300 yards, 600 yards, and 700 yards above the ground. The ground is 200 yards above sea level.

    a. How many *feet* above sea level are the three planes flying?
    b. If a fourth plane is N yards above the ground, how many feet above sea level is it?
    c. If the ground is K feet above sea level, how many feet above sea level is the plane which is N yards above the ground?

2. If it were suddenly discovered that Christ was actually born 50 years earlier than had been supposed, and therefore everyone decided to readjust the calendar so that the letters A.D. would still have historical meaning, (a) what year would it be now? (b) what would be the new designation for the year that was previously called 1650? (c) for the year previously called 'X'?

3. Convert the following Fahrenheit temperatures into centigrade:

$$0, 32, 70, 98.6, 212, -40$$

4. Convert the following centigrade temperatures into Fahrenheit:

$$0, 37, 100, 24, -40$$

5. Convert all the temperatures given above into Kelvin (absolute temperature). Note: $0°$ Kelvin is equal to $-273°$C.

6. What relation is kept constant (unchanged, or invariant) when we translate from height above ground to height above sea level for the three airplanes in problem 1? For the dates in the revised calendar? When we change from Fahrenheit to centigrade temperature?

The numerals assigned to the classes of an interval scale behave in many respects like true numbers. For example, they can be averaged, and the average numeral will correspond to the magnitude of the average object, as we shall see in Chapter 5. Statements such as '40°F. is as much warmer than 20°F. as 20°F. is warmer than 0°' have both mathematical and empirical meaning. If we were to convert these Fahrenheit temperatures to centigrade by the formula given above, we should say instead: '+4.4°C. is as much warmer than −6.7°C. as −6.7°C. is warmer than −17.7°.' But we can*not* say that 40°F. is twice as warm as 20°F. When those temperatures are converted to centigrade we then find ourselves claiming that

+4.4° is twice as warm as −6.7°, which looks like, and is, a non-sensical statement.

The reasons that we cannot make a statement like '20°F. is twice as warm as 10°F.' is that the Fahrenheit temperature scale, being only an interval scale, has an arbitrary zero point. Any change in the zero point will change the *ratio* of one number to another.

Let's look further into this problem of ratios. This time we shall assign numerals to the lengths of wire on spools. The spools are so designed that only a certain amount of wire can be unrolled. We

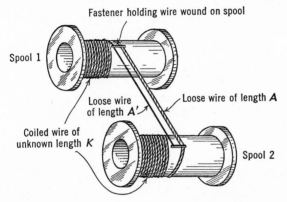

FIG. 2.3   Measurement of length without an absolute zero.

A is compared to A′ and they are found to be equal. The wire on spool 1 therefore has length $K + A'$. The wire on spool 2 has length $K + A$. Since $A = A'$, the two wires have equal length even though that length is not known. For fuller explanation, see text.

know that the amount of wire left on the spool is the same for all the several spools with which we shall be concerned, but we do not know what this amount is. Let us call it K. The spools, with their coiled and uncoiled wires, are shown in Figure 2.3.

The tests for the criteria of addition will be identical with those we used when we were working with sticks, except that we shall be working only with the loose ends of the coiled wires. Our operation for addition will again be the laying of the uncoiled portions of the wires end to end. We assign numerals according to the rule for an interval scale.

We find that the uncoiled portion of wire B is twice as long as the uncoiled portion of wire A, so we assign to B the numeral 2, and to

A the numeral 1. Can we now say that wire *B* is twice as long as wire *A*? No, because the actual lengths of *A* and *B* are unknown. When the spool is unwound *B* may be found to be 61 feet long while *A* is 60. Since the coiled length may be anything at all, we cannot even make a guess about ratios, even though we are perfectly safe in talking about intervals or differences.

Only when an absolute, as opposed to an arbitrary, zero point can be established can we compare one class of objects to another in terms of ratios. A scale that meets all the other criteria of measurement and, in addition, has an absolute zero point is therefore called a **ratio scale**. The sticks in Figure 2.1 were measured on a ratio scale because we could actually add the lengths of the whole sticks, while the coiled wires of Figure 2.2 were measured only on an interval scale, since we could not tell where the wires 'started'— that is, we could not establish a true zero point.

Once we have established an interval scale, and have shown that our measurements are made from a true zero point, we are ready to assign numerals. Numerals are assigned to the classes on a ratio scale by the following rule:

The number or numeral assigned must be proportional to the absolute size of the class of objects to which it is assigned.

Thus, if one object, *A*, has been shown to be twice as big as some other object, *B*, the numeral assigned to *A* must be twice as big as the numeral assigned to *B*. The numerals may be 2 and 1, or 64 and 32, or 2000 and 1000, or any other pair of numerals so chosen that the first is twice the second. Once numerals have been assigned on a ratio scale, new numerals may be substituted if they obey the rule above. The equation showing permissible substitutions of new for old numerals is:

$$N' = CN \qquad \text{where } C > 0$$

Multiplying the old numerals by some constant is simply a way of changing the unit of measurement. Thus, if *I* stands for height in inches, and *F* for height in feet, we may write

$$I = 12F$$

This equation states that to change our unit of measurement from feet to inches, we must multiply by a constant factor, 12.

The numerals assigned to classes of objects on a ratio scale have all the properties of real numbers. They may be added and subtracted, ratios may be formed, logarithms taken; they may be squared or square-rooted, and other exponential transformations may be made. If we can measure our objects on a ratio scale, we have acquired a very powerful tool.

Questions

1. For which of the following qualities is it possible to establish and measure deviations from an absolute zero? Explain when necessary.

Dollars earned per year	Degrees of fever in a sick man
Height of schoolgirls	Sympathy
Intelligence	Socio-economic status
Scholastic aptitude	Difficulty of arithmetic problems
Time	Distance of cities from New York

2. What relation is kept invariant when we convert from feet to inches? From pounds to ounces? Is this the same kind of relation that was held invariant when we converted from Fahrenheit to centigrade temperatures? Discuss.

3. In problem 1, page 66, the second airplane was twice as high above the ground as the first one. Is it also twice as high above sea level? With reference to problem 2, page 66, the year 100 was twice as long after the birth of Christ as the year 50 on the old calendar. Is the same thing true on the new calendar?

2.4 Measurement and Statistics

We have already seen that an average obtained from the numerals assigned on a nominal or ordinal scale is meaningless, but an average obtained from the numerals of an interval or ratio scale is legitimate and meaningful. What has been said of an average is also true of many other statistics. Any statistic can be used when measurement has been made on a ratio scale; a few are eliminated when the scale is only an interval one. Many more are excluded from application to an ordinal scale, while very few may properly be applied to a nominal scale.

The appropriateness of various statistics is cumulative: if the scales are ranked in order of restrictions on numeral assignment the nominal scale is the least restrictive, the ratio scale the most restrictive. Any statistic that can be used with a nominal scale can also be used with any other kind of scale; statistics appropriate to ordinal scales may also be used with interval and ratio scales but not necessarily with nominal scales; and finally statistics usable with interval scales can also be applied to ratio scales but not necessarily to the other two kinds.

However, given a choice of two statistics which are otherwise equally desirable, we are usually wise if we select the one that uses all the information in the data. If we use a statistic appropriate to an ordinal scale when our objects have been measured on an interval scale, we are not making use of the unit of measurement so painstakingly established, and valuable information is therefore being wasted or ignored. Other things being equal, it is therefore desirable to use the statistics most appropriate to the particular scale on which our objects or variables have been measured.

In actual practice there is sometimes doubt about what kind of a scale we are dealing with. Classifying occupations along the dimension of socio-economic status, for example, seems to give us a scale which is much better than nominal but not quite good enough to be called ordinal. When we measure IQ's, we get what looks like a pretty good unit of measurement but we have no proper operation for addition. In any kind of classification or abstraction there are likely to be borderline cases and exceptions to the rules, and this is as true of our classification of measurement into four kinds of scales as of any other. (For a different classification, see Coombs, references 2 and 3.) If, in practice, we have a scale with a good unit of measurement but no operation for addition, we have two choices: we can limit ourselves to ordinal-scale statistics and throw away information, or we can use interval-scale statistics and run the risk of getting an answer that may not quite correspond to reality. Which of these alternatives is the lesser evil depends upon the use to which the statistics are to be put. It is a question which has to be decided in each individual case and which may be answered differently by different investigators.

2.5 The Plan of This Book

In Chapter 1, we said that in using statistics to describe the world around us we should be trying to answer five questions:

1. What is the over-all picture given by the data?
2. What is average or typical? If we know that an individual is a

member of our group, what is our best prediction or guess about him?

3. How good or bad is whatever prediction we make? How well does the typical represent the group? How much variability is there within the group?

4. To what extent does knowing about one thing help us to predict another? To what extent are variables related?

5. How does a single individual compare with the rest of the group?

In Chapter 2 the four principal kinds of measurement scale have been introduced. In Chapters 3 through 8 we shall take up each of the four scales in turn and consider what methods are available to us to answer each of the five questions. At the end of Chapter 8, you should be able to decide what kind of measurement you have and what question you want to answer and then know immediately the best statistic to use. All of descriptive statistics can be summarized by filling in the blanks in the 4×5 table below, which lists the chapter and section where the statistic is considered. Chapter 9 will summarize the results and present the filled-in table. The rest of the book will be devoted to statistical inference.

Question

		Over-all Descr.	'Best Guess'	'How Bad?'	Related-ness	Individ. Position
	NOMINAL	3.1	3.2	3.3	3.4	3.5
	ORDINAL	4.2	4.4	4.5	4.6	4.3
SCALE	INTERVAL	5.1 6.1 6.2 6.4	5.2	5.3	7.1 7.2 7.3	6.5
	RATIO	8.2	8.3	8.4	8.6	8.5

Table 2.1

Summary

Measurement is the assignment of numerals to objects according to rule. Basically, the rule that governs all numeral assignment is that

Table 2.2. Summary of Scales of Measurement

SCALE	DESCRIPTION	CRITERIA	SUBSTITUTION EQUATION	EXAMPLES OF NUMERALS THAT MAY BE SUBSTITUTED FOR 1, 2, 3	RELATIONSHIP UNCHANGED
NOMINAL	Names applied to discriminable classes	Discriminability	$N' = s(N)$ s is 'any direct substitution for'	Heb, Nuv, Lub, K Z F 41, 57, 94‖11, 12, 13‖4, 8, 12	Identities of classes
ORDINAL	Ordered numerals applied to ordered classes	If $A \neq B$ then $A > B$ or $A < B$. If $A > B$, $B \not> A$. If $A > B$ and $B > C$ then $A > C$	$N' = o(N)$ o is 'any order preserving substitution for'	41, 57, 94 F, K, Z 11, 12, 13‖4, 8, 12	Order of classes
INTERVAL	Numerals equally different from one another applied to classes equally different from one another	Equality: $A = B$ if and only if $A \not> B$, $A \not< B$. If $A > C$, $B > C$. If $A < C$, $B < C$. Addition: $A + B = B + A$. If $A = A'$ and $B > A'$ then $A + B > A'$. If $A = A'$ and $B = B'$ then $A + B = A' + B'$. $(A + B) + C = A + (B + C)$. Criteria above applied to deviations from arbitrary zero	$N' = CN + K$ C is any multiplying factor K is any constant	2200, 2400, 2600 63, 66, 69 11, 12, 13 4, 8, 12	Equality of differences
RATIO	Numerals that are multiples of a standard applied to classes that are the same multiples of a standard class	Criteria above applied to deviations from absolute zero	$N' = CN$ C is any multiplying factor	4, 8, 12 10, 20, 30 13, 26, 39	Equality of ratios or multiples

the properties of the objects must be represented in the properties of the numerals assigned to them. Later manipulations carried out with the numerals must correspond to manipulations that can be carried out with the objects.

Four general kinds of measurement may be distinguished:

1. **The nominal scale,** where different numerals are assigned to distinguishable classes. The numerals assigned on a nominal scale have scarcely any of the properties of numbers and cannot be manipulated as numbers can.

2. **The ordinal scale,** where classes are distinguishable and can be placed in one and only one order. The order inherent in the formal system of numerals must correspond to the order empirically established among the classes. The numerals of an ordinal scale behave like numbers only in so far as both have a conventional order.

3. **The interval scale,** where classes are distinguishable and can be ordered, and where a unit of measurement has been established. Numerals from an interval scale may be added or subtracted, but they cannot be related to each other as ratios or multiples.

4. **The ratio scale,** where classes can be distinguished and placed in order, a unit of measurement has been established, and an absolute, rather than an arbitrary, zero exists. The numerals assigned on a ratio scale have all the properties of real numbers.

The characteristics of the various scales of measurement are summarized in Table 2.2.

As we progress from the nominal to the ratio scale, the rules for the assignment of numerals become more stringent, but as a result the number of manipulations of numerals that correspond to manipulations of the objects increases. Thus increasing numbers of statistics become available as we proceed from the nominal to the ratio scale. The best statistic to use, however, is usually the one that utilizes all the information available in the data. In the remainder of this book we shall consider the four scales in turn, starting with the nominal, and discuss the statistics appropriate with each.

Questions

1. For each kind of measurement listed below decide whether the scale is nominal, ordinal, interval, or ratio. Briefly defend your decision or if you are in doubt explain your doubt.

    a. Human age in years
    b. Goodness of handwriting
    c. Numbers on football players' backs
    d. IQ
    e. Serial numbers on automobiles
    f. Notes on the musical scale
    g. Subjective pitch (apparent highness or lowness of a tone)
    h. Kelvin (absolute temperature)
    i. Saturation (apparent richness of a color)
    j. Calendar time
    k. Numbers on alternative answers in a multiple-choice test

2. Give three examples not mentioned in the text of each of the four kinds of scales.

3. The numerals 6, 13, and 24 have been assigned to three measured objects. For each kind of scale, give two sets of three numerals which could properly be substituted for these three.

References

1. Brown, C. W., and Ghiselli, E. E. *Scientific Method in Psychology*, New York, McGraw-Hill, 1955, pp. 105–30. An elementary review of the material covered in this chapter.

2. Coombs, C. H. *A Theory of Psychological Scaling*, Ann Arbor, Univ. of Mich. Press, 1952. A highly technical presentation of an approach to scaling different from that presented here. Several scales other than the four discussed in this chapter are described.

3. Coombs, C. H. Theory and Methods of Social Measurement, in *Research Methods in the Behavioral Sciences*, Festinger, L., and Katz, D. (eds.) New York, Dryden, 1953. A much more elementary presentation of the material in reference 2.

4. Morgan, C. T. *Introduction to Psychology*, New York, McGraw-Hill, 1956, pp. 188–92. A very brief and elementary summary of the principles of measurement.

5. Newman, J. R. (ed.), *The World of Mathematics*, New York, Simon and Schuster, 1956. Many of the selections in this four-volume set are interesting and authoritative. The following are relevant to the problems of measurement:

> Conant, L. L. Counting, pp. 432–41.
>
> Smith, D. E., and Ginsburg, J. From Numbers to Numerals and from Numerals to Computation, pp. 442–64.
>
> Campbell, N. R. Measurement, pp. 1797–1813.

Campbell, N. R. Numerical Laws and the Use of Mathematics in Science, pp. 1814–29.

6. Reese, T. W. 'The application of the theory of physical measurement to the measurement of psychological magnitudes, with three experimental examples,' *Psychol. Monogr.*, 1943, **55**, No. 3. An intensive examination of the principles of measurement and their application. Very difficult.

7. Stevens, S. S. 'On the theory of scales of measurement,' *Science*, 1946, **103**, pp. 677–80. This reference and the next are the sources from which most of this chapter was derived. Neither is beyond the ability of a serious student.

8. Stevens, S. S. Mathematics, Measurement, and Psychophysics, in *Handbook of Experimental Psychology*, Stevens, S. S. (ed.) New York, Wiley, 1951, pp. 1–49.

Answers

Page 66.

1. a. 1500, 2400, 2700; b. $3N + 600$; c. $3N + K$
2. b. 1700; c. $x + 50$
3. $-17.8°$, $0°$, $21.1°$, $37°$, $100°$, $-40°$
4. $32°$, $98.6°$, $212°$, $75.2°$, $-40°$
5. $255.2°$, $273°$, $294.1°$, $310°$, $373°$, $233°$, $273°$, $310°$, $373°$, $297°$, $233°$

THE NOMINAL SCALE

The nominal scale consists simply of a set of names applied to distinguishable classes. When we classify mental-hospital patients according to their psychiatric diagnoses, Rorschach responses according to the part of the blot to which they were made, answers to a multiple-choice question according to the response alternative chosen, people according to sex or place of national origin, we are using nominal scales. In this chapter we shall see what answers to the five basic questions of descriptive statistics are available when the data come from a nominal scale.

3.1 An Over-all Picture of the Data—Frequency Distributions

Once we have decided upon the categories or classes of our scale, we may then ask how many individuals from some specified group fell into each of these classes. Given 100 animals, we may say that there are 50 horses, 25 dogs, 24 cows, and 1 sea serpent. We may also obtain ratios, proportions, and percentages. For example:

Ratios: The ratio of cows to all animals is 25:100, or 1:4. The ratio of cows to sea serpents is 25:1. The ratio of sea serpents to cows is 1:25.

Proportions: In this oddly assorted barnyard, the proportion of horses is .50, of dogs .25, of cows .24, and of sea serpents .01.

Percentages: 50 per cent of the animals are horses, 25 per cent dogs, 24 per cent cows, and 1 per cent sea serpents.

Graphic representations: There are several ways of representing counts, or frequencies, graphically. Of these, the most generally satisfactory is the bar graph. In a bar graph, each bar represents one category, and the height of the bar represents the frequency. Figure 3.1 is a bar graph for the barnyard data given above.

In a bar graph the order of the bars and the relative spaces between the bars are chosen arbitrarily. We could, for example, interchange the positions of the bars for sea serpents and horses, which would give the graph a very different appearance but would not change its meaning. We could crowd the bars together at one end of the graph and spread them out at the other end, and that change, too, would leave the meaning of the graph unaffected.

In fact, the only thing that is not arbitrary about a bar graph is the relative heights of the bars. Once we have said, 'One square on this graph paper will represent five animals,' we are no longer free to let it represent anything else. It might be convenient to let one

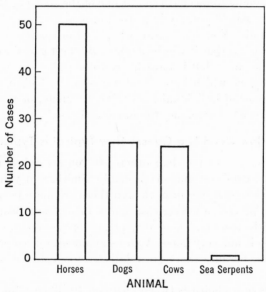

Fɪɢ. 3.1   Frequencies of animals in hypothetical barnyard.

square equal ten horses but only one sea serpent, but should we try it, the graph would lose all its meaning and validity. If we are to keep the relative heights of the bars constant, the y-axis (vertical) of the graph must start at zero. Suppose the sea serpent were to pass on, leaving only 99 animals. You might think that since no class has fewer than 24 animals, it would be convenient to start the frequency axis at 20. To see how that would look, turn to Figure 3.1 and hold a ruler horizontally across the graph at the level of '20' on the y-axis. Note that from the resulting picture, a reader would conclude that there were many times more horses than dogs, while actually there are still only twice as many. The relative heights of the bars must be proportional to the numbers of cases falling into the various categories.

Other kinds of graphic representation, such as pie charts and pictographs, are sometimes used to represent data from a nominal scale. All of these are simply ways of showing the relative proportions of cases falling into the different categories.

3.2 The Typical—The Best Guess

If you were going to receive as a gift one of the zoological specimens listed above, should you lay in a stock of oats, hay, dog biscuits, or mermaids' tails? You don't know what kind of beast you'll get, but your best guess is that it will be a horse. By 'best guess' we mean, in this case, the guess that is most likely to be right.

That category which is our best guess, and which has in it the largest number of individuals, is called the **mode,** or modal class.[1] In this overworked example, the mode is 'horse.'

3.3 How Good Is a Guess? How Typical Is Typical?[2]

Some guesses are better than others. If you are asked to guess a man's name, your best guess is probably 'Smith,' but you're almost certain to be wrong, because, though there are more people named Smith than named anything else, many many more people are *not* named Smith than are. There are so many names a man might have that a guess is not very good. A guess about his eye color would be much better, because there are relatively few colors a man's eyes can be.

If you have a choice between two equally likely alternatives, a mere guess will be right half the time, while if you must choose among four, you will be right only one fourth of the time, and so on. Clearly, then, as the number of alternatives from which we must choose goes up, our uncertainty about which to choose goes up, and the goodness of the guess goes down.

But what if the alternatives are not equally likely? If in school *A* there are 500 boys and 500 girls, while in school *B* there are

[1] The mode, defined in this way, is sometimes called the 'crude mode' to distinguish it from a more elegant but rarely used statistic which is computed from two other measures of the typical: the mean and the median. Whenever we speak of the mode in this text, we refer to the crude mode.

[2] Before reading this section, you should study logarithms (section 0.2.6) and the summation sign (section 0.3.1).

999 boys and 1 girl, a guess about the sex of a student is better when applied to school B than when applied to school A. If we guess 'boy' we shall be right 99.9 per cent of the time in the one case and only 50 per cent of the time in the other. Yet in both cases the number of alternatives is two. In general, the closer the alternatives are to being equally likely, the more uncertain we are and the poorer is our guess.

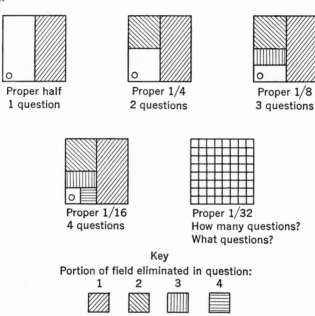

Key
Portion of field eliminated in question:

Fig. 3.2 Number of questions required to locate a ball in some specified fraction of a field when alternatives are equally likely.

What we need is a measure of uncertainty, or of 'poorness of a guess,' which will be high when the number of alternative possibilities is high, and low when some of the possibilities are much more likely than others. One possible measure is the *average number of questions we have to ask to specify the correct alternative.*

Suppose a ball is lost in a square field, and you have only to determine which side of the field it is in. It may be in either the left or the right half, and for the time being we shall assume that it is equally likely to be in either place. One guess will give you your answer (if you guess 'left' and you're wrong, then obviously the ball is in the right half). If you guess the *quarter* of the field the ball is in, does it require two, three, or four questions? Two, because you first ask, 'Top or bottom?' This eliminates half of the possibilities and leaves you with your original two-choice situation. If you must specify the eighth of the field holding the ball, you need add only one more guess, since you can get rid of half the alternatives on the first guess, reducing the situation to the four-choice one. How many questions or guesses would be required to locate the sixteenth of the field holding the ball? The thirty-second? Each time the number of alternatives is doubled, the number of guesses is increased by one. If A stands for the number of alternatives and $\hat{H}$ for the number of guesses required, then

$$A = 2^{\hat{H}}$$

as shown in the table below:

A	$\hat{H}$	$2^{\hat{H}}$
1	0	$2^0 = 1$
2	1	$2^1 = 2$
4	2	$2^2 = 4$
8	3	$2^3 = 8$
16	4	$2^4 = 16$
32	5	$2^5 = 32$

$\hat{H}$, and not A, is to be our measure of uncertainty. We must therefore solve the above equation for $\hat{H}$, which requires the use of logarithms. Remember that *the logarithm of A to the base b is the power to which b must be raised to make the result equal A*. Since $A = 2^{\hat{H}}$ we may take 2 as the base of our logarithms. Then $\hat{H} = \log_2 A$. $\hat{H}$ is the power to which 2 must be raised to make the result equal A.

When the alternatives are equally likely, therefore, the formula for $\hat{H}$, a measure of uncertainty, is

$$\hat{H} = \log_2 A \qquad (3.3.1)$$

where A is the number of equally likely alternatives.

Now let's consider a situation where the alternatives are not equally likely. Again a ball is lost in a field which this time is divided into three parts—call them A, B, and C. We know from experience that half the time the ball lands in part A, one-fourth of the time in B, and one-fourth of the time in C.

PART OF FIELD	PROPORTION OF CASES
A	$\frac{1}{2}$
B	$\frac{1}{4}$
C	$\frac{1}{4}$

How do you go about locating the ball, and how many questions will it take you?

You first ask, 'Is it in A?' If the answer is 'Yes,' you can stop guessing. That will happen half the time. If the answer is 'No,' you must then ask, 'Is it in B?' Whatever the answer, you have finished, since if the answer is 'No,' you know that the ball must be in C. Half the time, therefore, one guess will be required, and the other half of the time, two guesses will be required. On the average, one and a half guesses will be needed.

PART OF FIELD	PROPORTION OF TIME	NUMBER OF GUESSES	PRODUCT
A	$\frac{1}{2}$	1	$\frac{1}{2}$
B	$\frac{1}{4}$	2	$\frac{1}{2}$
C	$\frac{1}{4}$	2	$\frac{1}{2}$
		Total	$\frac{3}{2}$

The uncertainty, $\hat{H}$, about the location of the ball is $1\frac{1}{2}$.

There is a simple formula which will enable us to compute $\hat{H}$ when the alternatives are not equally likely (as well as when they are[3]) and which can be used easily when the proportions are not all convenient powers of 2. Let $p(i)$ (which is read: p of i) stand for the proportion of cases in an individual category. Then

$$\hat{H} = -\Sigma p(i) \log_2 p(i) \qquad (3.3.2)$$

This formula tells us to find the logarithm of the proportion of cases in a particular category, multiply the result by the proportion, repeat for each of the several categories, and then sum the numbers so obtained.

Fortunately, tables have been made up which give us the product of the proportion and its logarithm. Table A is a table of values of

[3] The student who is familiar with logarithms will have no trouble in proving that formula 3.3.1 is mathematically equivalent to formula 3.3.2 when the alternatives are equally likely.

$-p(i) \log_2 p(i)$. We merely look up the proportion in the table, copy out the corresponding value of $-p(i) \log_2 p(i)$, and, when we have done this for every category, obtain the sum of the numbers we have listed. Let us carry out this computation for the three-part ball field, using the table instead of the direct method.

CATEGORY (i)	$p(i)$	$-p(i) \log_2 p(i)$
A	.50	.50
B	.25	.50
C	.25	.50
		1.50

When alternatives are not equally likely formula 3.3.2 may be used to find the uncertainty of the distribution; when alternatives are equally likely, either formula 3.3.1 or 3.3.2, whichever is more convenient, may be used. Both describe the average number of two-alternative questions needed to specify the class to which an individual belongs.

We have not yet specified a unit of measurement for $\hat{H}$, and we must do so now. All our calculations have used the number 2 as a base. This comes about largely because the uncertainty measure was developed by engineers for use by engineers, and the measure is of great value in specifying the properties of communication channels. In these channels and networks, relays and tubes are among the most important components. A typical relay can be either open or closed, a tube can fire or not. Thus, relays and tubes correspond to men giving answers to true-false or yes-or-no questions, and a binary (base 2) system seems to be the most convenient one to use. $\hat{H}$ is therefore measured in binary digits, which has been shortened to 'bits.' We say that the uncertainty is one and a half **bits.**

Psychologists are just beginning to make use of the uncertainty measure. One example of a situation where it proved useful was in a choice-reaction-time experiment. In this experiment the subject is shown a panel of lights. When one of these lights is turned on, the subject is to respond as quickly as possible. He makes a different response to each of the different lights on the panel, and the time between the turning on of the light and the subject's response is accurately measured. The more lights the subject has to choose

among, and the closer the different lights are to being equally likely
to come on, the longer is the subject's reaction time. In fact, if we
use our knowledge about the number of lights and the proportion of
the time each is used to compute $\hat{H}$, we shall find that as $\hat{H}$ increases
the subject's reaction times increase roughly in direct proportion (1).
This is just one example of the many ways in which psychologists
are using the uncertainty measure.

While you are just beginning to use $\hat{H}$ the numbers you get won't
mean much to you. The bit is an unfamiliar unit and will take some
getting used to, just as any new unit of measurement does. For instance, if you were told that something cost 500 yen you wouldn't
know whether that was a lot or a little until you had translated the
price into dollars. Gradually, though, if you kept hearing prices expressed in yen, you'd get a feeling for what the numbers meant. The
same thing is true of bits. If you're told that the uncertainty of a
particular distribution is 3.32 bits, you may want to translate that
statement to: 'Equivalent to a choice among 10 equally likely alternatives.' As you get accustomed to talking in bits, you'll find that
kind of translation becoming unnecessary.

Relative uncertainty, $\hat{H}_{rel}$: $\hat{H}$ describes the actual uncertainty or
unpredictability of a distribution. Sometimes this is precisely the
figure we need to draw conclusions or make decisions. There are
other situations, however, when our interest centers in a comparison
of the actual uncertainty with the uncertainty that might possibly
exist if all the cases were divided equally among the various possible
alternatives. The ratio of actual uncertainty to the maximum
possible uncertainty is called the relative uncertainty.

$$\hat{H}_{rel} = \frac{\hat{H}}{\hat{H}_{max}} \qquad (3.3.3)$$

If the cases in the distribution are divided evenly among all the
possible alternatives, then $\hat{H} = \hat{H}_{max}$, and the relative uncertainty,
$\hat{H}_{rel}$, is 1.00, which may be translated to 100 per cent. If all the cases
fall into just one category, then $\hat{H}$ is zero, and hence $\hat{H}_{rel}$ is also zero.
Between these two extremes lies an infinite number of possible
values for $\hat{H}_{rel}$. Let's consider, for example, our three-part ball field
in which the ball spends one-half its time in one section and one-
quarter of its time in each of the other two sections. We found that
in this situation the actual uncertainty was one and one-half bits.

The maximum possible uncertainty would be that which would occur if the ball spent one-third of its time in each of the three parts. This would be:

$$\hat{H}_{max} = \log_2 3 = -.333 \log_2 .333 - .333 \log_2 .333 - .333 \log_2 .333$$
$$= 1.5849 \text{ bits.}$$

The relative uncertainty is therefore

$$\frac{1.5000}{1.5849} = .95$$

The relative uncertainty is .95, or 95 per cent.

$\hat{H}_{rel}$ can be especially useful for comparing two or more distributions. Suppose a psychologist is looking for a short, efficient personality test which will detect differences among people. He has settled on the procedure of presenting the subject with a list of adjectives and asking him to check the *one* that best applies to himself. On one test the psychologist tries there are 64 adjectives, and on another test, 32. Both tests are tried out on large groups of subjects. On the 64-item test, some adjectives are chosen much more often than others, and the actual uncertainty is 5.2 bits out of a possible 6. ($64 = 2^6$, hence $\log_2 64 = 6$.) On the 32-item test all adjectives are equally popular, and the uncertainty is 5 bits out of a possible 5. Which is the better test? The psychologist will learn slightly more from the long test, but he will pay dearly for the extra two-tenths of a bit in the form of a longer time for administration, increased paper and printing costs, and so on. The short test, with a relative uncertainty of 1.00, will be more efficient than the long test, whose uncertainty is only $\frac{5.2}{6}$ or .87.

Questions

1. An appliance company asks 584 people which new appliance they would like most to buy. The results are given below.

APPLIANCE	NUMBER DESIRING
Refrigerator	147
Washer	189
Dryer	84
Stove	71
Freezer	71
Ironer	22

a. What is the ratio of people desiring each appliance to the total number of people? What is the ratio of people desiring freezers to people desiring refrigerators? Of people desiring refrigerators to those desiring freezers?

b. Convert the ratios in problem a to proportions; to percentages.

c. Plot a bar graph of the data.

d. What is the mode?

2. A certain college tabulated the number of students of each sex majoring in each academic department. The results are given below.

DEPARTMENT	MEN	WOMEN	ALL STUDENTS
Anthropology	1	2	3
Arts and letters	42	66	108
Biology	22	20	62
Business administration	100	22	122
Chemistry	20	8	28
Education	27	42	69
Engineering	75	3	78
Geology	8	0	8
History and political science	25	25	50
Home economics	5	50	55
Mathematics	10	6	16
Music	3	10	13
Physics and general science	38	18	56
Psychology	24	28	52
	400	300	700

a. Find the percentage of men, of women, and of all students majoring in each department.

b. What percentage of the students majoring in each department are men?

c. Draw a bar graph of the results, using open bars for men and shaded bars for women. Will a bar graph be more meaningful if it is drawn in terms of percentages or if it is drawn in terms of absolute numbers?

d. What is the modal subject for men? For women? For all students?

e. What is the ratio of men to women in this college? Of women to men?

3. Compute the following: 2^1, 2^2, 2^3, 2^5, 2^8, 2^{12}

4. Solve for x:

     a. $x^1 = 3$ d. $x^4 = 1$

     b. $x^1 = 2$ e. $x^4 = 16$

     c. $x^0 = 1$ f. $x^3 = 1000$

5. Solve for x:

     a. $x^{\frac{1}{2}} = 1$ d. $x^{\frac{1}{2}} = 2.5$

     b. $x^{\frac{1}{2}} = 2$ e. $x^{\frac{1}{3}} = 2$

     c. $x^{\frac{1}{2}} = 4$ f. $x^{\frac{1}{4}} = 2$

6. Find the following logarithms:

     a. $\log_2 2$, $\log_3 3$, $\log_7 7$, $\log_b b$

     b. $\log_2 4$, $\log_3 9$, $\log_7 49$, $\log_b b^2$

     c. $\log_2 8$, $\log_2 32$, $\log_3 27$, $\log_b b^d$

     d. $\log_2 \dfrac{1}{2}$, $\log_2 \dfrac{1}{4}$, $\log_2 \dfrac{1}{32}$ $\log_3 \dfrac{1}{9}$, $\log_b \left(\dfrac{1}{b^d}\right)$

     e. $\log_2 .50$, $\log_2 .25$, $\log_2 .03125$

7. Solve for x:

     a. $x^{-1} = 1$ c. $x^{-1} = 2$

     b. $x^{-1} = \frac{1}{2}$ d. $x^{-2} = \frac{1}{4}$

8. By direct calculation, obtain the following:

     a. $1.00 \log_2 1.00$ c. $.25 \log_2 .25$

     b. $.50 \log_2 .50$ d. $.125 \log_2 .125$

Check your results by comparing them to the values in Table A.

9. Obtain from Table A the value of $-p(i) \log_2 p(i)$ for the following values of $p(i)$:

     a. .040   c. .099   e. .504

     b. .046   d. .104   f. .766

10. A telephone message must go through 5 relay stations before it is received. Experience has shown that when there is trouble in reception the source of the trouble is more likely to occur at some stations than at others.

16 messages out of every thousand are lost at station	A
4 " " " " " " " " "	B
32 " " " " " " " " "	C
4 " " " " " " " " "	D
8 " " " " " " " " "	E

What procedure should the repair department use for tracking down a difficulty in reception? On the average, how many stations would they have to examine before locating the difficulty? (Calculate by the direct method; then check your result by using formula 3.3.2.) What is the uncertainty about the station causing the trouble?

11. Two items are being considered for inclusion in a multiple-choice test. The distribution of responses for each of the items is given below:

ALTERNATIVE	ITEM A	ITEM B
a	20 %	0 %
b	20 %	25 %
c	20 %	50 %
d	20 %	10 %
e	20 %	15 %

What is the uncertainty, $\hat{H}$, for each item? Other things being equal, which would be the more useful test item? Why?

12. An animal psychologist is interested in the extent to which animals will seek 'variety' in their diets. He therefore makes careful studies of the food choices of four groups of animals. Each group is presented with a certain number of foods, each of which contains all the necessary elements of a balanced diet. He determines the quantities of each food eaten by each group and converts these quantities to per cent of total eaten by that group. His results are given below. Use $\hat{H}$ and $\hat{H}_{rel}$ to provide the basis for a discussion of his problem.

FOOD	GROUP I	GROUP II	GROUP III	GROUP IV
A	50	25	35	4
B	50	25	6	37
C		25	25	29
D		25	9	6
E			10	6
F			15	10
G				2
H				6

How to read the table above: Numbers in the table refer to per cent of total food intake of group specified. Thus, Group I was offered only foods A and B, and ate equal amounts of the two. Group II was offered foods A, B, C, and D, and 25 per cent of its diet consisted of each of the 4 foods. Group III was offered a choice of 6 foods, and Group IV, of 8.

3.4 Measures of Relatedness

We saw in the last section that some guesses or predictions are better than others. If we predict that an individual will fall in the modal class, we can sometimes be fairly sure that we'll be right; at other times we know that we'll probably have to guess again—and again and again. We have developed a measure, $\hat{H}$, which describes the extent of our uncertainty. We have said, for purposes of illustration, that our uncertainty in guessing a man's name would be very high. But now let us suppose that we have some additional information about this man: we know that he is of Japanese descent. Now we should have a very much easier time guessing his name, because a lot of possible names which we previously had to consider are highly improbable for a man of Japanese descent. When we say that we should have an easier time guessing, we mean that our uncertainty will be reduced. Name and nationality are related, and relatedness means that knowing about one thing reduces our uncertainty about the other. In order to study relatedness between two variables, every individual in the group must have been classified on both.

3.4.1 Bivariate Frequency Distributions: When every individual in a group can be classified simultaneously on two scales, we may describe the results by the use of a bivariate frequency distribution. As the name implies, this is a distribution showing the frequency of cases in each category of the two scales or variables. Suppose, for example, we classify people as male or female, and also as adults or children. We find that in the group there are 20 men (adult) and 30 women, 30 boys and 20 girls. These results are presented in a two-way table, as shown below:

	MALE	FEMALE	TOTAL
Adult	20	30	50
Child	30	20	50
Total	50	50	100

In this table the upper-left square represents individuals who are *both* adult and male; the upper-right square, people who are both adult and female; the lower-left square, non-adult males, and the lower-right square, non-adult females. The number 20 in the upper-left square means that there are 20 adult males. The numbers in these squares are called the 'cell-entries.' In the margin at the right are the totals—one for adults, of whatever sex, and one for children. At the bottom are the totals for the two sexes, whatever the age. The numbers in the right-hand and bottom margins are called the marginal totals. The number 100 in the extreme lower-right corner is the total number of cases in the group, which, now and forever after, will be called N. In this example, N = 100.

Whenever we can make up a bivariate frequency distribution, we can study the strength of relationship between the two variables represented on it.

3.4.2 Uncertainty Reduction, $\hat{T}$: A woman claims that she can tell without looking at the cards in a deck whether they will be red or black, and we wish to study this claim. We shuffle an ordinary deck of playing cards and put it on a table. The lady in question then calls off the colors of the cards from top to bottom. Has she proved her ability? Is there a relationship between the actual color of the card and the color she has assigned to it? If we know what color the card really is, does that reduce our uncertainty about what she will say? If we know what she said, does that reduce our uncertainty about the card's color? Let's consider some possible results:

FIRST POSSIBILITY

CARD COLOR

		Red	Black	Total
Color called by lady	Red	26		26
	Black		26	26
	Total	26	26	52

According to this table, every black card was called black, and every red card, red. Let's see how much our uncertainty was reduced.

Our original uncertainty, that is, our uncertainty about card color before we know what the lady calls, is one bit. That is because the cards are equally divided between red and black, and naming a card's color requires one choice between two equally likely alternatives. But if we consider separately those cards which our subject said were black, we have no uncertainty. The card is certain to have been black. Similarly, we have no uncertainty about those cards which the subject said were red: they were. Our uncertainty about card color, once we know what the subject said, is zero.

Our original uncertainty was one bit.

Our new uncertainty, with knowledge of what the subject said, is zero.

We have therefore *reduced our uncertainty* by *one bit*. If we let $\hat{T}$ stand for the amount by which our uncertainty is reduced, then

$$\hat{T} = \text{original uncertainty} - \text{new uncertainty}$$
$$\hat{T} = 1 - 0 = 1$$

SECOND POSSIBILITY

| | | CARD COLOR | | |
		Red	Black	Total
Color called by lady	Black	26		26
	Red		26	26
	Total	26	26	52

As before, our original uncertainty is one bit, and again, our new uncertainty, based upon what the woman has said, is zero. If she called a card red we know that it is black, and vice versa. She got her signals crossed, but her answers reduce our uncertainty just as much as they did when she was 'right.' $\hat{T}$ is again equal to one bit.

THIRD POSSIBILITY

| | | CARD COLOR | | |
		Red	Black	Total
Color called	Black	13	13	26
	Red	13	13	26
	Total	26	26	52

Our original uncertainty about the color of a card is again one bit. Now let's consider the cards the subject called black: half of them really are black, and the other half are red. The same is true for the cards she called red. Knowing what color she called makes no difference to us. In either case our new uncertainty is still one bit.

$$\hat{T} = 1 - 1 = 0$$

There is no uncertainty reduction.

FOURTH POSSIBILITY

CARD COLOR

		Red	Black	Total
Color called	Black	6	20	26
	Red	20	6	26
	Total	26	26	52

In this instance the subject does a good, but not a perfect job. We should expect, therefore, that the uncertainty reduction would be somewhere between one and zero.

The original uncertainty is one bit. We now compute the new uncertainty for the occasions when the subject says the card is black:

$$\hat{H} = -\Sigma p(i) \log_2 p(i)$$
$$\hat{H} = -\frac{6}{26} \log_2 \frac{6}{26} - \frac{20}{26} \log_2 \frac{20}{26}$$
$$\hat{H} = -.231 \log_2 .231 - .769 \log_2 .769$$
$$\hat{H} = .4883 + .2941$$
$$\hat{H} = .7797 \text{ bits}$$

The same figure will be obtained for the cards called red since the proportions are the same. On the average, then, our new uncertainty is .7797 bits.

$$\hat{T} = \text{original uncertainty} - \text{new uncertainty}$$
$$\hat{T} = 1.0000 - .7797 = .2203 \text{ bits}$$

Our uncertainty has been reduced *from* one bit *to* .7797 bits. It has been reduced *by* .2203 bits. Since the original uncertainty was one bit, we can also say that our uncertainty has been reduced 22.03 per cent.

In summary, then, one way to measure relationship is to measure the extent to which our uncertainty, $\hat{H}$, is reduced by a knowledge of some other factor. To do this, we compute the original $\hat{H}$, without knowledge of the added factor, and then find the average $\hat{H}$ *with* knowledge of that factor. The difference between the old and the new uncertainties is $\hat{T}$, the measure of uncertainty reduction. If we call the thing we are trying to predict (in the above example, card color) y, then we can call our original uncertainty $\hat{H}(y)$. If we call the thing we are predicting *from* (in this example, the color called by the subject) x, we can call the new uncertainty, that is, the uncertainty about y once we know x, $\hat{H}_x(y)$. (This last term is read: $\hat{H}$ sub x of y.) Then

$$\hat{T} = \hat{H}(y) - \hat{H}_x(y) \qquad (3.4.1)$$

$\hat{H}_x(y)$, the uncertainty about y with knowledge of x, is not always so simple to compute as it was in the examples above. Since in those examples the lady always called half the cards red and half black, to get the *average* uncertainty was no problem for us. Suppose, instead of using a whole deck of cards, we use just 30 cards drawn at random from the deck. It turns out that these are equally divided between red and black, but our subject does not know this. The results are as follows:

| | | CARD COLOR | | |
		Red	Black	Total
Color called	Black	5	15	20
	Red	10		10
	Total	15	15	30

Our original uncertainty, $\hat{H}(y)$, is still one bit. What about our reduced uncertainty? When the lady says that the card is red, we have no uncertainty about what it actually is—it's red. When she says that it's black, there is some uncertainty:

$$\hat{H} = -.25 \log_2 .25 - .75 \log_2 .75 = .8113 \text{ bits}$$

When she says it's black, our uncertainty is .8113 bits. But two-thirds of the time she says the card is black, while she calls it red only one-third of the time. Therefore, two-thirds of the time our uncertainty is .8113 bits, while only one-third of the time is it zero.

The *average* new uncertainty, therefore, is

$$\hat{H}_x(y) = \frac{1}{3}(0) + \frac{2}{3}(.8113) = .5408 \text{ bits}$$

and

$$\hat{T} = 1.0000 - .5408 = .4592 \text{ bits}$$

When the x categories are not equally likely, the uncertainty of each category must be multiplied by the proportion of cases in that category in order to find the correct average.

Let us summarize the way in which $\hat{T}$ is computed and then carry through a complete computational example. After that we shall consider more fully the interpretation of $\hat{T}$.

To compute $\hat{T}$:

1. Make up a bivariate frequency distribution.
2. Call one of the variables, which we are trying to predict, y. Call the other variable x.
3. From the marginal totals of the y variable compute $\hat{H}(y)$.

    a. Divide the number of cases in each y category by the total number of cases to obtain $p(i)$.
    b. From Table A, obtain $-p(i) \log_2 p(i)$ for each $p(i)$.
    c. Sum the numbers found in step b.

4. From the cell entries, compute $\hat{H}(y)$ separately for each x category.
5. Find, from the marginal totals of the x variable, the proportion of cases in each x category.
6. Multiply each value found in step 4 by the corresponding proportion found in step 5.
7. Sum the results found in step 6. The result is $\hat{H}_x(y)$.
8. Subtract the result of step 7 from the result of step 3. This is $\hat{T}$.
$\hat{T} = \hat{H}(y) - \hat{H}_x(y)$.

As an illustration, we'll consider another experiment on extrasensory perception (ESP). In this case, a more ambitious subject maintains that he can predict in advance the suit of a card drawn from a deck. He makes his prediction and the card is drawn. It is then replaced in the deck. The process is repeated 200 times, and the results are shown below:

STEP 1: Construct a bivariate frequency distribution:

| | | SUIT CALLED BY SUBJECT | | | | |
		H	D	C	S	Total
	S	10	8	6	24	48
Card drawn	C	17	12	9	16	54
	D	14	10	10	6	40
	H	19	10	5	24	58
	Total	60	40	30	70	200

STEP 2: We shall try to predict the suit of the card drawn, so we shall call this variable y. The suit called by the subject will be x.

STEP 3(a):

$$\frac{48}{200} = .24 \qquad \frac{54}{200} = .27 \qquad \frac{40}{200} = .20 \qquad \frac{58}{200} = .29$$

STEP 3(b):

When $p(i)$ is .24, $\qquad -p(i) \log_2 p(i)$ is .4941
" " " .27 " " .5100
" " " .20 " " .4641
" " " .29 " " .5179

STEP 3(c):

$$\hat{H}(y) = .4941 + .5100 + .4644 + .5179 = 1.9864 \text{ bits}$$

STEP 4:

Hearts:	$p(i)$	$-p(i) \log_2 p(i)$
	$\frac{10}{60} = .167$	.4312
	$\frac{17}{60} = .283$	.5154
	$\frac{14}{60} = .233$	.4897
	$\frac{19}{60} = .317$	.5254
		1.9617

$$-\Sigma p(i) \log_2 p(i) = 1.9617 \text{ bits}$$

Diamonds:	$p(i)$	$-p(i) \log_2 p(i)$
	$\dfrac{8}{40} = .20$	.4644
	$\dfrac{12}{40} = .30$	.5211
	$\dfrac{10}{40} = .25$	.5000
	$\dfrac{10}{40} = .25$	.5000
		1.9855

$$-\Sigma p(i) \log_2 p(i) = 1.9855 \text{ bits}$$

Corresponding calculations are carried out for clubs and spades.

For clubs $-\Sigma p(i) \log_2 p(i) = 1.9450$ bits
For spades $-\Sigma p(i) \log_2 p(i) = 1.8504$ bits

STEP 5:

The proportion of cards called hearts   by the subject is $\dfrac{60}{200} = .30$

"   "   "   "   "   diamonds "   "   "   " $\dfrac{40}{200} = .20$

"   "   "   "   "   clubs   "   "   "   " $\dfrac{30}{200} = .15$

"   "   "   "   "   spades   "   "   "   " $\dfrac{70}{200} = .35$

STEP 6:

$$.30 \times 1.9617 = .5885$$
$$.20 \times 1.9855 = .3971$$
$$.15 \times 1.9450 = .2918$$
$$.35 \times 1.8504 = .6476$$

STEP 7:

$$\hat{H}_x(y) = .5885 + .3971 + .2918 + .6476 = 1.9250 \text{ bits}$$

STEP 8:

$$\hat{T} = \hat{H}(y) - \hat{H}_x(y)$$
$$\hat{T} = 1.9864 - 1.9250 = .0614 \text{ bits}$$

Our uncertainty is reduced by .0614 bits.

In this example our uncertainty is reduced by only six one-hundredths of a bit, which seems like a pretty small amount. Our subject is apparently not as clever as he thinks he is.

How do we decide what is a 'small amount'? How do we go about interpreting a result?

If the uncertainty is reduced by one bit, we can cut the number of alternatives among which we must choose by one-half. Thus, if our uncertainty about a card's suit had been reduced one bit by a knowledge of what the subject called, then knowing his call would be equivalent to knowing the card's color. We should have only two things to choose between, instead of four. If uncertainty is reduced by two bits, that is equivalent to reducing the alternatives among which we must choose to one-quarter of what it was originally. Each bit of uncertainty reduction cuts the number of alternatives in half.

Sometimes our interest centers in the absolute amount by which uncertainty is reduced, sometimes in the percentage reduction. The subject who claims that he can tell the suits of the cards, but who actually calls red cards either hearts or diamonds pretty much at random, and calls black cards randomly clubs or spades, is doing just as good a job of clairvoying as the man who claims only to be able to predict color and does. Relative to what he claims to be able to do, the first man is only shooting 50 per cent, and the second man 100 per cent, but in absolute terms both are discriminating color equally well. $\hat{T}$, the absolute measure of uncertainty reduction, enables us to make the absolute comparison. If we wish to get a relative figure, we can compare the amount by which the uncertainty *is* reduced with the amount by which it *could be* reduced.

For a given bivariate frequency distribution, the maximum amount by which the uncertainty can be reduced is the original uncertainty of the x variable, $\hat{H}(x)$, or of the y variable, $\hat{H}(y)$, whichever is smaller. In the last example, for instance, the original uncertainty about what the subject will say, when we know that 30 per cent of his responses were hearts, 20 per cent diamonds, 15 per cent clubs, and 35 per cent spades, can be calculated, and turns out to be 1.9261 bits. If we limit the subject to that distribution of responses, the uncertainty cannot be reduced by more than 1.9261 bits. On the other hand, a theoretically perfect subject, who guessed every card correctly and whose responses would therefore be distributed in the same way as the numbers of cards drawn from the deck, could show an uncertainty reduction of 1.9864 bits. The particular purpose for which we are using the measure will determine whether we are more interested in the theoretically perfect condition or in the situation as it actually exists.

The measure of uncertainty reduction, $\hat{T}$, does not measure correctness. The subject who says 'black' for every red card, and 'red' for every black card reduces our uncertainty just as much as the one who names every card correctly, and this uncertainty reduction is the only thing that $\hat{T}$ measures. Furthermore, it makes no difference which variable we choose to predict and hence call y, and which we predict *from* and call x. Provided that we are consistent and don't interchange x's and y's in the middle of the calculation, $\hat{T}$ will be the same whichever way we compute it.

What we have been calling 'uncertainty reduction' is usually referred to in the literature as 'information transmitted.' That is a consequence of the history of the measure as an engineering concept and tool. The engineers who developed the system of $\hat{H}$, $\hat{T}$, and other measures which we cannot consider now were actually interested in the transmission of information over wires, and they rather naturally adopted that name for their measure. It was very easy for psychologists to adopt the engineers' terminology—in fact it has become quite fashionable to talk about people as 'transmission channels,' with information being transmitted from the stimulus to the response. There's nothing wrong with doing this—it can be a fruitful and provocative way of thinking about an organism—but the word 'information' often turns out to be value-loaded. It seems, somehow, to convey the impression of good information, or true information, or important information, none of which is necessarily implied. Furthermore, $\hat{T}$ can be such a useful statistic in situations that just can't be thought of as communication channels that the word 'transmission,' too, seems to be too limiting. So we'll go on calling the measure 'uncertainty reduction' and wishing there were some less polysyllabic term available. Be alerted, though, to understand the term 'information transmitted' when you run across it in your reading.

Questions

1. List five instances of situations in which knowledge of one variable will reduce our uncertainty about another.

2. Make up a two-dimensional table to display the following information: There are 256 students in a college graduating class. Of these, 125 are men and the rest (naturally) are women. 57 people are definitely planning to go to graduate school, 15 think they may go, and the rest are definitely not going. 35 of those who say they are definitely going to graduate school are men, and 10 of the 15 who aren't sure are women.

NOTE: the table should have 6 cell entries and 5 marginal totals in addition to N. Only 6 of the 12 necessary figures are listed in the paragraph above. Be sure to fill in the rest.

3. Three factory workers are engaged in making a small radio part. When the parts made by the workers are inspected, it is found that 200 are defective: 50 are cracked; 50 are unfinished; 50 are oversized; 50 are undersized. The defective parts are traced back to the workers who made them. It is found that:

Joe Bloke contributed 50 of the defective articles, of which 25 were cracked and 25 undersized.

Mabel Mullins also contributed 50 articles. 25 of her articles were unfinished and 25 oversized.

Jack Whifflebottom contributed 100 defective parts, equally divided among the four defects.

    a. Make up a bivariate frequency distribution showing these results.

    b. Compute $\hat{T}$. You should be able to do it without having to refer to the $-p(i) \log_2 p(i)$ table at all.

    c. Interpret your results.

4. In many modern airplanes, the handles or controls that operate the wheels, flaps, throttle, and other parts are shaped differently to prevent confusion. When the pilot has to wear flying gloves, however, he may not be able to detect these differences in shape. Psychologists and human engineers must design control knobs that can be distinguished with and without gloves. One way of studying the distinguishability of knobs of different shapes is to conduct 'blind grasping' experiments in which the subject must grasp the knob without looking and decide which one of several possible knobs it is. The results of one such experiment are given below.

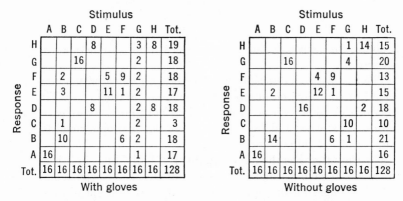

With gloves

| | Stimulus | | | | | | | | |
	A	B	C	D	E	F	G	H	Tot.
H				8			3	8	19
G			16				2		18
F		2			5	9	2		18
E		3			11	1	2		17
D				8			2	8	18
C		1					2		3
B		10				6	2		18
A	16							1	17
Tot.	16	16	16	16	16	16	16	16	128

(Response)

Without gloves

| | Stimulus | | | | | | | | |
	A	B	C	D	E	F	G	H	Tot.
H							1	14	15
G			16				4		20
F					4	9			13
E		2			12	1			15
D				16				2	18
C							10		10
B		14				6	1		21
A	16								16
Tot.	16	16	16	16	16	16	16	16	128

(Response)

Use $\hat{H}$, $\hat{T}$, and a large quota of common sense to answer the following questions:

  a. Which knobs are identified most certainly without gloves? With gloves? Which knobs are identified least certainly with and without gloves?
  b. Do you think knob C would be a good one to use? Discuss.
  c. How good is the subject at identifying knobs when he is without gloves? When he is wearing gloves.
  d. How much do the gloves affect the subject's discrimination?
  e. Which knob or knobs are most affected by the wearing of gloves? Which are affected least?

5. From the data in Problem 2, page 85, determine how much our uncertainty about a person's major subject is reduced by a knowledge of his sex.

6. Construct a numerical example to show that for a given bivariate frequency distribution $\hat{T}$ can never be larger than $\hat{H}(x)$ or $\hat{H}(y)$, whichever is smaller.

7. List three situations in which a psychologist might find $\hat{T}$ a useful measure.

3.5 Comparing an Individual with the Rest of the Group

Since the classes of a nominal scale are only names and don't have any describable kind of relationship to each other, there is no way to compare an individual with the other members of the group. All we can do is to name the class to which the individual belongs, and perhaps state whether or not that class is also the mode.

Summary

A nominal scale consists of a set of names applied to distinguishable classes.

The best over-all description of the data obtained from a nominal scale is a count of the number of individuals in each class. The results of this count can be presented in a bar graph, where each bar represents a class, and the height of the bar is proportional to the number of individuals in the class.

The class that has the largest number of individuals in it is called the mode. If we must make a guess about the class to which an individual belongs, our best guess is the mode. By 'best guess' we mean the guess that is most likely to be right.

We feel most certain about our guess when most individuals fall into a few categories, least certain when the individuals are equally divided among many categories. A quantitative measure of our uncertainty is $\hat{H}$, the average number of choices between two equally likely alternatives that would be required to specify the category to which an individual belongs.

If every individual has been measured on two scales, a knowledge of the class to which he belongs on one scale will sometimes reduce our uncertainty about his class on the other scale. When this is the case, the two variables are said to be related. To measure the amount of uncertainty reduction, we can use $\hat{T}$, which is the difference between our uncertainty about the second variable without knowledge of the first and our uncertainty when we use our knowledge of the first variable. $\hat{T}$ can be computed for a table of any dimensions, is always positive, and varies from zero to the uncertainty in bits of the less uncertain of the two variables being related. Each bit by which the uncertainty is reduced halves the number of alternatives among which we must choose.

When data come from a nominal scale, there is no way to describe the position of an individual relative to the group.

References

1. Hyman, R. 'Stimulus information as a determinant of reaction time,' *J. Exp. Psychol.*, 1953, **45**, pp. 188–96. This article reports the reaction time study mentioned on pp. 82–3.
2. Miller, G. A., 'What is information measurement?' *Am. Psychologist*,

1953, **8,** pp. **3–11.** A relatively elementary discussion of the uncertainty measures and their use in psychology.
3. Quastler, H. (ed.), *Information Theory in Psychology*, Glencoe, The Free Press, 1955. A collection of articles on information theory and its use in psychology. The articles vary in difficulty level.
4. Reid, Constance, *From Zero to Infinity*, London, Routledge & Kegan Paul, 1956, pp. 28–40. A brief, non-mathematical account of the number 2 and the binary system.

Answers

Page 84f.:

1. a.		b.		d. Washer
147:584		25.2%		
189:584		32.4%		
84:584		14.4%		
71:584		12.2%		
71:584		12.2%		
22:584		3.8%		
71:147		48.3%		
147:71		207.0%		

2. Men per dept.	Women per dept.	Students per dept.	Men of students
0.2%	0.7%	0.4%	33.3%
10.5%	22.0%	15.4%	39.0%
5.5%	6.7%	8.9%	35.5%
25.0%	7.3%	17.4%	82.0%
5.0%	2.7%	4.0%	71.4%
6.8%	14.0%	9.9%	39.1%
18.8%	1.0%	11.1%	96.2%
2.0%	0.0%	1.1%	100.0%
6.2%	8.3%	7.1%	50.0%
1.2%	16.7%	7.9%	9.1%
2.5%	2.0%	2.3%	62.5%
0.8%	3.3%	1.9%	23.1%
9.5%	6.0%	8.0%	67.9%
6.0%	9.3%	7.4%	46.2%

   d. Bus. ad.; arts & let.; bus. ad.
   e. 4:3; 3:4
3. a. 2; b. 4; c. 8; d. 32; e. 256; f. 4096
4. a. 3; b. 2; c. insol.; d. 1; e. 2; f. 10
5. a. 1; b. 4; c. 16; d. 6.25; e. 8; f. 16
6. a. 1, 1, 1, 1; b. 2, 2, 2, 2; c. 3, 5, 3, d; d. $\bar{1}, \bar{2}, \bar{5}, \bar{2}, \bar{d}$; e. $\bar{1}, \bar{2}, \bar{5}$
7. a. 1; b. 2; c. $\frac{1}{2}$; d. 2
8. a. 0; b. $-.50$; c. $-.50$; d. $-.3750$

9. a. .1858; b. .2043; c. .3303; d. .3396; e. .4982; f. .2946

10. C, A, E, B or D; 1.875   11. Item A: 2.3220 bits
                                                  Item B: 1.7427 bits

12. Gp. I: $\hat{H} = 1$ bit, $\hat{H}_{rel} = 1.00$; Gp. II: $\hat{H} = 2$ bits, $\hat{H}_{rel} = 1.00$; Gp. III: $\hat{H} = 2.3290$ bits, $\hat{H}_{rel} = .90$; Gp. IV: $\hat{H} = 2.4100$ bits, $\hat{H}_{rel} = .80$

Page 97f.:

3. $\hat{T} = .5$ bits   5. $\hat{T} = .2750$ bits

THE ORDINAL SCALE

An ordinal scale is one in which the criteria of connectedness, transitivity, and asymmetry have been established and which therefore allows items to be placed in an ordered relationship to each other. Examples of ordinal scales are the scale of hardness of minerals established by the operation of scratching, attitude scales, letter grades describing academic performance, and many different kinds of rating scales.

4.1 Kinds of Ordinal Scales—Continuous and Discrete Variables

Consider peas and pea soup. You can have a pot with 500 peas in it and a pot with 501 peas in it, but (unless the peas have been squashed) you can't have a pot with $500\frac{1}{2}$ peas in it. On the other hand, you can have a pot with two cups of pea soup, another pot with $2\frac{1}{2}$ cups, one with $2\frac{1}{4}$ cups, one with 2.0000001 cups, or one with 2.0000000000001 cups. Theoretically there is no limit to the fineness of the gradations that can be used in describing the amount of pea soup. Number of peas, which can be measured by *counting* the peas, is a discrete variable; amount of pea soup, which cannot be measured by counting, is a continuous variable. Whenever numerals are assigned by counting, the variable to which they are assigned is said to be **discrete.** When they cannot be assigned by counting, the variable is called **continuous.**

Let's take another example—art appreciation. Presumably this is a continuous variable with an infinite number of fine gradations, but how do we go about measuring it? One way is to administer an art-appreciation test and count the number of items answered correctly. The number of items right, that is, the score on the test, is a discrete variable that is used to represent a continuous variable, art appreciation. Any ordered discrete variable forms an interval or ratio scale, and if our interest were really in the number of items answered correctly we should not be considering the problem in this chapter. However, our interest is usually in art appreciation itself, not in test scores. The latter are just a device (and often a poor one) for getting at the underlying continuous variable. If three people take the test and get scores of 15, 20, and 25 respectively, then the third man is as much better than the second as the second is than the first—in terms of number of items answered correctly. But the differences in art appreciation may not be equal at all. Those extra five items might all be very difficult ones which indicate a very much higher degree of appreciation. So if we are interested in the continuous variables underlying psychological tests, we consider scores as numerals from an ordinal rather than a ratio scale.

A continuous variable is usually more amenable to mathematical treatment than a discrete variable, and for that reason we sometimes treat a discrete variable *as if* it were continuous. (In section 4.2, where we discuss the real limits of an interval, you will encounter one example of treating a discrete variable as continuous.) When the discrete variable is being used to represent an underlying continuous variable, the treatment of the data as continuous makes fairly good sense.

The ordinal scales psychologists use are not always based on test scores. Sometimes we have nothing better than general subjective impressions to go on, and descriptive categories with ordinary words for numerals may be the only measurements we have. We might watch our subjects on a trip through an art museum and classify their behavior as:

1. 'Very appreciative. Hair stands on end when looking at great art.'

2. 'Quite appreciative. Looks ecstatic, but no physiological symptoms.'

and so on down the scale to 'totally unappreciative.' When people are classified in this way, they are being placed on a crudely subdivided ordinal scale. We might substitute the letters A, B, C, D, and F for the descriptive phrases, or we might substitute actual numbers. In any case we should have an ordinal scale for the measurement of a continuous variable. Given such a scale, how shall we go about answering the five basic questions of descriptive statistics?

4.2 General Description of the Data

In Chapter 3 we said that, for the nominal scale, the bar graph is the principal means of representing graphically the relative frequencies of items in various categories. For the ordinal scale this is still the case. When a bar graph was constructed for a nominal scale, only the relative heights of the bars were of mathematical significance, but for an ordinal scale the order of the bars, as well as their relative heights, is significant and cannot be manipulated at will for the sake of prettier pictures. In addition, when the variable is continuous or is being treated as if it were continuous, bars for adjacent categories should be contiguous. A bar graph for continuous data is called a **histogram.**

4.2.1 The Histogram or Bar Graph: To construct a bar graph or histogram for an ordinal scale, we list the categories of the scale in order, and determine, by counting, the number of items or individuals falling in each category. Consider a typical rating scale of job performance, with results like those shown below:

CATEGORY	NUMBER OF EMPLOYEES
Excellent	54
Very good	65
Good	31
Average	18
Below average	15
Unsatisfactory	17
Total	200

We wish to plot these results. The bars on the graph must be contiguous, for quality of job performance is a continuous variable ranging from utter horror at one end to fondest superlatives at the other. We therefore plot the data in the form shown in Figure 4.1: the order of the bars is determined by the order of the descriptive categories, and the fact that the bars have no spaces between them is determined by the fact that they represent a continuous variable. The relative heights of the bars are determined, of course, by the relative frequencies of occurrence in the various categories.

Notice that we have made the bars equal in width. Actually, they probably should not be equal, but since we don't know how wide they should be relative to each other, we have resorted in our ignorance to equality. Looking at the relative frequencies, we might suspect that the category 'very good' covers a much wider range of performance than any other and hence should be the widest bar on the graph. On the other hand, the two end categories—excellent and unsatisfactory—should perhaps also be extra wide. If an employee is unsatisfactory for a particular job because he has low mechanical aptitude he gets an 'unsatisfactory' rating, but so does the worker who shows up for work two days out of five, comes in

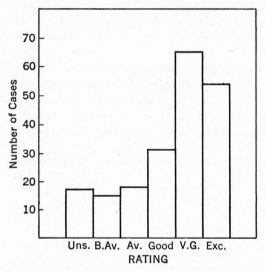

FIG. 4.1   Histogram of the data on job-performance ratings.

dirty and unshaven, tries to seduce all the secretaries, and rifles the company safe. Yes, we might do well to give 'unsatisfactory' an extra-wide bar, but we just don't know how wide. In our ignorance, therefore, we make all bars equally wide, remembering, however, that this equality has no mathematical significance.

4.2.2 The Frequency Polygon: When relative frequencies in different categories are to be compared for two or more groups, a frequency polygon may be used instead of a histogram. A frequency polygon can be constructed by simply connecting with straight lines the midpoints of the tops of the bars for different categories. The frequency polygon for the data given above is shown in Figure

4.2. Since the widths of the bars are without mathematical significance the slopes of the lines connecting their midpoints are also meaningless. Figure 4.3 is a graphic representation of the same set of data. It is just as valid a picture as that given in Figure 4.2.

The use of a frequency polygon for the representation of a discrete variable is, strictly speaking, illogical, because the frequency can be read off of any point on the x-axis instead of just off the integral

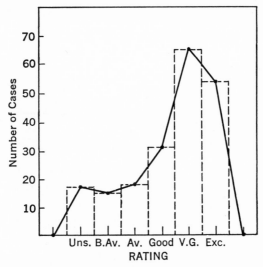

Fig. 4.2 Frequency polygon of the data on job-performance ratings. Broken lines show where the bars of the histogram used to be. These bars are not to be drawn when you are plotting a frequency polygon. They are included here only to show the relation between the two types of graph.

points obtained by counting. But a frequency polygon is an exceedingly convenient way of representing data, and its use with discrete variables is one of the more common examples of the treatment of discrete data as if they were continuous.

4.2.3 Grouped Frequency Distributions: Ordinal scales have one big advantage over nominal scales: since the order of the categories is determinate and meaningful, it makes sense to talk about 'adjacent categories.' This fact, in turn, makes it possible to group frequencies from adjacent categories into one new category. This is particularly useful when there are many categories to begin with and few cases in any individual category. For example, we might have a

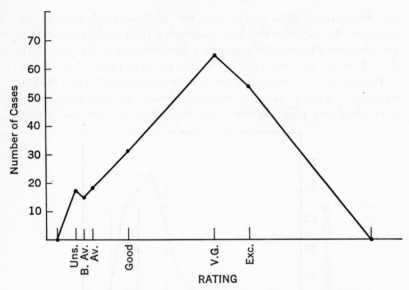

FIG. 4.3 Data on job ratings replotted to make a symmetrical figure. The relative distances between the different categories are meaningless and may be manipulated at will.

list of scores on an intelligence test. There may be 50 children in the group, with only two or three obtaining any one score, as shown below:

INTELLIGENCE TEST SCORES

85	102	108	119	134
87	103	109	120	136
90	104	111	121	140
92	104	112	124	143
93	104	114	125	145
97	106	114	127	152
100	107	117	127	155
101	107	119	128	157
101	108	119	129	164
102	108	119	130	179

If a bar graph were made from these data, in the form in which they are given above, it would be long, spread out, and not particularly helpful, as shown in Figure 4.4.

The fact that the categories are adjacent, however, allows us to group together all the scores falling within a certain range. We may decide on some convenient number of categories, or **intervals,** and group the scores into them. For example, using the same data, we might decide to use ten intervals, each one being ten score points in width. The data are retabulated in this form below and plotted in

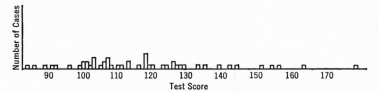

FIG. 4.4   Histogram of ungrouped intelligence-test scores. It is very difficult to get an over-all picture of the data from such a graph.

Figure 4.5. This new figure gives us, at a glance, a much better idea of the actual distribution of test scores in the class.

SCORES	NUMBER OF CASES
170–179	1
160–169	1
150–159	3
140–149	3
130–139	3
120–129	8
110–119	9
100–109	16
90– 99	4
80– 89	2
	50

Before we can use a grouped frequency distribution we must answer many practical questions which were neatly glossed over in the example above. How many intervals shall there be? How wide shall the intervals be? Where shall the intervals start? How shall the intervals be named?

Number, width, and starting points of intervals. How many intervals to use is determined by the use to which the grouped data are to be put and by the number of cases in the group. Of course the width of the intervals will depend upon the number of intervals to be used and the range of the scores, so we must consider interval width at the same time that we are deciding upon the number of intervals to be used.

Usually the principal purpose of grouping data is to make it easier to get a general picture of what happened. For this purpose, a number of intervals which is neither too large nor too small is best. Too many small intervals gives us a picture like Figure 4.4. Too few intervals will result in the loss of a great deal of potentially useful

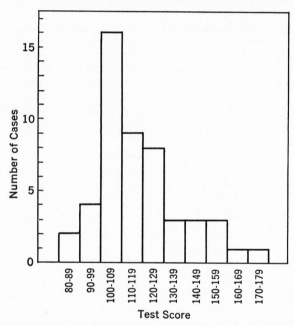

FIG. 4.5   Histogram of intelligence-test data grouped in intervals of ten points.

information. The larger the number of cases in the group, the more intervals it is desirable to use. As a rough rule of thumb, we may say that ten intervals is a good number, with more to be used when the number of cases in the group is very large, and fewer intervals to be used when the group is small. Sometimes it is a good idea to group the data into a large number of small intervals, plot the results, and then, if the resulting histogram is flat and ragged, regroup the data into fewer intervals of larger size.

The decision about the number of intervals to be used should often be modified by a consideration of how wide the intervals are to be. It was convenient, when grouping the intelligence-test data, to use an interval of ten points because this made it possible to disregard the last digit of the scores in grouping them. On the other hand, if further computations are to be carried out on the grouped data, every score in an interval will be treated as if it were at the midpoint of that interval. It is very convenient, therefore, to have midpoints that are integers—whole numbers. If the number of units in each interval is odd, the midpoint will be an integer, but if the number of units is even, the midpoint will have a most annoying .5 stuck on the end of it. If the data are just going to be looked at, this consideration is of no importance.

Usually the lowest interval may start anywhere. For example, our first interval used in grouping the intelligence-test data started at 80, but it might have started at 78 or 82 or 85. If the data seem to come in clumps which occur at regular spaces along the scale, it's a good idea to arrange to have these clumps near the midpoints of the intervals selected. Census figures show more people aged 10, 15, 20, 25, and so on than aged 11, 16, and 21, or 8, 13, 18, 23, and so on. This peculiarity, which turns out to be true no matter what the year in which the census is taken, probably results from a tendency to use round numbers when reporting ages of people other than oneself. If the intervals chosen were:

$$5-\ 9$$
$$10-14$$
$$15-20$$

and so on, all those clumps at ages that were multiples of five would fall at the bottoms of intervals. The cases in those intervals would then be represented in later computations by the interval midpoints. The result is that the population would then appear to be older than it actually reports itself as being. This matter of grouping may be of great concern when the data come from an interval or ratio scale, but is less important with data from ordinal scales. In this latter case the relative widths of the intervals are not assumed to be constant, and inequalities of interval widths can cause more distortions of the data than can grouping errors.

Limits of intervals. On most tests a person can get 85 items right or 86 items right, but not $85\frac{1}{2}$ items right. Nevertheless, the discrete variable—number of items right—represents some underlying continuous variable such as intelligence, and of those people who get scores of 86, some are more intelligent than others. The single number, 86, really represents a range of intelligence, and some of the people who got that score just barely exceeded 85, while others were almost 87. We acknowledge this fact by saying that the score 86

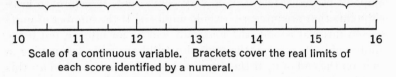

Scale of a continuous variable. Brackets cover the real limits of each score identified by a numeral.

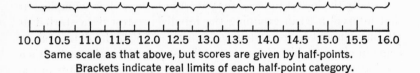

Same scale as that above, but scores are given by half-points. Brackets indicate real limits of each half-point category.

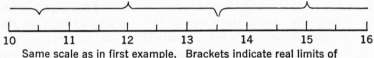

Same scale as in first example. Brackets indicate real limits of the intervals 8-10, 11-13, 14-16.

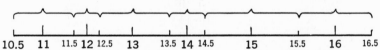

Scale of a continuous variable where the various scores are not equal in width. Arithmetically, the point 13.5, for example, is halfway between 13.0 and 14.0, but on this scale of unequal intervals it is not.

FIG. 4.6 Real limits of intervals.

covers the range from 85.5 to 86.5, thus treating the discrete scores as if they were a continuous variable. The numbers 85.5 and 86.5 are called the **real limits** of the score 86.

When several scores are grouped together in a grouped frequency distribution, the intervals into which they are grouped have as their real limits the lower real limit of the lowest score and the upper real limit of the highest score. For example the interval that includes the scores 80–89 has as its real limits 79.5 (the lower real limit of the score 80) and 89.5 (the upper real limit of the score 89). The next interval, which includes scores from 90 to 99 inclusive, has 89.5 and 99.5 as its real limits. The lowest and highest *scores* in an interval are called its **score limits.** The score limits in the two intervals discussed above are 80–89 and 90–99.

If half-points were actually given on a test, so that a person might receive the score $85\frac{1}{2}$, that score must be thought of as covering the range from $85\frac{1}{4}$ to $85\frac{3}{4}$. The score 86 would then cover the range from $85\frac{3}{4}$ to $86\frac{1}{4}$, and so on. It is rather ironical that real limits are values that can never really occur in practice.

Real limits are frequently put to use when computations are made on data from a grouped frequency distribution, and they are used in labeling a cumulative frequency or cumulative percentage graph, as we shall see in the next section. For the job of tallying scores in a grouped distribution, however, or for labeling a histogram, it is usually more convenient to list the score limits of an interval. Figure 4.6 may help to clarify the meaning of the terms *real limits* and *score limits.*

4.2.4 Cumulative Graphs: Because the categories of an ordinal scale bear an ordered relation to each other, it is possible to construct a very convenient and useful kind of graph called a **cumulative frequency graph.** Such a graph plots the number of cases falling in all categories *below and including* the specified one. The grouped intelligence-test data are reproduced below, and a cumulative frequency graph is constructed from them.

SCORE	NO. OF CASES	CUM. FREQUENCY
170–179	1	50
160–169	1	49
150–159	3	48
140–149	3	45
130–139	3	42
120–129	8	39
110–119	9	31
100–109	16	22
90– 99	4	6
80– 89	2	2

50

Note that the points on this curve are plotted against the *upper real limits* of the intervals to which they correspond. This is because all the cases in the lowest interval, for example, fall *below* 89.5, the upper real limit of that interval.

Such a curve can be very convenient and useful. Often our interest is actually in the number of cases falling above or below a certain

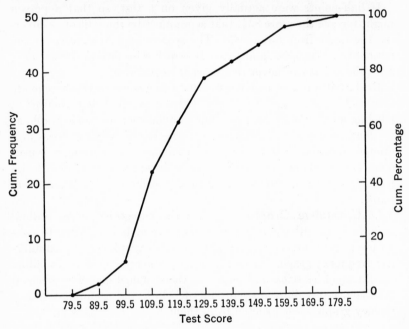

FIG. 4.7 Cumulative frequency curve and cumulative percentage curve of intelligence test data. Note that the points are plotted against the upper *real* limits of intervals.

point. While this number can be obtained from a histogram or frequency polygon, it can be obtained more directly and easily from a cumulative frequency curve. Furthermore, the curve can be easily converted to a **cumulative percentage curve,** which is often even more useful than the frequency curve itself. Often the most convenient way to make the conversion is to do it on the graph itself. The highest point on the curve, the number of cases in the group, is, of course, 100 per cent. Label it as such. Then divide the distance between 0 and 100 per cent into four or five or ten parts, whichever is most convenient, and label them with the appropriate percentages. This has been done on the right-hand side of the graph in Figure 4.7.

Now, by reading off the graph, we can make such statements as: '90 per cent of the students in the class have scores of 149.5 or below. Half the members of the class have scores of 113 or below. If those with scores of 110 or less are to be placed in another class, 42 per cent of the class will be involved.'

It is, of course, perfectly possible, and sometimes easier, to construct a cumulative percentage graph without going through the intermediate step of drawing the cumulative frequency curve. The cumulative frequencies are converted to percentages by dividing them by N, the number of cases in the group, and these percentages are then plotted directly on the graph paper.

Questions

1. Which of the variables below are continuous and which discrete?

    a. bridge-playing ability
    b. size of a country's gold reserve
    c. time required to complete a task
    d. size of salary
    e. scholastic aptitude
    f. shoe size
    g. age at last birthday

2. How would you measure the continuous variables in the list above? Would your measurements be discrete or continuous variables?

3. Explain what is meant by the statement that the slopes of the lines connecting the points on a frequency polygon are without mathematical significance.

4. Explain fully why the use of a frequency polygon with discrete data is illogical.

5. What are the real limits of the following scores:

    a. 16   b. $27\frac{1}{2}$ c. 101.3   d. 24.379

6. If people are asked to report their ages to the nearest birthday, what is the youngest that a man who reports his age as 48 can be? The oldest? What are the real limits of the reported age 29?

Answer the same questions for ages that are reported to the *last* birthday.

7. Student A during his four years at college received the following grades in his courses:

Grade	Freq.
A+	0
A	1
A−	2
B+	2
B	4
B−	6
C+	12
C	7
C−	4
D+	0
D	1
D−	1
F	0

a. Plot a histogram for these data.

b. The registrar's office does not record plus signs and minus signs. Plot a histogram of this student's grades as they would be recorded by the registrar's office.

c. Plot a cumulative percentage graph of the grades (with plus signs and minus signs).

8. Student B's grades are given below:

Grade	Freq.
A − and above	0
B+	1
B	4
B−	10
C+	12
C	8
C−	3
D+	2
D and below	0

a. On the same set of axes, draw two frequency polygons, one for student A and one for student B. From looking at the graphs what can you say about the relative abilities of the two students?

b. Draw a cumulative percentage graph for student B.

9. Below are 100 scores on a scale of attitude toward the church. A high score indicates a favorable attitude.

0.2	1.4	2.6	4.0	4.8	5.3	5.7	6.4	7.1	8.3
0.4	1.4	2.6	4.0	4.8	5.4	5.8	6.4	7.3	8.4
0.5	1.7	2.6	4.0	4.9	5.4	5.8	6.4	7.4	8.5
0.6	1.8	2.8	4.1	4.9	5.4	5.9	6.5	7.4	8.5
0.8	1.8	2.9	4.3	5.0	5.4	5.9	6.6	7.6	8.7
0.9	2.0	3.2	4.3	5.1	5.5	6.0	6.6	7.7	8.8
1.0	2.1	3.4	4.5	5.1	5.5	6.1	6.7	7.8	8.8
1.0	2.1	3.5	4.6	5.1	5.6	6.2	6.7	7.9	9.0
1.1	2.3	3.7	4.8	5.2	5.6	6.2	6.9	8.1	9.2
1.2	2.4	3.7	4.8	5.3	5.6	6.3	6.9	8.2	9.7

a. Plot a histogram of the data in the form in which they are given (i.e. without grouping them further).

b. Group the data into ten intervals with score limits 0.0–0.9, 1.0–1.9, etc.

   (1) What are the real limits of these intervals?

   (2) Plot a histogram and a frequency polygon for the grouped data.

d. Plot a cumulative percentage graph for the *grouped data* and from it answer the following questions:

   (1) What per cent of the group have scores of 6.8 or below? (Remember to use real limits.)

   (2) What per cent have scores of 3.5 or above?

   (3) What point splits the group in half?

   (4) Below what point falls 25 per cent of the group? 75 per cent?

4.3 Relative Position of an Individual

One of the most frequent uses of descriptive statistics is to describe the position of an individual relative to his fellows. To know your score on a test means little by itself; to know that your score places you in the upper tenth of the group is much more informative. On the nominal scale there was no way to make such comparisons because there was no meaning to the terms 'better' or 'worse,' 'higher' or 'lower.' The ordinal scale makes these terms meaningful and makes it possible to place an individual relative to the other members of the group.

4.3.1 Ranks: If scores are listed in order, and the number 1 assigned to the lowest score, 2 to the next lowest, 3 to the next, and so on, ending with N for the highest score, these numbers are called **ranks**. Any individual's position relative to his fellows is specified by naming his rank. A rank of 3 means that the person equaled or surpassed 3 members of the group; a rank of n means that the person equaled or surpassed n members. For the intelligence-test data of p. 108, the score of 85 corresponds to a rank of 1, 87 to a rank of 2, and so on, with 179 corresponding to a rank of 50. If two or more individuals are tied—that is, receive the same score—each receives for a rank the average of the ranks that would be assigned had there been no ties. For example, there are two intelligence-test scores of 101. These occupy the 8th and 9th positions, and therefore both receive the rank 8.5, which is the average of ranks 8 and 9. The score 102 would then receive the rank of 10, were it not for the fact that there are two scores of 102. Both of these receive the average of the ranks 10 and 11, or 10.5, and the score 103 receives a rank of 12.

A rank by itself means nothing unless we know how many individuals there are in the group. To receive a rank of 10 means one thing if there are 10 people in the group and quite another if there are 1000. Sometimes we specify the size of the group, saying, for example: 'His rank is nine in a group of ten,' or whatever the particular numbers may be.

4.3.2 Percentile Ranks and Percentiles: To avoid the cumbersome necessity for specifying each time the number of individuals in the group, and to make groups of different sizes more directly comparable, we frequently convert an individual's rank, which is the number of cases he equals or surpasses, to the number of cases he would equal or surpass if there were 100 cases in the group. A person who equals or surpasses two cases in a group of ten would equal or surpass twenty cases in a group of 100. When ranks are converted to 'equivalent rank in a group of 100' they are called **percentile ranks.** To find an individual's percentile rank from a knowledge of his rank, therefore, we simply divide the rank by the number of cases in the group and multiply by 100.

$$\text{Percentile rank} = \frac{\text{Rank}}{N} \times 100 \qquad (4.3.1)$$

For a group of large size this is not a very practical approach. It would be convenient to have some method whereby, knowing a person's score on a test, we could immediately figure out his percentile rank without having to go through the process of counting. Let's suppose that Joe Doakes was one of the group of 50 which took the intelligence test previously discussed and see how we'd go about finding his percentile rank. Joe got a score of 112.

Looking at the cumulative frequency distribution on p. 113, we see that Joe is one of the 9 individuals in the step interval 110–119. Twenty-two people had scores in the three intervals below that one, so we know that Joe's rank must be at least 23, and, since a total of 31 people had scores in and below that interval, Joe's rank cannot be above 31. That means that his percentile rank must be between

$(\frac{23}{50}) \times 100$ and $(\frac{31}{50}) \times 100$, or between 46 and 62. The interval in which Joe's score falls is 110–119, while Joe's score is 112, so his score places him near the bottom of the interval but not at the very bottom. We therefore expect that his percentile rank will be higher than 46 but much lower than 62. To get an exact figure, we make the assumption that the 9 scores in the interval 110–119 are equally distributed throughout that interval. That means that the lowest score takes up the bottom ninth of the interval, the second lowest score the next-to-the-bottom ninth, and so on, as shown in Figure 4.8. Since there are 10 score points in the interval, and each individual takes up one-ninth of them, each individual takes up 1.11 score points.

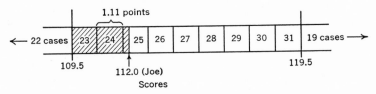

Fig. 4.8 Linear interpolation in finding a percentile rank. The shaded area represents the individuals (and fractions thereof) that Joe surpasses. For further explanation, see text.

Joe's score of 112.0 places him 2.5 score points from the lower (real) limit of the interval, which is 109.5. Since each individual in the interval takes up 1.11 score points, Joe must surpass $\frac{2.5}{1.11}$ of those individuals. He surpasses 2.25 of the individuals in the interval 110–119. Of course, he surpasses all the individuals whose scores are in intervals below that one—there are 22 such cases—so in all he surpasses $22 + 2.25$ or 24.25 cases. His rank is 24.25, and his percentile rank is therefore $100 \times \frac{24.25}{50}$, or 48.5, which we round off to 48.

Notice that we've stopped saying 'equals or surpasses' and started saying just 'surpasses.' Ranks are a discrete variable, obtained by counting. Percentile ranks, obtained as described above, are treated as a continuous variable. They are found by measuring. Joe's score of 112 is treated as a *point* on a scale of scores, and a point has no width. Therefore Joe, who is at the point 112.000 . . . , is said to surpass 24.25 cases and to be surpassed by $(50 - 24.25)$, or 25.75

cases. Treating people and scores as continuous variables in this way is artificial and slightly in error, but so convenient and practical that we usually overlook its disadvantages.

The procedure we used to find Joe's percentile rank from a grouped frequency distribution can be expressed by a formula, and computations can then be carried out mechanically. The formula is

$$S = L + i \left(\frac{pN - f_L}{f_i} \right) \qquad (4.3.2)$$

where S is the score for which the percentile rank is to be found
L is the lower real limit of the interval in which the score lies
i is the width of the interval
p is the proportion of individuals surpassed
N is the number of cases in the group
f_L is the number of cases below the interval in which S lies
f_i is the number of cases in the interval in which S lies.

To find a percentile rank, this equation is solved for p and the result multiplied by 100. Let us make the substitutions and find Joe's percentile rank by the use of the formula.

S, Joe's score, is 112.0

112 is in the interval 110–119. The lower real limit of that interval, L, is 109.5

The interval is 10 points wide. $i = 10$.

p is unknown.

$N = 50$.

There are 22 cases below the interval 110–119. $f_L = 22$.

There are 9 cases in the interval 110–119. $f_i = 9$.

Substituting:

$$112.0 = 109.5 + 10 \left(\frac{50p - 22}{9} \right)$$
$$1008.0 = 985.5 + 500p - 220$$
$$.485 = p$$

A percentile rank, in summary, is the percentage of cases in the distribution falling below a specified point on the scale of scores.

If we know an individual's percentile rank we can find, from the grouped frequency distribution, the score which enabled him to receive that rank. All we have to do is solve formula 4.3.2 for S instead of for p. *The point on the scale of scores below which fall p*

per cent of the cases in the distribution is called the pth **percentile.** If Sammy Samovar had a percentile rank of 91 on the intelligence test, what was his score?

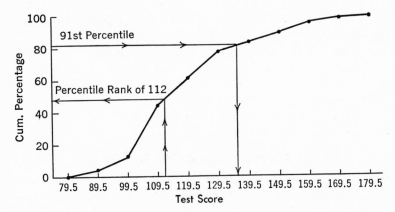

Fig. 4.9 Finding percentiles and percentile ranks from a cumulative percentage curve. To find the 91st percentile, lay a ruler horizontally at the point, 91, on the cumulative percentage axis. Where the ruler intersects the curve, drop a perpendicular. The point where the perpendicular intersects the x-axis is the 91st percentile.

To find the percentile rank of the point, 112.00, lay a ruler vertically at the point, 112.00, on the x-axis. Where the ruler intersects the curve, draw a line at right angles to the ruler. The point where the line intersects the y-axis is the per cent of cases falling below the point, 112.00, or, in other words, the desired percentile rank.

If Sammy's percentile rank was 91, his rank in the group of 50 must have been 50 × .91, or 45.5. That would mean that his score was in the interval 140–149. Now we are ready to substitute in the formula:

S is unknown

L is 139.5 $\qquad S = 139.5 + 10 \left(\dfrac{.91 \times 50 - 45}{3} \right)$

i is 10 $\qquad\qquad 3S = 418.5 + 455.0 - 450.0$

p is .91 $\qquad\qquad 3S = 423.5$

N is 50 $\qquad\qquad\ \ S = 141.17$

f_L is 45

f_i is 3

Below the point 141.17 fall 91 per cent of the cases in the distribution. Rounding to the nearest score point we conclude that Sammy's score was 141. The point 141.17 is the 91st percentile.

A **percentile rank,** then, specifies the per cent of the cases falling below some given point on the scale of scores. A **percentile** specifies the point below which a given per cent of the cases fall.

If a cumulative percentage graph has been drawn, both percentiles and percentile ranks can be read directly off the graph, as shown in Figure 4.8. If you solved problem 9d(1) on page 117, you were finding the percentile rank of the point 6.85 by reading it from a graph; if you solved problem 9d(4) you were finding the 25th and 75th percentiles from a graph.

4.4 The Most Typical—The Best Guess

When data come from a nominal scale it does not make much sense to talk about an average. There are just categories with various numbers of cases in them. If we want to select a 'typical' individual, the best we can do is to select one from the modal category.

The mode is still a useful statistic when applied to an ordinal scale. It can be very handy to know which category has the largest number of cases in it. In the case of the job ratings, the modal category is 'very good.'[1] In the distribution of intelligence-test scores the mode lies in the interval from 100–109, and if we want to describe it by a single figure we take the midpoint of that interval, 104.5. The mode is one kind of average and in some ways a very pleasant one because it is so easy to 'compute.'

This advantage is, however, offset by a great disadvantage. The exact value of the mode is completely dependent upon the size of the interval used and upon the starting points of the intervals. For the grouped intelligence-test data the mode is 104.5, while for the ungrouped data it is 109. If we had chosen to start our intervals at some other point on the scale, we might have altered radically the value of the mode. Furthermore, if two new children, both with scores of 104, had entered the class, the mode of the ungrouped data would take a sudden tumble from 109 to 104. All these objections add up to the fact that the mode is an unstable measure, depending upon a particular concatenation of circumstances for even its approximate value.

[1] But see question 1, p. 127

Another way of thinking about the average of data measured on an ordinal scale is to specify the point that splits the group in half. The **median,** our new measure of the typical, *is the point above and below which lie 50 per cent of the cases.* In other words, the median is the 50th percentile. If we know only that an individual was a member of a group and must guess his score, we may guess the median. The median is the best guess in the sense that it is just as likely to be too high as too low.

If the data are already grouped into a frequency distribution, the median is found by solving formula 4.3.2 for S when p equals .50. In other words, we simply find the 50th percentile. Or the 50th percentile can be read from the cumulative percentage curve if one has been prepared. The median intelligence-test score is 112.8, as calculated from the grouped frequency distribution.

Finding the median from ungrouped data is very easy. What we want to do is find the score of the 'middle' individual. For example, if there are 25 cases in a group, arranged in order from smallest to largest, the 13th man will be at the median. (Note that we don't have to say '13th from the top' or '13th from the bottom.' Since the 13th score is the middle score we can count in either direction.) If N is even there are two middle individuals. In a group of 26, the 13th and 14th individuals represent the middle. There are 12 cases below individual number 13, and 12 cases above individual number 14. In this case the median is half the distance between the 13th score and the 14th scores. The median intelligence-test score is half the distance between the 25th and 26th scores. Both these scores turn out to be 114, so the median is 114. If the 26th score had been 115, the median would be 114.5. If the 26th score had been 116, the median would be 115.

Because the median makes use of the ordering of the data, it is usually a better measure of the average or typical than the mode when the data come from an ordinal scale.

4.5 Unpredictability or Variability

The median temperature may be 50° in both San Francisco and Omaha, but life in these two cities can be very different indeed. In San Francisco the lowest temperature may be 35° and the highest 78°, while in Omaha the temperatures may range from −14° to 114°. Omaha has a more variable temperature than San Francisco, and no comparison of the temperatures in the two cities would be complete without a report of this variability.

4.5.1 The Use of $\hat{H}$ with Ordinally Scaled Data: In the previous chapter we discussed the uncertainty measure, $\hat{H}$, which depends upon the proportions of cases falling in different categories. Its use requires no assumptions about the relative widths of different categories or the distributions of individual cases within any category or group of categories. But there is one major disadvantage to the use of this measure with data from an ordinal scale. This disadvantage is illustrated in Figure 4.10. The order of the categories is ignored in computing $\hat{H}$. This means that, whether the high-frequency events are close to the median or all the way out at the ends of the scale, the uncertainty will be the same.

$\hat{H}$ was introduced with the question 'How good is a guess?' In the case of a nominal scale a guess could be wrong or right, but when the variable is ordered a guess may be very wrong or only a little bit wrong. A miss is by no means so bad as a mile. If, therefore, we wish to include the concept of degree of wrongness in our measure of uncertainty, we must seek a measure other than $\hat{H}$.

4.5.2 Percentile Measures of Variability: There are many measures which do make use of the ordinal nature of the data and which involve little or no distortion when intervals are unequal. All these involve a description of the range of the variable included in some specified percentage of the distribution.

The range. The range is the simplest of these measures. It is a measure of the spread of scores covered by the whole distribution— 100 per cent of the cases. The best way to present the range is usually to name the highest and lowest scores, since this tells the reader not only how great the distance between them is but also what the extremes themselves are. If a single figure is needed, it may be obtained by subtracting the lowest score from the highest and adding 1. Thus the range of the intelligence test scores is $(179 - 85) + 1$, or 95 points.

The naming of extreme values may be very useful in practice, for these numbers describe the outside limits—the most widely divergent occurrences for which one must prepare. To know that the temperature in San Francisco will never be lower than 35° or higher than 78° may be more help in planning a wardrobe or a house than any other set of figures that could be given. But the range depends

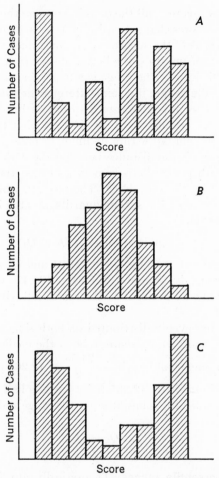

FIG. 4.10 $\hat{H}$, the uncertainty, will be the same for all the distributions. The same column heights occur in all of them, but the order of the columns is different for the three. If we must make a guess, the one that stands the best chance of being 100 per cent right is a guess of the most frequent, or modal score. We guess the score corresponding to the highest column. If that is wrong, our next-best guess is the score corresponding to the second-highest column, and so on. In figure B, the highest column is the column for the middle score. If that guess is wrong, there is a very good chance that the correct answer will be in one of the categories adjacent to it. We will, therefore, have been only *slightly* wrong. On the other hand, in figure C, our best guess is the highest score. If that guess is wrong, the score we seek is most likely to be the lowest score, and we have made as big an error as it is possible to make. Figure A represents an intermediate case.

entirely upon two scores—all the ones in between them are ignored. If either of these scores changes radically, the range, too, will change radically. This makes the measure very unstable. In general, the more data any measure uses, the better and more stable it is likely to be, and in this respect the range is a poor measure indeed.

The interquartile range, the semi-interquartile range. The range tells us that *any* score is guaranteed to fall within its limits. The interquartile range permits us to say, instead, that the chances are equal that a score will fall within its limits or outside of them. The interquartile range is the distance between the 25th and 75th percentiles. The 25th percentile is sometimes called the **first quartile** and represented by the symbol Q_1. The median, which is the 50th percentile, is also called the **second quartile,** and the 75th percentile is the **third quartile,** Q_3.

$$\text{Interquartile range} = Q_3 - Q_1 \qquad (4.5.1)$$

For the intelligence-test data, $Q_3 = 127.94$ and $Q_1 = 103.41$. The interquartile range is therefore $127.94 - 103.41$, or 24.53 score points. The middle 50 per cent of the scores fall within a range of 24.53 points.

If the scores are evenly distributed on both sides of the median, and we guess an individual's score to be at the median, 50 per cent of the time our guess will be within $\frac{24.53}{2}$ or 12.265 points of being right. We'll be in error by 12.265 points or less half the time. The figure 12.265 is called the semi-interquartile range and is symbolized by the letter Q.

$$Q = \frac{Q_3 - Q_1}{2} \qquad (4.5.2)$$

Other interpercentile ranges. Theoretically any interpercentile range could be used as a measure of variability, or unpredictability. We could lop off symmetrically any specified per cent of the cases at the top and bottom of the distribution and describe the range covered by the remaining cases. In practice two other interpercentile ranges are frequently used. These are the distance between the 7th and 93rd percentiles, and the distance between the 10th and 90th percentiles. Both these measures tend to be quite close to the range, but they are not so radically influenced by one or two very extreme scores.

The interpretation of interpercentile ranges. If the interquartile ranges of two groups are computed and found to be the same in numerical value, does this mean that the distance between the first and third quartiles is really the same for these two groups? Since we know nothing about the widths of intervals on an ordinal scale, it does not. In one group, the first and third quartile points may be, for example, 10 and 20, and in the other group 30 and 40. Both these intervals contain 10 score points. But we have no guarantee that the distance between 10 and 20 is the same as the distance between 30 and 40. Therefore the best way to employ interpercentile ranges with an ordinal scale is to describe or name the percentile points themselves—that is, to say: 'One fourth of the cases had scores below 10 and one fourth had scores above 20.' These values describe some actual state of the variable being measured, and a person familiar with the measuring instrument can then make the proper interpretation of the results.

Questions

1. Consider the distribution of job ratings given on p. 105. Suppose it were decided to split the category 'very good' into two categories: 'very, very good indeed' and 'very good.' Examination of the records shows that 30 of the 65 employees previously rated 'very good' now rate 'very, very good indeed,' while the remaining 35 new rate 'very good.' Plot a new histogram and frequency polygon for the revised data. What has happened to its shape, as compared with Figures 4.1 and 4.2? What has happened to the mode?

This example should convince you that if the variable is continuous, the mode is not invariant under a permissible transformation, such as the one above. For that reason it is not a good measure for continuous data from an ordinal scale.

2. For the distribution of attitude scores given in problem 9, p. 116:

    a. Find the ranks of subjects with scores of

$$0.9, \ 2.0, \ 6.0, \ 1.0, \ 4.0, \ 5.4, \ 9.7$$

    b. Find the percentile ranks of these subjects by the use of formula 4.3.1 and also by reading them off your cumulative percentage curve. Are the two sets of answers the same? If not, explain why not (two reasons).

   c. Find the median by three methods: (1) computed from the grouped frequency distribution; (2) read off of the cumulative percentage curve; and (3) by direct examination of the raw scores. Explain any differences in the results of the three methods.

   d. Do the same for Q_1 and Q_3.

   e. Find the range, the interquartile range, and the semi-interquartile range by all three methods.

3. Find the median letter grades of the students in problems 7 and 8, p. 116.

4. Below is a frequency distribution of scores on a test of social maturity.

SCORE	FREQ.
10–14	8
15–19	10
20–24	9
25–29	16
30–34	18
35–39	12
40–44	20
45–49	22
50–54	14
55–59	15
60–64	6

$N = 150$

   a. Plot a histogram.

   b. Plot a cumulative percentage curve.

   c. Find the 3rd, 21st, and 72nd percentiles.

   d. Find the percentile ranks of scores 27, 40, 51, and 64.

   e. Find and interpret the median, Q, and the range.

   f. Find the mode.

5. Officers are rated in proficiency from 0 to 4, 4 being the highest rating. Below are the ratings received by two lieutenants, Snodgrass and Todhunter, from 20 senior officers.

LT. SNODGRASS		LT. TODHUNTER	
Rating	Times received	Rating	Times received
4	4	4	1
3	1	3	4
2	10	2	10
1	1	1	4
0	4	0	1

a. Plot a histogram for each of the men, and compare the two histograms. Is either man more proficient than the other? Which man is more predictable in his performance?

b. Compute $\hat{H}$, Q, and the range for the two men, and use your results as the basis for a discussion of the relative merits of these three measures of unpredictability.

4.6 Measures of Relatedness

When the terms 'high' and 'low' have no meaning, as is the case for nominally scaled data, one cannot ask whether something that is high in one respect is also high in another. But when the data are ordered, the terms 'high' and 'low' take on meaning and importance, and *degrees* of highness and lowness are important too. Not only can we ask whether the person who is good at tennis is good at badminton—we can also ask whether the man who is very good at one is also very good in the other, and even whether the man who is best at one is likewise best at the other. Several new measures of relatedness are available when the data come from an ordinal scale; before we consider them, however, let's take another look at $\hat{T}$ and consider what happens when we use it with ordered data.

4.6.1 Uncertainty Reduction: We have already seen that $\hat{H}$, uncertainty, is a poor measure of unpredictability for ordinally scaled data because it makes no distinction between a very wrong guess and a guess that is just a little bit wrong. $\hat{T}$ is a measure of the amount by which knowledge of one variable reduces our uncertainty about another variable. It is, essentially, a comparison of two values of $\hat{H}$. Since $\hat{H}$ is not a good measure of unpredictability to use with an ordinal scale, it follows that $\hat{T}$ is not a good measure of relatedness for such a scale.

Furthermore, $\hat{T}$ cannot give us any measure of the direction of a relationship—which is reasonable enough, since 'positive' and 'negative' are seldom meaningful when applied to nominally scaled data. But the concept of direction is meaningful when applied to data from an ordinal scale, and we want to know whether any particular relationship is positive or negative. Consider the example below. Four hundred people have received letter grades in art, political science, and physics. Is ability in art related to ability in physics? To ability in political science? We'll hypothesize some perfectly outrageous results:

	ART				
	D	C	B	A	Tot.
POLI. SCI. A				100	100
B			100		100
C		100			100
D	100				100

	ART				
	D	C	B	A	
PHYSICS A			100		100
B	100				100
C				100	100
D		100			100

In both cases our uncertainty is reduced from two bits to zero, and $\hat{T}$ is therefore 2.0 bits in both examples. But the relationship is direct and obvious between art and political science—all who get A's in one subject get A's in the other, the B students get B's in both courses, and so on. On the other hand, an A in art goes with a C in physics, an art B with a physics A, an art C with a physics D, and an art D with a physics B. Common sense tells us that these are very different situations, but $\hat{T}$ tells us they are the same. The moral of the story is that $\hat{T}$ is not a good statistic to use with ordered data. Let's take a look at some statistics that are.

4.6.2 The Index of Order Association, o: [2] Suppose we have letter grades for 25 students who have taken both psychology and statistics. One of these, Joe Zilch, got a C in both courses, while another, Arbuthnot, got an A in psych. What guess would you make about Arbuthnot's grade in statistics? If you think that people who are good in one subject tend to be good in the other, you may conclude that since Arbuthnot was better than Zilch in psych, he was probably better in stat too, and you'd guess that he got an A or B in that subject. If you compared Zilch to every member of the class and found that those who were better than he in psych were also better in stat, and those who were worse in psych were also worse in stat, you'd begin to think that abilities in the two subjects were positively related. But you wouldn't want to base this conclusion just on comparisons with Zilch. Why pick Zilch? There are 25 students in the class. Why not compare every student with every other student? Then we can count the number of comparisons in which one student excels the other in both subjects, which we'll call 'S' for 'same,' and

[2] L. A. Goodman and W. H. Kruskal, 'Measures of association for cross classifications,' *J. Amer. Stat. Assoc.*, 1954, **49**, 732.

the number of comparisons in which one student excels the other in one subject but is worse in the second, which we'll call '*D*' for 'different.' (When the two students being compared are tied in either of the two subjects we'll ignore them.) If there are a lot more *S*'s than *D*'s, we'll conclude that people who are good in psych tend also to be good in stat; if there are a lot more *D*'s than *S*'s, we'll conclude that psych students were never meant to be statisticians, while if there are about the same number of *D*'s and *S*'s we must infer that ability in stat has nothing to do with ability in psych. If 75 per cent of the comparisons are *S*'s and 25 per cent *D*'s, then the excess of *S*'s over *D*'s is 50 per cent. The excess of *S*'s over *D*'s, expressed as a proportion of the total number of comparisons, is *o*, the index of order association. Let's try a problem.

The number of A's, B's, and C's in psych and in stat is shown in the bivariate frequency distribution below. (Both instructors were jolly fellows and gave no D's or F's.) Notice that we follow the convention of putting high grades at the right-hand side of the horizontal axis and at the top of the vertical axis.

GRADES IN STATISTICS

		C	B	A	Total
	A	2	3	6	11
GRADES IN	B	1	5	2	8
PSYCHOLOGY	C	3	2	1	6
	Tot.	6	10	9	25

Let's consider the 3 students who got C's in both courses. They were surpassed in both psych and stat by all the people who got the grade combinations A-A, A-B, B-A, and B-B. There were $6 + 2 + 3 + 5 = 16$ such people. Each of the C-C students is compared with each of these 16, and thus we have 3×16, or 48, comparisons in which those who excelled in one subject also excelled in the other. We repeat this process for the C-B students, the B-C students, and the B-B students, multiplying the frequency in each cell by the sum of the frequencies in the cells that are both above and to the right of it.

CELL	FREQ.	FREQ. ABOVE AND TO RIGHT	NO. OF S COMPARISONS
C-C	3	$3 + 5 + 6 + 2 = 16$	$3 \times 16 = 48$
C-B	1	$3 + 6 \qquad = 9$	$1 \times 9 = 9$
B-C	2	$2 + 6 \qquad = 8$	$2 \times 8 = 16$
B-B	5	$6 \qquad\qquad = 6$	$5 \times 6 = 30$

Total 103

There are a total of 103 comparisons which result in a verdict of 'same.' Now we want to find out how many comparisons result in a verdict of 'different.' To do this, we multiply each cell frequency by the sum of all the frequencies that are both above and to the left of it.

CELL	FREQ.	FREQ. ABOVE AND LEFT	NO. OF D COMPARISONS
A-C	1	$2 + 3 + 1 + 5 = 11$	$1 \times 11 = 11$
B-C	2	$2 + 1 \qquad = 3$	$2 \times 3 = 6$
A-B	2	$2 + 3 \qquad = 5$	$2 \times 5 = 10$
B-B	5	$2 \qquad\qquad = 2$	$5 \times 2 = 10$

Total 37

Thirty-seven comparisons result in a verdict of 'different.' There are 66 more verdicts of 'same' than of 'different.' The total number of comparisons made is $103 + 37 = 140$, so the proportion of excess 'same' judgments is $\frac{66}{140}$, or .43. The index of order association, o, is .43.

To sum up the method for computing o:[3]

1. Prepare a bivariate frequency distribution with high values of one variable at the right side of the horizontal axis and high values of the other at the top of the vertical axis.

2. Multiply each cell frequency by the sum of the frequencies in the cells that are both above and to the right of it.

3. Sum the numbers found in step 2. Call the result S.

4. Multiply each cell frequency by the sum of the frequencies in the cells above and to the left of it.

5. Sum the numbers found in step 4. Call the result D.

6. $o = \dfrac{(S - D)}{(S + D)}.$

[3] The accuracy of your calculations may be checked as follows:
1. Square each column total and each row total (but not N, the grand total)

The statistic o ranges from -1.00 through zero to $+1.00$. Positive values close to 1 indicate strong direct associations; negative values close to 1, strong inverse associations; and values close to zero, the lack of association or relationship.

4.6.3 The Rank-Order Correlation, r_0: In section 4.2.1 ranking was described and defined. When items or individuals are ranked, the ranks themselves form an interval scale—a scale that measures the number of individuals equaled or surpassed. The interval quality of this scale attaches to the ranks only, not to the variable underlying the ranking procedure. Remember good old Whifflebottom—his *rank* in tennis-playing ability was just one below Jones's, but his tennis-playing ability was in a different universe.

A correlation measure has been developed to describe the relationship between two sets of ranks. This measure, the rank-order correlation, describes with mathematical exactness the relation between the *ranks*, but does not describe the relation between the two underlying variables being compared. If this restriction is remembered, the rank-order correlation can readily be used with an ordinal scale.

There is a common superstition that brains and beauty are incompatible attributes in a female. 'Not, "beautiful but dumb," ' says one young man in the course of a bull session, 'but "beautiful *and* dumb"! The two things go together.' An intelligent fellow whose fiancée is a junior Phi Bete and a glamour girl challenges this statement and proposes a scientific test. Why not pick ten girls known to all, have the group rank them in pulchritude, and then

---

and add up all the squares. In our example:

$$6^2 + 10^2 + 9^2 + 11^2 + 8^2 + 6^2 = 438$$

2. Square each cell entry and add up all the squares. In our example:

$$2^2 + 3^2 + 6^2 + 1^2 + 5^2 + 2^2 + 3^2 + 2^2 + 1^2 = 93$$

3. Subtract the result of step 2 from the result of step 1.

$$438 - 93 = 345$$

4. To the result of step 3 add $2(S + D)$.

$$345 + 2(140) = 625.$$

5. Square N. If your calculations are right N^2 will equal the number found in step 4.

$$25^2 = 625$$

get their academic averages? Then it can be determined whether the girls who rank highest in beauty are also those with the best averages. The scheme is enthusiastically undertaken.

Before considering the results of this scientific investigation, let us consider some of the possible outcomes. Let beauty be the x variable, and academic average the y variable. Each girl will receive a rank in beauty. Her academic average will be converted from a grade to a rank. Then, if the old superstition is right, the girl with the highest rank in beauty will have the lowest rank in academic

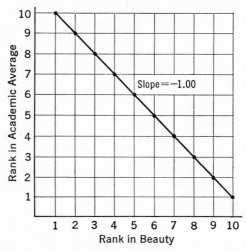

Fig. 4.11   Relation between ranks in beauty and in academic average when the relationship is a perfect negative one. Each point represents one girl, who has been ranked on both variables.

achievement, the one with the second-best appearance will be next to the dumbest, and so on. The results can be plotted and will yield a graph like that of Figure 4.11.

If, on the other hand, it turns out that beauty queens are likely to be Phi Betes, and numbskulls to be hags, the two sets of ranks will go together. A high rank on one variable will go with a high rank on the other, and the results when plotted will look like the graph of Figure 4.12.

It may be that the two variables are totally unrelated. In that case, the points on the graph will be scattered in a random sort of fashion. Figure 4.13 or something like it might result.

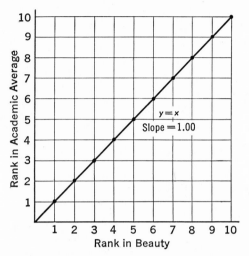

FIG. 4.12   Relation between ranks in beauty and in academic average when the relationship is a perfect positive one.

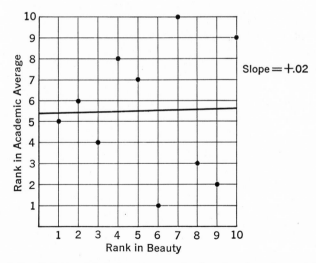

FIG. 4.13   Relationship between two sets of ranks when the variables are actually unrelated. The line that best fits all the points is the one drawn, which has a slope of +.02, or practically zero. It passes through the average rank of both the x and y variables—in this case, 5.5.

The slope of the line connecting the points in Figure 4.11 is -1.00. The slope of the line connecting the points in Figure 4.12 is $+1.00$. No straight line can be drawn through all the points of Figure 4.13, but, for any set of points, what is called a 'line of best fit' can be drawn. This line will not touch all the points—in fact it may touch none of them. The points will, however, cluster around it better than around any other straight line that can be drawn.

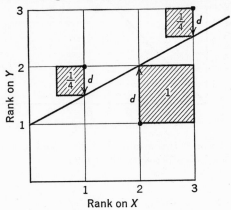

FIG. 4.14   Explanation of the term 'least squares fit.'

Pairs of Ranks		Line of best fit for 3 pairs of ranks. d represents the distance between the point and the line. The shaded area is the square of d, and the numeral inside each area is its size. The sum of the squared deviations in this case is $1 + \frac{1}{4} + \frac{1}{4} = 1\frac{1}{2}$. The slope of this line is $\frac{1}{2}$. Any other slope will give a larger figure for the sum of the squares of the deviations of the points from the line. You are invited to test this statement for yourself.
x	y	
1	2	
2	1	
3	3	

What do we mean by 'better'? In this case we mean that the *sum of the squares of the deviations of the points from the line will be as small as possible*. The line of which this is true is said to be a **least squares fit**. The principle of using a least squares fit is illustrated and explained in Figure 4.14.

The rank-order correlation is the slope of the best-fitting straight line relating two sets of ranks. Its formula is:

$$r_o = 1 - \frac{6\Sigma D^2}{N(N^2 - 1)} \qquad (4.6.1)$$

Where D is the difference between ranks on the two variables,
        N is the number of cases in the distribution.

The derivation of this formula is quite complicated, but the principles underlying it will become clearer when we take up the product-moment correlation in Chapter 7.

To compute a rank-order correlation:

1. Assign ranks in both variables to each individual. When several individuals are tied for one rank, each receives the average of the ranks that would have been assigned had there been no ties.[4]

2. Subtract one rank from the other. (Since these differences will be squared, the sign of the difference can be ignored.) Call the difference D.

3. Square each of the numbers obtained in step 2. The result is D^2.

4. Sum the squares obtained in step 3. This is ΣD^2.

5. Substitute in formula 4.6.1.

Now let's go back to the scientific investigation of brains and beauty. Ten girls have been selected, and ranked in beauty, and the academic average of each has been obtained. The results and computations are shown below:

GIRL	RANK IN BEAUTY	ACADEMIC AV.	RANK IN AC. AV.	D	D^2
Clarissa	3	B	7.5	4.5	20.25
Eloise	2	C$-$	2	0	0
Elvira	6	B$+$	9	3	9
Lucille	8	C	4	4	16
Margot	4	C	4	0	0
Marlene	10	A$-$	10	0	0
Myrna	7	B$-$	6	1	1
Nina	1	D$+$	1	0	0
Sylvia	9	B	7.5	1.5	2.25
Vesta	5	C	4	1	1

$$49.50$$

$$r_o = 1 - \frac{6(49.50)}{10(100 - 1)} = 1 - \frac{297}{990} = 1 - .30 = +.70$$

[4] If more than 5 scores are tied for one rank, a correction formula should be used to get the proper rank for the tied scores. It is:

$$R_t = \sqrt{A^2 + \frac{n^2 - 1}{12}}$$

Where R_t is the corrected rank of the tied scores.

A is the average rank of the tied scores.

n is the number of scores tied for one rank.

The slope of the line relating the two sets of ranks is +.70. The points and line are shown in Figure 4.15. Clearly, brains and beauty are positively but not perfectly related, and the chap who proposed the experiment departs happily, humming 'All things bright and beautiful' as he goes.

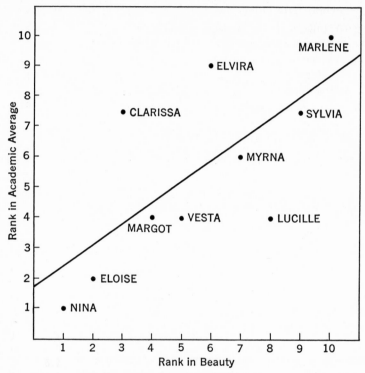

FIG. 4.15   Results of the experiment to determine the relation between brains and beauty. The slope of the best-fitting straight line is +.70.

Like o, r_o can assume values between -1.00 and $+1.00$. In Chapter 7 we shall discuss in detail the interpretation of correlation coefficients; for the present, however, we shall be content with the statement that high values of r_o, whether positive or negative, represent strong relationships and values close to zero represent a relative absence of relationship.

The ranking of objects in a set is a very quick and easy business when there are only a few of them. When N is large—say 30 or more

—ranking can be a tedious process. Furthermore, the number of ties is likely to increase as N increases, and if there are too many tied scores, r_o is not a very accurate measure. The method is most to be recommended, therefore, when N is 30 or less and there are few scores tied for any one rank. When you use r_o, be sure to remember that *it is a measure of the strength and direction of relationship of ranks, not of the variables underlying those ranks.*

4.6.4 One Variable Nominal, One Ordinal: If individuals have been simultaneously classified on two scales, one nominal and one ordinal, neither o nor r_o can be used, but $\hat{T}$ can be. If for example, we were interested in studying the intelligence of different national groups we could use uncertainty reduction as our measure.

Questions

1. Construct an example to show the advantage of o over $\hat{T}$ for data from ordinal scales.

2. Three observers, A, B, and C, have rated the activity levels of 125 schizophrenic patients. Use the index of order association to determine which pair of observers exhibits the closest agreement.

OBSERVER A

		Lethargic	Inactive	Average	Above average	Hyperactive	Total
	Hyper.			2	2	10	14
	Above		1	5	15	6	27
OBS.	Aver.	1	8	18	7	1	35
B	Inac.	4	20	4			28
	Leth.	1	15	4	1		21
	Tot.	6	44	33	25	17	125

OBSERVER A

		Lethargic	Inactive	Average	Above average	Hyperactive	Total
	Hyper.					16	16
	Above				15	1	16
OBS.	Aver.	1	6	19	10		36
C	Inac.	1	17	11			29
	Leth.	4	21	3			28
	Tot.	6	44	33	25	17	125

OBSERVER *B*

		Lethargic	Inactive	Average	Above average	Hyperactive	Total
	Hyper.			1	7	8	16
	Above			2	9	5	16
OBS.	Aver.	1	4	19	11	1	36
C	Inac.	1	18	10			29
	Leth.	19	6	3			28
	Tot.	21	28	35	27	14	125

Could $\hat{T}$ be used to make the same comparison?

3. A subject is given 100 pairs of tones and asked to judge whether the second tone of each pair is louder or softer than the first. Each decision is timed. He is also asked whether he is sure of the decision, doubtful about it, or guessing blindly.

After the experiment, the experimenter groups the 100 decision times into four sets of 25 each. The shortest 25 times make up one group, the next shortest 25, a second group, and so on. Determine from the data below whether there is any relation between the subject's reported certainty in making a decision and the time it took him to make the decision.

DECISION TIMES

		Shortest $\frac{1}{4}$	Second $\frac{1}{4}$	Third $\frac{1}{4}$	Longest $\frac{1}{4}$	Total
S's	Certain	18	20	2		40
CERTAINTY	Doubtful	6	4	7	2	19
	Guess	1	1	16	23	41
	Total	25	25	25	25	100

4. A subject in a dial-reading experiment makes 100 readings on each of 8 dials and then ranks the dials in order of preference. A rank of 8 is assigned to the best-liked dial and a rank of 1 to the least-liked dial. His preferences and the number of errors made on each dial are given below. Is the subject a good judge of readability?

DIAL	S'S RATING	NO. OF ERRORS
A	3	0
B	7	59
C	2	26
D	4.5	0
E	4.5	8
F	6	19
G	1	24
H	8	21

5. From the data below determine whether, among the 15 subjects studied, there is a relationship between IQ and anti-Semitism. (A high score on the anti-Semitism inventory indicates a high degree of prejudice.)

SUBJ.	IQ	ANTI-SEM.	SUBJ.	IQ	ANTI-SEM.
A	102	10.1	I	124	5.9
B	116	8.4	J	112	8.3
C	108	7.6	K	102	5.4
D	139	2.6	L	100	11.2
E	94	9.8	M	125	4.7
F	99	10.1	N	117	4.3
G	112	6.6	O	112	9.1
H	123	3.2			

6. Find in the literature or devise three situations in which a psychologist might use the index of order association and three in which he might use the rank-order correlation.

7. Below are two sets of ranks.

Rank on x	Rank on y
4	2
3	4
2	1
1	3

a. On a piece of finely ruled graph paper plot the data points as given.

b. Compute r_o.

c. Draw a straight line of slope r_o through the point where $x = 2.5$ and $y = 2.5$.

d. Measure the distance* from each data point to the line.

* Unless otherwise specified the distance from a point to a line is considered to be the length of a vertical dropped from the point to the line. See Figure 4.14.

    e. Compute the sum of the squares of the distances found in step d.

    f. Now draw another line with any slope except r_o through the point where $x = 2.5$ and $y = 2.5$. Repeat steps d and e above. How does this answer compare with the one you obtained in step e? Discuss the meaning of your results.

4.7 Common Errors in the Use of Ordinal Data

Numerals, you remember, are simply symbols, while numbers are symbols among which a set of logical relations has been agreed to exist. One of these relations among numbers is that they have a serial order. There is meaning to the expressions 'greater than' and 'less than.' This relationship, and only this relationship, must be demonstrated among objects for them to be placed on an ordinal scale. Only the order of the numbers, therefore, can be used in representing the data.

In our everyday thinking most of us make surprisingly few errors in using ordinally scaled data. In setting up a game of doubles at tennis or choosing partners at bridge few of us would assume that the best player and the worst player would necessarily be an even match for the two intermediate players. And most students know that it is somewhat easier to raise their grades from C's to B's than to raise them from B's to A's.

It is when the novice in his ignorance or the expert in his carelessness tries to get technical and 'scientific' that errors are most likely to be made. The most common of these errors is the averaging of ordinally scaled data. A flagrant example of this practice is the computation of 'grade point averages.' A letter grade is a grade on an ordinal scale, and there is absolutely no guarantee that the difference between an A and a B is the same as the difference between a B and a C, yet at practically every college in the country the registrar's office ploughs sturdily ahead averaging these letter grades. Sometimes ranks are averaged as if they were numbers. The magnitude of the error introduced by these practices may be negligible, but when the differences between numerals assigned to the objects do not correspond to the differences between the objects themselves, considerable distortion may be introduced into the results. When there is no real way to measure the differences between objects, there is no way to correct for the errors thus introduced.

Occasionally an inappropriate measure of unpredictability or of correlation may be used with ordinally scaled data, but this is less common than the use of the wrong average. Another fairly common error is the interpretation of the rank-order correlation as representing the strength of relationship between variables, rather than between ranks.

Summary

Ordinal scales may represent either continuous or discrete variables, or the actual measurements may be a discrete variable representing an underlying continuous variable.

For an over-all description of a set of data from an ordinal scale we have available the bar graph (for discrete data), the histogram (for continuous data), the frequency polygon, grouped frequency distribution, cumulative frequency and cumulative percentage graphs.

To specify the position of an individual relative to the rest of the group, we may name the rank or the percentile rank of the individual. A percentile is the score point corresponding to a specified percentile rank.

Our 'best guess' about an individual known to belong to the group under study may be the mode, which has several disadvantages, or the median, which is the 50th percentile.

The badness of that guess may be described by any interpercentile range, such as the range itself, the interquartile or semi-interquartile range, or any of several other interpercentile ranges.

To measure the strength and direction of relationship between two ordinally scaled variables, we may use the index of order association or the rank-order correlation. Both range from -1.00 through 0 to $+1.00$.

The most common error in the use of ordinal data is the computation of an arithmetic average, which may lead to completely erroneous interpretations of the data.

Answers

Page 115

5. 15.5–16.5; b. $27\frac{1}{4}$–$27\frac{3}{4}$; c. 101.25–101.35; d. 24.3785–24.3795

6. $47\frac{1}{2}$; $48\frac{1}{2}$; $28\frac{1}{2}$–$29\frac{1}{2}$; 48.0; 48 yrs., 364 days; 29.0–29.9999

9. d. (1) 77.8%; (2) 27.8%; (3) 5.24; (4) 2.95; 6.62

Page 127

2. a. 6, 16, 66, 7.5, 32, 53.5, 100
   c. (1) 5.24; (3) 5.3
   d. (1) $Q_1 = 2.95$; $Q_3 = 6.62$; (3) $Q_1 = 3.05$; $Q_3 = 6.6$
   e. 9.6, 3.55 or 3.67, 1.78 or 1.84

3. $C+$, $C+$
4. c. 12.3, 25.9, 47.9; d. 23, 50, 79, 99.6; e. 40, 10.6, 55.0; f. 47

Page 139

2. $o_{AB} = +.801$; $o_{AC} = +.916$; $o_{BC} = +.902$

3. $o = -.841$ 4. $r_0 = +.077$ 5. $r_0 = -.790$

INTERVAL AND RATIO SCALES, PART I

Frequency Distributions, Measures of the Typical,

and Measures of Unpredictability

An interval scale is one for which a unit of measurement has been established and a satisfactory operation for addition demonstrated. The numerals assigned to an interval scale behave in most respects like true numbers, but they have no absolute-zero point. When an absolute zero exists, the scale is called a ratio scale.

Very few statistical measures make use of the absolute-zero point of a ratio scale. Therefore, the statistics that are most appropriate for an interval scale are the same ones that are likely to be used with a ratio scale. For this reason, this chapter and the two that follow it are entitled 'Interval and Ratio Scales.' In Chapter 8, we shall consider those few measures that are appropriate only when we have an absolute zero to measure from.

5.1 An Over-all Description of the Data

5.1.1 The Histogram: The histogram is the basic tool for getting an over-all picture of the data from interval or ratio scales, just as it is for the data from ordinal scales, and its construction involves exactly the same steps. Data are grouped into some appropriate number of intervals. The number of cases in each interval is determined by counting or tallying, and the height of the bar on the graph is made proportional to the number of cases in the interval. As it was on the ordinal scale, the order of the bars is determined by the order of the various intervals on the scale of measurement.

There is, however, one important difference between a histogram as used with data from an ordinal scale and as used with data from interval or ratio scales. When we made the bars displaying ordinally scaled data equal to each other in width, we did so because we had

no way of deciding how wide each should properly be. But when we
have a unit of measurement, we know that one unit is equal to any
other unit. Therefore, we make the bars that include the same
number of units equally wide. The heights of the bars, their order,

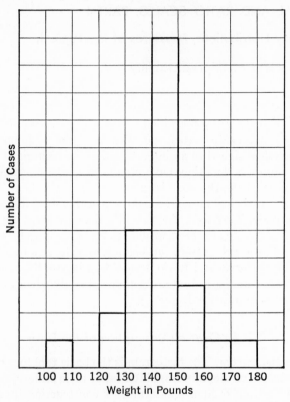

FIG. 5.1   Histogram showing distribution of weights. Each individual is
represented by one square on the histogram. The number of squares
inside the bars of the histogram between any two points on the x-axis is
proportional to the number of cases falling within those limits.

and the relative widths of the bars are all meaningful when the data
come from an interval or a ratio scale. At last we can talk sensibly
about the *shape* of a histogram.

When we have a unit of measurement, and hence a histogram on
which the widths of the bars are mathematically meaningful, we
acquire an additional advantage, which will be illustrated by the

example below, a frequency distribution of weights. This distribution is plotted as a histogram in Figure 5.1. We have let one square

WEIGHTS	FREQUENCY
100–109	1
110–119	0
120–129	2
130–139	5
140–149	12
150–159	3
160–169	1
170–179	1

$$N = 25$$

on the graph paper stand for one case. Therefore, the total number of squares inside the bars of the histogram is 25. Furthermore, if we want to know the number of cases having weights between, say, 120 and 159 inclusive, we have but to count the squares between those limits. We find that there are 22 squares and conclude that there are 22 such cases. If we had let one square on the graph paper represent two men (instead of one) there would be 11 squares between the limits, and we should again conclude that there were 22 cases having those weights. *The area inside the bars of a histogram between any two points on the* x-*axis is proportional to the number of cases falling within those limits.* You will see how important this fact can be when we study the normal distribution and other theoretical distributions, in Chapter 6.

Unequal intervals. When we had only an ordinal scale we had no information about the widths of bars, hence no injustice was done to the data by grouping different numbers of the original categories into the various step intervals. For example, on the employment rating form, 'good' and 'very good' could have been considered together and plotted as one bar. With an interval or ratio scale, however, we have a different situation. Two intervals containing the same number of units are mathematically equal, and if we combine two such intervals out of many, we make one new interval larger than all the rest. In general that is not a good idea. The resulting histogram may be confusing at best, or may lead at worst to totally wrong interpretations. There are a few situations, however, where the advantages of the procedure outweigh the disadvantages. Let us consider two examples.

Occasionally you will encounter what is called an 'open-ended' distribution. A frequency distribution of family salaries in the United States might have as its first category '$1000 and below,' and as its last category '$10,000 and above.' The reason for presenting the data this way is usually the fact that a few cases of extreme value may occur. If the graph were to have to stretch by thousand-dollar intervals to include the one family with an income

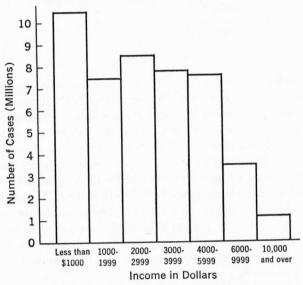

Fɪɢ. 5.2 Histogram showing number of families and unrelated individuals by income level in 1949. Based on a 20 per cent sample. 'Family' refers to a group of two or more related persons living in the same household, and 'unrelated individual' refers to a person living alone or with persons not related to him. From Statistical Abstract of the United States, 1955, p. 295.

of one million dollars, it would have to be yards long. If, on the other hand, we decided to work by ten-thousand-dollar intervals, more than 99 per cent of our cases would be lumped together in one bar, and we should lose a great deal of valuable information. When we plot our data with unequal intervals as in Figure 5.2, we must be careful to draw no conclusions from the shape of the graph alone. To interpret the graph it is necessary to read the labels very carefully and draw conclusions accordingly.

Another instance of a situation that might suggest the use of unequal intervals is the following: An airline wishes to get an estimate of the distribution of flying proficiency, including such nebulous things as skill in manipulating controls, knowledge of traffic procedures, and good judgment in emergencies, among its pilots. No good measure of flying proficiency is available, but there is reason to believe that, in general, proficiency is related to experience. Since each pilot must enter all his flying hours in a log book, it is very easy to determine the amount of experience each man has had. It is also generally accepted as a fact that 50 hours of experience will improve the performance of a very inexperienced man more than it will the performance of a man with a great many flying hours to his credit. Thus, for the most inexperienced pilots, it is important to know fairly exactly the number of flying hours they have had, while for pilots of many thousands of hours of flying time, a much rougher description will suffice. The frequency distribution might be as follows:

FLYING TIME	NUMBER OF PILOTS
200– 299	2
300– 399	4
400– 499	3
500– 749	6
750– 999	10
1000–1499	6
1500–1999	5
2000–2999	3
3000–4999	2

What has actually happened here is that the airline, perhaps without any idea of what it was doing, has tried to make intervals that represent equal intervals of flying proficiency. Of course there is no reason to believe that all the criteria of equality and additivity have been satisfied, hence no reason to apply interval-scale statistics to these intervals in their present form. If, however, the intervals were numbered from one through nine, an ordinal scale of flying proficiency would probably have been established. (This statement assumes as a minimum that flying proficiency does turn out to be related to experience.) Ordinal-scale statistics could then be applied to these newly assigned numerals. A histogram for these data, now treated as ordinally scaled, is shown in Figure 5.3.

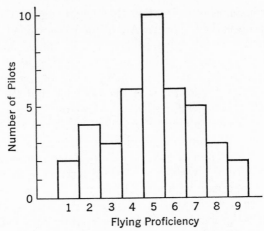

FIG. 5.3 Distribution of flying proficiency among pilots of X Airline. The scale of proficiency is an ordinal scale derived from number of hours of flying experience.

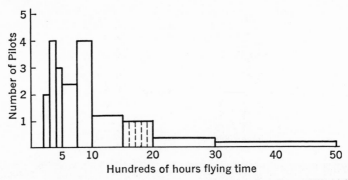

FIG. 5.4 Distribution of hours of flying time among pilots of X Airline, showing proper treatment of unequal intervals. The three narrow bars represent intervals of 100 hours each. The fourth and fifth bars represent intervals of 250 hours, and they are therefore made two and one half times as wide as the 100-hour bars, and so on. Notice that in the interval from 1500–1999 hours there are 5 pilots, but the height of the bar is only one unit. This is because the interval is 500 hours wide, and we make the assumption that the flying hours of these pilots are equally spaced throughout the interval. It is as if one pilot fell in the interval 1500–1599, one in the interval 1600–1699, and so on. When the widths of the bars are multiplied, for example, by 5, their heights must be divided by 5 in order to keep the area within the bars of the histogram proportional to the number of cases in the distribution.

If the histogram is to be plotted as the data are originally given—in terms of number of flying hours—we must make adjustments for the unequal intervals. The crucial thing to remember in making these adjustments is that the area inside the bars is proportional to the number of cases in the distribution. The bar standing for the interval 3000–4999 hours includes a range of 2000 hours, while the interval 2000–2999 includes only 1000 hours. There are two pilots in the larger interval, three in the smaller. Therefore, if the height of the bars of the histogram is one square for each pilot in a 1000-hour category, the height for the 2000–2999 interval will be three units; but for the 3000–4999 interval there are two pilots to be distributed over two 1000-hour units, or an average of one pilot per 1000-hour unit. It is just as if we had divided that last interval into two, and found one pilot in each of the two new intervals. A properly drawn histogram for these data is shown in Figure 5.4.

5.1.2 Frequency Polygons: As with ordinally scaled data, a frequency polygon can be constructed for data from interval or ratio scales by connecting with line segments the midpoints of successive bars of the histogram. Since the horizontal distances between the points on a frequency polygon, as well as their vertical distances, are now determined by the nature of the data, the shape of the frequency polygon has mathematical and logical significance. It cannot be stretched and squeezed at will as was done with the job-rating data in Figure 4.3.

When we connect the midpoints of successive bars of a histogram, we cut off a little triangle from the top of each bar, but we also add a little triangle that wasn't there before. The triangle we cut off can be shown to be exactly equal in area to the triangle we add. Since the area under the bars of the histogram between any two points on the x-axis is proportional to the number of cases falling between those points, the same thing must be true of the frequency polygon, at least to a close approximation. This important fact is further explained in Figure 5.5.

5.1.3 Cumulative Curves: Cumulative frequency and cumulative percentage curves can be constructed for data from interval and ratio scales in exactly the same way in which we constructed them for data from ordinal scales. The horizontal spacing of points on these graphs is now mathematically meaningful, because we have a unit of measurement.

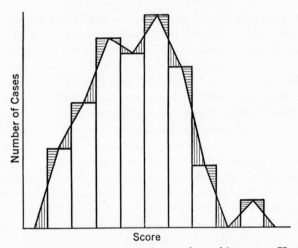

Fig. 5.5 Frequency polygon superimposed on a histogram. Horizontally shaded triangles represent areas included in the histogram which are not included under the frequency polygon. Vertically shaded triangles represent areas included under the frequency polygon which were not included in the histogram. Each horizontally shaded triangle is matched with a vertically shaded triangle. Hence, as much is added to the polygon as is taken from it. The areas under the histogram and polygon are therefore equal, and both are proportional to the number of cases in the distribution. You can also see by inspection of the figure, however, that the area under the polygon between two points on the x-axis is not necessarily identical to the area under the histogram between those same two points.

5.2 The Typical. The Best Guess

The mode and the median can both be used with data that come from interval and ratio scales, and in certain circumstances they are more desirable measures of the 'typical' than is the **mean,** which is the measure generally to be preferred for the two 'strongest' kinds of scales. Let us first talk about what the mean is and how it works, and then discuss the relative desirability of the three measures.

5.2.1 The Mean: Undoubtedly you are already familiar with the mean, though perhaps not with that name for it. The arithmetic mean is nothing more than what we usually intend when we say 'average.' It is the sum of the scores, or measurements, divided by the number of scores. It is conventional in statistics to let the capital letter X stand for 'any score or measurement.' Then the mean, identified by the symbol $\overline{X}$, (read: 'X bar') is:

$$\bar{X} = \frac{\Sigma X}{N} \tag{5.2.1}$$

where N is, as always, the number of cases in the distribution. The mean of the numbers 1, 2, and 3 is equal to

$$\frac{1 + 2 + 3}{3} = 2.$$

If anybody (your instructor, for example) should ask you for a definition of the mean, you may give formula 5.2.1. That is the most basic definition, but there are several others. Each of these results from some interesting or unique mathematical property of the mean as defined in the formula above.

The mean is the point about which the sum of the positive and negative deviations is zero. By deviations, we mean 'differences.' The deviation of a score from the mean is the difference between that score and the mean, and the deviation of any score from any other is the difference between them. A score of 15 deviates from 10 by $+5$. A score of 6 deviates from 10 by -4. Let us prove our definition of the mean by letting K stand for 'any constant point from which deviations are taken' and then solving for it.

$$\Sigma(X - K) = 0.$$

This equation is a statement of the fact that we can subtract from each score some number such that, when the results of the subtractions are summed, they will equal zero.

Now we apply the rules for the summation sign to the equation above. K is a constant, so when we 'sum' it, we shall multiply it by N. (See preparatory chapter, section 0.3.1.)

$$\Sigma X - NK = 0, \qquad \text{and therefore} \qquad \Sigma X = NK$$

Now we divide both sides by N.

$$\frac{\Sigma X}{N} = K$$

But $\frac{\Sigma X}{N} = \bar{X}$, the mean. Therefore, the point about which the sum of the deviations equals zero is the mean, and the mean may be defined, as it was above, in terms of this property.

The symbol x is conventionally used by many statisticians to signify the deviation of a score from the mean.

$$x = (X - \overline{X})$$

What we have been saying in the paragraph above is that

$$\Sigma(X - \overline{X}) = 0, \qquad \text{hence that} \qquad \Sigma x = 0.$$

Later on, when we are deriving more complicated formulas, we shall sometimes encounter an algebraic expression which includes the term Σx. It will help if you can remember to think to yourself 'zero' when you see that expression.

The mean is the fulcrum, or balance point, of a distribution. This property is related to the last one. If a histogram or frequency polygon were constructed for a set of data and then cut out of sheet metal or cardboard, it would balance on a wedge if and only if the wedge were placed underneath the mean value. This property is illustrated in Figure 5.6.

Computation of the mean. Usually the best way to find a mean is to add up all the scores and divide by the number of scores, using the definition formula, 5.2.1.

Occasionally you may get your scores already grouped into a frequency distribution. In that case, you will not know what the original scores were, and you must treat each score as if it fell in the very middle of the interval in which it lies. Consider the grouped frequency distribution below:

INTERVAL	MIDPOINT (X')	f	fX'
0– 4	2	4	8
5– 9	7	12	84
10–14	12	9	108
15–19	17	3	51
		28	251

There are 4 scores in the interval $0 - 4$. These scores may all be zeros, or they may all be fours; we either do not know or do not care. We treat them all as if they fell in the middle of the interval and had the value 2. The twelve scores in the interval 5–9 are all treated as if they were 7's and so on. Then, instead of adding $2 + 2 + 2 + 2 + 7 + 7 \ldots$ etc., we use that magnificent short cut known as multiplication. The midpoint of each interval, X', is multiplied by the number of cases in the interval, f. We then find the sum of the products and divide it by the number of cases in the

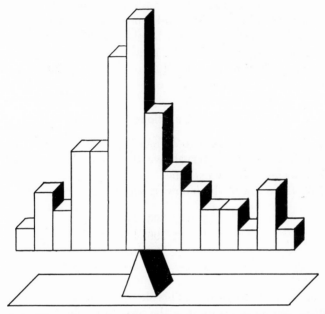

FIG. 5.6 The mean as the balance point of a distribution. In this figure, the wedge has been placed at the mean, and the distribution balances. If the wedge were moved to the left, the distribution would be unbalanced and would tip toward the right, and vice versa.

distribution. The result is the mean (or at least a sufficiently close approximation to it for all practical purposes.)

$$\overline{X} = \frac{\Sigma f X'}{N} \tag{5.2.2}$$

where X' is the midpoint of an interval and f is the number of cases in the interval. $\Sigma f = N$.

When we compute a mean from a grouped frequency distribution in this way, we are making the assumption that all the cases in a particular interval are spread evenly throughout the interval. Only then will the midpoint of the interval be a good 'average' value to represent all the cases. Of course this assumption is seldom fulfilled completely, for in most instances there will be more scores in the end of the interval near the middle of the distribution than in the end near the extreme. So for low intervals, the midpoint is likely to be lower than the average of the scores in the interval, and for high intervals, higher. Hence the 'too-lowness' of the midpoints of the low intervals should be balanced by the 'too-highness' of the midpoints of high intervals, and the mean should be about the same when computed from a grouped frequency distribution as when computed from the original raw scores.

Questions

1. Explain the statement that 'In most instances there will be more scores in the end of the interval near the middle of the distribution than in the end near the extreme.'
2. Obtain the mean of the following set of numbers:

$$1, 052, 796, 436$$
$$1, 052, 796, 438$$
$$1, 052, 796, 432$$
$$1, 052, 796, 430$$

What short cut did you use? This short cut can always be used in computing the mean. State it in the form of a rule.
3. Construct two numerical examples to show that if a constant is added to (or subtracted from) every score in a distribution, the mean is increased (or decreased) by that constant.
4. Prove the statement above mathematically.
5. Obtain the mean of the following set of numbers:

$$15, 000, 000, 000, 000$$
$$7, 000, 000, 000, 000$$
$$8, 000, 000, 000, 000$$

What short cut did you use? This short cut can always be used in computing the mean. State it in the form of a rule.
6. Construct two numerical examples to show that if every score is multiplied (or divided) by a constant, the mean is multiplied (or divided) by that constant.
7. Prove the statement above mathematically.

8. You now have available two short cuts to use in finding the mean:

   (1) Subtract a constant from each score and add it back later.
   (2) Divide each score by a constant and multiply back later.
       Use both these short cuts in finding the mean of the grouped
       frequency distribution below.

X	f
40–44	3
35–39	8
30–34	10
25–29	7
20–24	2
	$N = 30$

Find the midpoint of each interval and then subtract from each the
constant 32. Divide the resulting numbers by the constant 5. Don't
forget to multiply back and add back at the end. Check your results
by computing the mean directly from formula 5.2.2.

Why did we suggest the use of 32 and 5 as constants?

9. Use similar short-cut procedures to find the mean of the grouped
frequency distribution below. What will be the most convenient
constant to subtract? To divide by?

X	f
1064–1065	14
1062–1063	21
1060–1061	39
1058–1059	37
1056–1057	16
1054–1055	17
1052–1053	8
	153

10. By examining what you did in problems 8 and 9, can you find
one new short cut that combines both of the original ones? (Hint:
the new short cut is sometimes referred to as 'the use of coded
intervals.')

Make up a set of instructions for computing a mean from a
grouped frequency distribution using this new short cut.

11. Construct three numerical examples to show that the sum of the positive and negative deviations about the mean is zero.

5.2.2 Choice of a Measure of the Typical:

When the data came from a nominal scale, we had but one measure of the typical available: the mode. The advance to an ordinal scale added the median. Now we have a choice among three measures: the mode, the median, and the arithmetic mean. Which measure is best when? And why?

Before we answer those questions, let us first ask what we want a measure of the typical to do for us. What makes a measure good? What characteristics are desirable in a measure of central tendency, as an average of any kind is sometimes called?

1. As a general rule, the best statistic is the one that makes use of all the information contained in the data. If the numbers come from an ordinal scale, the measure should make use of their order. If they come from an interval scale, the measure should make use of the unit of measurement that is available.

2. The best measure is one that is not likely to be greatly changed by a small change in the frequency distribution. If we add a case here or take one away there, we expect to see some change in our measure of central tendency, but we don't want to see it change too radically. A measure that fulfills this condition is called *stable*.

3. If we change the size or starting point of our step intervals we don't want the measure of central tendency to be greatly affected. After all, how we group the data is really arbitrary, and we don't want our notion of the 'typical' to be determined largely by arbitrary considerations.

4. The best measure is, in fact as well as in name, a reasonable description of a typical case.

5. The best measure is the one that gives appropriate importance to extreme scores. Sometimes we want our conceptions to be influenced by the extreme cases, but at other times we want to minimize the effects of these unusual cases. What is 'appropriate' therefore depends upon the use to which the measure is to be put.

6. The best measure is one that is fairly easy to compute. Since all three of these measures are easy to compute, we shall not linger long on that point. We may add, however, that when further computations are going to be carried out on the same data, it's nice if the measure of central tendency either can be used in doing these computations or emerges automatically as a by-product.

Now, with these characteristics in mind, let's take a look at the mode, the median, and the mean to see how they compare. We shall always be discussing the application of these measures to data from interval and ratio scales.

The mode is ordinarily to be scorned.

    a. It uses less of the available information than any other measure.
    b. It is highly unstable.
    c. It is highly susceptible to changes in step intervals.
    d. It is totally uninfluenced by extreme scores.
    e. No other computations take the mode as their starting point.

On the other hand, the mode has a few advantages.

    a. It almost always gives a reasonable picture of a typical individual. The modal number of children in a family will never turn out to be a fraction of a child, and there's something reassuring about being able to say that 'this thing actually happened more often than anything else.'
    b. It is delightfully easy to 'compute.'

There are two situations that call for the use of the mode in preference to either the median or the mean. The first is the occurrence of a multimodal distribution. If, when a frequency polygon or histogram is constructed, it appears to have two or more separate peaks rather than one, it is called multimodal. If there are only two peaks the distribution is bimodal. Bimodal distributions are most likely to occur when two distinct subgroups have been placed together in one distribution. For example, a county-wide French contest is held every year for high-school students. If the scores of all those taking the examinations were grouped into a frequency distribution it would probably look like Figure 5.7. Further investigation might then reveal that the individuals whose scores appeared in the small hump at the top end were students who had lived in France or came from French-speaking families or had attended schools in which French was spoken and taught from the primary grades up. The best way to describe the central tendency of such a distribution as this would be to say: 'The distributon has two modes, one at such-and-such a score, and a second, smaller one at such-and-such a score.'

Failure to use the mode as the measure of central tendency in bimodal distributions can have ridiculous results. On the eve of a very close election, the distribution of political attitudes measured on an ordinal scale ranging from 'very Republican' at one end, through 'neutral' in the middle, to 'very Democratic' at the other

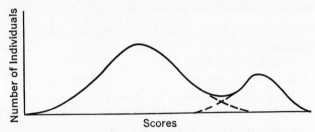

FIG. 5.7 Probable distribution of scores among individuals taking part in a county-wide French contest. The hump at the upper end is composed of individuals who have had special opportunities to speak and read French.

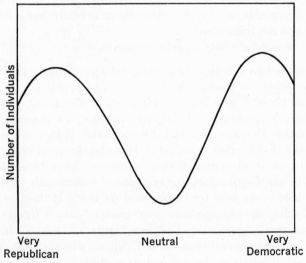

FIG. 5.8 Probable distribution of political attitudes on the eve of a very close election.

might be like that shown in Figure 5.8. The median of this distribution would be somewhere near the 'neutral' point, but that would certainly not be descriptive of any but a few very atypical individuals.

The other situation that calls for the use of the mode in preference to the median or the mean is that in which only one class of individuals can be 'fitted' or satisfied. If a shoe salesman can take only one demonstration pair with him, he will do better to take a pair of the modal size than a pair of the median or mean size. Nobody may have feet that are fitted by either of the latter, and a shoe that *almost* fits is not much better than a shoe that is much too big or too small. What the salesman wants is the shoe that will fit perfectly the largest number of people, and a shoe of the modal size is just what he needs.

The median, while it is a much better measure than the mode, also has some disadvantages:

a. It doesn't make use of the unit of measurement.

b. It is much more stable than the mode but less stable than the mean.

c. It is practically unaffected by extreme scores. This may be an advantage rather than a disadvantage, as will be shown below.

d. It is usually less easy to compute than either of the other measures, primarily because it does not lend itself readily to machine-computation methods. It is an integral part of the percentile system, but it is not used in any further computations.

The median has some very real advantages, however.

a. It is usually a reasonable description of a typical case except when the distribution is multimodal.

b. It is relatively uninfluenced by extreme scores. This can be a very real advantage when the distribution is highly unbalanced or when a few extreme cases distort the mean badly. For example, the owner of a sweatshop wants to demonstrate that his employees are well paid. The actual distribution of annual wages is given below:

WAGES	f	
$20,000–$20,499	1 (the owner)	
4,500– 19,999	0	Median wages: $749.50
4,000– 4,499	1 (his son)	
2,000– 3,999	0	Mean wages: $1219.50
1,500– 1,999	3	
1,000– 1,499	10	
500– 999	20	
0– 499	15	

50

By including his own salary in the distribution and obtaining the arithmetic mean, the owner is able to demonstrate that 'The average annual wage of those who work in my plant is $1219.50.' He fails to add, however, that at least 35 out of his 50 workers make lower than average wages. The median and the mode, which in this case are the same, tell us that a more realistic estimate of an employee's earnings would be $749.50. Furthermore, if the employer were to raise his own salary to $1,000,000, the median would be unchanged but the mean would be drastically increased. When a company advertises that the average annual earnings of its employees have risen from so much in 1948 to so much in 1958, it is always worth while to inquire: 'Which average? Which employees?'

Since the median remains unaffected by changes in extreme scores, it can be used when the distribution is open-ended, as in the case of the income distribution of Figure 5.2. A mean cannot be computed for such a distribution.

c. We have said that the median is the 'best guess' in the sense that it is no more likely to be too high than too low. There is another sense in which the median is the best guess. On the average, we shall be less in error when we guess the median (or use it as a measure of central tendency) than when we use the mode or the mean. We'll explain this fact more fully when we take up the average deviation in section 5.3.1.

The mean has more advantages and fewer disadvantages than either of the other measures of central tendency. Its disadvantages are:

a. If the distribution is multimodal or lopsided the mean is not a reasonable description of a typical case.

b. It is greatly affected by extreme scores. Sometimes that is desirable, but sometimes, as in the example above, it is not.

The advantages of the mean are many:

a. It is the only measure of the three which uses all the information contained in the data. It is an *algebraic* function of all the scores in the distribution—which means that it depends upon the size and sign of each of the scores.

b. It is the most stable measure available.

c. It is relatively unaffected by changes in the sizes or starting points of intervals.

d. It is usually a description of a typical case.

e. It is easy to compute and, more important, it is used as the starting point for later computations, and it emerges as a by-

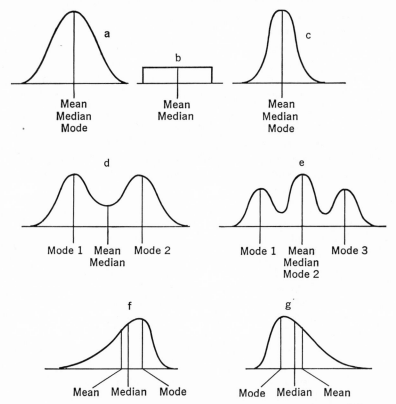

FIG. 5.9   Relationships among mean, median, and mode for different kinds of distribution.

Distributions *a* and *c* are symmetrical and unimodal; mean, median, and mode are identical. Distribution *b* has no mode but the mean and median are identical.

In a symmetrical, multimodal distribution, mean and median are identical, and they may coincide with one mode, as in distribution *e*, or not, as in distribution *d*.

When the distribution is skewed (asymmetrical), the mean is farthest out along the 'tail,' the median next, and the mode least.

product of computations for the standard deviation, correlation coefficient, and many other statistics. This is one of the most important advantages of the mean over either of the other measures.

In summary, then, the mean is usually to be preferred to the median, and the median to the mode. But, unfortunately for overworked students, there's no law that says that if you've found one measure you mustn't find the others. If you really want to give a complete description of a set of data, one good way to start is to compute all three measures of central tendency.

5.2.3 Relationships among the Mode, Median, and Mean: If a distribution is perfectly symmetrical and has only one mode, the mode, median, and mean are identical. If the distribution is symmetrical but multimodal, the mean and the median will be the same, but there will be several modes. If the distribution is unimodal but lopsided, the mode will be least influenced by the few extreme scores, the median next, and the mean most influenced. These relationships are illustrated in Figure 5.9.

If we compute and present all three measures of central tendency, we may give our readers some idea of the shape of the distribution. If the three are identical, for example, the reader may conclude that the distribution is probably symmetrical. (And he stands a good, though not a perfect, chance of being right.) If the mean is higher than the median, which in turn is higher than the mode, he may conclude correctly that the distribution is lopsided, with most people getting fairly low scores but a few unusual ones getting extremely high values.

Questions

1. Which measure of central tendency would be preferred in each of the following situations, and why?

    a. You have to select a birthday card for your nephew, Alphonse, who is in the fourth grade. You can't remember how old Alphonse is, but you know that the modal age of fourth-grade children is 9, the median age 10, and the mean age, 11.

    b. The chairman of the board of education of Splinterville, who is a candidate for re-election, wishes to prove to the voters that the teachers in the Splinterville Public Schools are highly experienced. There are 47 teachers, and their actual years of experience are as follows:

1 year	12 teachers
2 years	15 teachers
3 years	8 teachers
4 years	6 teachers
5 years	2 teachers
7 years	1 teacher
11 years	1 teacher
17 years	1 teacher
24 years	1 teacher

c. Abernathy, who is a candidate for the office of chairman of the board of education of Splinterville, wishes to prove that Splinterville teachers are grossly lacking in experience.

d. You, as a Splinterville voter, wish to get a fair idea of the amount of experience the teachers actually have.

e. You have made 100 measurements of a subject's reaction time, and you wish to obtain some kind of average.

f. Two groups of 10 rats learn a maze. The numbers of trials required by the rats in each group are given below. You wish to compare the groups:

GROUP I		GROUP II	
TRIALS	f	TRIALS	f
10	1	15	1
12	3	17	2
13	3	18	3
14	2	19	3
24	1	29	1

2. Comment on the case of the statistics student who drowned in a river with an average depth of four feet.

3. It has been said that 'Statistics don't lie, but statisticians do.' Describe one of the ways statisticians can do it.

5.3 Measures of Unpredictability

Once we have decided on what to predict, we want, as usual, to know how much in error our prediction is likely to be. What measures are available for this purpose?

$\hat{H}$, the uncertainty measure, is a very poor one to use for interval and ratio scales, for the same reason that it was poor for ordinal scales. It makes no distinction between a large error and a small error.

The interpercentile measures of unpredictability, or variability, have certain advantages. When these measures are used with interval or ratio scales their absolute size—that is, the distance between the percentile points—is expressed in units of measurement and hence has logical and mathematical meaning. This means that these measures are more useful with data from the two 'strongest' kinds of scales than they were with data from an ordinal scale. We can now compare, for example, the interquartile ranges of two distributions and state definitely that one is larger or smaller than the other. Furthermore, these measures are fairly easy to compute and very easy to interpret.

The principal objection to them—and it is an important objection—is that they do not use all the data or depend upon all the scores. Below are several sets of eight numbers. Sets A and B have

A	B	C	D
100	0	0	0
101	101	101	15
102	102	101	59
103	103	101	101
104	104	101	121
105	105	101	147
106	106	101	169
107	200	200	200

the same interquartile deviation, but look at the difference in their ranges! You can make a much wronger guess in set B than in set A. Lest this example lead you to believe that the range is the measure we need, look at sets C and D. They have the same range, but in set C all the numbers except the two extreme ones are the same, while in set D the numbers vary all over the lot. No, the range, by itself, won't do the trick.

What is needed is a measure that depends upon every score in the distribution and uses the unit of measurement that is now available.

The logical way to develop such a measure would be to find the difference between every score and the mean (or median or mode) and average the results. We have already shown, however, that the positive and negative deviations about the mean always add up to zero, so we must find a way to get rid of the minus signs. We can do this either by ignoring the minus signs and using only the absolute values of the deviations, or by squaring the deviations. If we do the first, we are using the **average deviation;** if the second, we are using the **standard deviation** or the **variance** as our measure of unpredictability.

5.3.1 The Average Deviation: This measure is just what its name implies. It is the average of the deviations of the scores from some measure, usually the mean, when we ignore the signs of the deviations.

$$AD = \frac{\Sigma|X - \overline{X}|}{N} \tag{5.3.1}$$

where $|X - \overline{X}|$ means the absolute value of the difference between some score, X, and the mean, $\overline{X}$.

This formula gives us the average amount by which we are in error if we let the mean represent every score in the distribution. We might, instead, find out what our average error would be if we let the median represent every score. In that case the formula would be:

$$AD_{\text{Mdn}} = \frac{\Sigma|X - \text{Mdn}|}{N} \tag{5.3.2}$$

Presumably we could do the same thing for the mode, or for any other arbitrarily chosen point in the distribution. The interesting fact is that the average deviation will be less when taken about the median than when it is taken about any other point. It is this fact that led us to say earlier that the median was the best guess in the sense that it would lead, on the average, to the smallest error in prediction.

The average deviation can be a very useful measure if we are not going to do any further calculations. It is perhaps easier to understand than any other measure of unpredictability except the range, and it intuitively 'makes sense' to most people. It is not easy to compute, because there are no calculating-machine short cuts, but an even greater disadvantage is that it is never used in any later calculations. The average deviation used to be a very popular measure and you may encounter it in your reading. For practical statistical work, however, the average deviation has been almost entirely supplanted by the variance and the standard deviation.

5.3.2 The Variance and Standard Deviation: The variance is the average of the squares of the deviations of the scores from the mean.

$$s^2 = \frac{\Sigma(X - \overline{X})^2}{N} = \frac{\Sigma x^2}{N} \qquad (5.3.3)$$

where s^2 stands for the variance.

The standard deviation is the square root of the variance.

$$s = \sqrt{\frac{\Sigma(X - \overline{X})^2}{N}} = \sqrt{\frac{\Sigma x^2}{N}} \qquad (5.3.4)$$

where s is the standard deviation.

These measures are used continuously in advanced statistical work. They will be mentioned or used in every chapter after this one. Though you will probably feel ill at ease with them for a while, you should soon come to feel that they are old familiar friends. Let us see how they are computed and then consider some of their properties.

Calculating the variance and standard deviation from the definition formulas. The formula that defines the variance requires that we subtract the mean from each score, square the results, add the squares, and divide the result by N. To find the variance of the numbers 4, 5, 6, 7, and 8 we first find the mean, which is 6. Now 6 is subtracted from each number:

$$
\begin{array}{rcr}
X - \overline{X} = & & x \\
8 - 6 = & & 2 \\
7 - 6 = & & 1 \\
6 - 6 = & & 0 \\
5 - 6 = & & -1 \\
4 - 6 = & & -2 \\
\end{array}
$$

Next each x is squared, and the squares are added.

$$
\begin{array}{rcr}
(x)^2 = & & x^2 \\
(2)^2 = & & 4 \\
(1)^2 = & & 1 \\
(0)^2 = & & 0 \\
(-1)^2 = & & 1 \\
(-2)^2 = & & 4 \\
\hline
\Sigma x^2 & & 10 \\
\end{array}
$$

Σx^2 is 10. This number is now divided by N, which in this case is 5. $\frac{10}{5} = 2$. The variance of these five numbers is 2 and the standard deviation is $\sqrt{2}$.

Calculating the variance and standard deviation by raw-score formulas. The use of the definition formula as a set of computational instructions works well on those rare occasions when the mean is an integer and the number of scores in the distribution is small. When these two conditions do not hold (and they usually don't) this method of computing is time-consuming and difficult. For instance, it would be much harder to find the variance of the numbers 4, 6, 7, 8, and 9 by the method above than it was to find the variance of the numbers 4, 5, 6, 7, and 8, because the mean of the new set is 6.8. The new x's would therefore be 2.2, 1.2, 0.2, -0.8, and -2.8. The squares of these numbers would be written with two decimal places, and computation would be considerably more laborious than before.

Instead of subtracting the mean from each score and then squaring, we can, instead, develop a formula that permits us to square the original scores and do our subtracting later.

$x = (X - \overline{X})$ by definition
$x^2 = (X - \overline{X})^2$
$x^2 = X^2 - 2X\overline{X} + \overline{X}^2$ by expansion
$\Sigma x^2 = \Sigma X^2 - 2\overline{X}\Sigma X + N\overline{X}^2$ by application of the rules for the use of summation signs. Remember that X is a variable, $\overline{X}$ a constant.

$\overline{X} = \dfrac{\Sigma X}{N}$ by definition of the mean. We substitute in the equation above:

$$\Sigma x^2 = \Sigma X^2 - 2\left(\frac{\Sigma X}{N}\right)(\Sigma X) + N\left(\frac{\Sigma X}{N}\right)\left(\frac{\Sigma X}{N}\right)$$

$$\Sigma x^2 = \Sigma X^2 - \frac{2(\Sigma X)^2}{N} + \frac{(\Sigma X)^2}{N} \text{ by canceling } N\text{'s}$$

$$\Sigma x^2 = \Sigma X^2 - \frac{(\Sigma X)^2}{N} \text{ by collecting terms}$$

This is the numerator of the definition formula for the variance, and we have only to divide the result by N to obtain the variance.

There are many different forms of raw score formulas, all of which take this as their starting point. Two alternative ones are listed below:

$$s^2 = \frac{1}{N^2} [N\Sigma X^2 - (\Sigma X)^2] \qquad (5.3.5)$$

$$s = \frac{1}{N} \sqrt{N\Sigma X^2 - (\Sigma X)^2} \qquad (5.3.6)$$

$$s^2 = \frac{\Sigma X^2}{N} - \bar{X}^2 \qquad (5.3.7)$$

$$s = \sqrt{\frac{\Sigma X^2}{N} - \bar{X}^2} \qquad (5.3.8)$$

If you have a calculating machine available you can find ΣX and ΣX^2 in one machine operation. Your instructor can show you how to do this. You need not, and should not, write down each X^2. Every additional writing step in your calculations is an additional opportunity for error to creep in, so try to make your machine do your remembering and recording for you.

In the example below, we compute again the variance and standard deviation of the numbers 4, 5, 6, 7, and 8. The cumulative ΣX and ΣX^2 is written beside each X, just as it would appear in a calculating machine.

X	Cum. ΣX	Cum. ΣX^2			
8	8	64	$\Sigma X = 30$	$N = 5$	$\bar{X} = \frac{30}{5} = 6$
7	15	113	$\Sigma X^2 = 190$		
6	21	149	$s^2 = \dfrac{\Sigma X^2}{N} - \bar{X}^2$		
5	26	174	$s^2 = \frac{190}{5} - 6^2$		
4	30	190	$s^2 = 2$		
			$s = \sqrt{2}$		

Note that when you use a calculating machine to find ΣX^2, you also find ΣX as a kind of by-product. That means that if you are told to find the mean and variance of a distribution, you start by getting the quantities necessary to compute a variance and then you will not have to repeat the step of adding the scores. That was what we meant when we said earlier that the mean could be obtained as a by-product of further computations.

Calculating the variance and standard deviation from a grouped frequency distribution. If your data are grouped into a frequency distribution, you have only to remember that each score is treated as if it were at the midpoint of its interval, which we have called X'. Therefore ΣX is very closely approximated by $\Sigma f X'$, and ΣX^2 is closely approximated by $\Sigma f X'^2$. The formula for the variance from a grouped frequency distribution is therefore

$$s^2 = \frac{\Sigma f X'^2}{N} - \left(\frac{\Sigma f X'}{N}\right)^2 \qquad (5.3.9)$$

An illustrative computation is performed and the steps described below:

X	f	X'	X'²	fX'	fX'²
20–24	5	22	484	110	2420
15–19	10	17	289	170	2890
10–14	11	12	144	132	1584
5– 9	9	7	49	63	441
0– 4	5	2	4	10	20
	40			485	7355

1. Prepare a grouped frequency distribution in the usual way, listing the number of cases in each interval in a column labeled 'f.'

2. List the midpoint of each interval in a column headed X'.

3. Find the square of each interval midpoint, and list it in a column headed X'^2.

4. Multiply the number of cases in each interval, f, by the midpoint of that interval, X'. List the results in a column headed fX'. Obtain the sum of this column. This is $\Sigma f X'$. In the example above, $\Sigma f X' = 485$.

5. Multiply the number of cases in each interval, f, by the square of the interval midpoint, X'^2. List the results in a column headed fX'^2 and sum this column. The result is $\Sigma f X'^2$, in the example above 7355.

6. Substitute in formula 5.3.9. For the example above

$$s^2 = \frac{\Sigma f X'^2}{N} - \left(\frac{\Sigma f X'}{N}\right)^2$$

$$s^2 = \frac{7355}{40} - \left(\frac{485}{40}\right)^2$$

$$s^2 = 183.9 - (12.1)^2 = 37.5$$

$$s = 6.1$$

This method, like the one you used for finding the mean from a grouped frequency distribution, is based upon the assumption that the midpoint of each interval is an accurate representation of all the scores in that interval. For the same reason that this assumption was not wholly true when you used it in finding the mean, it is not wholly true now. There are usually more scores in the end of the interval near the middle of the distribution than in the end near the extreme. This means that the interval midpoints of low intervals are actually too low to represent the scores accurately, and interval midpoints of high intervals are too high. When we used the interval midpoints to find the mean, the highs and the lows canceled and left the mean unaffected. When we use the midpoints to find a variance, however, we are not concerned with the direction of the error. Whether a midpoint is 'too high' or 'too low' it is, in any case, 'too different' from the mean. Therefore, $\Sigma f X'^2$ will almost always be larger than ΣX^2, and the variance and standard deviation, as found by formula 5.3.9, will be larger than the variance and standard deviation of the same set of data found by a raw-score formula. There is a formula called Sheppard's correction[1] which will shrink these measures down to their proper size. It is usually enough, however, to be aware of the fact that they are slightly too high.

Short cuts for computing the variance and standard deviation from a grouped frequency distribution. The same short cuts that you developed in the exercises on page 157 can be used in finding the variance and standard deviation from grouped data. They would ordinarily not be used, however, unless a calculating machine were not available, a situation that virtually never arises in practical statistical work. Therefore we shall not consider them here. Should you ever need them, you can find them described in almost any elementary statistics book except this one.

Properties of the variance and standard deviation

1. The standard deviation and variance are taken about the mean. That is to say, we square the deviation of each score from the mean, rather than from some other point such as the median

---

[1] Sheppard's correction is:

$$s_c = \sqrt{s^2 - \frac{i^2}{12}}$$

where s_c is the corrected value of the standard deviation,
    s is the standard deviation from the grouped frequency distribution,
    i is the size of the step interval.

or the mode. *The variance and standard deviation will be smaller when the deviations are taken about the mean than when they are taken about any other point.* This fact leads to a new definition of the mean: it is *the point about which the sum of the squared deviations will be as small as possible.*

2. *If a constant is added to (or subtracted from) every score in the distribution, the standard deviation and variance will be unchanged.* The reason for this is that, as you may remember, the addition of a constant to every score increases the mean by that constant. The first step in finding the variance is to find the difference between every score and the mean. If the score is increased by K, and the mean is increased by K, the difference between these two values is the same as the difference between the mean and the score.

$$X - \overline{X} = (X + K) - (\overline{X} + K)$$

This means that we can often shorten our computations by subtracting some convenient constant from every score.

3. *If every score in the distribution is multiplied by a constant, the standard deviation is multiplied by the constant and the variance by the square of the constant.* This fact can be used in developing computational short cuts, and it can also be used in converting figures from one unit of measurement to another. If we know that the standard deviation of a set of measurements, expressed in yards, is 4, then the same standard deviation, expressed in feet, is three times that, or 12. The variance of the same set of measurements, expressed in yards, is 16. Expressed in feet it is $(3)^2 \times 16$, or 144.

Table 5.1.[2] Ratios of the Total Range to the Standard Deviation in a Distribution for Different Values of N

N	$\dfrac{\text{Range}}{s}$	N	$\dfrac{\text{Range}}{s}$	N	$\dfrac{\text{Range}}{s}$
5	2.3	40	4.3	400	5.9
10	3.1	50	4.5	500	6.1
15	3.5	100	5.0	700	6.3
20	3.7	200	5.5	1,000	6.5

[2] Abridged from Tippett, L. H. C., 'Mean values of the ratio, $\dfrac{\text{range}'}{\sigma}$, *Biometrika*, 1925, **17**, 386. By permission of the author and editor.

4. When the number of cases in the distribution is large (200–700) the standard deviation is usually about one-sixth of the range. *The relation between the range and standard deviation is given in Table 5.1 for various sizes of N.* After you have computed a standard deviation it is a good idea to use this table to see whether it is approximately the right size. If you have forgotten to take a square root, or made some other such hideous error, the table may help you find it.

Questions

1. Prove the statement that 'if every score in the distribution is multiplied by a constant, the variance is multiplied by the square of that constant.'

2. Prove that $\Sigma(X - \overline{X}) = 0$. (Note: the proof is given on p. 153, but see if you can do it without looking at the book.)

3. Fill in the blanks in the following sentences.

    a. The _____ is the point about which the sum of the squared deviations is a minimum.

    b. The _____ is the point about which the sum of the deviations, considered without regard to sign, is a minimum.

    c. The _____ is the 'best guess' in the sense that it is as likely to be too high as too low.

    d. The _____ is the 'best guess' in the sense that it is most likely to be absolutely right.

    e. The _____ is the point about which the sum of the deviations is zero.

    f. The _____ is the measure of central tendency which is least affected by extreme cases, while the _____ is most affected.

    g. The _____ cannot be computed for an open-ended distribution, but the _____ and the _____ can be.

4. Given the three lines below:

    a. Find the mean length geometrically—that is, without measuring the lines or using numbers.

    b. Find the average deviation geometrically.

    c. Find $\Sigma(X - \overline{X})^2$ geometrically.

      a   b   c

    _____ _____ _____

5. For the set of numbers below:

    a. Find the mean and median.
    b. Find AD and AD_{Mdn}. Show that AD_{Mdn} is lower than AD.
    c. Find $\Sigma(X - \overline{X})^2$ and $\Sigma(X - \text{Mdn})^2$ and show that the former is smaller than the latter.
    d. Find the variance and standard deviation by the use of the definition formula.

$$1, 2, 4, 5, 13$$

6. Make up three sets of numbers. For each set, compute AD and AD_{Mdn} and compare them. Compute $\Sigma(X - \overline{X})^2$ and $\Sigma(X - \text{Mdn})^2$ for each set, and compare them.

7. Find the variance and standard deviation of the following set of numbers by both the definition formula and the raw-score formula.

$$10, 11, 14, 15.$$

8. In a set of 40 measurements, the lowest measurement is 116 and the highest 136. You have computed the standard deviation and found it to be 21. Do you think your answer is approximately right?

9. Below are given the highest and lowest scores for four sets of measurements of size N. Approximately what would you expect the standard deviation to be in each case?

Lowest X	Highest X	N	s
0	125	10	
1074	1110	750	
.647	.891	36	
5	15	7	

10. Find either ΣX and ΣX^2 or $\overline{X}$, s^2, and s for the following sets of numbers:

    a. 21, 29, 34, 48, 61
    b. 0, 6, 9, 10, 14
    c. 5117, 5119, 5124, 5128
    d. 17.5, 17.8, 18.0, 18.2, 18.6, 18.7

11. Below are given the times, in one-hundredths of a second, required by 50 subjects to complete a perceptual motor task. Find $\overline{X}$, s^2, and s. Convert your answers to seconds.

21	19	31	34	26	$\Sigma X = 1680$
40	33	44	38	28	$\Sigma X^2 = 60,626$
38	26	25	36	31	
35	34	28	25	42	
22	32	33	31	18	
32	27	32	20	65	
36	41	29	26	39	
24	33	40	39	40	
53	27	22	41	44	
48	30	50	37	35	

12. Below are given the numbers of trials required by 25 subjects to learn a list of nonsense syllables. Find $\overline{X}$, s, and s^2.

12	31	9	16	12
12	11	26	11	10
14	13	24	13	9
8	12	17	21	20
19	10	15	19	16

13. Below are given the scholastic-aptitude scores of 100 students.

  a. Prepare a grouped frequency distribution, using as many intervals as you think wise.
  b. Plot the data in the form of a histogram.
  c. Plot a cumulative percentage curve.
  d. Find the median, the range, and Q.
  e. Find s and s^2 from the grouped data.
  f. Find $\overline{X}$ from the grouped data.
  g. Find $\overline{X}$, s, and s^2 from the raw scores. $\Sigma X = 50,378$, and $\Sigma X^2 = 26,347,786$.

Explain any discrepancy between results from grouped data and results from raw scores.

264	424	480	524	587
302	426	481	530	591
314	431	481	536	598
326	433	484	538	600
338	439	485	538	604
342	441	492	540	609
350	442	493	543	617
361	447	497	545	622
369	447	498	547	628
378	448	501	550	633

387	449	501	554	641
391	450	504	558	642
394	451	507	559	649
399	453	509	562	662
400	460	511	567	674
406	464	513	568	681
410	466	519	570	690
411	468	521	572	703
417	471	522	581	733
421	479	524	585	755

Summary

An interval scale is one for which a unit of measurement has been established and a satisfactory operation for addition demonstrated. If, in addition, the scale has an absolute-zero point, it is called a ratio scale. Statistics for interval and ratio scales are considered together because there are few measures that utilize the zero point of a ratio scale.

Grouped frequency distributions, histograms, frequency polygons, and cumulative frequency and percentage curves can all be used to provide an over-all picture of data from interval and ratio scales. The horizontal distances between points on these graphs are mathematically meaningful. This means that we can now talk about the shapes of distributions, and it means, further, that the area under the curve between any two points on the x-axis is proportional to the number of cases between those points.

The arithmetic mean is a measure of central tendency that is available for use with interval and ratio scales. The mean is also:

1. The point about which the positive and negative deviations are equal.

2. The fulcrum or balance point of a distribution.

3. The point about which the sum of the squared deviations is a minimum.

The mode and the median, as well as the mean, can be used to describe the typical case when the data come from interval or ratio scales. In general, however, the mean is the most desirable of these measures because it makes use of all the data and forms the basis for further calculations.

Interpercentile measures of variability are relatively easy to compute and to interpret, but they do not use all the data, nor do they use the unit of measurement that is now available. Two new measures of variability, the average deviation and the standard deviation (or its square, the variance), can be used instead.

The average deviation is the average of the absolute values of the deviations of the scores from the mean. While this measure is easy to understand, it is relatively difficult to compute and is never used in further calculations.

The variance is the average of the squares of the deviations of the scores from the mean. The standard deviation is the square root of the variance. This measure is easy to compute and is used continually in further calculations. Its interpretation may throw the beginner for a loop, but before too long familiarity should breed content.

References

1. Huff, D., *How To Lie with Statistics*, New York, Norton, 1954. Many excellent suggestions on how to lie (and how to detect lying) with examples. Amusingly written, but it repays thoughtful reading.

Short cuts for non-machine calculation can be found in many elementary statistics texts. For further specific instructions on machine calculation see:

2. Pease, Katherine, *Machine Computations of Elementary Statistics*, New York, Chartwell House, 1949.

Answers

Page 156

2. 1,052,796,434.   5. 10,000,000,000,000.   8. 32.5.

9. Subtract 1058.5, divide by 2. $\overline{X} = 1059.1$.

Page 174

3. a. mean; b. median; c. median; d. mode; e. mean; f. mode, mean; g. mean, median, and mode.
5. $\overline{X} = 5$, Mdn. = 4; b. $AD = 3.2$, $AD_{\text{Mdn}} = 3.0$; c. $\Sigma(X - \overline{X})^2 = 90$, $\Sigma(X - \text{Mdn.})^2 = 95$; d. $s^2 = 18$, $s = 3\sqrt{2}$ or 4.24.

7. $s^2 = 4.25$, $s = 2.06$.   8. No.   9. 40, 5.9, .06, 4.2.

ANSWERS 179

10. (Answers, in order, are ΣX, ΣX^2, $\overline{X}$, s^2, and s): a. 193, 8463, 38.6, 202.64, 14.23; b. 39, 413, 7.8, 21.76, 4.66; c. 20,488, 104,939,610, 5122, 18.5, 4.30; d. 108.8, 1973.98, 18.13, .300, .548.

11. $\overline{X}$ = 33.6 hundredths or .336 sec.; s^2 = 83.56 hundredths or .008356 sec.; s = 9.14 hundredths or .0914 sec.

12. $\overline{X}$ = 15.2; s^2 = 32.16; s = 5.67.

13. g. $\overline{X}$ = 503.78; s^2 = 9683.57; s = 98.4.

INTERVAL AND RATIO SCALES, II

Theoretical Distributions and Measures of Individual Position

In the last chapter we said that when measurements are made on interval or ratio scales, the horizontal distances between or within the bars of a histogram, or between the points of a frequency polygon, are mathematically meaningful. This fact makes it possible to talk about the shapes of frequency distributions and about the relation of obtained to theoretical shapes. In this chapter we shall consider two related kinds of theoretical distribution, the binomial and the normal distributions, say a few more words about skewness, introduce the concept of kurtosis (the relative flatness or peakedness of a frequency distribution), and, finally, discuss measures of the position of an individual with respect to the group.

Before we launch into a discussion of theoretical distributions, let us think for a minute about why they are being considered in a section of the text devoted to descriptive statistics. Descriptive statistics are measures that describe a population or a sample; they do not tell us anything about extrapolations that can be made from an obtained sample to some hypothetical population. A great many obtained distributions, however, have shapes that are very similar to the shapes of certain theoretical distributions. For example, many obtained distributions have approximately the symmetrical, bell-shaped form that characterizes the normal distribution. If we are willing to treat such obtained distributions *as if* they were of the normal form, we have available to us a great deal of information about proportions and percentages, about variability, and about other characteristics of the distribution as well. Of course we make an error in treating any data that are not distributed in a perfectly normal fashion as if they were so distributed, but the error is small compared to the additional information gained and the computational labor saved. Needless to say, if the obtained distribution differs too much from the theoretical distribution, the error will be too large to justify the saving.

With these considerations in mind, we shall go ahead to talk about two important kinds of theoretical distribution—the binomial distribution and the normal distribution.

6.1 The Binomial Distribution

If you toss a nickel, you may find yourself looking at the visage of an indian brave or at the broad side of a buffalo. These two states

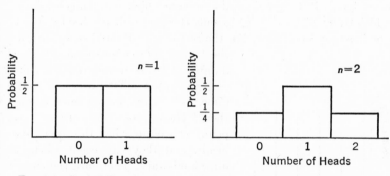

Fig. 6.1 Probability distribution resulting from one toss of a coin.

Fig. 6.2 Probability distribution resulting from the toss of two coins.

of affairs are referred to, respectively, as heads and tails. Since there are two possible outcomes to the toss of a coin, and since, for an honest coin, these outcomes are equally likely, we say that the probability of either one is $\frac{1}{2}$. If we roll a die, we may obtain any one of six possible results, which are assumed to be equally likely. We therefore say that the probability of obtaining any one result—a two-spot, say—is $\frac{1}{6}$. In general, if there are k equally likely outcomes of an event, we can say that the probability[1] of any one of them is $\frac{1}{k}$.

On the toss of one coin we can obtain either no heads or one head, and the probability of each outcome is $\frac{1}{2}$. These results are plotted

[1] The important and complex topic of probability is discussed more fully and more formally in Chapter 10, pp. 335ff. Readers who feel disturbed by the incompleteness of the discussion here can study the treatment on those pages before continuing with the section on the binomial distribution.

as a bar graph in Figure 6.1. Suppose we toss two coins, a nickel and a penny, what can happen then?

OUTCOME		RESULT
Heads	*Tails*	
nickel-penny	—	2 heads
nickel	penny	1 head
penny	nickel	1 head
—	penny-nickel	0 heads

There are four possible, equally likely outcomes. The probability of each is $\frac{1}{4}$. If, however, we do not care which coin lands heads and which lands tails, we recognize only three possible results: two heads, one head, and no heads. For the rest of this discussion we shall use the word *result* to refer to some specified number of heads on the toss of n coins.

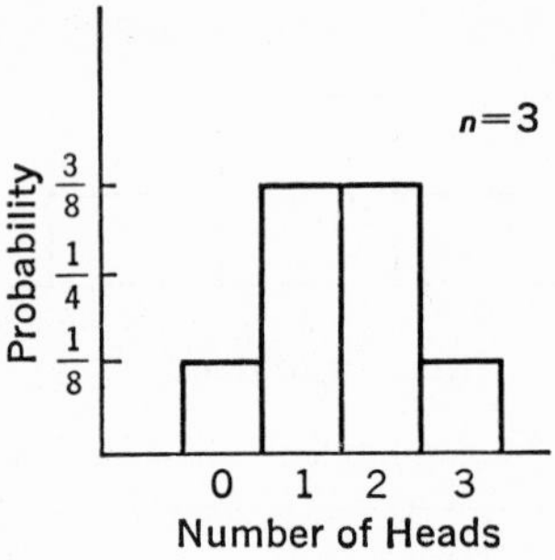

FIG. 6.3   Probability distribution resulting from the toss of three coins.

If we toss a nickel, a penny, and a dime, how many possible outcomes are there? The four outcomes of nickel and penny can occur when the dime lands heads, and they can occur when the dime lands tails. There are therefore 8 possible outcomes of the toss of three coins. If we include a quarter as well, then each of these 8 outcomes can occur when the quarter lands heads and when it lands tails, thus giving us 16 outcomes. In general, each time we add a coin, we double the number of possible outcomes. If there are n coins, the number of possible outcomes is 2^n. For three coins, the 8 outcomes are:

OUTCOME		RESULT
Heads	*Tails*	
penny-nickel-dime	—	3 heads
penny-nickel	dime	2 heads
penny-dime	nickel	2 heads
nickel-dime	penny	2 heads
penny	nickel-dime	1 head
nickel	penny-dime	1 head
dime	penny-nickel	1 head
—	penny-nickel-dime	0 heads

These 8 outcomes are equally likely; the probability of each is $\frac{1}{8}$. There are only four possible *results*, however: no heads, 1, 2, or 3 heads. To determine the probability of each result we must find out how many of the 8 outcomes will yield it. The probability of the result is the sum of the probabilities of these outcomes.

For example, consider the result 'two heads.' There are three ways of selecting two coins from three to yield this result: the penny and the nickel may be heads, or the penny and the dime, or the nickel and the dime. Each of these ways of selecting two coins from three is called a **combination.** Since each outcome, or combination, has a probability of $\frac{1}{8}$, the probability of the result 'two heads' is $\frac{1}{8} + \frac{1}{8} + \frac{1}{8}$, or $\frac{3}{8}$.

There is a formula that tells us immediately how many combinations will yield one result. Let n stand for the number of things to be arranged—in our case the number of coins to be tossed; and let r stand for the number that are to be of one kind—in our case the number that are to be heads. Then, if $\binom{n}{r}$ stands for the number of combinations of n things, such that r are of one kind and $(n - r)$ are of the other:

$$\binom{n}{r} = \frac{n!}{r!(n - r)!} \tag{6.1.1}$$

(The symbol '!' does not mean 'Gad!' It is read 'factorial,' and $n!$ is defined as $n(n - 1)(n - 2) \ldots 2 \cdot 1$. Thus 3! means $3 \times 2 \times 1$. We define 0! as being equal to 1.)

Let us apply this formula to the three-coin case. How many ways can three coins be arranged so that the number of heads is zero?

$$n = 3 \qquad r = 0$$
$$\binom{n}{r} = \frac{3!}{0!3!}$$

Since 0! equals 1:
$$\binom{3}{0} = \frac{3!}{1 \times 3!} = 1$$

There is one such combination. For one head, $n = 3$ and $r = 1$, so

$$\binom{n}{r} = \frac{3!}{1!2!} = \frac{3 \times 2 \times 1}{1 \times 2 \times 1} = 3$$

The formula is applied in the same way to find the number of combinations yielding two heads and three heads.

The probabilities of the various results on the toss of two coins are plotted in Figure 6.2, and on the toss of three coins in Figure 6.3. In plotting Figures 6.1, 6.2, and 6.3 we have made the area inside the bars the same in all to correspond to the fact that the total probability must always equal 1.0. That is to say, one of the possible results must always occur. The widths and the heights of the bars in the graphs change from graph to graph, but the area always remains constant.

To summarize the technique for finding the probability of any particular result:

1. Find the total number of possible outcomes for n things, each of which can be in k equally likely states. This number is k^n.

2. The probability of any one of these outcomes is $\frac{1}{k^n}$.

3. Find the number of combinations of the n things such that r are of one kind and $(n - r)$ are of the other. This number is $\binom{n}{r}$.

4. $\binom{n}{r}$ is multiplied by the probability obtained in step 2. This is the probability of a result such that r things are of one kind and $(n - r)$ are of the other.

For example, let us find the probability of obtaining exactly three heads on five tosses of a coin (or on the toss of five coins—an identical problem.)

1. We have 5 coins, each of which can be in 2 states. The number of outcomes is therefore 2^5, or 32.

2. The probability of one of these outcomes is $\frac{1}{32}$.

3. The number of combinations of 5 coins, such that 3 are heads and 2 are tails is $\binom{5}{3}$, or $\frac{5!}{3!2!} = 10$.

4. The probability of obtaining 3 heads is $10 \times \frac{1}{32}$, or $\frac{5}{16}$.

This procedure will work only when the k states are equally likely. If we roll a die, it may land with any one of six faces up, and these six are equally likely, but if we then go on to talk about 'two-spots' and 'not-two-spots,' these two states are not equally likely. There are five ways of obtaining something other than a two-spot and only one way of obtaining a two-spot, so the probability of a two-spot is $\frac{1}{6}$ and of a not-two-spot, $\frac{5}{6}$. If we are to work with more than one die, these different probabilities will have to be considered, and in the next section we shall introduce an easier method of dealing with this kind of situation.

Questions

1. If four coins are tossed, how many possible outcomes can result? List them.

2. If two dice are rolled, how many outcomes can result? List them.

3. You go to four men in turn and ask each man to 'pick a number from one to ten (inclusive).' Assume that the ten possible numbers are equally likely. How many different outcomes can result? What is the probability of each of these outcomes?

4. If you toss five coins, what is the probability of obtaining each of the following outcomes:

    a. Heads on coin one, heads on coin two, tails on coin three, heads on coin four, and tails on coin five.

    b. Tails on coins one, two, and three, and heads on coins four and five.

    c. Tails on all five coins.

5. How many combinations of six coins will yield four heads?

6. Two representatives are to be chosen from a group of eight people. How many ways can these two be chosen?

7. How many ways can one bridge hand of 13 cards be chosen from a deck of 52 cards?

8. How many ways can a poker hand of 5 cards be chosen from a deck of 52?

9. What is the probability of obtaining exactly two heads on four tosses of a coin?

10. Compute the probabilities of obtaining 0, 1, 2, 3, or 4 heads on four tosses of a coin and plot a bar graph of the results.

11. Do the same for the probabilities of 0, 1, 2, 3, 4, or 5 heads on the toss of 5 coins.

12. If 3 coins are tossed, what is the probability of obtaining *either* two heads or three heads? Of obtaining either one, two, or three heads?

13. If 20 coins are tossed, what is the probability of getting 20 heads? What is the probability of getting some number of heads from zero to 19 inclusive?

There is another method for finding the probabilities of various combinations. That is to expand the binomial

$$(P + Q)^n$$

Where P is the probability of one particular outcome—for example, that one coin will land heads. Q is $1 - P$, and n is the number of events—for example, the number of coins to be tossed.

If two coins are to be tossed, n is 2 and the binomial is expanded to

$$(P + Q)^2 = P^2 + 2PQ + Q^2$$

Each of the terms in the expansion corresponds to one of the three possible results that can occur. The first term tells us the probability of getting two heads, the second term the probability of getting one head, and the third term the probability of no heads. Since $P = \frac{1}{2}$, and therefore $Q = \frac{1}{2}$, the values of the three terms are $\frac{1}{4}$, $\frac{1}{2}$, and $\frac{1}{4}$, which is, of course, the same answer we previously obtained.

If we toss three coins, n is three, and the expanded binomial is

$$(P + Q)^3 = P^3 + 3P^2Q + 3PQ^2 + Q^3$$

These four terms are the probabilities of getting 3, 2, 1, and 0 heads, respectively. Substituting $\frac{1}{2}$ for P and for Q, we find that the probabilities are, as we expected, $\frac{1}{8}$, $\frac{3}{8}$, $\frac{3}{8}$, and $\frac{1}{8}$.

In the binomial, P and Q are the probabilities of two mutually exclusive, independent outcomes of an event, one of which must occur. Thus a coin cannot be simultaneously a head and a tail, nor, we assume, will it stand on edge. Therefore, $P + Q$ equals 1, and $(P + Q)^n$ must also equal one. The sum of all the terms in the binomial expansion will always equal one. The outcomes in this case are independent, because the fall of the second coin is not influenced by the fall of the first.

There is no necessity for P and Q to be equal. Let us consider the probabilities of rolling 0, 1, or 2 two-spots on two rolls of a die. The probability of obtaining one two-spot on one roll is $\frac{1}{6}$, so $P = \frac{1}{6}$ and $Q = \frac{5}{6}$. We therefore expand

$$\left(\frac{1}{6} + \frac{5}{6}\right)^2 = \left(\frac{1}{6}\right)^2 + 2\left(\frac{1}{6}\right)\left(\frac{5}{6}\right) + \left(\frac{5}{6}\right)^2 = \frac{1}{36} + \frac{10}{36} + \frac{25}{36}$$

The probability of rolling two two-spots is $\frac{1}{36}$; of rolling exactly one, $\frac{10}{36}$; and of rolling none, $\frac{25}{36}$.

The number that appears before each term of the binomial expansion is called its coefficient. The binomial coefficients for $(P + Q)^2$ are 1, 2, and 1. For $(P + Q)^3$ the binomial coefficients are 1, 3, 3, and 1. Each binomial coefficient tells the number of combinations of the n items which will permit the result in question. Thus, when two coins are tossed, there is one way of getting 2 heads, two ways of getting 1 head, and one way of getting 0 heads. Table B gives the binomial coefficients for various values of n. It is known as Pascal's Triangle, and budding numerologists may enjoy figuring out the relationships among the numbers there.

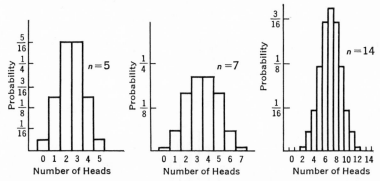

Fig. 6.4. Probabilities of various numbers of heads when n coins are tossed.

Since we already have a formula for determining the number of combinations of n items such that r are of one kind, we can write a formula for the generalized binomial:

$$(P + Q)^n = P^n + \binom{n}{n-1} P^{n-1}Q + \binom{n}{n-2} P^{n-2}Q^2$$

$$+ \ldots + \binom{n}{1} PQ^{n-1} + Q^n \quad (6.1.2)$$

for example:

$$(P + Q)^4 = P^4 + \binom{4}{3} P^3Q + \binom{4}{2} P^2Q^2 + \binom{4}{1} PQ^3 + Q^4$$

Figures 6.4 and 6.5 show the probability distributions resulting from binomial expansions when n becomes larger, both for $P = Q$

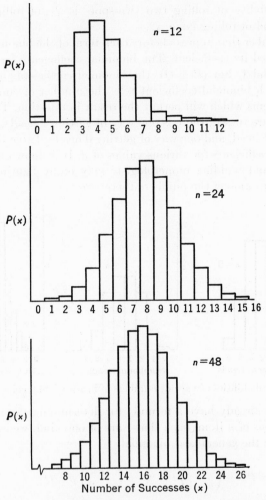

FIG. 6.5 Probabilities of various numbers of successes out of n trials when the probability of one success is $\frac{1}{3}$. Note that the mode of each distribution is always at nP, or $\frac{1}{3}n$. (Areas are not identical.) (From Hoel, P. G., *Introduction to Mathematical Statistics*, New York, Wiley, 1954 by permission of the author and publisher.)

$= \frac{1}{2}$ and for $P = \frac{1}{3}$ and $Q = \frac{2}{3}$. Notice that as n becomes larger and larger the distribution becomes smoother and smoother, and when P and Q are different the distributions also become more and more symmetrical.

Since, if we know n and P, we can figure out the exact shape of the distribution that will result, we can also determine in advance the mean of the distribution. If we toss ten coins many many times, what will be the average number of heads that will occur? Common sense suggests that the average number of heads would be 5, one-half of ten. That is what the formula says too.

$$\mu = nP \qquad \text{where } \mu \text{ stands for the arithmetic mean} \qquad (6.1.3)$$

(The letter μ (mu) is used instead of $\overline{X}$ to conform to modern statistical usage, which distinguishes between theoretical and obtained distributions by using Greek letters for the former and Roman letters for the latter. If we actually tossed ten coins dozens and dozens of times, and computed the mean from the obtained results, we should call it $\overline{X}$. When we speak of the theoretical standard deviation of the binomial distribution we shall use the Greek letter σ (sigma) instead of the Roman s. But if a standard deviation were computed from obtained data, it would be called s.)

Thus, if we were to keep rolling a set of six dice, we should expect that, on the average, one die would be a two-spot. This is because the probability of a two-spot, P, is $\frac{1}{6}$, and the number of dice, n, is 6.

The formula for the standard deviation of the binomial distribution is

$$\sigma = \sqrt{nPQ} \qquad (6.1.4)$$

Later on in this chapter we shall see how useful formulas 6.1.3 and 6.1.4 can be in making predictions.

We have seen that as n becomes larger and larger, each rectangle in the bar graph becomes narrower and narrower. Nevertheless, the binomial distribution is a theoretical distribution of a *discrete* variable—if you toss 2000 coins you can get 1000 heads or 1001 heads but not $1000\frac{1}{2}$. That means that the graph of a binomial distribution will always contain some definite number of bars, no matter how narrow these bars must be. If, however, we are willing to treat the discrete possibilities as if they represented a continuous variable, then we can talk about $1000\frac{1}{2}$ heads, or $1000\frac{1}{4}$ heads, and so on. In that case, as n becomes larger and larger the bars become narrower and narrower, until finally, as n becomes infinitely large, the bars become infinitely narrow—that is to say, each bar ceases to be a rectangle and becomes just a line with no width. The curve connecting the tops of the bars then loses its step-like nature and becomes a smooth, continuous curve. When that happens, the resulting curve is known as the **normal distribution.**

Questions

1. By direct multiplication expand $(P + Q)^4$.

2. By the use of the generalized binomial (formula 6.1.2) write out the expansion of $(P + Q)^6$. Reduce the coefficients to integers.

3. By reference to Pascal's Triangle, write out the expansion of $(P + Q)^8$.

4. (a) Which term in the expansion above would tell you the probability of getting exactly 6 heads on 8 tosses of a coin? If $P = \frac{1}{2}$, compute the actual probability.

   (b) Which term would tell you the probability of rolling 6 two-spots on 8 rolls of a die? Compute the actual probability.

5. Plot the bar graphs showing the probabilities of getting 0, 1, 2 . . . n two-spots on n rolls of a die when $n = 1, 3, 5, 8,$ and 10. What happens to the graphs as n gets larger?

6. What is the probability of obtaining *no* three-spots on 15 rolls of a die? Of obtaining at least one three-spot on 15 rolls?

7. What is the probability of rolling either 2 or 3 six-spots on 4 rolls of a die?

8. (a) If you made 160 tosses of a set of 4 coins, how many tosses would you expect to result in no heads? In one head? In 2, in 3, and in 4 heads?

   (b) Assume that your results correspond exactly with your expectations and compute the mean of the obtained distribution by the formula $\overline{X} = \dfrac{\Sigma fX}{N}$. Compute the theoretical mean by the formula $\mu = nP$ and compare the results.

   (c) Assuming that your obtained results correspond exactly with the expected results, compute the standard deviation by the formula

$s = \sqrt{\dfrac{\Sigma f(X - \overline{X})^2}{N}}$. Compute the theoretical standard deviation by the formula $\sigma = \sqrt{nPQ}$ and compare the results.

9. Actually make 160 tosses of 4 coins and compare your results with the expected ones. Compute the mean and standard deviation of your obtained distribution and compare these with the expected ones.

10. If you were asked to compute the probabilities of getting 0, 1, 2, 3, 4, or 5 spades in a poker hand of 5 cards, you could not do it correctly by expanding $(\frac{1}{4} + \frac{3}{4})^5$. Why not?

11. If one-third of the eggs laid in a certain dairy farm are brown, and two-thirds are white, and if these eggs are sold in boxes of one dozen,

  a. What would be the probability of getting a box with 11 brown eggs?

  b. What would be the probability of getting a box with 11 white eggs?

  c. What would be the mean number of brown eggs per box?

  d. What proportion of the boxes would you expect to contain exactly four brown eggs?

  e. If a grocer buys 100 boxes of eggs from this farm, how many boxes would he expect to contain all white eggs?

6.2 The Normal Distribution

6.2.1 Areas under the Curve: To repeat, the binomial distribution is the theoretical distribution that tells us the probability of 0, 1, 2, . . . n outcomes of one kind among n events when the probability of an outcome of that kind is P. The events in question must be independent; that is, results on one toss of a set of coins, for example, must not affect the results of the next toss. The binomial distribution is a distribution of a discrete variable. If we can conceive of the variable as continuous, and think of n as getting larger and larger and finally approaching infinity, we shall end up with a continuous curve instead of a series of little steps. The theoretical curve obtained in this manner is called the normal distribution.[2]

[2] If P and Q are different the binomial distribution becomes more and more symmetrical as n gets larger and larger. But if either P or Q is very small the distribution will be asymmetrical even when n is very large. In practice, a binomial distribution can be treated like a normal distribution when nP and nQ are both greater than 5.

The equation for the normal curve is

$$y = \frac{1}{\sigma \sqrt{2\pi}} e^{-\frac{1}{2}z^2} \tag{6.2.1}$$

where

$$z \text{ is } \frac{X - \mu}{\sigma} \tag{6.2.2}$$

μ is the mean of the distribution and σ is the standard deviation

e is a natural constant, 2.718.

π is a natural constant, 3.142.

y is the height of the curve at point z. That is, y is the ordinate or y-value corresponding to an abscissa or x-value of z.

We would like to say that y corresponds to the probability of obtaining value z, but we cannot, for z is now merely a point without any width. Hence the rectangle erected above it is infinitely narrow —without width—while we have seen that probability corresponds to an *area*, inside a rectangle or under a curve. The area under a continuous curve between two specified points on the abscissa corresponds to the proportion of cases between those points, or to the probability that any case chosen at random will have a score between the specified values.

For a continuous curve, these areas are found by a mathematical process called **integration,** which is represented by the **integral sign,** $\int$. The area under a curve between any two points is called the **definite integral** between those points, and the points are listed at the top and bottom of the integral sign. For example, integration tells us that the area under the normal curve between the mean ($z = 0$) and a point one standard deviation above the mean ($z = +1$), expressed as a proportion of the total area, is .3413, as shown in Figure 6.6. We write that this way:

$$\int_{z=0}^{z=+1} \frac{1}{\sigma \sqrt{2\pi}} e^{-\frac{1}{2}z^2} \, dz = .3413$$

(The 'dz' in the expression above need not bother you. It has a mathematical reason for being there, but to explain it would require a short course in calculus. Until you have studied calculus, you can look on the 'dz' as a sort of mathematical convention.)

The mathematical expression above is equivalent to saying, in words: 'The proportion of cases in the distribution having values between the mean and a point one standard deviation away from the mean is .3413; or: 34.13 per cent of the cases have scores between the mean and one standard deviation above or below it.' Perhaps this verbal translation gives you an idea of why we are so interested

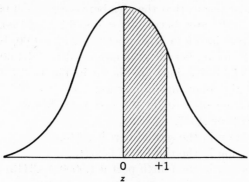

FIG. 6.6   To find the proportion of cases between $z = 0$ and $z = 1$, we must determine the size of the shaded area.

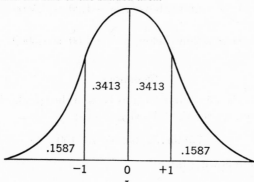

FIG. 6.7   A normal distribution divided into four parts, with proportions given for each of the four.

in areas under the curve. As we shall see in the rest of this chapter and in many of the chapters to follow, our ability to specify the proportion of cases falling between any two specified values of z is one of our most useful statistical tools. So important is it that tables have been made up giving the area, or proportion of cases, under the normal curve between the mean and values of z from 0 to 3.09. Table C is such a table.

Before we go on to look at that table, however, let us see how much we can do with our knowledge of the normal curve, and of the fact that the area under the curve between $z = 0$ and $z = +1.00$ equals .3413. First, the normal curve is symmetrical. That means that 50 per cent of the cases lie below the mean and 50 per cent above it. It also means that the area between $z = -1.00$ and $z = 0$ is the same as the area between $z = 0$ and $z = +1.00$. So we can divide the curve into four parts: below a z of -1.00, between $z = -1.00$ and the mean, between the mean and $z = +1.00$, and above $z = +1.00$. These divisions are shown in Figure 6.7. From them we can make the following statements:

The proportion of cases in the first part, below $z = -1.00$, is (.5000 − .3413) or .1587.

The proportion in the second part is .3413.

The proportion in the third part is .3413.

The proportion in the fourth part is (.5000 − .3413) or .1587.

The proportion falling between $z = -1.00$ and $z = +1.00$ is .3413 + .3413, or .6826.

The proportion falling above $z = -1.00$ is (.5000 + .3413) or .8413.

The proportion falling below $z = +1.00$ is (.5000 + .3413) or .8413.

Questions

1. If the mean of a distribution, μ, is 75, and the standard deviation, σ, is 20, compute z for the following scores:

$$75, 95, 55, 65, 85, 78, 100$$

2. Fill in the following table:

X	μ	σ	z
600	500	100	a)
b)	1000	50	+1.00
37	c)	3	−1.00
61	58	d)	+.75
4.2	7.1	1.0	e)

3. If the mean of a normal distribution is 50 and the standard deviation is 10:

    a. What proportion of the cases fall between 50 and 60?
    b. Between 40 and 50?
    c. Below 50?
    d. Above 50?
    e. Between 40 and 60?
    f. Below 40?
    g. Above 60?
    h. Above 40?
    i. Below 60?

For each answer draw a little sketch of a normal curve and shade in the area you are finding.

Table C gives the areas, or proportions of cases, under the curve between the mean and every other point. For example, if we have a normal distribution of measurements with a mean of 80 and a standard deviation of 10, and we wish to know what proportion of the cases in the distribution are between 80 and 100, we first convert the 100 to a value of z. That is to say, we find out how many standard deviations away from the mean the measurement is. In this instance,

$$z = \frac{100 - 80}{10} = 2$$

Now we turn to Table C and look up $z = 2$. We find that the proportion of cases between the mean and $z = 2$ is .4772. In other words, 47.72 per cent of the cases in our distribution fall between 80 and 100.

What proportion of the measures fall between 65 and 90? This is a problem in simple addition. We find the proportion of measures falling between 65 and 80, and the proportion falling between 80 and 90. The sum of these two proportions is our answer.

$$z = \frac{65 - 80}{10} = -1.5$$

The area between a z of 1.5 (or -1.5) and the mean is found, from Table C, to be .4332.

$$z = \frac{90 - 80}{10} = 1.0$$

The area between the mean and a z of 1.0 we know to be .3413. The area between a z of -1.5 and $+1.0$ is therefore $(.4332 + .3413)$

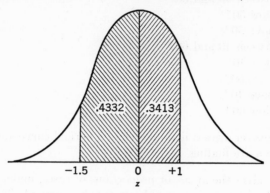

Fig. 6.8   The proportion of cases between $z = -1.5$ and $z = +1.0$ is the sum of the two cross-hatched areas, each of which can be found from Table II.

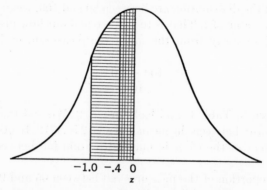

Fig. 6.9   The area between the mean and $z = -1.00$ has been shaded horizontally. The area between the mean and $z = -0.4$ has been shaded vertically. The area shaded horizontally but *not* vertically is the difference between these two.

or .7745. Thus, 77.45 per cent of the measures are between 65 and 90.

What proportion of the measurements are between 70 and 76? This is a problem in subtraction, as shown in Figure 6.9. We must find the area between 70 and the mean, and the area between 76 and the mean. The difference between these areas is the area between 70 and 76.

$$z = \frac{70 - 80}{10} = -1$$

The corresponding normal curve area is .3413.

$$z = \frac{76 - 80}{10} = -.4$$

The corresponding normal curve area is found from Table C to be .1554. The difference between these two areas is .1859. Thus, 18.59 per cent of the cases have scores between 70 and 76.

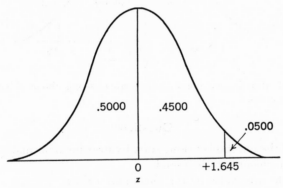

FIG. 6.10 Finding the value of z above which lie 5 per cent of the cases.

We can find proportions from scores, as we have been doing above, and we can also find scores from proportions. Suppose we wish to select the top 5 per cent of the cases in our distribution. What score must an individual have to be included in this special group? We want to find the score that will include between itself and the mean 45 per cent of the cases; 50 per cent, of course, lie below the mean, so this score will be the one below which lie 95 per cent of the cases. This time we look in the body of Table C, for a proportion of .4500. We find, opposite a z of 1.64, a proportion of .4495, and opposite a z of 1.65, a proportion of .4505. Interpolating between these values we find that our required z must be 1.645.

$$z = \frac{X - \overline{X}}{s} \qquad 1.645 = \frac{X - 80}{10}$$

Solving for X, we find that $X = 96.45$. The required score is 96.45, or, since the lower real limit of the score 97 is 96.5, we may say that by including only those cases with scores of 97 or above we shall include almost exactly the top 5 per cent in our group.

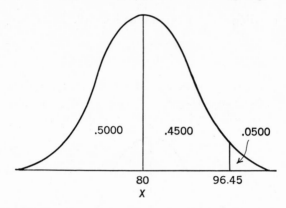

Fig. 6.11   Finding the point on the scale of scores above which lie 5 per cent of the cases.

Questions

For all of the questions below, start by drawing a normal curve and shading in the area to be found.

1. Find the area between the mean and a z of:

$+1.000, -2.000, +3.000, -2.670, +1.445,$
$$-0.565, +1.645, -1.960$$

2. If the mean of a distribution is 500 and the standard deviation is 100, find the per cent of the cases between 500 and the following points:

$$400, 700, 350, 447, 681, 900, 553$$

3. If the mean of a distribution is 30 and the standard deviation 3, find the proportion of the cases having scores between the mean and the scores listed. Remember that a *score*, unlike a *point*, has width, extending from its lower real limit to its upper real limit. For scores below the mean, therefore, you should find the difference between the mean and the lower real limit of the score, and for scores above the mean, the difference between the mean and the

upper real limit of the score. Show exactly what you are doing in your diagrams.

$$31, 29, 36, 26, 38$$

4. Find the normal curve areas that lie:

   a. Above $z = +1.96$
   b. Between $z = -.44$ and $z = +.89$
   c. Above $z = -1.77$
   d. Below $z = -.95$
   e. Below $z = +2.00$
   f. Between $z = -1.00$ and $z = +1.00$
   g. Between $z = -.67$ and $z = +.96$
   h. Between $z = -1.00$ and $z = -.50$
   i. Between $z = +.50$ and $z = +1.50$
   j. Between $z = -.50$ and $z = +.50$

5. If the heights of 200 boys are normally distributed with a mean of 60.0'' and a standard deviation of 2.4'', how many of the boys would you expect to find in the following groups? (Remember to use real limits—the boys have been measured to the nearest inch.)

   a. $60'' - 65''$ (translate: $59.5'' - 65.5''$)
   b. 55'' to 65''
   c. 55'' to 58''
   d. Just 60'' (translate: $59.5'' - 60.5''$)
   e. Just 59''
   f. Just 61''
   g. $59'' - 61''$

6. Find z if

   a. The normal curve area above z is .1587
   b. The normal curve area between 0 and z is .4750
   c. The normal curve area below z is .8413
   d. The normal curve area below z is .0500
   e. The normal curve area between $-z$ and $+z$ is .9500

7. A group of children has taken a spelling test, and the scores are normally distributed. The mean grade is 57 and the standard devia-

tion is 4. Find the numerical grades required to achieve the letter grades A, B, C, and D if

The top 5 per cent are to receive A's
The next 15 per cent are to receive B's
The middle 60 per cent are to receive C's
The next 15 per cent are to receive D's
The lowest 5 per cent are to receive F's

6.2.2 Relation between the Binomial and Normal Distributions:

We have said that when $(P + Q)^n$ is expanded, and n becomes very large, the resulting distribution is approximated by the normal distribution. Since expanding the binomial when n is very large is an exceedingly laborious chore, the ability to approximate the results by the use of the normal distribution is most convenient at times.

For example, suppose we toss 100 coins, and we want to know the probability of getting some number of heads between (and including) 47 and 53. We *could* solve the problem by taking the middle seven terms of the expansion of $(.5 + .5)^{100}$, but it would be quite a job! Instead we can proceed as follows:

The distribution of 'number of heads' is approximately normal, with a mean of nP and a standard deviation of $\sqrt{nPQ}$.

$$nP = 100 \times .5 = 50$$
$$\sqrt{nPQ} = \sqrt{100 \times .5 \times .5} = 5$$

Now we have a simple and straightforward normal curve problem. We have only to remember that we are treating our discrete variable, number of heads, as if it were continuous, and that we must therefore use real limits, and we can procede in routine fashion.

$$z_1 = \frac{46.5 - 50}{5} = -.7 \qquad z_2 = \frac{53.5 - 50}{5} = +.7$$

The normal curve area corresponding to a z of .7 is .2580, and the probability of getting some number of heads from 47 to 53, inclusive, is therefore $2 \times .2580$, or .5160.

The hardest part of such problems is usually thinking out the approach. Once the problem has been neatly formulated and translated into conventional statistical terms, the rest is easy and can be done by a chimpanzee who has been taught to read tables. The following questions may help you to organize your thinking:

1. Does the problem deal with a true binomial expansion?

    a. Are we trying to find the probability of getting r outcomes of one kind and $n - r$ outcomes of some other kind?

    b. Are the n events truly independent?

    c. Can we specify P, Q, and n?

2. Can the binomial distribution be approximated by a normal distribution? We have said that a binomial distribution can be approximated by a normal distribution if n is large and P (or Q) is not too small. A good rule of thumb is: if neither nP nor nQ is less than 5, the approximation will be satisfactory.

3. What are the mean and standard deviation of the distribution? A sketch will help at this point.

4. What does the problem ask? How is this problem to be translated to normal curve areas? Shade in the required area on your sketch.

If you've been able to give satisfactory answers to all of these questions, you can then go ahead like any literate chimpanzee and solve your problem.

Questions

Some of the questions below can be solved by normal curve techniques and some cannot. Some can be solved by these techniques only if we are willing to make certain assumptions. For each problem, state whether normal curve techniques are appropriate. If they are not, explain why not. If assumptions are necessary, state them. If the problem is soluble by these techniques, solve it.

1. If 16 coins are tossed, what is the probability of getting exactly 8 heads?

2. If half the children in the world are boys, what is the probability that a class of 25 children will contain 15 or more boys?

3. If the probability that a baby will be born defective is $\frac{1}{213}$, what is the probability that 2 or more of the first 500 children born in a certain hospital will be defective?

4. If one person in 20 spends some part of his life in a mental hospital, what is the probability that 5 or more of the 144 people on my Christmas-card list will spend (or have spent) some part of their lives in such hospitals?

5. If half the people in the world have brown eyes, what is the probability that at least 9 of the 10 children in one family will have brown eyes?

6. If a multiple-choice test consists of 100 four-choice questions, what is the probability that a student who makes blind guesses on all the questions will get 30 or more of them right?

7. If a matching question contains 20 answers to be matched with 20 questions, what is the probability that a guessing student will get 5 or more right?

8. In a certain mental hospital, 600 out of the 1000 patients are diagnosed as schizophrenic. What is the probability that 25 or more of the patients in one 30-bed ward will be schizophrenic?

9. What is the probability that 12 or more of the men in one platoon of 16 men will have scores below the median on the Army General Classification Test? What is the probability that at least half of the men in a platoon will have scores below Q_3?

6.2.3 Characteristics of the Normal Distribution:

Parameters. To compute the proportion of cases between any two points, we need to know two things: the mean and the standard deviation of the distribution. The mean and standard deviation are constant for any one distribution, but they are different for different distributions. Quantities that vary from distribution to distribution, but are constant for any single distribution, are called **parameters.** The normal distribution, expressed in terms of proportions, has two parameters, μ and σ. If we wish to work with actual frequencies of cases, rather than proportions, we must know N so that the proportions can be converted to frequencies. Thus the normal curve, expressed in terms of frequencies, has three parameters, N, μ, and σ. Once these three have been specified, everything else about the distribution is also specified.

Relations among measures of central tendency. Since the normal curve is symmetrical and unimodal, the mean, median, and mode are identical, There is no necessity to choose among them.

Relations among measures of variability. We have said that when the two or three parameters of the normal distribution are specified, everything about the distribution is specified. Among the things that are specified are all the measures of variability that we have discussed so far.

H^3 depends upon the proportions in the various categories of a distribution. Since proportions have been completely described for a normal distribution, the value of H can be determined. Since a high value of H goes with unpredictability, and a high value of σ goes with unpredictability, we should expect that H should be large when σ is, and small when σ is small.

$$H = \log_2 \sqrt{2\pi}\, \sigma = 1.31 + \log_2 \sigma \qquad (6.2.3)$$

Percentile measures of variability depend upon the limits within which specified proportions of the cases fall. Since these proportions can be obtained from a normal curve table, the percentile measures can also be completely specified in terms of σ. For example, Q_1 is the point below which lie 25 per cent of the cases; therefore, the proportion of cases lying between Q_1 and the mean is .2500. By reference to the normal curve table, we find that the value of z which includes the proportion .2500 between itself and the mean is .6745. Therefore, the range between Q_1 and Q_3 is the range between $-.6745\sigma$ and $+.6745\sigma$.

$$Q = .6745\sigma \qquad (6.2.4)$$

The range between the highest and lowest scores in the distribution depends upon the number of cases in the distribution. Theoretically, if N is large enough, no value of X is impossible. The crucial question therefore becomes: what proportion of the cases will lie above and below certain specified values of X? If the proportion is, for example, .01, then we should expect that, if N is 100, exactly one such case would actually occur, while if N is 20, only two-tenths of a case would occur. Since two-tenths of a case is less than half a case, that value of X probably will not occur, and therefore, the range when there are 20 cases should be smaller than when there are 100. Thus the relation between the range and the standard deviation depends upon the number of cases, and the relationships have already been stated in Table 5.1 on p. 173.

The average deviation is computed by taking the average of the absolute values of the deviations of the scores about the mean.

---

[3] H, rather than $\hat{H}$, is used for the same reason that μ is used instead of $\overline{X}$ and σ instead of s. The hat on the $\hat{H}$ tells us that we are talking about an obtained sample, while the absence of the hat means that we are talking about a theoretical population.

The standard deviation is computed by averaging the squares of these deviations, and then taking the square root. Hence these two measures must be related. The relationship is:

$$AD = .7979\sigma \qquad (6.2.5)$$

Points of inflection. A brief glance at any normal curve shows that most of the cases are clustered near the center of the curve with fewer and fewer cases at more and more extreme values of X (or z). Near the center of the distribution the height of the curve falls off rapidly as we get farther away from the mean, but near the extremes,

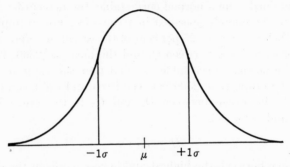

FIG. 6.12   A normal distribution showing the change from convexity to concavity at $+1\sigma$ and -1σ. This figure is, of course, greatly exaggerated.

the height falls off quite slowly with increasing distance from the mean. The curve is convex near the center but concave near the extremes. The two points where the curve stops being convex and becomes concave are called the **points of inflection,** and they occur at -1σ and $+1\sigma$. This fact is shown, in greatly exaggerated form, in Figure 6.12.

6.2.4 The Cumulative Form of the Normal Distribution: A cumulative percentage curve, you may remember, is a curve showing the per cent of cases lying below any point on the scale of scores. Of course a cumulative percentage curve can be drawn for normally distributed data. If each point is converted to a z-score before the curve is plotted, the curve is said to be in standard form. In Figure 6.13 a cumulative percentage curve for a normal distribution is plotted in standard form. Notice that it is S-shaped in appearance. An S-shaped curve of this type is sometimes called 'sigmoid,' which means, translated, 'S-shaped.'

If the scores are not converted to z-scores before being plotted, the curve will still be sigmoid, but its relative steepness will depend upon the size of the standard deviation. The smaller the standard deviation, the steeper will be the curve, and vice versa. Two cumulative normal curves with different standard deviations are plotted in Figures 6.14 and 6.15.

The fact that the cumulative percentage form of the normal curve is completely determined, or predictable, permits the use of normal

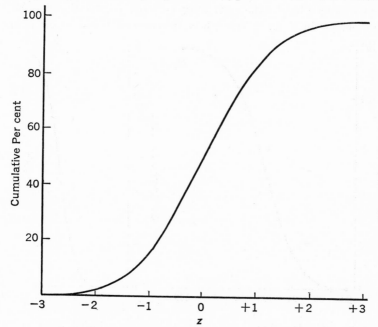

Fig. 6.13 Cumulative normal curve in standard form.

curve graph paper, or **normal-probability paper.** You will notice that at the bottom of the S in Figure 6.13 a fairly large change on the x-axis results in a fairly small change on the y-axis. The same thing is true at the top of the S. Near the middle, small changes in x result in fairly large changes in y. Now suppose we think of the paper on which this graph is plotted as being like an old-fashioned girdle— one-way stretch. Suppose the paper can be pulled and stretched so that the y-axis can be lengthened without changing the x-axis. Imagine, now, that the paper is stretched out near the top and bottom of the curve, but is squeezed together near the middle. Before this stretching process, a large change in x at one end of the curve resulted in only a small change in y. But now the y-axis is stretched in that part of the curve, so that a small change in per cent nevertheless looks pretty big on paper. On the other hand, near the center, where a small change in x formerly resulted in a large change in y, the paper has been squashed together, so that what was once a large change now looks pretty small. You can see that if we squeezed and stretched in just the right way, we could arrange things so that any change in x, no matter where it occurred, would result in the

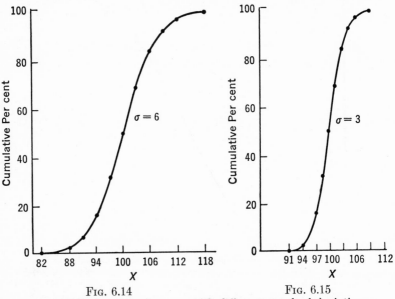

FIG. 6.14   FIG. 6.15

Two cumulative normal curves with different standard deviations.

same change in y. In other words, the curve that was previously sigmoid would now appear as a straight line. Normal-probability paper is paper whose y-axis has been pushed around in exactly this way, and any normal distribution, plotted on normal-probability paper, will appear as a straight line.

One of the most important uses of this paper is to help us decide whether an obtained distribution is really normal. To use it in this way, we proceed in exactly the same way as when we are going to plot an ordinary cumulative percentage curve. For each class interval we determine the frequency and then the cumulative frequency. The cumulative frequencies are then divided by N to give the per cent of cases lying below the upper real limit of that interval. Now results are plotted on normal-probability paper. The point for 100 per cent always has to be omitted from the plot, and sometimes a few other points near 0 per cent or 100 per cent have to be omitted too, because the paper extends only from .01 per cent to 99.99 per cent. That is because a theoretical normal distribution extends from minus infinity at the low end to plus infinity at the high end, while, we need hardly say, an obtained distribution never does.

INCHES	NUMBER OF BOYS	CUM. FREQ.	CUM. PER CENT
73	1	359	100.0
72	1	358	99.9
71	3	357	99.2
70	11	354	98.6
69	14	343	95.6
68	17	329	91.8
67	47	312	87.0
66	53	265	73.9
65	50	212	58.9
64	44	162	45.1
63	41	118	32.9
62	26	77	21.5
61	19	51	14.2
60	11	32	8.9
59	13	21	5.7
58	4	8	2.2
57	2	4	1.2
56	2	2	0.6

359

Usually a glance at the plot is enough to tell us whether the distribution is essentially normal or not. The points are usually either clearly fitted or clearly not fitted by a straight line. If they are well fitted, normal curve statistics are appropriate even though the obtained distribution may be slightly irregular. If the points do not lie along a straight line, normal curve statistics are not properly applied to the data no matter how convenient it would be if they could be. The use of a visual criterion such as this may seem like a rather loose and casual approach to a mathematical problem. Actually, there are rigorous statistical tests which enable us to make an unequivocal decision about a distribution's normality or non-normality, but a discussion of them is postponed until we study inferential statistics.

In Figure 6.16 the following set of data is plotted as a histogram. In Figure 6.17 the same data are plotted on normal-probability paper. The data represent the heights of 359 sixteen-year-old Boston schoolboys. They were collected (the data, that is) in 1877.[4]

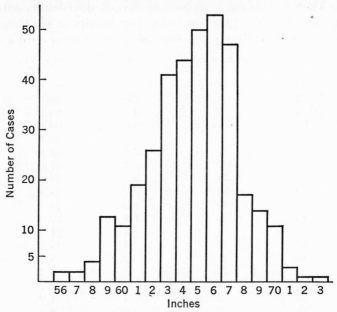

FIG. 6.16   Histogram showing the distribution of heights of 359 sixteen-year-old Boston schoolboys.

From Figure 6.17 it can be seen that the fit of the points to a straight line is good but not excellent. The points tend to lie above the line at the ends and below it in the middle, suggesting that there were more extremely tall and extremely short boys, in relation to the total group, than would be predicted if the distribution were truly normal. With a fit as good as this it is usually safe to use normal curve statistics, though if the concavity occurred repeatedly with the same kind of data one would certainly like to know the reason why.

[4] Walker, Helen M., *Studies in the History of Statistical Method*, Baltimore, Williams and Wilkins, 1929, p. 99. Data from Bowditch.

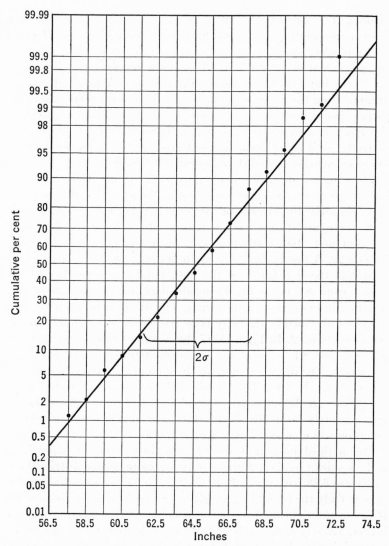

Fɪɢ. 6.17   Same data as in figure 6.16 plotted on normal-probability paper.

A second important use of normal-probability paper is to obtain a quick approximation of the mean and standard deviation of a set of data. The mean is the 50 per cent point (remember that in a normal distribution the mean and median are identical). To find it graphically, all we have to do is locate the 50 per cent point on the y-axis and observe where a horizontal line drawn at this point intersects the line fitted to the data points. A perpendicular is dropped from the intersection to the x-axis, and the point where the perpendicular intersects the x-axis is the mean. From Figure 6.17 the mean is seen to be 64.5 inches. The data do not fit the line perfectly, so it is not surprising to learn that the mean obtained by direct calculation is slightly different—64.6 inches.

The standard deviation is obtained from the graph by using our knowledge of normal curve proportions. We have already seen that approximately 16 per cent of the cases in a normal distribution lie below -1σ, and 16 per cent lie above $+1\sigma$. The range between 16 per cent and $(100 - 16)$ per cent, or 84 per cent, will therefore include 2σ. A line is drawn from 16 per cent on the y-axis until it intersects the line fitted to the data points, and another line is drawn from 84 per cent. Perpendiculars are dropped from the resulting intersections to the x-axis. The distance between the two X values obtained in this way is 2σ. To obtain σ, we simply divide the distance by 2. In Figure 6.17 the X values corresponding to 16 per cent and 84 per cent are approximately 61.6″ and 67.6″ respectively. The distance between these points is 6.0 units, and half this distance is 3.0″. The standard deviation obtained by direct numerical calculation is 2.9″—which suggests that, if the data are approximately normally distributed, the quick graphical determination will give amazingly precise results.

Still a third important use of normal-curve graph paper is to make a quick visual comparison of two or more normal distributions. In Figure 6.18, two normal distributions have been plotted on this paper. (Only the fitted lines are given.) Since the line for distribution B lies to the right of the line for distribution A, its mean must be higher. Exactly how much higher can, if desired, be calculated by determining the horizontal distance between the lines at the 50 per cent point on the y-axis. Even more important than our ability to compare the means of these distributions, however, is our ability to compare their standard deviations. For just as with a plain cumulative percentage curve, the slope of the line—its steepness—is inversely proportional to the size of the standard deviation. The

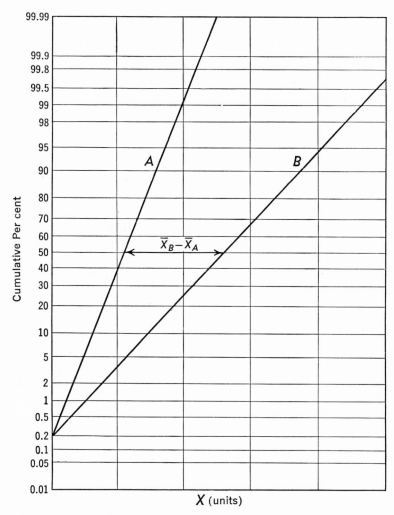

FIG. 6.18 Two distributions plotted on normal-probability paper. The mean of distribution B is higher than that of distribution A. The slope of line A is 2, that of line B, 1, indicating that the standard deviation of distribution B is double that of A.

steeper the line, the higher its slope and the lower its standard deviation. The slope of line A in Figure 6.18 is 2—that is, $67\frac{1}{2}°$ to the x-axis—while the slope of line B is only 1—45° to the x-axis. The slope of line A (the tangent of the angle made by line A with the x-axis) is twice the slope of line B, and we can therefore conclude that the standard deviation of distribution A is only half the standard deviation of distribution B. There are many occasions where actual numerical values of statistics are not important, while relations between those values are. The use of normal-probability paper is especially indicated in such circumstances.

6.2.5 When To Expect a Normal Distribution and When Not To: It used to be thought that normal distributions were everywhere. As a matter of fact, the normal curve does have an amazing ubiquity, with many many variables of different kinds being normally distributed. Anthropometric data, such as measurements of height, weight, chest expansion, length of leg, and so on, are usually normally distributed if they are collected from large groups of the same age and sex. Measures of performance, such as strength of grip or batting averages, tend to be normally distributed. Some social and economic variables, such as birth, death, and marriage rates obtained from large samples under uniform conditions, are distributed in this way. So are errors of measurement. That is, if many measurements are made of a single object, many different results will be obtained (assuming that the measuring instrument is not infinitely fine). We try to measure a table with a ruler. On repeated attempts we find that our measurements range from, let us say, $35\frac{3}{4}''$ to $36\frac{1}{4}''$. Within this range they will probably be normally distributed. The fact that errors of measurement are normally distributed seemed very important to the men who did the early work on the normal curve, and some of them went so far as to refer to it as 'the normal law of error.' Sometimes a normal distribution is called a **Gaussian distribution** after the German scientist, Gauss, who studied its characteristics and made great use of it.

We have already seen that a normal distribution is a good approximation to a binomial distribution provided n is large and neither P nor Q is too small. It is not easy, however, to generalize about the conditions that will lead to the normal distribution of a variable. It is much easier to describe the conditions that will *not* lead to one.

1. When the probability of one kind of outcome is higher than the probability of the other kind, and n is small, the distribution is more likely to be skewed than normal. For example, if a true-false test is given to a group of college students, it is usually the case that any particular question is more likely to be answered right than wrong. For a relatively short test, then, the distribution of 'total number of questions answered correctly' will probably be asymmetrical.

2. When the probability of one of the outcomes is very low, the distribution resulting will not be normal even when n is very large. For example, the distribution of number of deaths per year per Prussian Army Corps which resulted from the kick of a mule will never be normal no matter how many corps we study or how large each one is. This is the classic example of another kind of theoretical distribution, the **Poisson distribution.**

3. When an upper or lower limit is imposed upon the distribution it will not be normal. Reaction times are not normally distributed because there is a physiological limit below which a reaction time cannot go. Reading speeds in a remedial-reading class will not be normally distributed because the upper end of the distribution has been chopped off.

4. If a selective factor is operating, the curve may not be normal. The effects of a selective factor are similar to the effects of imposing an upper or lower limit, except that they happen gradually rather than all at once. Thus, the distribution of some measure of academic performance is likely to be less normal among college seniors than among freshmen, since there is a tendency for those with the poorest performance to fall by the wayside over the years.

5. If results from several subgroups that do not belong together are grouped into one distribution, the resulting curve is likely to be multimodal or flat rather than normal.

Questions

1. If a normal distribution has a mean of 321 and a standard deviation of 16, what is:

    a. The mode
    b. The median
    c. The uncertainty (H)

    d. The interquartile range

    e. Q

    f. the average deviation

    g. The distance between the 10th and 90th percentiles

2. Plot the data from problem 13 p. 176 as a cumulative percentage curve, on regular graph paper and also on normal-probability paper. If the distribution appears normal, estimate the mean and standard deviation from the plot and compare them with the results you got by direct computation.

3. With the help of Table C, make yourself a piece of normal-probability paper. On the y-axis label the following points:

1%, 2%, 5%, 10%, 15%, 20%, 30%, 40%, 50%, 60%, 70%, 80%, 85%, 90%, 95%, 98%, and 99%

This problem will take some thought, but if your work it out you will really understand normal-probability paper.

3. On normal-probability paper draw the lines of three normal distributions: one with a mean of 50 and a standard deviation of 10; one with mean of 50 and standard deviation of 5, and one with mean of 60 and standard deviation of 5.

4. Plot the three distributions below as histograms. Which ones, if any, do you think are normal? Check your hypotheses by plotting the cumulative percentage curves on normal-probability paper.

	DISTRIBUTION		
	A	B	C
X	f	f	f
200–209	2	1	4
190–199	20	3	16
180–189	31	8	21
170–179	41	21	25
160–169	35	43	26
150–159	26	54	29
140–149	18	40	23
130–139	12	19	20
120–129	6	9	16
110–119	8	1	16
100–109	1	1	4
	200	200	200

5. Which of the following variables would *not* be normally distributed? For each variable you think would not be normally distributed, give an explanation of the reason(s), or draw a sketch to show what you would expect.

   a. The typing speeds of 50 government stenographers.
   b. The percentages of brown-eyed children born in each of 100 hospitals in one year.
   c. The scores on a psychology test made by 100 graduate students in psychology.
   d. The heights of 150 trees of many different species.
   e. The weights of 500 college students, half men and half women.
   f. The income taxes of 1000 randomly selected U.S. citizens.
   g. The weights of 50 adult male albino rats.
   h. The percentages of students 'flunked out' each year by U.S. colleges.
   i. The ages of children in one elementary school.

6.3 Normal Curve Scaling, or How To Make a Silk Purse from a Sow's Ear

Statistically speaking, an ordinal scale is a sow's ear. It is an unattractive sort of thing and, compared to interval and ratio scales, relatively useless. Many a researcher has been stymied by the fact that he needed interval-scale statistics but could not use them because he had only an ordinal scale to work with. The registrar who averages letter grades is not stymied—he or she (and others of that ilk) is simply wrong, and the results of such averaging are, mathematically speaking, even less valuable than the most battered of sow's ears.

It would be nice if there were some way of converting ordinal scales into interval scales even when all the operations listed in Chapter 2 cannot be carried out. If we are willing to make some assumptions about the distribution of the trait or variable underlying the ordinal scale, we can accomplish that end. The usual assumption is that the variable is distributed normally.

Consider the distribution of job ratings plotted in Figures 4.1 and 4.2. We pointed out in connection with these data that the horizontal distances between the points are mathematically meaningless and can be manipulated at will. In Figure 4.3 (p. 108) the same points are replotted in such a way as to make a more symmetrical figure. This is the general principle involved in transforming ordinal scales to interval ones.

Once again, think of the paper on which the data are originally plotted as 'one-way stretch,' but this time it is the x-axis which is to have the stretchable nature. The areas under the normal curve are then used as the basis for stretching and squeezing the axis. The median of the distribution is placed at the center of the graph and is given a numerical value of zero. Remember, now, that between the mean (or median) of a normal distribution and a point one standard deviation away is included 34.13 per cent of the cases. Below a score of $+1\sigma$ lie 84.13 per cent of the cases. Therefore, in transforming the ordinal data, the 84.13rd percentile is found—i.e. the point below which lie 84.13 per cent of the cases in the distribution. It is assigned a value of $+1.00$. The point above which lie 84.13 per cent of the cases is assigned a value of -1.00. From tables of the normal curve it can be determined that 97.72 per cent of the cases lie below $+2\sigma$. The 97.72th percentile is therefore called $+2.0$, and the point above which lie 97.72 per cent of the cases is called -2.0. And so on for intermediate and for more extreme values.

The *unit* of the newly formed interval scale is the standard deviation of the normal distribution which is assumed to underlie the variable being measured. Once this unit has been established, it may be treated like any other unit of measurement. The scale is only interval, not ratio, because zero has been arbitrarily set at the median of the obtained distribution.

In what sense is one standard deviation unit equal to another? Certainly not in the sense that the standard criteria of equality (see p. 59) have been met, for there is no direct way to test these criteria. But *if* the assumption of a normal distribution of the variable is justified, then units along the baseline *must* be equal to yield the specified normal curve proportions. Equality is established by an indirect, but nevertheless logically watertight method.

This technique is called **normalizing,** and the newly assigned scores are called **normalized scores.** The method is just about as good as the assumption underlying it. If the assumption that the underlying variable is normally distributed is a sound one, the method will work very well and give extremely useful results. Unfortunately, there is no way to test the assumption, since, to test it, we should need to be able to measure the variable on an interval scale. If we could do that, we shouldn't need the method. To quote Stevens:

> In psychometrics the need for equal units is distressingly acute, because the paraphernalia of metric statistics (means, standard deviations, coefficients of correlation, etc.) seem to be essential tools of the trade. The assessor of human abilities is usually knee deep in statistical problems to which most statistics do not apply unless his units can be equalized. Out of this quandary he hoists himself by an act of faith in the 'normal distribution' of nature's errors. If this faith is firmly founded—if in truth it is legitimate to use the distribution of scores as a criterion for the sizes of units—then the equalization of units is possible. It is certainly not unreasonable to believe that this faith is often justified. What haunts us is the difficulty of knowing when it isn't.[5]

There is one practical problem in using the technique that deserves special mention. Not only must the underlying variable be assumed to be normally distributed, but it must be assumed to be normally distributed in the *particular group from which the data have been obtained*. If intelligence is normally distributed in the world's population, it is *not* normally distributed in that portion of the population which is not incarcerated in schools for the feeble-minded. If job ability is normally distributed in the general population, it is not so distributed in the employed population. And so on. Not only must the assumption of a normal distribution of the variable be valid in general, but it must be valid for the particular group under study. Otherwise we work with only a part of the normal distribution, but stretch and distort it until it looks like the whole distribution.

The common use of normalized scores leads to some fascinating philosophical problems. You will sometimes see the statement (though not often in psychology books) that 'intelligence is normally distributed.' This statement can mean either of two things: it can mean that there is a thing, intelligence, which we *assume* to be normally distributed in spite of the impossibility of testing the assumption; or it can mean that intelligence-test scores are normally distributed. If it means the first, it is a speculative, rather than a

[5] Stevens, S. S., 'Mathematics, Measurement, and Psychophysics,' Chap. I in *Handbook of Experimental Psychology* (S. S. Stevens, ed.), New York, Wiley, 1951, p. 39.

factual, statement. If it means the second, it is merely a statement of the fact that psychometricians, in developing intelligence tests, have used some rather fancy statistical techniques to make the scores distribute themselves normally. As it is generally made, the statement that intelligence (or scholastic aptitude, or will power, or any other such variable) is normally distributed is hardly worth the ink used to print it.

Questions

1. The author of a popular psychology book advances the following argument:

In a financial way, society does not treat its members fairly. For we know that intelligence is normally distributed, while the distribution of incomes in the general population is anything but normal. The figure below shows the two distributions. Thus it must be that many members of the population are not paid in accordance with their intelligence.

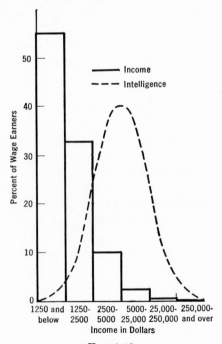

FIG. 6.19

Analyze this author's argument thoroughly. Pay particular attention to the way his graphs are drawn. The argument contains at least three major fallacies. See how many you can find.

2. In the light of all that you know about the normal distribution, discuss the pros and cons of assigning letter grades 'on the curve' in college classes.

6.4 Skewness and Kurtosis

We have referred frequently in foregoing pages to distributions that were symmetrical or asymmetrical, and have also introduced the term **skewness** in a general way. A distribution that is symmetrical is one in which the half above the mean is identical with the half below the mean in size and shape. If you folded the distribution in the middle, the two halves would match perfectly. Figure 5.9, parts a–e, (p. 163) gives five different examples of symmetrical distributions. A distribution that is symmetrical is not skewed. It is said to have zero skewness.

On the other hand, an asymmetrical distribution is a skewed distribution. *If the long tail is on the right* or upper end, *the distribution is* said to be **positively skewed;** *if the long tail is on the left,* or lower end, *the distribution is* **negatively skewed.** Some distributions of different kinds and directions of skweness are shown in Figure 6.20.

There are many ways of measuring the degree of skewness of an obtained distribution, none of which is particularly useful. In practice, one often says, 'the distribution has a high degree of positive skewness,' or 'the distribution is slightly skewed in the negative direction,' but there are only a few very specialized situations where a quantitative estimate of skewness is desirable. Should you ever encounter one of these, you can find the necessary techniques described in an advanced statistics text.

The term **kurtosis** refers to the flatness or peakedness of a curve, relative to the size of the standard deviation. Figure 6.21 shows three curves, one of which has most of its cases bunched in the center, making a high peak, but also has a few cases of rather extreme value. The second curve is a normal curve, while the third one has many cases near the extremes and relatively few in the central portion. These three kinds of curves are called, respectively, **leptokurtic** (tall and thin), **mesokurtic** (medium), and **platykurtic**

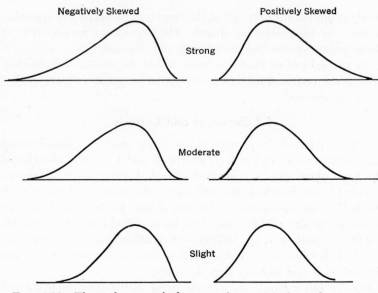

FIG. 6.20 Three degrees of skewness for positively and negatively skewed distributions.

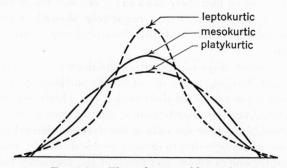

FIG. 6.21   Three degrees of kurtosis.

(flat). Walker reports that: '"Student" [the pseudonym of a very famous British statistician] once suggested that platykurtic curves, like the platypus, are squat with short tails, while leptokurtic curves are high with long tails like the kangaroo which "leps."'[6]

After you have studied Figure 6.21, take a look at Figure 6.22,

[6] Walker, Helen M., *Elementary Statistical Methods*, New York, Holt, 1943, p. 159.

which shows three mesokurtic curves with different standard deviations. By comparing these two figures, you will be able to distinguish between a normal curve with a large standard deviation and a platykurtic curve, between a normal curve with a small standard deviation and a leptokurtic curve.

There are formulas that enable us to compute the exact degree of kurtosis in a distribution, but the occasions demanding their use

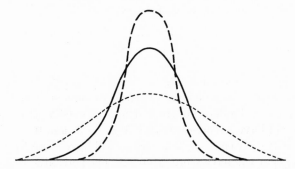

FIG. 6.22   Three mesokurtic curves with different standard deviations.

are rare indeed. Suffice it to say that the kurtosis of a normal distribution, computed by these formulas, is 3. A lower figure indicates a platykurtic curve, and a higher figure a curve that is leptokurtic.

6.5 Measures of the Relative Position of an Individual

In addition to the ranks and percentile ranks which were available to us to describe the position of an individual even when the data come from an ordinal scale, several new measures are now at hand. The choice among them depends largely upon the form of the distribution of scores.

1. *If the obtained distribution of scores is approximately normal* (and a rather wide latitude is permitted here) an individual's position can be conveniently specified by some form of standard score. By 'standard score,' we mean a score that is expressed in units of the standard deviation.

The most fundamental form of standard score is the z-score, which we have already defined.

$$z = \frac{x}{s} \quad \text{or} \quad \frac{(X - \overline{X})}{s}$$

(Since we are now dealing with an obtained rather than a theoretical distribution, we use the symbols $\overline{X}$ and s rather than μ and σ.) A z-score tells us how many standard deviations a given point is above or below the mean. If the mean of a distribution is 69 and the standard deviation is 12, what z-score shall be assigned to an individual who obtained a score of 63 on the test?

$$z = \frac{(63 - 69)}{12} = -.5$$

The individual's z-score is $-.5$.

Table C enables us to convert z-scores to percentile ranks. From that table it can be determined that approximately 19 per cent of the cases will have z-scores between .5 (or $-.5$) and 0. This means that $(50 - 19)$ per cent, or 31 per cent, will have scores below this, and 69 per cent will have scores above it. The percentile rank of this individual is therefore 31.

Because decimals are a nuisance and negative values are clumsy to manipulate, variants on the z-score are sometimes used. One example is the Z-score, where

$$Z = 10z + 50 \qquad (6.5.1)$$

The mean of the distribution of z-scores is 0, and its standard deviation is 1. The mean of the distribution of Z-scores is 50, and its standard deviation is 10. An individual who is one standard deviation above the mean has a z-score of $+1$, and a Z-score of 60. The procedure of converting z-scores to Z-scores has the advantage that the latter roll more trippingly off the tongue (and onto the keyboard of a calculating machine) than numbers with minus signs in front and decimal points behind. Sometimes, if we want to make fine distinctions between individuals, we set the mean of the distribution equal to 500 and the standard deviation equal to 100. This is frequently done on college-entrance examinations and on graduate-record examinations.

Below are illustrated some raw scores which have been converted to z-scores, Z-scores, and percentile ranks on the assumption of a normal distribution of scores.

RAW SCORE, X	$\bar{X}$	s	z-SCORE	Z-SCORE	PERCENTILE RANK
49	47	8	.25	52	60
11	15	3	-1.33	37	9
105	85	10	2.00	70	98
38	38	5	0.00	50	50

Percentile ranks and standard scores are really two different kinds of language for presenting the same information. To the lay reader, percentile ranks carry more information and are more readily understood. To the mathematician or statistician, standard scores, being expressed in a familiar unit of measurement which has an important mathematical meaning, are more meaningful and usually preferable. If we are to use the measures in later calculation, standard scores are distinctly preferable.

2. *If the obtained distribution of scores is not normal, but it is assumed that the variable underlying these scores is normally distributed,* the 'silk purses' method can be used. To summarize this method briefly, each individual is assigned the standard score which *would* correspond to his percentile rank *if* the distribution were normal. Scores obtained in this way are sometimes called T-scores, or normalized scores.

T-scores can be treated like measurements on an interval scale, and they are, by their very nature, normally distributed. Both of these facts make them convenient measures to use as the basis of later calculations. Of course percentile ranks can also be used, and as before they have the advantage of being easy for the lay reader to interpret.

3. *If the obtained distribution is not normal, and it is not assumed that the variable underlying the distribution is normally distributed,* either percentile ranks or standard scores can be used. When presented with standard scores, however, the sophisticated reader tends to think of a normally distributed variable; it therefore makes sense to give him *both* percentile ranks and standard scores to serve as a continual reminder of the non-normality of the distribution.

Questions

1. Scores on a certain test are normally distributed with a mean of 68 and a standard deviation of 4. Express the following raw scores as z-scores, as Z-scores, and as percentile ranks:

$$57, 59, 60, 64, 68, 70, \text{ and } 77$$

2. Fill in the following table, assuming a normal distribution in all cases:

$\bar{X}$	X	s	z	Z	PERCENTILE RANK
100	110	10	a	b	c
.64	.70	d	2.0	e	f
g	488	8	h	35	i
180	j	40	k	l	16

3. Describe the shape of the distribution of percentile ranks. Approximately what is its mean?

4. If the raw scores are normally distributed, what is the shape of the distribution, and the mean and standard deviation of the distribution of:

    a. z-scores

    b. Z-scores

    c. T-scores

Summary

The binomial distribution is a frequency distribution giving the probability of 0, 1, 2, . . . n outcomes of one kind, out of n independent trials, when the probability of an outcome of that kind is P. The distribution is obtained by expanding the binomial $(P + Q)^n$, and is a distribution of a discrete variable. If we think of the variable as continuous and allow n to approach infinity, the distribution will become more and more like the normal distribution, provided neither P nor Q is too small. Any normal distribution is completely described by its three parameters, the mean, the standard deviation, and N. Tables of areas under the normal curve between the mean, and points so-many standard deviations away from the mean, permit many useful manipulations of scores from normally distributed variables.

The cumulative percentage form of the normal distribution yields a straight line when plotted on normal-probability paper. This fact permits a visual test of the normality of a distribution, a quick estimate of the mean and standard deviation of a normal distribution, and a comparison of these parameters for two or more distributions.

Ordinal scales can be converted to interval scales, with the standard deviation of the distribution as the unit of measurement, if we are willing to assume that the variable underlying the ordinal scale is distributed normally. The method is as valid as the assumption.

An asymmetrical distribution is called 'skewed,' and the direction of skewness—positive or negative—specifies the direction of the long tail. The flatness or peakedness of a distribution is called its kurtosis.

When measurements are made on interval or ratio scales, the position of an individual relative to his fellows can be specified by a percentile rank, a standard score, or a normalized score, depending on the normality or non-normality of the obtained distribution or of the variable assumed to underlie the distribution.

References

1. Guilford, J. P., *Psychometric Methods*, New York, McGraw-Hill, 1936. Extensive treatment of the principle of normal curve scaling, both in mental testing and in psychophysics.
2. Walker, Helen M., *Studies in the History of Statistical Method*, Baltimore, Williams and Wilkins, 1929, Ch. II. A scholarly survey of the history of the discovery and use of the normal distribution.

Different textbooks print normal curve tables in a variety of forms. A particularly useful one can be found in:
3. Guilford, J. P., *Fundamental Statistics is Psychology and Education*, New York, McGraw-Hill, 1950, pp. 602–608.

For further reading on probability, the binomial, and theoretical frequency distributions, see references following Ch. 10, p. 353.

Answers

Page 185

1. 16.

2. 36.

3. 10^4 or 10,000. $\dfrac{1}{10,000}$ or .0001.

4. (a) $\frac{1}{32}$; (b) $\frac{1}{32}$; (c) $\frac{1}{32}$.

5. 15.

6. 28.

7. $\dfrac{52!}{13!39!}$ or 635, 013, 535, 000.

8. $\dfrac{52!}{5!47!}$ or 2, 598, 960.

9. $\frac{3}{8}$.

10. $\frac{1}{16}, \frac{1}{4}, \frac{3}{8}, \frac{1}{4}, \frac{1}{16}$.

11. $\frac{1}{32}, \frac{5}{32}, \frac{10}{32}, \frac{10}{32}, \frac{5}{32}, \frac{1}{32}$.

12. $\frac{1}{2}, \frac{7}{8}$.

13. $\dfrac{1}{2^{20}}, 1 - \left(\dfrac{1}{2^{20}}\right)$.

Page 190

1. $P^4 + 4P^3Q + 6P^2Q^2 + 4PQ^3 + Q^4.$
2. $P^6 + 6P^5Q + 15P^4Q^2 + 20P^3Q^3 + 15P^2Q^4 + 6PQ^5 + Q^6.$
3. $P^8 + 8P^7Q + 28P^6Q^2 + 56P^5Q^3 + 70P^4Q^4 + 56P^3Q^5 + 28P^2Q^6 + 8PQ^7 + Q^8.$
4. (a) 3rd, $\frac{7}{64}$; (b) 3rd, $\frac{7}{46,656}$.   6. $(\frac{5}{6})^{15}$, $1 - (\frac{5}{6})^{15}$.   7. $\frac{85}{648}$.
8. (a) 10, 40, 60, 40, 10; (b) 2; (c) 1.   10. Non-independence.
11. (a) $12(\frac{1}{3})^{11}(\frac{2}{3})$; (b) $12(\frac{2}{3})^{11}(\frac{1}{3})$; (c) 4; (d) 14080/59049; (e) 1.

Page 194

1. 0, +1, −1, −.5, +.5, +.15, +1.25.
2. (a) +1; (b) 1050; (c) 40; (d) 4; (e) −2.9.
3. (a) .3413; (b) .3413; (c) .5000; (d) .5000; (e) .6826; (f) .1587; (g) .1587; (h) .8413; (i) .8413.

Page 198

1. .3413, .4772, .4987, .4962, .4258, .2140, .4500, .4750.
2. .3413, .4772, .4332, .2019, .4649, more than .4990, .2019.
3. .1915, .1915, .4849, .4332, .4977.
4. (a) .0250; (b) .4833; (c) .9616; (d) .1711; (e) .0228; (f) .6826; (g) .5801; (h) .1498; (i) .2417; (j) .3830.
5. (a) 114; (b) 196; (c) 51; (d) 33; (e) 30; (f) 30; (g) 93.
6. (a) +1.00; (b) ±1.96; (c) +1.00; (d) −1.645; (e) 1.96.
7. A: 63.6, B: 60.4, C: 53.6, D: 50.4.

Page 201

1. .1974.   4. .8485.   8. .0078.
2. .1587.   6. .1020.   9. .0401, .9953.

(Assumptions are involved in some of these answers.)

Page 213

1. (a) 321; (b) 321; (c) 5.31; (d) 21.58; (e) 10.79; (f) 12.77; (g) 41.02.

Page 223

1. −2.75, 22.5, 0.30; −2.25, 27.5, 1; −2.0, 30, 2; −1.00, 40, 16; 0, 50, 50; +.5, 55, 69; +2.25, 77.5, 99.
2. (a) +1.00; (b) 60; (c) 84; (d) +.03; (e) 70; (f) 98; (g) 500; (h) −1.5; (i) 7; (j) 140; (k) −1.00; (l) 40.
3. rectangular, 50.
4. (a) normal, 0, 1; (b) normal, 50, 10; (c) normal, 50, 10.

INTERVAL AND RATIO SCALES, III

Measures of Correlation

Correlation means the reduction of unpredictability. If two things are related, then knowing about one of them will help us to make better predictions about the other. Better predictions are predictions with less uncertainty, whether uncertainty means $\hat{H}$, Q, range, AD, s^2, or s. We have reason to believe, for example, that age and school grade are related. This means that knowing Johnny Jones's school grade will help us to predict, or guess, his age. If we do not know Johnny's grade, our best guess about his age is the mean age of all school children, and the badness of our guess can be described by the standard deviation of the ages of all school children. If we know that Johnny is in the second grade, our best guess about his age is the mean age of second graders, and the badness of our guess is described by the standard deviation of the ages of second graders. Since second graders are more alike in age than children of all grades together, the standard deviation of second graders' ages will be less than the standard deviation of the ages of all children. By knowing Johnny's grade, we have reduced the unpredictability of his age. Age and school grade are therefore said to be **correlated.** All measures of correlation are basically measures of the extent to which knowledge of one variable reduces the unpredictability of another.

The first measure of correlation that we encountered was $\hat{T}$, whose very name, 'uncertainty reduction,' described exactly what it was. $\hat{T}$ is designed for use with data from nominal scales, so our measure of unpredictability was, of necessity, $\hat{H}$.

$$\hat{T} = \hat{H}(y) - \hat{H}_x(y)$$

where $\hat{H}(y)$ means 'the original uncertainty of the variable to be predicted, y' and $\hat{H}_x(y)$ means 'the average uncertainty of the y

variable for different subgroups of the x variable.' We might, for the sake of brevity, refer to $\hat{H}(y)$ as 'total uncertainty' and to $\hat{H}_x(y)$ as 'within-groups uncertainty.'

Sometimes we wish to express the amount by which uncertainty was reduced as a proportion of the amount by which it could have been reduced.[1] One way to do this is to compare the uncertainty reduction with the original uncertainty:

$$\frac{\hat{T}}{\hat{H}(y)}, \quad \text{or} \quad \frac{\hat{H}(y) - \hat{H}_x(y)}{\hat{H}(y)} \quad \text{or} \quad 1 - \frac{\hat{H}_x(y)}{\hat{H}(y)}$$

These three expressions are identical, as a few minutes with pencil and paper should convince you. They all mean 'the ratio of actual to possible uncertainty reduction.'

We have seen that $\hat{H}$ is not a good measure of unpredictability for data from ordinal, interval, or ratio scales. In general, the best measure of unpredictability for interval and ratio scales is the variance or the standard deviation. And our new measures of correlation are going to be practically identical with relative $\hat{T}$ except that the word 'variance' should be substituted for the word 'uncertainty,' the symbol s^2 for the symbol $\hat{H}$. The most basic of these measures, E^2, is:

$$E^2 = 1 - \frac{\text{within-group variance}}{\text{total variance}} = 1 - \frac{s_w^2}{s_y^2}$$

where s_w^2 stands for 'within-group variance' and s_y^2 for total variance of the y variable. Compare that with the expression above, where the ratio of actual to possible uncertainty reduction was shown to be

$$1 - \frac{\text{within-groups uncertainty}}{\text{total uncertainty}}$$

The two measures of correlation are identical except for the substitution of the word 'variance' for the word 'uncertainty.'

---

[1] See pp. 96ff. for a fuller discussion of the comparison of actual and possible uncertainty reduction.

7.1 E, the Correlation Ratio[2]

The most basic measure of correlation for interval or ratio scale data is E^2, the square of the correlation ratio. One formula for E^2 is

$$E^2 = \frac{1 - \text{within groups variance}}{\text{total variance}} = 1 - \frac{s_w^2}{s_y^2} \qquad (7.1.1)$$

(E^2 is easier to interpret than E, and we shall ordinarily talk about it rather than its square root.) Let us start with a numerical example.

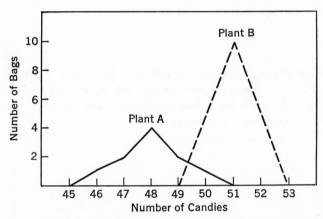

FIG. 7.1 Frequency polygons showing the number of bags containing each number of candies. Plants A and B are considered as two separate groups.

7.1.1 A Numerical Example: Two plants package Icky-Licky Gum Drops. Fifty candies are supposed to be placed in each Icky-Licky bag, but complaints from customers have led to an investigation of the counting and packaging accuracy of the plants. Thirty Icky-Licky bags are examined. The mean number of candies per bag turns out to be 50, as it should be, but the variance is $\frac{82}{30}$, which suggests to the supervisor that there is more variability from bag to bag than there ought to be. He then begins to wonder if there is any relationship between the number of candies per bag and the plant at which the bag was filled. He sorts out the 30 bags into two

[2] The symbol η (eta) is ordinarily used for the correlation ratio, but to be consistent we are using E to indicate that we are talking about a measure actually obtained from a sample.

groups, one for each of the plants. It turns out that 10 of the bags were filled at Plant A and 20 at Plant B. Here are the results:

NO. OF CANDIES	PLANT A (f)	PLANT B (f)	TOTAL
52		5	5
51		10	10
50	1	5	6
49	2		2
48	4		4
47	2		2
46	1		1
	10	20	30

Figure 7.1 shows the frequency polygons for Plants A and B, and Figure 7.2 shows the frequency polygon for the whole set of 30 bags. From these data it is immediately apparent that there is a relationship between the plant packaging the bag and the number of candies.

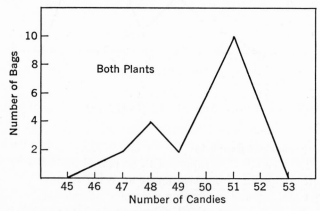

FIG. 7.2   Frequency polygon showing the number of bags containing each number of candies when bags from Plants *A* and *B* are considered as one group. Note that the spread for the total group is much wider than the spread for either of the plants considered singly.

Plant B is overgenerous, while the workers of Plant A appear to have sweet teeth and little self-control. The mean number of candies per bag is 48 for Plant A and 51 for Plant B.

To measure the strength of the relationship between plant and

number of candies, we must determine the within-groups variance.
By within-groups variance we mean the average of the subgroup
variances. For Plant A:

X	$(X - \overline{X}) = x$	x^2	f	fx^2	
50	+2	4	1	4	
49	+1	1	2	2	$s^2 = \dfrac{\Sigma fx^2}{N}$
48	0	0	4	0	
47	−1	1	2	2	$s^2 = \dfrac{12}{10} = 1.20$
46	−2	4	1	4	
			10	12	

Plant A's variance is 1.20. For Plant B:

X	x	x^2	f	fx^2	
52	+1	1	5	5	
51	0	0	10	0	$s^2 = \dfrac{10}{20} = .50$
50	−1	1	5	5	
			20	10	

Plant B's variance is .50. Now we want to find the average of these
two subgroup variances, but in doing so, we want to take into
account the fact that 20 bags came from Plant B and only 10 from
Plant A. We do it this way:

$$\text{Within-groups variance} = s_w^2 = \frac{(10 \times 1.20) + (20 \times .50)}{30} = \frac{22}{30}$$

By 'within-groups variance' we mean the weighted average of the
subgroup variances, just as by 'within-groups uncertainty' we mean
the weighted average of the subgroup uncertainties. Now we are
ready to compute E^2 from formula 7.1.1.

$$E^2 = 1 - \frac{s_w^2}{s_y^2}$$

$$E^2 = 1 - \frac{\frac{22}{30}}{\frac{82}{30}} = 1 - \frac{22}{82} = .74$$

What that number means is that we have reduced the unpredictability 74 per cent, by using our knowledge of the plant at which the
bag was packaged. Unpredictability in this case means specifically
'variance.' Another way of saying the same thing is that the average

variance of the subgroups is only 26 per cent as big as the variance of the total group.

Question

In a certain college, the ages of the students in the four classes are as given in the table below:

CLASS

Age	Freshman	Sophomore	Junior	Senior	Total
22			5	50	55
21		18	55	40	113
20	5	65	50	30	150
19	70	60	40	5	175
18	75	30			105
17	48	7			55
16	2				2
Total	200	180	150	125	655

a. On one graph draw the four frequency polygons showing the ages of the four different classes. Draw a separate frequency polygon showing the distribution of ages in the college as a whole.

b. Use $\hat{T}$ to measure the strength of relationship between class and age and interpret your result.

c. Use E^2 to measure the strength of relationship between class and age and interpret your result.

d. Explain why E^2 is a better measure than $\hat{T}$ for these data.

e. What would be your best guess about the age of a student if you did not know his class? If you knew that he was a freshman? A sophomore? A junior? A senior? About which guess would you feel least uncertain? Explain.

f. Plot a graph with 'year in college' on the x-axis and 'mean age' on the y-axis. Save the results. We shall use them as a basis for discussion later in this chapter.

7.1.2 Partitioning the Variance (or Sum of Squares): At this point we interrupt our discussion of the correlation ratio to bring you an important announcement from our sponsor. This announcement concerns one of the most important theorems in statistics, and not only will an understanding of it help you to know what you are doing—it will also save you a lot of work. The theorem says this:

If a group is composed of two or more subgroups, the variance of the total group is made up of two parts. One of these parts comes from the variance of each subgroup about its own mean; the othe part comes from the differences between the means of the subgroups and the mean of the combined group.

Suppose we have a total group that can be broken down into two subgroups, as in the Icky-Licky example, where the original 30 bags of candy can be subdivided into those packaged at Plant A and those packaged at Plant B. We now define some terms:
N_a = no. of cases in subgroup a; N_b = no. of cases in subgroup b; and N_t = no. of cases in total group.

$$N_t = N_a + N_b$$

s_a^2 and s_b^2 = variances of subgroups a and b; s_y^2 = variance of total group. $\overline{Y}_a$ and $\overline{Y}_b$ = means of subgroups a and b; $\overline{Y}_t$ = mean of total group. $\overline{Y}_t = \dfrac{N_a\overline{Y}_a + N_b\overline{Y}_b}{N_t}$.

$$d_a = \overline{Y}_a - \overline{Y}_t, \qquad d_b = \overline{Y}_b - \overline{Y}_t.$$

Then:

$$N_t s_y^2 = N_a s_a^2 + N_b s_b^2 + N_a d_a^2 + N_b d_b^2 \qquad (7.1.2)$$

The first two terms represent the part of the total variance (or sum of squares, as it is expressed here) which comes from the variance of each subgroup about its own mean. The last two terms represent the part that comes from the differences between the means of the subgroups and the mean of the total group. We are now going to prove this theorem. Follow the algebra carefully, without skipping a step, and you will see where the theorem comes from.

$$s_y^2 = \frac{\Sigma(Y - \overline{Y}_t)^2}{N_t} \qquad \text{(definition of variance)}$$

$$N_t s_y^2 = \Sigma\,(Y - \overline{Y}_t)^2 \qquad \text{(clearing fractions)}$$

$$Y - \overline{Y}_t = (Y - \overline{Y}_a) + (\overline{Y}_a - \overline{Y}_t) \quad \text{or} \quad (Y - \overline{Y}_b) + (\overline{Y}_b - \overline{Y}_t)$$

Let

$$y_a = (Y - \overline{Y}_a) \qquad \text{and} \qquad y_b = (Y - \overline{Y}_b)$$

Let

$$d_a = (\overline{Y}_a - \overline{Y}_t) \qquad \text{and} \qquad d_b = (\overline{Y}_b - \overline{Y}_t)$$

Then:

$$(Y - \overline{Y}_t) = y_a + d_a \quad \text{or} \quad y_b + d_b \quad \text{(substitution)}$$

$$N_t s_y^2 = \sum^{N_a} (Y - \overline{Y}_t)^2 \quad \text{(from definition above)}$$

$$N_t s_y^2 = \sum_1^{N_a} (y_a + d_a)^2 + \sum_1^{N_b} (y_b + d_b)^2 \quad \text{(substitution)}$$

$$N_t s_y^2 = \sum_1^{N_a} (y_a^2 + 2y_a d_a + d_a^2) + \sum_1^{N_b} (y_b^2 + 2y_b d_b + d_b^2)$$

$$\text{(expansion)}$$

y_a and y_b are variables; d_a and d_b are constants, so when we sum:

$$N_t s_y^2 = \sum_1^{N_a} y_a^2 + 2d_a \sum_1^{N_a} y_a + N_a d_a^2 + \sum_1^{N_b} y_b^2 + 2d_b \sum_1^{N_b} y_b + N_b d_b^2$$

$$\text{(summation)}$$

But $\sum_1^{N_a} y_a$ and $\sum_1^{N_b} y_b$ equal 0. Do you remember why? So:

$$N_t s_y^2 = \sum_1^{N_a} y_a^2 + N_a d_a^2 + \sum_1^{N_b} y_b^2 + N_b d_b^2$$

And if we substitute $N_a s_a^2$ for $\sum_1^{N_a} y_a^2$, and similarly for the b group, and rearrange our terms, we have what we started out to prove:

$$N_t s_y^2 = N_a s_a^2 + N_b s_b^2 + N_a d_a^2 + N_b d_b^2$$

Let us substitute numbers from the Icky-Licky data. In that example:

$N_t = 30$	$\overline{Y}_t = 50$	$s_y^2 = \dfrac{82}{30}$	$d_a = 48 - 50 = -2$
$N_a = 10$	$\overline{Y}_a = 48$	$s_a^2 = 1.20$	$d_b = 51 - 50 = +1$
$N_b = 20$	$\overline{Y}_b = 51$	$s_b^2 = .50$	

Substituting:

$$30 \times \frac{82}{30} = [10 \times 1.20] + [20 \times .50] + [10 \times (-2)^2] + [20 \times (1)^2]$$
$$82 = 12 + 10 + 40 + 20$$
$$82 = 82$$

This theorem works for many groups as well as for the special case of two groups. If there were k groups altogether, we should write it this way:

$$N_t s_y^2 = N_a s_a^2 + N_b s_b^2 + \ldots + N_k s_k^2 + N_a d_a^2 + N_b d_b^2 + \ldots + N_k d_k^2$$
$$(7.1.3)$$

$N_a s_a^2 + N_b s_b^2 + \ldots + N_k s_k^2$ is the sum of the squares of the deviations of all the scores from the means of their own subgroups. This sum is commonly called the 'within-groups sum of squares.'

$N_a d_a^2$ is the sum of the squares of the deviation of the mean of group a from the total mean. (Sum of squares may sound strange here, where there is no summation sign, but remember that we have simply replaced Σ by N because d is a constant. We are really dealing with a sum even though we found it by multiplying instead of adding.) So

$N_a d_a^2 + N_b d_b^2 + \ldots + N_k d_k^2$ is the sum of the squares of the deviations of the subgroup means from the grand mean. It is commonly called the 'between-groups sum of squares.'

Now we can state that:

The total sum of squares is the sum of the within-groups sum of squares and the between-groups sum of squares.

If all the subgroups have the same mean, then the between-groups sum of squares will be zero, and the total sum of squares will be identical with the within-groups sum of squares. If the means of the various subgroups are quite different from each other (and hence from the grand mean), but the groups are quite homogeneous within themselves, then the between-groups sum of squares will be large compared to the within-groups sum of squares. In the next section we shall see how this partitioning of the total sum of squares can be used to provide some useful shortcuts in computing E^2. In a later chapter we shall see how this theorem provides the basis for an extremely important technique of inferential statistics, the analysis of variance.

Questions

1. Prove that $N_t s_y^2 = N_a s_a^2 + N_b s_b^2 + N_a d_a^2 + N_b d_b^2$. Of course the proof has just been worked out for you, but see if you can do it by yourself, referring to the book only when you get stuck. If you have to refer to the book often, make a second try.

2. Below are given the scores for two subgroups, A and B. Find the mean of each subgroup and the mean of the total group. Then express each $(X - \overline{X}_t)$ as the sum of two parts, $X - \overline{X}_a$ or $X - \overline{X}_b$, and $\overline{X}_a - \overline{X}_t$ or $\overline{X}_b - \overline{X}_t$. From these two parts, find directly the within-groups sum of squares, the between-groups sum of squares, and the total sum of squares. Find the total variance and the variance of each subgroup.

A	B
7	14
8	15
8	16
9	

3. Make up a numerical example in which the within-groups sum of squares is zero and the between-groups sum of squares is large.

4. Make up a numerical example in which the between-groups sum of squares is zero and the within-groups sum of squares is large.

5. Compare the examples you have given in answer to questions 3 and 4, and state a generalization about the conditions that determine the relative sizes of the within- and between-groups sums of squares.

6. In a reaction-time experiment the subject is given 25 trials a day for four days. Each day's mean and standard deviation is given below. Compute the mean and standard deviation for all 100 trials.

Day 1	Day 2	Day 3	Day 4
$\overline{X} = 250$	$\overline{X} = 245$	$\overline{X} = 243$	$\overline{X} = 244$
$s = 15$	$s = 12$	$s = 13$	$s = 12$

7. Three sections of one psychology class take a test. The mean and standard deviation, as well as number of students, is given for each section. Find the mean and standard deviation for the whole class.

SECTION	A	B	C
$\overline{X}$	500	488	501
s	100	95	101
N	50	35	25

7.1.3 Finding the Correlation Ratio from the Sums of Squares:
By using the theorem developed in the last section, and by making some other substitutions, we are now in a position to simplify the procedure for computing E^2.

First, whereas we originally defined E^2 as

$$1 - \frac{\text{within-group variance}}{\text{between-group variance}}$$

we can now make use of our knowledge of the fact that a variance is simply a sum of squares divided by N. So:

$$E^2 = 1 - \frac{\dfrac{\text{Within-groups } SS}{N_t}}{\dfrac{\text{Total } SS}{N_t}} = 1 - \frac{\text{Within-groups } SS}{\text{Total } SS} \qquad (7.1.4)$$

Second, we can make use of the fact that the total SS is the sum of the within-groups SS and the between-groups SS. $T = W + B$.

$$E^2 = 1 - \frac{W}{T} = 1 - \frac{W}{(W + B)} = \frac{B}{T}$$

$$E^2 = \frac{\text{Between-groups sum of squares}}{\text{Total sum of squares}} \qquad (7.1.5)$$

This formula is really going to save some work, because it enables us to compute E^2 without going through the intermediate step of computing the sum of squares for each subgroup. We need only compute the subgroup means and the grand mean, and from these we can easily find the between-groups sum of squares, which is, you will remember:

Between-groups sum of squares $= N_a(\overline{Y}_a - \overline{Y}_t)^2 + N_b(\overline{Y}_b - \overline{Y}_t)^2$
$$+ \ldots + N_k(\overline{Y}_k - \overline{Y}_t)^2$$

Let's try this with the Icky-Licky data. We found from those data that the total sum of squares was 82, the mean of the total group, 50, the mean of group A, 48, and the mean of group B, 51. N_a was 10 and N_b, 20. So:

Between-groups sum of squares $= 10(48 - 50)^2 + 20(51 - 50)^2$
$$= 60$$

$E^2 = \frac{60}{82} = .74$, the same answer that we previously obtained by the much longer method.

Let us sum up the technique for computing E^2 by formula 7.1.5. We start with one total group that has been divided into subgroups on the basis of some variable which we shall call 'X.' In the Icky-

Licky example, the X variable was the plant at which the candy was packaged. The members of the group (and, of course, of the subgroups) have been measured on some other variable which we will call Y. In the Icky-Licky example, the Y variable was the number of candies per bag. Then, to compute E^2,

1. Find the total sum of squares. Ordinarily, you will use the raw score formula:

$$\text{Total } SS = \Sigma Y^2 - \frac{(\Sigma Y)^2}{N_t}$$

2. Find the mean of the total group, $\overline{Y}_t$.

3. Find the mean of each subgroup, which we shall call $\overline{Y}_i$.

4. Find the difference between the mean of each subgroup and the mean of the total group, $\overline{Y}_i - \overline{Y}_t$. Call the result d_i.

5. Square each d_i.

6. Multiply each $(d_i)^2$ by the number of cases in the subgroup from which the d_i was computed. Call this number of cases N_i. What you have just found are the several $N_i(d_i)^2$s.

7. Obtain the sum of the numbers found in step 6. This is the between-groups sum of squares.

8. Divide the result of step 7 by the result of step 1. This is E^2.

9. $100E^2$ is the per cent of the total variance (or sum of squares) contributed by the between-groups variance (or sum of squares). It is the per cent by which unpredictability has been reduced by a knowledge of the X variable, when unpredictability means 'variance.'

7.1.4 The Use and Interpretation of E and E^2:

We started our discussion of correlation by talking about prediction and the improvement of prediction. Let us return now to that important topic.

Suppose we wish to predict an individual's score on some variable called Y. Our best prediction is $\overline{Y}$, and the measure of the amount of error left in our prediction is s_y^2, the variance of Y. Thus, if we know only that a package contains Icky-Licky gumdrops, our best guess about the number of gumdrops in the bag is 50, the mean, and the error of our prediction is $\frac{82}{30}$, the variance.

If we know, however, that an individual (in this case a candy bag) is a member of a particular subgroup (was packaged at a particular plant) we may be able to improve our prediction, and we certainly cannot make it worse. We predict not the grand mean but the sub-group mean, $\overline{Y}_i$. And now we measure our error in prediction not in terms of the variance of the total group but in terms of the variance of that subgroup, s_i^2. Has our prediction been improved by a knowledge of the subgroup? We can answer that question by comparing the subgroup variance, s_i^2, with the variance of the total group, s_y^2. If different subgroups have different variances, we want to get an average in order to measure the average improvement in prediction. This average subgroup variance we have called the 'within-groups variance,' s_w^2. If the within-groups variance is—let us say—one-fourth of the total variance, then we have reduced our error by three-fourths. E^2 is the statistic which tells us how much we have reduced our error in predicting Y by making use of our knowledge of X.

In the example we have been using, the Y variable was number of candies per bag, a variable that was measured on a ratio scale. If we are to use E^2 as our measure of correlation, the variable we are trying to predict must be measured on an interval or ratio scale, else we could not find a mean or a variance. But the X variable, the plant packaging the candies, was measured only on a nominal scale. E^2 can be used, then, when one variable comes from any kind of scale—nominal, ordinal, interval, or ratio—provided the variable to be predicted comes from an interval or ratio scale.

E^2 (or E) is often used when both variables come from interval or ratio scales. For example, if we were to determine the reading rates of a great many people of different ages, we might obtain results like those shown in Figure 7.3. In this graph, which is called a **scatter-plot** or **scatter diagram,** each point represents a single individual whose reading speed and age have both been measured. Notice that reading speed tends to increase with age up to about 25 years, after which it remains unchanged for some years and then, at about age 45, begins slowly to decrease. The question we should like to ask is, how much will a knowledge of a person's age improve our prediction of his reading speed?

To obtain E^2 from these data, we should first have to divide the age range into step intervals of some convenient size, as shown by the vertical bars in Figure 7.4. We could then determine the mean reading speed for each interval, or, as shown in Figure 7.4, each column. We could also determine the variance for each column,

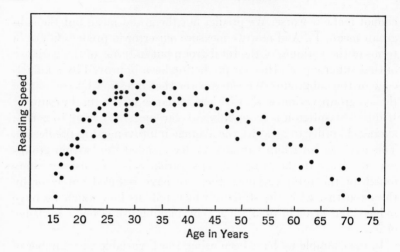

Fig. 7.3 Relation between reading speed and age (hypothetical data). Each point represents a single individual who has been measured on both variables.

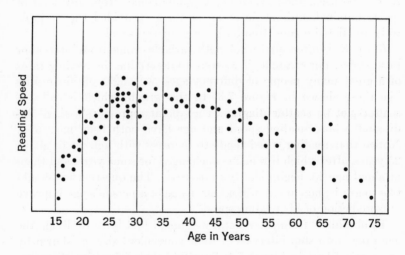

Fig. 7.4 To compute E^2 from these data, it is necessary first to divide the age range into step-intervals. Each column in the figure is a step-interval, or subgroup.

and the weighted average of these column variances would be our within-groups variance. The mean and variance of the total distribution of reading speeds for all ages lumped together would be computed and compared with the within-groups variance. From the comparison, E^2 and E could be computed. Perhaps this example will help you to understand why E is sometimes called the **coefficient of curvilinear correlation**. There is, apparently, a relation between reading speed and age, but it is not a simple one. We cannot say that reading speed increases with age or decreases with age.

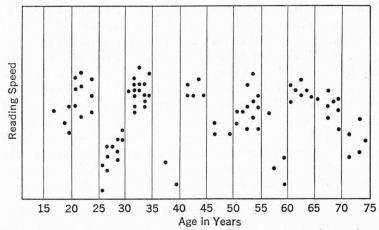

Fig. 7.5 If the relation of reading speed to age were as shown above, E^2_{yx} would be the same as it was for the data shown in figure 7.4. This is because the order of the columns in that figure has been rearranged, but within each column the points are identical with those in figure 7.4. Would E^2_{xy} be the same in these two cases?

It does both at different times. Since the relationship must be described by a curve, rather than a straight line, we say that the relation between reading speed and age is curvilinear, and E^2 and E measure the strength of this curvilinear relationship.

One might object that the use of E in the situation described above will throw away much useful information. E would be unchanged if the various columns in Figure 7.4 were shifted about as shown in Figure 7.5. E takes no account of the ordering of the columns, or of the distances between them. This is certainly a potential disadvantage, but for certain types of data, we find ourselves forced to use E in spite of it.

When both variables have been measured on interval or ratio scales, the decision to call one variable X and the other Y is made arbitrarily. No rule tells us which letter goes with which variable. In our discussion of E^2 we have talked always of predicting the Y variable from a knowledge of X, but we might want to predict X from a knowledge of Y. In the age and reading-speed example, for instance, we might want to use our knowledge of a person's reading speed to help in predicting his age. If you study Figure 7.4, you will be able to see that reading speed will be less help in predicting age than age was in predicting reading speed. E^2, computed from the 'before and after' variances of the X variable, age, will be lower than when computed from the variances of the Y variable, reading speed. To distinguish between these two kinds of E^2 we use identifying subscripts. E^2_{yx} means the reduction Y variance from a knowledge of X, and E^2_{xy} means the reduction of X variance from a knowledge of Y. The variable we are trying to predict is given first in the subscript.

E^2 ranges in value from 0 to 1.00, and when we find E we always take the positive square root. E and E^2, unlike r, which we shall study in the next section, tell us only about the strength of a relationship, not about its direction.

Questions

1. From the data on p. 232, recompute E^2 from formula 7.1.5 and compare the new answer with the original.
2. Use these same data to predict year in college from a knowledge of a student's age. Compare the new measure of relationship, E^2_{xy}, with the old one, E^2_{yx}.
3. Why do we find it more convenient to talk about the reduction of *variance* than about the reduction of a *standard deviation?* (Hints: (1) Consider formula 7.1.3. (2) If $a^2 = b^2 + c^2$, does $a = b + c$?)
4. Name several pairs of variables that you think might show a curvilinear relationship. Sketch a graph for each pair, showing the kind of relationship you might expect.

7.2 The Coefficient of Correlation, r

$\hat{T}$, we have seen, is a measure which results from a comparison of the uncertainty ($\hat{H}$) of a total group with the average uncertainty of the subgroups. E is a measure that results from a comparison of the variance of a total group with the average variance of the sub-groups. The coefficient of correlation, r, is a measure that compares the variance of a total group with the variance left in our prediction of Y when we take X into account. r is much like E, but it can be used only when both variables come from interval or ratio scales, and it can be used sensibly only when the two variables are **linearly related.**

7.2.1 A General Description of r: Let us explain what we mean by 'linearly related.' If you answered the questions on p. 232, you

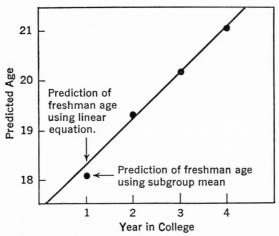

Fig. 7.6   Predicted (mean) age as a function of year in college, showing a linear relationship. When we utilize this linear relationship in making a prediction, we predict a point on the straight line, rather than the mean age for each subgroup. From data on p. 232.

computed the mean ages of freshman, sophomores, juniors, and seniors at a certain college, and you plotted mean age as a function of year in college. If you did it correctly, your results looked like Figure 7.6. In that figure the four points appear to lie in almost a straight line. Age is therefore said to be linearly related to year in college.

When you were asked what your best prediction would be for the age of a student if you knew he was a freshman, your answer was (or should have been) the mean age of all freshmen, 18.14. When you predicted the age of a sophomore, you gave the mean sophomore age, and so on. But since the means of the classes form almost a straight line when they are plotted against college year, it should be possible to develop an equation that will describe *in general* the relation between age and year. Then, if we know a student's year in college we can predict his age merely by substituting in that equation. Because the four points do not lie exactly along a straight line, we shall make a slightly larger error when we use the equation to make our predictions than when we use the means of the four columns. We can measure our error by computing the average of the squares of the deviations of the measures from the straight line, rather than the average of the squares of the deviations of the measures from the column means. Since we are using the line to estimate a student's age, we call the new measure of unpredictability the **variance of estimate.** The variance of estimate is almost identical with the within-groups variance.

$$\text{Within groups variance} = \frac{\Sigma(Y - \text{predicted } Y)^2}{N}$$

where 'predicted Y' means subgroup (column) mean.

$$\text{Variance of estimate of } Y = \frac{\Sigma(Y - \text{predicted } Y)^2}{N}$$

where 'predicted Y' means the point on the straight line relating X and Y.

The variance of estimate tells us how much error is left in our prediction when we use the straight line to predict from, and, like the within-groups variance, it can be compared with the total variance to see how much prediction has been improved.

$$r^2 = 1 - \frac{s^2_{\text{est}_y}}{s^2_y} \tag{7.2.1}$$

where r^2 is the square of the correlation coefficient
$s^2_{\text{est}_y}$ is the variance of estimate of y
s^2_y is the total variance of y.

If you compare this formula with the formula for E^2, you will see that they are identical except that s^2_w has been replaced by $s^2_{\text{est}_y}$.

This formula is an important one in showing us what r is and how it is related to $\hat{T}$ and to E. But it would be a highly unsatisfactory one to compute from because, in order to find $s^2_{\text{est}_y}$ we have to know

what to predict. In order to know what to predict we have to
know what line to draw. And in order to know what line to draw,
we almost have to know r. So we shall now leave the fair land of
variance ratios and (as the sunlight fades) stumble along over the
rocky trails of curve fitting.

7.2.2 Regression Lines: Suppose we are interested in finding out
how closely height and weight are related in a group of 25 college
women. The data are given below and plotted as a scatter diagram
in Figure 7.7.

WOMAN	X HEIGHT (INCHES)	Y WEIGHT (POUNDS)
1	60	95
2	65	131
3	67	133
4	66	151
5	63	164
6	61	110
7	64	125
8	69	152
9	62	141
10	64	140
11	65	140
12	66	132
13	70	180
14	59	91
15	63	126
16	72	171
17	65	123
18	68	128
19	64	114
20	66	130
21	67	103
22	65	162
23	66	145
24	65	136
25	64	111

Though our major interest is in the strength of the relationship
between these two variables, we shall start by considering a sub-
ordinate question: what is our best prediction of a woman's weight
if we know her height? We want to find the equation of the straight
line relating weight to height. Now obviously no one straight line
is going to touch all the points in the scatter-plot, but some lines

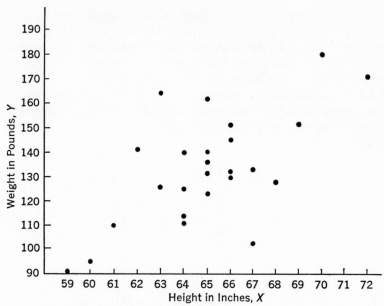

FIG. 7.7 Scatter diagram showing relation of weight to height for 25 college women.

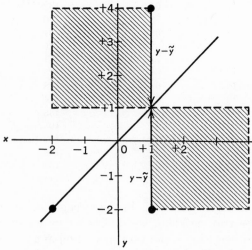

FIG. 7.8 Variance of estimate of y. The plotted line is the one which makes the average of the squares of the vertical deviations of the points from the line a minimum. The average of the shaded areas (that is, their sum divided by 3) is the variance of estimate, $s^2_{\text{est}_y}$.

will be better than others. Since we want to make the best possible prediction, and since the badness of a prediction is to be measured by the variance of estimate, the line we seek is the one that will make the variance of estimate as small as possible. It is the line about which the sum of the squares of the vertical deviations of the points from the line will be a minimum. This line will be called the **line of regression of** y **on** x. The reason for the use of the term 'regression' will be given later.

The equation for any straight line is

$$Y = a + bX$$

where a is the intercept of the line and b is its slope.
If the straight line goes through the origin, that is, through the point where both X and Y are zero, then a is zero and the equation is simply:

$$Y = bX$$

This second equation is simpler than the first because it has only one constant, b, while the general equation has two constants. If we call the mean height zero and the mean weight zero, then we can give the equation for the regression line in this simpler form. Every measurement of height and of weight will be expressed as a deviation from the means. We shall not plot X and Y, but $(X - \overline{X})$, or x, and $(Y - \overline{Y})$, or y. In Figure 7.9 the data have been replotted in this form. Note that the scatter diagram looks just like the original one except that the x and y axes have been shifted. The equation for the regression line of y on x will now be

$$(Y - \overline{Y}) = b(X - \overline{X}), \quad \text{or} \quad y = bx$$

Our problem now is to find b, the slope of the line. In order to find the slope that will make the variance of estimate a minimum we should have to use calculus if it were not for the fact that others have already used it and given us a formula. The formula for the slope of the line which enables us to predict y from x is

$$b_{yx} = \frac{\Sigma xy}{\Sigma x^2} \tag{7.2.2}$$

where b_{yx} is the slope of the regression line of y on x.

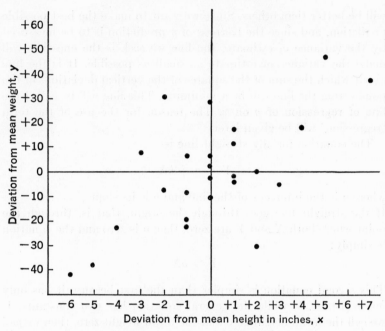

Fig. 7.9 Same data as figure 7.7 plotted as deviations from the means.

The computation has been done and the resulting line plotted in Figure 7.10. The slope turns out to be 4.97. If we let $\tilde{y}$ stand for 'predicted y' then

$$\tilde{y} = b_{yx}x \tag{7.2.3}$$

and in our case

$$\tilde{y} = 4.97x$$

If we know that a woman is three inches taller than the mean, what do we predict that she will weigh?

$$\tilde{y} = 4.97 \times 3 = 14.91$$

We predict that she will be 14.91 pounds heavier than the mean.

This equation will *not* do if we want to predict height from a knowledge of weight, rather than vice versa. For now, since we are estimating x, we want to minimize the variance of estimate of x; that is to say, we want to find the line that will make the sum of the squares of the *horizontal* deviations a minimum. This principle is illustrated in Figure 7.11, which should be compared with Figure

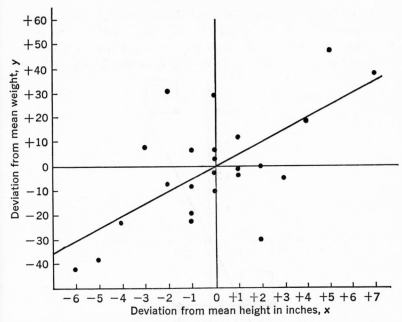

FIG. 7.10   Same data as figure 7.9, showing regression line of y on x. The slope of the line is 4.97, but the line drawn here does not have that slope because we are letting ten pounds equal one inch on the graph paper, while the figure 4.97 applies only when one pound equals one inch.

7.8, where we were minimizing the sum of the squares of the *vertical* deviations. The equation for the line which enables us to predict x from a knowledge of y will be

$$\tilde{x} = b_{xy}y \qquad (7.2.4)$$

where $\tilde{x}$ is the predicted x.
The formula for b_{xy}, is

$$b_{xy} = \frac{\Sigma xy}{\Sigma y^2} \qquad (7.2.5)$$

It has been computed and is found to be .08. It is plotted in Figure 7.12. If a woman is ten pounds above the mean in weight, how much taller than the mean height will she be?

$$\tilde{x} = .08y \qquad \tilde{x} = .08 \times 10$$

Our best prediction is that she will be .8 inches taller than the mean.

If we know the mean height and the mean weight, then we can substitute $(X - \overline{X})$ for x and $(Y - \overline{Y})$ for y, and get the actual equations that will enable us to predict height from a knowledge of weight and weight from a knowledge of height. The mean height

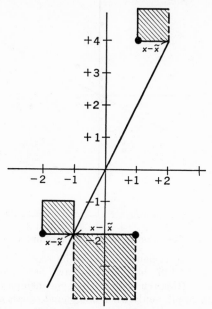

FIG. 7.11   Variance of estimate of x. The plotted line is the one which makes the average of the squares of the horizontal deviations of the points from the line a minimum. The average of the shaded areas is the variance of estimate of x, $s^2_{\text{est}_x}$. Compare this figure with figure 7.8, which shows the variance of estimate of y.

is 65.04 inches, and the mean weight, 133.36 pounds. Now we can write

$$\tilde{y} = b_{yx}x = 4.97x$$
$$(\tilde{Y} - 133.36) = 4.97(X - 65.04)$$
$$\tilde{Y} = 4.97X - 189.89$$

That is the actual regression equation of weight on height. To predict a woman's weight, we merely substitute her actual height for X and solve for $\tilde{Y}$. The corresponding equation for predicting height from a knowledge of weight is

$$\tilde{X} = .08Y + 54.37$$

The constants in the regression equations depend upon the units in which the data were measured. We have measured height in inches and weight in pounds, but if we measured weight in ounces instead of pounds, then the slopes and intercepts of the regression equations would be quite different. In a sense we have said, 'Let

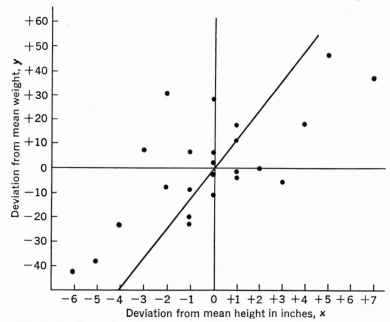

FIG. 7.12 Same data as figure 7.9, showing regression line of x on y. The actual slope of the line is .08, but it would be drawn with that slope only if one pound and one inch got the same amount of space on our graph paper.

one inch be equivalent to one pound.' The slopes of the two lines, 4.97 and $\dfrac{1}{.08}$, are the actual slopes of the plotted lines only when we let one horizontal unit on our graph paper equal one inch, and one vertical unit one pound. Since that would make a pretty silly-looking graph, we have not plotted the data that way.

Letting 'one inch be equivalent to one pound' sounds like a fairly arbitrary way of doing things. Why not 'one inch equivalent to ten pounds'? Or to twenty? Or any other number? Is there any logical way of deciding how many pounds are 'equivalent' to one inch?

Is there any unit in which we can measure both height and weight? What unit of measurement can possibly be common to two such unlike variables?

What, indeed, but the standard deviation? If we express each measurement not as so many inches above the mean but as so many standard deviations away from the mean, then we have a unit that

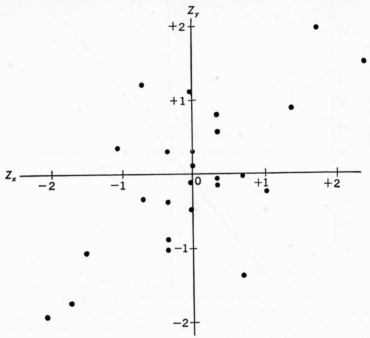

FIG. 7.13   Scatter plot of height and weight data in standard deviation units.

is comparable for height and weight. Our procedure, then, will be to convert all measurements to z-scores. We have done this in Figure 7.13, which you will notice no longer looks exactly like Figure 7.7 or Figure 7.9.

Next we wish to find the slope of the line which will enable us to predict $\dfrac{\tilde{y}}{s_y}$ from a knowledge of $\dfrac{x}{s_x}$. If

$$\tilde{y} = b_{yx}x$$

then we should be able, by the use of a little simple algebra, to find the required slope. Let us call this slope, which is unkown, r. Then we can solve for r in terms of b_{yx}, s_y, and s_x.

$$\frac{\tilde{y}}{s_y} = r\left(\frac{x}{s_x}\right) \qquad \text{where } r \text{ is the slope of the line, unknown}$$

$$\tilde{y} = r\left(\frac{s_y}{s_x}\right) x \qquad \text{multiplying both sides by } s_y$$

$$b_{yx}x = r\left(\frac{s_y}{s_x}\right) x \qquad \text{substituting for } \tilde{y}$$

$$b_{yx} = r\left(\frac{s_y}{s_x}\right) \qquad \text{dividing both sides by } x$$

$$r = b_{yx}\left(\frac{s_x}{s_y}\right) \qquad \text{dividing both sides by } \frac{s_y}{s_x} \text{ to solve for } r$$

We can simplify this expression further by substituting for b_{yx}.

$$b_{yx} = \frac{\Sigma xy}{Ns_x^2} \qquad \text{so}$$

$$r = \frac{\Sigma xy}{Ns_x^2}\left(\frac{s_x}{s_y}\right) \qquad \text{substitution}$$

$$r = \frac{\Sigma xy}{Ns_xs_y} \qquad \text{canceling the } s_x$$

A completely analogous procedure can, of course, be carried out if we wish to find the slope of the line which will enable us to predict $\frac{\tilde{x}}{s_x}$ from a knowledge of $\frac{y}{s_y}$. If we let r stand for the required coefficient and solve for it in terms of b_{xy}, s_x, and s_y, and later substitute for b_{xy}, we get a very interesting result. The coefficient that will enable us to predict $\frac{\tilde{x}}{s_x}$ from a knowledge of $\frac{y}{s_y}$ is identical with the slope of the line which will enable us to predict $\frac{\tilde{y}}{s_y}$ from a knowledge of $\frac{x}{s_x}$. In both cases,

$$r = \frac{\Sigma xy}{Ns_xs_y} \qquad (7.2.6)$$

What this fact means is shown graphically in Figure 7.14. Here we see a scatter diagram plotted in standard deviation units, and two regression lines are drawn through the points. The slope of the

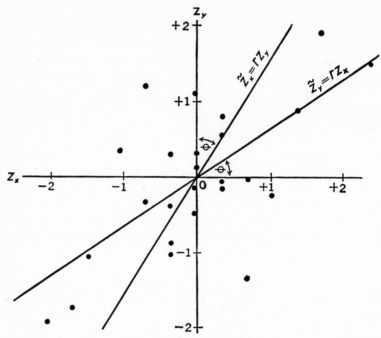

Fig. 7.14   Regression lines drawn through scatter plot of height and weight data, plotted in standard deviation units. The angle Θ made by the line of regression of z_y on z_x with the x axis is the same as the angle made by the line of regression of z_x on z_y with the y axis. The slope of the first line is r, of the second, $1/r$.

line relating $\dfrac{\tilde{y}}{s_y}$ to $\dfrac{x}{s_x}$ is r. But the angle made by the intersection of this line with the x-axis is the same as the angle made by the line of regression of $\dfrac{\tilde{x}}{s_x}$ on $\dfrac{y}{s_y}$ with the y-axis, so the slope of this second line is $\dfrac{1}{r}$. So

$$\frac{\tilde{y}}{s_y} = r\left(\frac{x}{s_x}\right) \qquad \text{and}$$

$$\frac{y}{s_y} = \left(\frac{1}{r}\right)\left(\frac{\tilde{x}}{s_x}\right) \qquad \text{which is the same thing as}$$

$$\frac{\tilde{x}}{s_x} = r\left(\frac{y}{s_y}\right)$$

The slope of the regression line of $\dfrac{\tilde{y}}{s_y}$ on $\dfrac{x}{s_x}$ is r, the coefficient of correlation.

That is a very important definition. What it means is that if we know an individual's z-score on one variable, we can predict his z-score on another variable by using the equation $z_x = rz_y$ or $z_y = rz_x$. If the correlation between two variables is $+1.00$, and an individual has a score two standard deviations above the mean on x, our best prediction of his score of y is that it will be two standard deviations above the mean of the y-scores. If the correlation between the variables is $+.5$, then the predicted y-score for an individual whose score on x is two standard deviations above the mean is *one* standard deviation $(r\left(\dfrac{x}{s_x}\right) = .5 \times 2 = 1)$ above the mean of y. If the correlation is zero, then our best prediction for the individual's y-score, regardless of what his score on x may have been, is the mean of the y-scores.

Let us find the correlation between height and weight for our 25 college women. We know that $b_{yx} = 4.97$, and it can be calculated that $s_x = 2.89$, and $s_y = 22.08$.

$$r = b_{yx}\left(\frac{s_x}{s_y}\right)$$
$$r = 4.97\left(\frac{2.89}{22.08}\right)$$
$$r = .65$$

Now if a woman is one standard deviation above the mean in height, we predict that she will be .65 standard deviations above the mean in weight. If she is one standard deviation above the mean in weight, we predict that she will be .65 standard deviations above the mean in height. In general, if her z-score in one variable is c, we predict that her z-score on the other variable will be rc, or in this case $.65c$.

Notice that we never predict that a woman's score on one variable will be farther away from the mean than it was on the other variable. The coefficient of correlation can never be higher than 1.00, which means that prediction will always be in the direction of the mean. It is for this reason that the term 'regression' is used. Regression means 'going back'—toward the mean. The phenomenon of regression was first observed by Sir Francis Galton, a British scientist of the late nineteenth century, who had become much interested in heredity. Galton made many studies of the extent to which such variables as tallness of stature tend to run in families. He found that, though tall parents were likely to have children who were taller than average, the children were unlikely to be *as much taller than average* as their parents. Galton also studied the hereditary transmission of talent and intelligence and concluded:

The law of Regression tells heavily against the full hereditary transmission of any gift. Only a few out of many children would be likely to differ as widely as the more exceptional of the two Parents. The more bountifully the Parent is gifted by nature, the more rare will be his good fortune if he begets a son who is endowed yet more largely. But the law is even-handed; it levies an equal succession-tax on the transmission of badness as of goodness. If it discourages the extravagant hopes of a gifted parent that his children will inherit all his powers; it no less discountenances extravagant fears that they will inherit all his weakness and disease. It must be clearly understood that there is nothing in these statements to invalidate the general doctrine that the children of a gifted pair are much more likely to be gifted than the children of a mediocre pair. They merely express the fact that the ablest of all the children of a few gifted pairs is not likely to be as gifted as the ablest of all the children of a very great many mediocre pairs.[3]

It was Galton who dubbed this phenomenon 'regression towards mediocrity,' coined the term 'regression line,' and later referred to the mutual relationship between two variables as 'co-relation.' Karl Pearson, a British statistician, is responsible for the mathematical development of the coefficient of correlation, and the coefficient is sometimes called, in his honor, the 'Pearson product-moment correlation,' or, more familiarly, 'Pearson r.'

Questions

1. If E^2 and r^2 are computed from the same set of data, E^2 is always equal to or higher than r^2, never lower. Explain why this should be so.

2. Name several pairs of variables that you think will be linearly related.

[3] Galton, F. *Natural Inheritance*, New York, Macmillan, 1889, p. 106. Quoted in Walker, Helen M., *Elementary Statistical Methods*, New York, Holt, 1943, p. 206. For a further description of Galton's interesting studies, see Walker.

3. One anthropologist measures the heights of 10 men in inches, and another anthropologist measures the heights of the same 10 men in centimeters (one inch equals 2.5 centimeters).

    a. Let X stand for 'height in inches' and Y for 'height in centimeters.'
       If $\tilde{Y} = b_{yx}X$, what is b_{yx}?
       If $\tilde{X} = b_{xy}Y$, what is b_{xy}?

    b. Draw two graphs showing the relation of X to Y. On the first graph, call height in inches X and height in centimeters Y. On the second, reverse the names. On both graphs, let one square on the graph paper equal one inch, and also let one square equal one centimeter. Measure the slopes of the two lines.

    c. If the standard deviation of the heights measured in inches was $1''$, what was the standard deviation of the heights measured in centimeters?

    d. Draw a new graph showing the relation of X and Y, but this time let one square of graph paper equal one standard deviation of each of the two variables. What is the slope of the line relating X and Y?

    e. If you know a man's height in inches, how much error is left in your prediction of his height in centimeters?

    f. What is s_y^2? What is $s_{est_y}^2$?

    g. What is the correlation between height in inches and height in centimeters? (Use: $r^2 = 1 - s_{est_y}^2/s_y^2$)

    h. If a man is one standard deviation shorter than the mean when his height is measured in inches, how many standard deviations shorter than the mean is he when his height is measured in centimeters?

4. If the correlation between the IQ's of identical twins is $+.95$, and the standard deviation of the IQ measures is 16 points, what would you predict Jimmy's IQ to be if you knew that his twin, Johnny, had an IQ of 68? (Mean IQ $= 100$.)

5. If the correlation between two variables is $-.75$, and

$$\bar{X} = 100 \qquad \bar{Y} = 500$$
$$s_x = 10 \qquad s_y = 50$$

a. What scores on X would you predict for individuals having the following scores on Y: 400, 450, 500, 525, 575.

b. What scores on Y would you predict for individuals having the following scores on X: 85, 95, 100, 110, 120.

c. Find the regression equation of $\tilde{X}$ on Y and the regression equation of $\tilde{Y}$ on X for these data.

(Hint: start with the fact that $\dfrac{\tilde{x}}{s_x} = r\left(\dfrac{y}{s_y}\right)$. For r, s_x, and s_y, substitute numerical values. For $\tilde{x}$, substitute $(\tilde{X} - \overline{X})$, and for y, substitute $(Y - \overline{Y})$. Then substitute numerical values for $\overline{X}$ and $\overline{Y}$ and solve.)

6. Two variables, X and Y are both normally distributed, the correlation between them is .50, and

$$\overline{X} = 50, \qquad s_x = 5, \qquad \overline{Y} = 150, \qquad \text{and} \qquad s_y = 12$$

One individual has a percentile rank of 95 on the X variable. What is his percentile rank on Y? (Don't jump to conclusions. This problem has several steps in its solution. The first step depends upon the words 'normally distributed.')

7. Prove that if $x = y$, $r = +1.00$. Use: $r = \dfrac{\Sigma xy}{N s_x s_y}$.

8. Prove that $\Sigma xy = \Sigma XY - N\overline{X}\,\overline{Y}$.

7.2.3 The Standard Error of Estimate: If we know the correlation between two variables, we can predict an individual's score on x from a knowledge of his score on y. The prediction, as we have said before is:

$$\frac{\tilde{y}}{s_y} = r\left(\frac{x}{s_x}\right) \qquad \text{or} \qquad \tilde{y} = r\left(\frac{s_y}{s_x}\right)x$$

We now return to our original definition of r and ask how much have improved our prediction from what it would have been if we had had no knowledge of x. How much error is left when we use our knowledge of x? The statistic which will answer that question is the variance of estimate of y, $s^2_{\text{est}_y}$, or its square root, the standard error of estimate of y. We have already defined the variance of estimate of y as

$$\frac{\Sigma(Y - \tilde{Y})^2}{N}$$

We can also write this as

$$\frac{\Sigma(y - \tilde{y})^2}{N}$$

Proof: $\quad y = Y - \overline{Y} \quad$ and $\quad \tilde{y} = \tilde{Y} - \overline{Y}$, so

$$y - \tilde{y} = (Y - \overline{Y}) - (\tilde{Y} - \overline{Y})$$
$$y - \tilde{y} = Y - \overline{Y} - \tilde{Y} + \overline{Y} = Y - \tilde{Y}$$

If we substitute for $\tilde{y}$ the actual value which we predict from our knowledge of x, we can solve the equation for $s^2_{est_y}$. The result is:

$$s^2_{est_y} = s^2_y(1 - r^2), \quad \text{and} \quad s_{est_y} = s_y \sqrt{1 - r^2} \quad (7.2.7 \text{ and } 7.2.8)$$

$$s^2_{est_x} = s^2_x(1 - r^2) \quad \text{and} \quad s_{est_x} = s_x \sqrt{1 - r^2} \quad (7.2.9 \text{ and } 7.2.10)$$

The variance of estimate is a statistic completely analagous to 'within-groups variance.' If we compare the variance of estimate of y with the total y variance, or the variance of estimate of x with the total x variance, we can see what proportion of error is left in our predictions when we use the linear relationship between x and y in making these predictions.

Notice what happens if r is $+1.00$ or -1.00—then $1 - r^2$ is zero, and there is no error in prediction. If, on the other hand, r is zero, then $1 - r^2$ is 1, and $s^2_{est_y}$ is equal to s^2_y. That is, knowledge of an individual's score on x leads to no reduction in uncertainty about his score on y, and vice versa. The higher the correlation, the lower will be $1 - r^2$ and, hence, the lower the variance of estimate. The lower r^2, the higher the variance of estimate and the poorer the prediction.

We have already said that $r^2 = 1 - \dfrac{s^2_{est_y}}{s^2_y}$. Like E^2, r^2 measures the reduction in the unpredictability of y which comes about from a knowledge of x. It is called the **coefficient of determination.**

$\dfrac{s^2_{est_y}}{s^2_y}$ measures the proportion of the original error which is left in our prediction. It is called the **coefficient of non-determination,** and has a symbol all its own, k^2. The square root of this ratio, k, is sometimes called the **coefficient of alienation.** To sum up, r^2 is the proportion of the y variance which is accounted for by the relationship of x and y, and k^2 is the proportion that is not accounted for by that relationship. Since the sum of the proportions must be 1, $k^2 + r^2 = 1.00$.

7.2.4 Definitions of r and r^2: The coefficient of correlation and its square, the coefficient of determination, are fascinating statistics because they are so many things all at once. For example, we have already seen that r tells us what to predict, and r^2 tells us how good the prediction is. From these facts, we can state two important definitions:

1. The coefficient of correlation r, and its reciprocal, $\frac{1}{r}$, are the slopes of the regression lines relating two variables, when both variables, are expressed in standard deviation units.

2. The coefficient of determination, r^2, is the proportion of the total variance which is accounted for by the relation of x and y. One hundred times the coefficient of determination is the percentage by which our error of prediction is reduced. (Error in this case means variance.)

There are other ways of thinking about r and r^2. For example, r^2 is the product of the two regression coefficients, b_{yx} and b_{xy}. This is easy to prove:

$$b_{yx} = \frac{\Sigma xy}{\Sigma x^2} \quad \text{and} \quad b_{xy} = \frac{\Sigma xy}{\Sigma y^2}$$

$$= \frac{\Sigma xy}{N s_x^2} \qquad\qquad = \frac{\Sigma xy}{N s_y^2}$$

$$b_{yx} b_{xy} = \frac{\Sigma xy}{N s_x^2} \cdot \frac{\Sigma xy}{N s_y^2} = \frac{(\Sigma xy)^2}{N s_x^2 N s_y^2} = r^2$$

r, of course, is the square root of this. This square root of the product of two numbers is called, as we shall see in the next chapter, the geometric mean of those numbers. So r *is the geometric mean of the two regression coefficients.*

r is sometimes called the *mean z-score product.*

$$z_x = \frac{x}{s_x} \quad \text{and} \quad z_y = \frac{y}{s_y}$$

The formula for r is

$$\frac{\Sigma xy}{N s_x s_y} \quad \text{which can also be written} \quad \frac{1}{N} \sum \frac{x}{s_x} \cdot \frac{y}{s_y}$$

And now, for $\frac{x}{s_x}$ we can substitute z_x, and for $\frac{y}{s_y}$ we can substitute

z_y. Then

$$r = \frac{\Sigma z_x z_y}{N}$$

We could find the coefficient of correlation by expressing every individual's scores on x and y as z-scores, obtaining the product of these z-scores for each individual, summing the products, and dividing by N. *The coefficient of correlation is the arithmetic mean of the product of the z-scores on two variables.*

Questions

1. From the data in problems 3, 4, 5, and 6 on pp. 257–8, compute and interpret:

$$s_{est_y}^2, \ s_{est_y}^2, \ s_{est_x}^2, \ s_{est_x}, \ b_{yx}, \ b_{xy}, \ r^2 \text{ and } k^2$$

2. From the data below, compute $\overline{X}$, $\overline{Y}$, s_x, and s_y. Then express each score as a z-score. Compute r from the formula: $r = \dfrac{\Sigma z_x z_y}{N}$

INDIVIDUAL	X	Y
A	1	10
B	2	8
C	3	12
D	4	16
E	5	14

(Suggestion: leave s_x and s_y under their radical signs. Do not extract square roots.)

3. Explain what is meant by a negative correlation.

4. For each of the following pairs of variables, decide whether the correlation would be positive, negative, or curvilinear, and whether it would be strong or weak.

a. Age and number of teeth.
b. Intelligence and school marks.
c. Family income and number of children per family.
d. Visual acuity and the intensity of the light.
e. The volume of a cube and the length of its side.
f. Standard deviations and variances.
g. The amount of truancy in children and the education of their parents.

    h. Age and intelligence of fifth-grade children.

    i. Age and intelligence of all children aged six to twelve.

5. From your reading in other subjects, collect reports of variables that have been found to be correlated. Where actual correlation coefficients have been given, interpret them.

6. Prove that

$$\frac{\Sigma xy}{Ns_x s_y} = \frac{N\Sigma XY - (\Sigma X)(\Sigma Y)}{\sqrt{N\Sigma X^2 - (\Sigma X)^2} \sqrt{N\Sigma Y^2 - (\Sigma Y)^2}}$$

7.2.5 Computation: Up to this point we have been talking theory.

We have discussed the meanings, interpretations, and inter-relationships of r, r^2, $s^2_{est_y}$, and the various other measures related to the correlation coefficient. Now we are ready to compute them. As an illustration we shall consider the heights and weights of the 25 females listed on page 245.

None of the formulas we have given so far will be much use when it comes to computation, because all these formulas are written in terms of x and y, deviations from the mean. Formulas in deviation form lead to hideous computational problems, while raw-score formulas, though formidable in appearance, are convenient to use. We shall therefore work with raw scores and raw-score formulas.

Our first step in computation is to find, by machine calculation, six quantities:[4] ΣXY, ΣX^2, ΣY^2, ΣX, ΣY, and N. (N, of course doesn't require the use of a calculating machine.) These quantities are going to be the raw material from which we shall obtain answers to the twelve questions below. For the height and weight data, these quantities are:

$$\Sigma XY = 217,875 \qquad \Sigma Y^2 = 456,808 \qquad \Sigma Y = 3,334$$
$$\Sigma X^2 = 105,964 \qquad \Sigma X = 1,626 \qquad N = 25$$

Now we are ready to start asking questions of our data.

[4] Finding these quantities on a calculating machine is exceedingly quick and easy. On a Marchant or Frieden calculator, ΣX and ΣX^2 are found in one set of machine operations, ΣY and ΣY^2 in a second, and ΣXY in a third. On certain types of Monroe calculator it is possible to find all five quantities in one set of machine operations. The calculation of these quantities in the illustrative problem here should take not more than 20 minutes on a Marchant or Frieden, and not more than 15 minutes on a Monroe.

1. How strongly are the variables related?

Answer: r

Formula: $r = \dfrac{N\Sigma XY - (\Sigma X)(\Sigma Y)}{\sqrt{N\Sigma X^2 - (\Sigma X)^2}\ \sqrt{N\Sigma Y^2 - (\Sigma Y)^2}}$

Computation:

$r = \dfrac{25 \times 217{,}875 - (1626)(3{,}334)}{\sqrt{25 \times 105{,}964 - (1626)^2}\ \sqrt{25 \times 456{,}808 - (3334)^2}}$

$r = .65$

The correlation between height and weight is .65. This is a moderately high degree of relationship.

2. What is the direction of relationship between the variables?

Answer: Positive if r is positive, negative if r is negative.

In our case r is positive, which means that people who are above average in height will also tend to be above average in weight, and vice versa.

3. What is our best prediction of X if we have no knowledge of Y?

Answer: $\overline{X}$

Formula: $\overline{X} = \dfrac{\Sigma X}{N}$

Computation: $\overline{X} = \tfrac{1626}{25} = 65.04$

Our best prediction of a woman's height, if we do not know her weight, is 65.04 inches.

4. How bad is this prediction?

Answer: s_x or s_x^2

Formulas:[5] $s_x = \dfrac{1}{N}\sqrt{N\Sigma X^2 - (\Sigma X)^2}$ $s_x^2 = \dfrac{1}{N^2}[N\Sigma X^2 - (\Sigma X)^2]$

Computation: $s_x = \dfrac{1}{25}\sqrt{25 \times 105{,}964 - (1626)^2}$

$s_x = 2.89, \qquad s_x^2 = 8.36$

If the data are distributed normally, we can conclude that when we

[5] Note that you have already found the quantity under the radical sign when you were computing r.

guess a woman's height to be 65.04 inches, we shall make an error of 2.89 inches or less 68 per cent of the time.

5. What is our best prediction of Y if we have no knowledge of X?

Answer: $\overline{Y}$

Formula: $\overline{Y} = \dfrac{\Sigma Y}{N}$

Computation: $\overline{Y} = \frac{3334}{25} = 133.36$

If we do not know a woman's height, our best guess about her weight is that it will be 133.36 pounds.

6. How bad is this prediction?

Answer: s_y or s_y^2

Formula:[5] $s_y = \dfrac{1}{N} \sqrt{N\Sigma Y^2 - (\Sigma Y)^2}$ $\qquad s_y^2 = \dfrac{1}{N^2}[N\Sigma T^2 - (\Sigma Y)^2]$

Computation: $s_y = \dfrac{1}{25} \sqrt{25 \times 456{,}808 - (3334)^2}$

$\qquad\qquad s_y = 22.08,\ s_y^2 = 487.43$

If the data are distributed normally, we can conclude that when we guess a woman's weight to be 133.36 pounds, we shall make an error of 22.08 pounds or less 68 per cent of the time.

7. What is our best prediction of X if we know Y?

Answer: Regression equation of $\tilde{X}$ on Y

Formula: $\tilde{X} = r\left(\dfrac{s_x}{s_y}\right)(Y - \overline{Y}) + \overline{X}$

Computation: $\tilde{X} = .65\left(\dfrac{2.89}{22.08}\right)(Y - 133.36) + 65.04$

$\qquad\qquad \tilde{X} = .08Y + 54.37$

If we know a woman's weight, we substitute it for Y in this regression equation, and solve the equation for $\tilde{X}$. If, for example, a woman weighs 100 pounds, we substitute 100 for Y and solve.

$\tilde{X} = .08(100) + 54.37 = 62.37$. Her predicted height is 62.37″.

[5] Note that you have already found the quantity under the radical sign when you were computing r.

8. **How bad is this prediction?**

Answer: s_{est_x} or $s_{est_x}^2$

Formula: $s_{est_x} = s_x \sqrt{1 - r^2}$ $\qquad$ $s_{est_x}^2 = s_x^2(1 - r^2)$

Computation: $s_{est_x} = 2.89 \sqrt{1 - (.65)^2} = 2.20$ $\qquad$ $s_{est_x}^2 = 4.84$

Whereas our error in predicting X without any knowledge of Y was 2.89 inches, our error in predicting X when we use our knowledge of Y is only 2.20 inches. We have improved our prediction by .69 inches. If the data for both variables are normally distributed, we can say that when we make our prediction from the regression equation we shall be in error by 2.20 inches or less 68 per cent of the time.

9. **What is our best prediction of Y if we know X?**

Answer: Regression equation of $\tilde{Y}$ on X

Formula: $\tilde{Y} = r \left(\dfrac{s_y}{s_x} \right) (X - \bar{X}) + \bar{Y}$

Computation: $\tilde{Y} = .65 \left(\dfrac{22.08}{2.89} \right) (X - 65.04) + 133.36$

$\qquad \tilde{Y} = 4.97X - 189.89$

If we know a woman's height, we substitute it for X in that equation and solve for $\tilde{Y}$. If a woman's height, for example, is **70″** we predict her weight to be

$$4.97(70) - 189.89 = 158.01 \text{ pounds}$$

10. **How bad is this prediction?**

Answer: s_{est_y} or $s_{est_y}^2$

Formula: $s_{est_y} = s_y \sqrt{1 - r^2}$ $\qquad$ $s_{est_y}^2 = s_y^2(1 - r^2)$

Computation: $s_{est_y} = 22.08 \sqrt{1 - (.65)^2} = 16.78$ $\qquad$ $s_{est_y}^2 = 281.57$

We have reduced our error of prediction from 22.08 to 16.78 pounds. If both X and Y are normally distributed, we can say that when we make our prediction from the regression equation, we shall be in error by 16.78 pounds or less 68 per cent of the time.

11. **How much does knowledge of one variable improve our prediction of the other**

Answer: r^2

Computation: $r^2 = (.65)^2 = .42$

Our error, measured in terms of variance, has been reduced 42 per cent.

12. How much error is still left in our prediction when we predict one variable from a knowledge of the other?

Answer: k^2

Formulae: $k^2 = 1 - r^2$ $k^2 = \dfrac{s^2_{esty}}{s^2_y}$ $k^2 = \dfrac{s^2_{estx}}{s^2_x}$

Computation: $k^2 = 1 - .42 = .58$

Our new error of prediction (variance) is 58 per cent of the original error.

—which is quite a lot of information to extract from six easily obtained quantities!

Questions

1. Find ΣX, ΣY, ΣX^2, ΣY^2, ΣXY, and N for the four sets of data given below:

a. INDIVIDUAL	X	Y
a	2	10
b	4	15
c	5	14

b. INDIVIDUAL	X	Y
a	.1	100
b	.3	121
c	.4	114
d	.2	103
e	.9	109

c. INDIVIDUAL	X	Y
a	1	1
b	4	4
c	2	2
d	5	5
e	3	3
f	6	6

d. INDIVIDUAL	X	Y
a	1	6
b	4	3
c	2	5
d	5	2
e	3	4
f	6	1

2. A certain reading test has two forms, X and Y. Both forms are administered to 100 subjects with the following results:

$$\Sigma X = 5341 \qquad \Sigma Y = 5004 \qquad \Sigma X^2 = 308{,}664$$
$$\Sigma Y^2 = 272{,}899 \qquad \Sigma XY = 289{,}811$$

Scores on both forms are normally distributed.

From these data answer the twelve questions in section 7.2.5.

3. A pencil-and-paper test of mechanical ingenuity (X) is given to 1000 subjects. The scores are normalized and converted to T-scores. These same 1000 subjects are then timed on the solution of an actual mechanical problem (Y). The mean time for solution is found to be 25 minutes, and the standard deviation 4 minutes. The correlation between the pencil-and-paper test and the time required to solve the practical problem is $-.72$. Answer the twelve questions in section 7.2.5.

4. A psychologist studied the relationship between subjects' reaction times to auditory stimuli and the latencies of their eyelid reflexes to sudden loud noises. His results are given below. Each time is the average time of 100 trials, given in milliseconds. Analyze his data.

SUBJECT	REACTION TIME	LATENCY
A	125	26
B	137	31
C	139	33
D	142	25
E	147	36
F	150	28
G	152	41
H	154	40
I	158	42
J	161	48
K	163	35
L	164	41
M	165	39
N	166	46
O	169	37
P	170	43
Q	171	32
R	173	37
S	180	40
T	182	39
U	188	49
V	193	44
W	195	52
X	201	51
Y	212	54

7.2.6 Interpretation of the Correlation Coefficient: The correlation coefficient ranges from -1.00 to $+1.00$. Whether any given correlation is high or low depends upon the circumstances under which it was obtained. If the correlation between measurements of height made by two anthropometrists turns out to be only .90, we would not feel that that was a very strong relationship; we would be amazed at how low it was and would look to the measurement technique to find the source of error. If the correlation between sunspot cycles and stock-market fluctuations turned out to be .30, we would be amazed by the unexpected evidence of a relationship and would consider the correlation to be astoundingly high. Then, too, we must consider the use we are going to make of the statistic. Sometimes the only use of the correlation coefficient is to describe the strength of a relationship. Sometimes, however, we study the relationship between two variables because we want to use one to predict another. We measure intelligence, for example, because we want to predict school success not for a group but specifically for individuals. In this case, a correlation of .5, while it indicates a definite and substantial relationship, nevertheless leaves considerable error in our predictions about individuals. The size of the error, relative to the original error, is $1 - r^2$, which, in the case of a correlation of .5, is .75. Our new error is 75 per cent of our original error—which indicates that individual prediction from intelligence measures to school success is pretty poor. Not until correlations reach .9 or so does prediction about individuals become dependable.

When two things are highly correlated, it is very easy to jump to conclusion that one of them must cause the other. If intelligence and school grades are found to be correlated many people will conclude that people who get high grades in school do so *because* they are intelligent. If there is a correlation between the heights of parents and of children, it is often assumed that the tallness of the parents somehow causes tallness in the children. In many cases this inference about causality is warranted. But suppose there is a high correlation between the heights of identical twins—does it then follow that one twin is tall because the other is? If so, how shall we know which is the 'cause' twin and which the 'effect' twin? Obviously it would be ridiculous to infer a causal relationship in this case. Many instances that are not so clear-cut as this one lead to difficulties. It is found, for example, that smoking and lung cancer have both increased markedly in the last twenty years. From this statement the jump to the conclusion that smoking causes lung cancer is an easy and erroneous one. The number of air conditioners has also increased markedly in the last twenty years, and we should be equally justified in concluding that air conditioners cause lung cancer as in concluding (on the basis of the correlations alone) that smoking causes lung cancer. Incidentally, from this set of correlations we might also conclude (erroneously) that air conditioners cause smoking, that smoking causes air conditioners, that lung cancer causes smoking, and that lung cancer causes air conditioners.

Correlation does not imply causality, but it may imply that both the correlated variables may be correlated with some other variable, and this third variable may or may not cause both. In years when the grapefruit crop in Florida is good, the orange crop is also likely to be good. Does one good crop cause another? Probably not, but the goodness of both crops might be found to be highly correlated with the amount of rainfall. It would be quite reasonable to suppose that a heavy rainfall caused both crops to be good.

Because of the fact that when two variables are correlated with a third variable they will be correlated with each other unless the effect of that third variable is held constant, the particular circumstances under which a correlation coefficient is obtained must be considered in interpreting it. If we find the correlation between height and weight for all children in a certain school, we shall probably find that it is very high—on the order of .90. But if we obtain a separate correlation for each grade, we may find that these new correlations are much lower—.5 to .6. Both height and weight are correlated with age, and if we do not hold age constant they will appear to be closely related to each other. By obtaining separate correlations for each grade we are, to some extent at least, holding age constant, and getting the correlation between height and weight in a 'purer' form. A correlation between two variables which comes about because both are related to a third variable that has not been controlled is called a *spurious correlation*, or the correlation is said to be *spuriously high*.

7.3 Many Measures of Relatedness

We have now talked about five different measures of relatedness: uncertainty reduction, the index of order association, the rank-order correlation, the correlation ratio, and the Pearson product-moment correlation coefficient. Directly or indirectly, all of these tell us how a knowledge of one variable reduces the unpredictability of another. In addition to these five there are many other measures of relatedness which you may some day encounter in your reading or need for your reasearch. Space does not permit a detailed discussion of these measures; nevertheless you should know their names and the special purposes for which they are used. Then if you ever need one you will at least know what to look up. The various measures of relatedness, old and new, are:

1. **Uncertainty reduction, $\hat{T}$.** This measure tells us how much a knowledge of one variable reduces the uncertainty, $\hat{H}$, of another. $\hat{T}$ is expressed in bits, a unit which is a 'pure number,' independent of the original units of measurement (if there are any such units). $\hat{T}$, can be converted to a relative measure by comparing the actual uncertainty reduction with possible uncertainty reduction. Although we have not discussed the techniques, $\hat{T}$ can be used when the interrelationships of three or more variables are to be investigated. This measure is particularly appropriate when both variables have been measured on nominal scales and it is also the only measure available when one variable has been measured on a nominal and the other on an ordinal scale.

2. **The contingency coefficient, C.** This measure can be used under exactly the same conditions as $\hat{T}$. It does not form part of a system of measurement as $\hat{T}$ does, and it cannot be used when more than two variables are to be investigated.

3. **The index of order association, o.** This measure is based on a comparison of every individual in the group with every other individual. It measures the extent to which the individual who is higher in one variable tends also to be higher in the other. It is most appropriate when both variables have been measured on ordinal scales.

4. **E, the correlation ratio.** This measure describes the extent to which a knowledge of one variable reduces the variance of the other. E_{yx}^2 is the proportion of the variance of y which is associated with variation in x. The measure can be used when one variable has been measured on an interval or ratio scale; the second variable may come from an ordinal or even a nominal scale. E can assume values between 0 and 1.00. It measures the strength of association but not the direction of relationship. The product-moment correlation is a special case of the correlation ratio.

5. r, **the Pearson product-moment correlation coefficient.** This is the basic measure of linear correlation. It assumes that both variables have been measured on interval or ratio scales and that the two variables are linearly related.

When there is any doubt about whether or not the relationship between two variables is linear, both E and r should be computed. E will always be equal to or greater than r in absolute value, but if the relationship is linear the difference will be small. A large difference indicates a non-linear relationship, in which case E rather than r should be used.[6]

All the other measures of correlation to be mentioned are derived from the product-moment correlation by making certain assumptions about the variables under study.

6. **The phi-coefficient,** ϕ. This measure describes the strength and direction of relationship between two dichotomous variables. It is derived from r by assuming that there are only two values a variable can assume, $+1$ and -1. ϕ can be used when both variables have been measured on ordinal or nominal scales if we are willing to make this assumption.

7. **Tetrachoric correlation.** When both variables are continuous and normally distributed but have been artificially dichotomized, the tetrachoric correlation should replace the ϕ coefficient. Like ϕ, is computed from a two-by-two table, but unlike ϕ it cannot be used for nominally or ordinally scaled measurements.

8. **Rank-order correlation,** r_o. If a product-moment correlation is computed for two sets of ranks, the results will be identical with the rank-order correlation obtained for the same data. The rank-order correlation is derived from the product-moment correlation on the assumption that the values assumed by both variables are 1, 2, 3, . . . N. The mean and variance of X are therefore identical with the mean and variance of Y, and both depend entirely upon N. When these relationships are taken into account, the formula for r can be simplified, and the ultimate result is the formula for the rank-order correlation. The rank-order correlation is a measure of the strength and direction of relationship between two sets of ranks and can be used when both variables have been measured on ordinal, interval, or ratio scales.

9. **Biserial correlation.** This is a measure of the strength and direction of relationship between two variables, one of which is

[6] See pp. 518ff. for a discussion of 'how large is large.'

normally distributed but artificially dichotomized, and the other of which has a continuous range of scores. For example, one might use a biserial correlation to study the extent to which the ability to pass a certain test is related to practice on the material. If the test scores are distributed normally but we know only that an individual passed or did not pass, and if we have quantitative measures of amount of practice, we can then compute a biserial correlation.

10. **Partial correlation.** We saw that the product-moment correlation between two variables, for example, height and weight, could be spuriously high because both are correlated with a third variable, age, which has not been controlled. Partial correlation is a technique for determining the true relationship between height and weight once the effect of the third variable, age, has been eliminated.

11. **Multiple correlation.** This is a measure which tells the strength and direction of relationship between one variable, called the 'criterion,' and the combination of many other variables. It also tells how much weight should be given to each of the many variables from which the criterion is being predicted. For example, a college may be interested in knowing how well it can predict the academic success of entering freshmen. For each freshman the college may have three examination scores, an IQ, and a high-school average. In order to find the multiple-correlation coefficient, it is necessary first to determine how each of these five variables taken individually correlates with college success. Then those that have the highest correlations are given the greatest weight, but all the variables are used together to make a prediction which is better than the prediction that would be made on the basis of any one variable alone. The multiple-correlation coefficient tells how good is the prediction made in this way.

Questions

1. Give an example of a situation in which E would be very much higher than an r computed from the same data.

2. If you computed a Pearson r between two variables, and then ranked the individuals on both variables and computed a rank-order correlation and found the two results to be identical, what could you conclude about the ranks?

3. Make up a table that will summarize the measures of relatedness

available when X is measured on a nominal, ordinal, or interval scale, and Y is measured on a nominal, ordinal, or interval scale.

4. Below are listed several problems that might be of interest to a research psychologist. Describe briefly an experiment you might conduct to solve each one and name the measure of relatedness that could most appropriately be used to describe your results. If your choice of a measure involves assumptions about the data, describe these assumptions.

You wish to determine:

a. Whether the effectiveness of psychotherapy for hospitalized patients is related to the length of time they have been hospitalized.

b. Whether Negroes' estimates of the intelligence of other Negroes is related to skin color of the latter.

c. The reliability of a certain test. Reliability is defined as the extent to which a test correlates with itself.

d. How well a man's skill as a pilot can be predicted from a knowledge of his scores on a battery of tests of special abilities.

e. Whether the tendency of a marriage to end in divorce is related to the age of the woman at the time of marriage.

f. Whether the subjective difficulty of arithmetic problems is related to the actual times required by a subject to solve the problems.

g. Whether children's estimates of the sizes of coins are related to the economic backgrounds of the children.

h. The strength of relationship between country of birth and intelligence.

i. The strength of relationship between political preference (Republican, Democratic, Socialist, etc.) and the section of the country in which a person lives (New England, Middle West, etc.).

Summary

Basically, all correlation measures describe the reduction in our uncertainty about one variable brought about by a knowledge of some other variable. When the data come from interval or ratio scales the variance serves as the most useful measure of uncertainty, and both the measures of correlation discussed in this chapter are measures of variance reduction.

E^2, the square of the correlation ratio, is the proportion of the total variance accounted for by the differences between subgroups. It is the ratio of the 'between-groups sum of squares' to the 'total sum of squares.' It is analogous to $\hat{T}$ in that it is a measure of uncertainty reduction, but s^2 is substituted for $\hat{H}$ as a measure of uncertainty. E^2 can be used whenever one variable comes from an interval or ratio scale. If both variables come from interval or ratio scales but the relationship between them is not linear, E^2 may be the best measure of relationship available.

The coefficient of correlation, r, can be used only when both variables have been measured on interval or ratio scales and the relationship between them is linear. When a scatter-plot of the data is prepared, two regression lines can be drawn between the points, one describing the way in which $\dfrac{\tilde{y}}{s_y}$ varies as a function of $\dfrac{x}{s_x}$ and the other describing the way $\dfrac{\tilde{x}}{s_x}$ varies as a function of $\dfrac{y}{s_y}$. The slope of the line describing how $\dfrac{\tilde{y}}{s_y}$ varies as a function of $\dfrac{x}{s_x}$ is r; the slope of the line describing the variation of $\dfrac{\tilde{x}}{s_x}$ with $\dfrac{y}{s_y}$ is $\dfrac{1}{r}$. When an individual's score on one variable is predicted from a knowledge of his score in the other, there will be some error in the prediction unless the two variables are perfectly related. This error is measured by the variance of estimate, which is the average of the squares of the deviations of the obtained scores from the predicted scores. The ratio of the variance of estimate to the total variance is a measure of the proportion of error still left in our predictions. One minus this proportion is a measure of the extent to which unpredictability has been reduced. It is called r^2, the coefficient of determination. The coefficient of correlation is thus a special case of the correlation ratio, with variance of estimate substituted for within-groups variance.

Machine computation of the correlation coefficient requires as a first step the calculation of six quantities: ΣX, ΣY, ΣX^2, ΣY^2, ΣXY, and N. From these six quantities we can find the coefficient of correlation, the means, variances, standard deviations, variances and standard errors of estimate, regression equations, the coefficient of determination, and the coefficient of non-determination, and thus carry out a fairly complete analysis of our data.

Many other measures of correlation have been developed for special purposes. Most of these are derived from the product-moment correlation by making certain assumptions about the nature of the measures to be correlated.

Answers

Page 232

(b) $\hat{T} = .6703$; (c) $E^2 = .588$; (e) 19.5, 18.1, 19.3, 20.2, 21.1, a junior.

Page 236

1. $E_{xy}^2 = .630$.

6. $\overline{X} = 45.5$, $s = 13.33$.   7. $\overline{X} = 496.4$, $s = 98.8$.

Page 257

3. (a) .4, 2.5; (c) 2.5; (d) $+1$; (e) 0; (f) 6.25 cm., 0; (g) 1.00; (h) 1.
4. 70.
5. (a) 115, 107.5, 100, 96.25, 88.75; (b) 556.25, 518.75, 500, 462.5, 425; (c) $\tilde{X} = -.15Y + 175$, $\tilde{Y} = -3.75X + 875$.
6. 79.46.

Page 261

1. (problem 3) 0, 0, 0, 0, .40, 2.5, 1.00, 0; (problem 4) 24.96, 5, 24.96, 5, .95, .9025, .0975; (problem 5) 1093.75, 33.1, 43.75, 6.6, -3.75, $-.15$, .5625, .4375; (problem 6) 108, 10.4, 18.75, 4.3, 1.2, .21, .25, .75.
2. $r = +.80$.

Page 266

1. (Answers are ΣX, ΣY, ΣX^2, ΣY^2, ΣXY, and N, in that order) (a) 11, 39, 45, 521, 150, 3; (b) 1.9, 547, 1.11, 60127, 210.6, 5; (c) 21, 21, 91, 91, 91, 6; (d) 21, 21, 91, 91, 56, 6.
2. (1) .983; (2) $+$; (3) 53.41; (4) 15.30 or 234.01; (5) 50.04; (6) 15.00 or 224.99; (7) $\tilde{X} = Y + 3.37$; (8) 2.82 or 7.95; (9) $\tilde{Y} = .964X - 1.45$; (10) 2.76 or 7.62; (11) 96.6%; (12) 3.4%.
3. (1) $-.72$; (2) $-$; (3) 50; (4) 10 or 100; (5) 25; (6) 4 or 16; (7) $\tilde{X} = -1.80Y + 95$; (8) 6.9 or 48; (9) $\tilde{Y} = -.29X + 39.5$; (10) 2.8 or 7.68; (11) 52%; (12) 48%.
4. $r = +.799$; $\overline{X} = 166.3$; $s_x = 20.8$; $\overline{Y} = 39.6$; $s_y = 7.7$; $\tilde{X} = 2.16Y + 80.8$; $s_{\text{est}_x} = 12.5$; $\tilde{Y} = .296X - 93.3$; $s_{\text{est}_x} = 4.6$; $r^2 = .638$; $k^2 = .362$.

THE RATIO SCALE

A ratio scale is a scale with a fixed unit of measurement and an absolute zero. If it is meaningful to talk about one quantity as being twice as great as another, or one-third as great as another, or any multiple of another, the scale is a ratio scale. Length, weight, electrical resistance, periods of time (as opposed to time from the beginning of time), and any measurements obtained by counting are instances of variables measurable on ratio scales.

Numerals that come from a ratio scale have all the properties of real numbers. That means that any manipulation that can be carried out with numbers can be appropriately employed with the numerals applied to variables measured on a ratio scale. Magnitudes can be expressed as ratios of each other, square roots can be extracted, numerals can be raised to powers or treated as exponents, logarithms can be obtained, and many other powerful kinds of mathematical analysis can be used. While there are very few *statistics* that are applicable to a ratio scale but not to an interval scale, there are many new mathematical techniques that are applicable only with a ratio scale. This chapter will be concerned primarily with those techniques. Specifically, we shall discuss many different kinds of equations. Of these, only the straight line can be applied to data from a scale weaker than a ratio scale. That is why we discuss these equations in this chapter, even though the general principles of scientific investigation to be discussed apply more generally.

8.1 Functional Relationships

8.1.1 The Search for Scientific Laws: The physical, biological, or social scientist is concerned with the examination of the universe around him and the attempt to find or establish orderly relationships underlying what is often a surface appearance of chaos. The universe he investigates is already partly structured for him; within the structure, however, there are gaps. Motivated by a belief in the lawfulness of nature and in the ability of man to find or express this lawfulness, the scientist seeks to fill the gaps, to reduce uncertainty, and, most of all, to derive new laws. The modern scientist brings to his work predictions based on theories, and hunches based on experience. Both of these lead him to carry out one particular experiment instead of any one of the hundreds of others he might have conducted. One of his aims in doing an experiment is to be able to specify a functional relationship between two or more variables.

For example, common observation suggests that the amount of light on a surface gets smaller and smaller as the surface is moved farther away from the source of light. If we let y stand for the amount of light on the surface and x for the distance of the surface from the light source, we can say that

$$y = f(x)$$

which is read: 'y is some function of x.' That means that y, the light on the surface, is in some way dependent upon the distance between the surface and the source, y. We should like to specify also that $f(x)$ (read 'f of x') is some *inverse* function—that is, the greater the distance the smaller will be the amount of light. But these statements leave a lot to be desired in the search for a scientific law. What we really seek is an exact specification of $f(x)$. We want to replace $y = f(x)$ by some equation that will tell us precisely *how* y is related to x. Experimental evidence as well as theoretical considerations show that the equation which will relate distance and amount of light is

$$y = \frac{k}{x^2}$$

where k stands for the amount of light emitted by the source.

The amount of light (or, more exactly, the total radiation) is inversely proportional to the square of the distance between surface and source. That statement, whether it is made in words or in symbols, is a scientific law. To be able to make statements as precise and explicit as the inverse-square law is the aim of all science.

The scientist conducts his experiment and collects his data. His next step is to plot these data, using the x-axis for the independent variable (the one he has manipulated), and the y-axis for the dependent variable (the one whose variation he has measured).This first plot of results is ordinarily just a sketch—something for the scientist himself to look at and think about, not something to display to the world. Plotting the data puts them in a form which permits him to get an over-all picture, something very difficult to do from long tables of numbers. When the data are plotted, he looks at the plot, and looks and looks.

If the dependent variable, y, appears to do anything definite as the independent variable, x, is changed, the scientist is probably safe in saying that y depends upon x, or $y = f(x)$; perhaps he can make some further verbal qualification such as 'y is related to x in a monotonically increasing fashion.' That would mean that as x increases, y always increases and never decreases. But, as in the case of light and distance, he wishes, if he can, to describe the relationship more exactly. Examination of the plot may suggest that the data will be fitted by some simple equation, or the theory that led to the experiment may predict that some simple equation will describe the data. If the theory predicts or the plot suggests that the data points lie along a straight line, for example, the scientist may draw a straight line along the points. Perhaps the shape of the curve suggests that as x increases by a constant *ratio* (that is, as each value of x becomes twice, or three times, or some other multiple of the preceeding value) y increases by a constant *amount*. That would mean that if y were plotted against the logarithm of x, instead of against x itself, the points would fall on a straight line. Equipped with a table of logarithms and a piece of graph paper, the scientist would then investigate this possibility.

And so on. Guided by hunch, intuition, and trial-and-error, the scientist tries various equations, various plots, seeking always the one that will yield a simple, meaningful mathematical relationship.

The words 'simple' and 'meaningful' are of crucial importance here. *Any set of points can be fitted exactly by some equation*, but this equation may be both complicated and meaningless. When we say that an equation is complicated, we mean that it has a great many constants.

$$y = ax$$

is a very simple equation. It has only one constant, *a*. This is also true of

$$y = a \log x, \quad \text{or}$$
$$y = e^x + a$$

(*e*, being a natural constant like π, does not really count.)
The equations

$$y = ax + b, \quad \text{or} \quad y = a \log x + b, \quad \text{or} \quad y = e^{ax} + b$$

are all slightly more complicated, since each of them has two constants, *a* and *b*. A really complicated equation would be:

$$y = ax^8 + bx^7 + cx^6 + dx^5 + ex^4 + fx^3 + gx^2 + hx + i$$

That equation has nine constants, and an equation of that form could fit any nine points we chose to plot, but it is a complex and probably a meaningless equation.

When we say that an equation is *meaningful*, we mean that the constants can be identified with aspects of the natural or experimental situation. The constants that appear in equations can be divided into three classes:

1. **Natural constants,** such as π, *e*, and *c* (the velocity of light). These could be called 'constant constants' because each is a specific number, the same at all times and in all circumstances. An equation such as

$E = mc^2$ (the energy is equal to the mass times the square of the velocity of light)

is the simplest form of equation because it involves only the two variables and a natural constant.

2. Constants which are specified by some aspect of the experimental or natural situation and which change as the situation changes. These are sometimes called 'variable constants' or, more properly, **parameters.** For example, the expression relating voltage and current (amperes) in a wire is

$$E = I \qquad \times \qquad k$$

volts   amperes   times   a constant

But the constant, *k*, in this equation is not just any old constant; it is the resistance of the wire, measured in ohms. The voltage is proportional to the current, but the rate at which voltage increases as the current is increased depends upon the resistance. A plot of this relationship, which is called Ohm's Law, and is properly stated as $E = IR$, is given in Figure 8.1. There are many straight lines, each one for a different value of the constant R.

In Figure 8.1, voltage is plotted as a function of current with resistance as a parameter. We could just as well plot voltage as a function of resistance with current as a parameter, as is done in Figure 8.2. In many cases like this one there is no way to decide

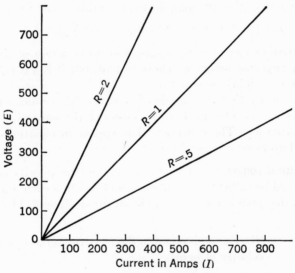

FIG. 8.1 Ohm's Law with resistance as a parameter.

which is a parameter and which is a variable, and graphs depicting relationships are often plotted in several different forms to make all the relationships explicit. In other instances, particularly in psychology and biology, the equations describe a general relationship which holds for all organisms, but the constants represent some characteristic of the individual, which, though specifiable, is not a variable of general interest. Such constants are seldom treated as independent variables.

3. **Arbitrary fitting constants.** These are constants whose values are manipulated in order to make the curve go through or near the

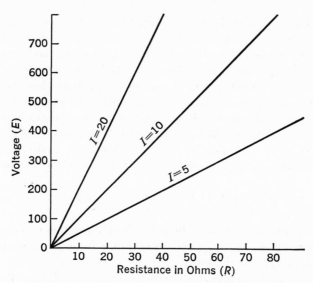

FIG. 8.2   Ohm's law with current as a parameter.

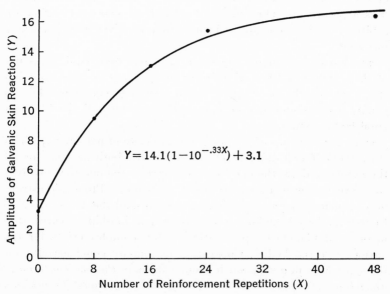

$$Y = 14.1(1 - 10^{-.33X}) + 3.1$$

FIG. 8.3   Data obtained by Hovland and quoted in Hull, C., *Principles of Behavior*, New York, Century, 1943, p. 103.

points on the graph. It is characteristic of a new science like psychology that many of its equations require the use of one or more such arbitrary constants. It is also characteristic of the history of a science that, as more knowledge is accumulated and more relationships are understood, meaning may be assigned to these arbitrary constants. Alternatively, equations requiring the use of many such constants may be replaced by equations whose constants can be related to natural conditions. An example of the use of arbitrary fitting constants, in addition to natural constants and parameters, is the description of the learning curve in Figure 8.3 by the equation

$$y = 14.1(1 - 10^{-.033x}) + 3.1$$

where y is the magnitude of the galvanic skin reaction to a tone, and x is the number of times the subject has been given an electric shock after hearing the tone.

In this equation, 1 and 10 are natural constants—they are the same from one experiment to the next. The 3.1 stands for the magnitude of the galvanic skin response before any shocks have been given; it is a parameter. The number 14.1 and the exponent $-.033$ are arbitrary fitting constants which cannot be given any particular meaning.

The most 'meaningful' equation is the one that requires the use of the smallest number of arbitrary fitting constants. An equation that uses no such constants is called a **rational equation,** while an equation containing one or more arbitrary constants is called an **empirical equation.**

One of the axioms of science is the **principle of parsimony,** which states that if two different explanations will both account for all the available data, the one to be preferred is the one that involves the fewer unverified assumptions. For example, Ptolemaic astronomy, which assumed that the sun goes around the earth, was able to account for all the known data about relationships of earth, sun, moon, and planets by postulating highly complex orbits for the various celestial bodies. Copernican astronomy could account for the same data in a very much simpler fashion. *Ptolemaic astronomy was relinquished not because it was 'disproved' but because it was highly unparsimonious.* An equation is really a scientific theory, and in this theory *every arbitrary constant is an unverified* (and unverifiable) *assumption.* Therefore, of two equations, both of which appear to fit the data equally well, the one with the fewer arbitrary fitting constants is to be preferred.[1]

Back now to the laboratory. Our scientist has just finished plotting his data and has reason to believe that they can be described by some simple equation. Let us suppose that he has found that $y = ax + b$. Now, if not before, he asks himself, 'What would this mean?' Suppose x were zero— could y (in fact, as well as in theory) equal b? Suppose x grows larger and larger—will y continue to increase as this equation says it does? If the general form of the equation makes sense, he next inquires about the constants. Do the constants a and b have any identifiable correlates in the natural world? Can they be specified in advance, or do their values depend upon the outcome of a particular experiment?

An equation is a theory, and once a simple rational equation which describes the data has been found, it must be tested. There are two basic kinds of tests available to determine the appropriateness of an equation or to choose between two alternative equations.

The first of these is the **statistical test**. In Chapter 7 we mentioned the principle of least squares. It is the principle that that curve best fits a set of points from which the sum of the squares of the deviations is a minimum. If, then, we have a choice of two possible equations for the description of a set of data, we may choose between them by the least-squares criterion. There are other statistical techniques that can also be used to test the goodness of fit of an equation to a set of points.

A much better test of the appropriateness of an equation is the **experimental test**. If the constants in the equation have been identified with correlates in the natural world, then these correlates should be varied in further experiments to see if the new data will follow the course predicted for them by the old equation. Suppose, for example, that Ohm's Law had not yet been formulated, and we, as scientists, were investigating the relation between voltage and current. All our measurements have been made on one piece of wire whose resistance is known to be 100 ohms. We find that the equation relating current and voltage is

Volts equals amps times 100

---

[1] As we said before, any set of points can be fitted by some equation provided the equation has enough constants. There is an old saying among scientists that 'with two constants you can draw an elephant and with three you can make his tail wag.'

'Aha!' we say, 'it may be just coincidence, but that number "100" is very suggestive. Perhaps that constant is really the resistance of the wire.' This theory we now proceed to test by repeating the experiment with many different kinds of wire of known resistances, and our results confirm our suspicion that volts equals amps times ohms. We have made an experimental test of our equation by varying the natural correlate of the constant in the equation, and observing that the old equation adequately predicts the new data.[2]

To summarize the steps involved in the search for a scientific law:

1. An investigator starts with a theory or a hunch. He thinks that some dependent variable, y, which he will measure, is related to some independent variable, x, which he will control.

2. He conducts his experiment and gathers his data. He plots his results, and then he broods.

3. He seeks, with all the methods at his disposal, a simple equation which will describe his data.

4. If a simple equation is found, the investigator tries to identify the constants in the equation with natural correlates.

5. He tests his equation and his theory by varying the natural correlates with which the constants have been identified and determining whether the old equation will satisfactorily predict new results.

8.1.2 An Illustrative Experiment:
Let us consider the application of these principles in a concrete experimental situation.[3]

If a man who is operating a complex machine has to read an instrument panel, common sense suggests that the time he requires to read the panel will depend upon the number of instruments on the panel. Common sense, however, cannot tell us *how* the time required for reading will increase as the number of instruments increases, and that was the question the experiment was designed to answer.

The independent variable in the experiment was the number of dials on a panel. Eight panels were made up containing 1, 2, 4, 8,

---

[2] That is not the way Mr. Ohm did it. He found that the relation between current and voltage was described by a straight line. The slope of the line was different for different kinds and sizes of wires, and Ohm *defined* resistance as the slope of the line.

[3] Senders, V. L., *The Effect of Number of Dials on Qualitative Reading of a Multiple Dial Panel*, WADC-TR 52–182, 1952.

16, 25, 32, and 45 dials. On each panel, all the pointers except one were pointing in the same direction, while one pointer was 'misaligned.' The subject's task was to find the dial with the misaligned pointer, and the time he required to do so was the dependent variable. In the actual experimental situation the subject pressed a button which opened a shutter and exposed the panel. When the subject had located the misaligned pointer he released the button and the shutter closed. The time between the pressing and the

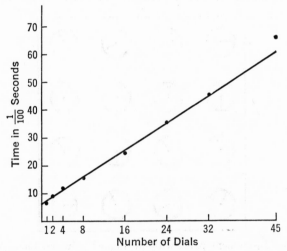

FIG. 8.4   Time to scan a panel as a function of number of dials on panel.

releasing of the button was accurately measured. The experiment was designed in such a way that such extraneous variables as learning, fatigue, and motivation would not materially affect the results.

The results of the experiment are shown in Figure 8.4. Time required to find the misaligned pointer increases as the number of dials on the panel is increased, and the points appear to lie along a straight line. Various other equations were tried, but no other simple equation could describe the data as well as the straight line. The equation for the line was found by the method described in Chapter 7. It was

$$\tilde{y} = 1.2x + 6.5$$

where $\tilde{y}$ = predicted time in one-hundredths of a second required to read panel, and x = number of dials on the panel.

Does this equation make sense? Suppose there were no dials on the panel—would it be reasonable to suppose that the time required would be 6.5 hundredths of a second? That supposition is reasonable, because some time is required by the subject just to press and release the button, even when there is nothing for him to look at. Suppose the number of dials was increased to 100 or 1000? Would the same equation still hold? The answer to that question is not so

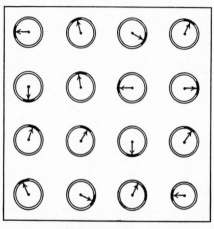

Fig. 8.5   Instrument panel without aligned pointers. Each pointer tip should be within the shaded 45° sector. Which one is not?

clear, but it is at least reasonable to conclude that within the range of 0–45 dials the equation provides a sensible description of the data.

Next, the constants in the equation were examined. The intercept constant, 6.5, is easily identified as the time required to operate the apparatus when no decision is required of the subject. The slope constant, 1.2, presents a problem. It can be called 'time per dial' but upon what factors does its magnitude depend? Perhaps a more difficult reading situation could be devised. Then the 'time per dial' should be increased, and the straight line describing the points should be steeper. To test that hypothesis a new set of dial panels was made up. A sample panel is shown in Figure 8.5. The subject's task is to locate the pointer that is not within the shaded sector.

The experiment was repeated using the new panels, and the

results are shown in Figure 8.6. It appears that these results will again be fitted by a straight line, whose equation is found to be:

$$\tilde{y} = 18.5x - 5.1$$

But this new equation, though it is of the same form as the old one, does *not* make sense, for it says that if there were no dials on the panel it would take the subject *less than no time* (5.1 hundredths of

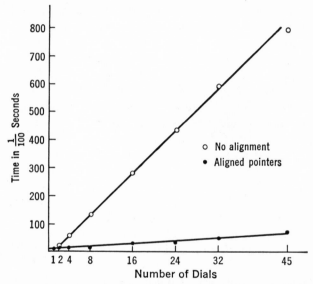

Fɪɢ. 8.6 Results of experiment without aligned pointers. The earlier results are given for comparison.

a second less) to operate the apparatus. Clearly, that is an impossibility, so the notion that the data are described by a straight line must be rejected.

Alternatively, it is possible to conceive of the data as being fitted by *two* straight lines, one through the points for $x = 0$, $x = 1$, and $x = 2$, and another through the points from $x = 4$ to $x = 45$. This would mean that the nature of the subject's task is different when there are four or more dials than it is when there are two or fewer, a notion that seems to make some sense in view of the reported difficulty of locating the deviant pointer when there are many dials on the panel. Two such straight lines were fitted to the data. There

were too few points to obtain an equation for the condition where
x is less than four, but when the number of dials is greater than or
equal to four

$$\tilde{y} = 18.6x - 5.3$$

That is the state in which conclusions are left. In many ways it
is an unsatisfactory state, since one set of data is described by one
equation, while two equations are required to describe a comparable
set. Furthermore, the intercept constant in the last equation cannot
be identified with any natural correlate. Perhaps future experi-
mentation will show that the original data really require two equations also, or perhaps one equation for a curve can be found which,
with a change of parameters, will fit both sets of data. It would take
a good deal experimental work to find out.

There is one bright spot in the situation as it stands. A more difficult reading situation was found to produce a line with a steeper
slope, and the slope of the line relating time to number of dials can
perhaps be used as a quantitative measure of reading difficulty.
Then by comparing the slopes of the lines for different kinds of dials,
an investigator would be justified in drawing such conclusions as:
'Dial A is 1.17 times as hard to read as Dial B.' With further experimental work, he could go on to establish the functional relationships between reading difficulty, so defined, and such physical
variables as the spacing of graduations on the dial, or the lengths
of dial pointers.

8.1.3 Kinds of Equations: Up to now there has been a 'right'
answer for every problem we have approached. When we look for
the *kind of equation* that best describes a set of data, there is usually
no one right answer. Furthermore there is no mechanical routine
by which we can find an answer. The only way to start the search
for an equation is to be familiar with many different kinds of equations and with the curves they generate. In this section we shall
consider several different kinds of curves so that you may have at
least some familiarity with them when you encounter them in your
reading or need them for research.

1. **The straight line.** By this time, you should be thoroughly
familiar with the straight line. Its general equation is

$$y = a + bx \qquad (8.1.1)$$

where the constant a is the intercept of the line, and the constant b its slope. Figure 8.7 shows the effects of changing the constants a and b. Whenever the dependent variable, y, is directly proportional to the independent variable, x, the data will appear as points along a straight line with a positive slope. When y is inversely propor-

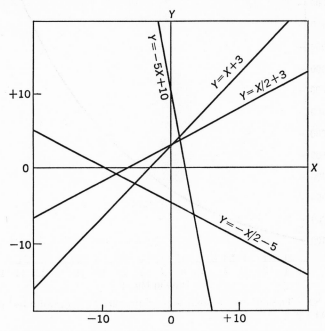

Fig. 8.7 Straight lines of the form $y = ax + b$, showing effects of changes in a and b.

tional to x the points will lie along a straight line with a negative slope.

2. **The exponential.** One general form of the exponential equation is

$$y = ab^x \qquad (8.1.2)$$

If, when x changes *arithmetically* (by constant amounts), y changes *geometrically* (by constant multiples) the points can be described by an exponential equation. For example, if, as x assumed the values given in Table 8.1, y assumed the corresponding values given in that table, x would be said to be increasing in arithmetic progression

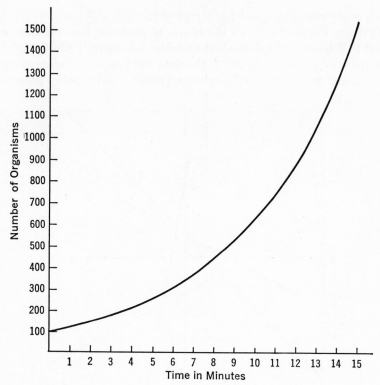

FIG. 8.8   The number of organisms, y, produced after x minutes, where $y = 100(1.2)^x$.

and y in geometric progression. Note that each time x is increased by 1, y is doubled. The equation for these numbers is

$$y = 2^x$$

Table 8.1

x	0	1	2	3	4	5
y	1	2	4	8	16	32

You may recognize that formula. If 'number of equally likely alternatives' is substituted for y, and '$\hat{H}$' is substituted for x, it is the formula relating the uncertainty in a distribution to the number of classes.

The exponential equation can also be used to describe the growth of populations under certain hypothetical conditions. In particular, the use of such an equation assumes that there is nothing to limit population growth. This is an unlikely assumption, since limitations of space and food will usually prevent a population from increasing faster and faster as time goes on. However, we might consider a hypothetical situation in which we have 100 micro-organisms in a culture with unlimited space and unlimited food supply. If each

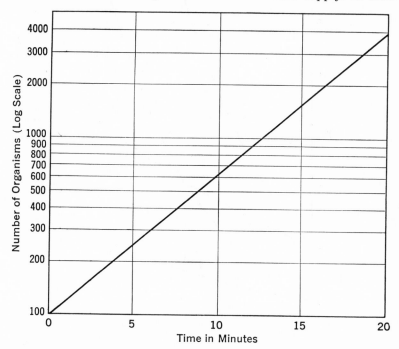

FIG. 8.9   Data from figure 8.8 plotted on semi-log co-ordinates.

organism divides into two on the average of once every five minutes, how many organisms will there be at the end of x minutes?

If each organism divides once every five minutes, then, on the average, at any particular minute there will be 1.2 times as many organisms as there were one minute before. If we started with 100 organisms, the equation describing the number of organisms as a function of time would be

$$y = 100(1.2)^x$$

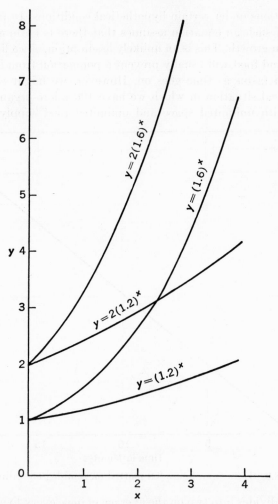

FIG. 8.10 The equation $y = ab^x$ where b is greater than 1, showing effects of changes in a and b.

where y is the number of organisms and x is the number of minutes since the start of the experiment.

These results are plotted in Figure 8.8.

Solving such equations by simple substitution is no easy job. If we wanted to find out how many organisms there would be at the end of 45 minutes we should have to raise 1.2 to the 45th power—

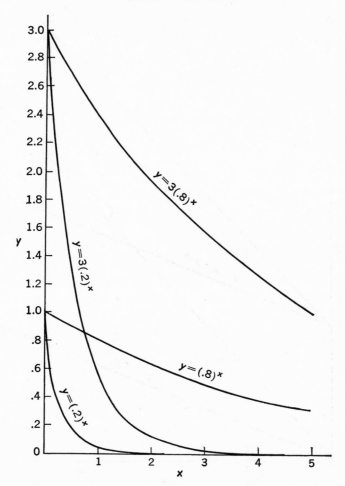

Fig. 8.11 The equation $y = ab^x$ where b is less than 1, showing effects of changes in a and b.

heaven forbid! This is where logarithms come to our aid. If

$$y = ab^x, \quad \text{then}$$
$$\log y = \log a + x \log b$$

But a and b are constants, and therefore $\log a$ and $\log b$ are constants. Let us call $\log a$ 'c' and $\log b$, 'd' Then:

$$\log y = c + dx$$

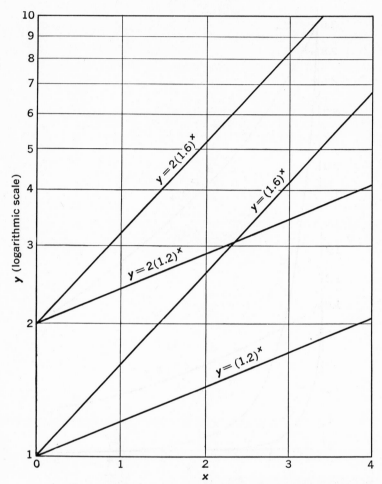

FIG. 8.12   Data of figure 8.10 plotted on semi-log co-ordinates.

This is our old friend, the equation for a straight line, with slope constant d and intercept c. The only difference is that it is now log y that is linearly related to x, whereas before, it was y itself. *If* y *is an exponential function of* x, *then log* y *is a linear function of* x.

Looking up logarithms is work, and there is a way to avoid doing it. One may purchase special graph paper known as semi-log paper, in which one axis is ruled in such a way that the spacing of successive numbers is proportional to the logarithms of those numbers. The numbers themselves, rather than their logarithms, are printed on the paper, so it is necessary only to plot points against the proper numbers, and the paper, in effect, converts from numbers to the

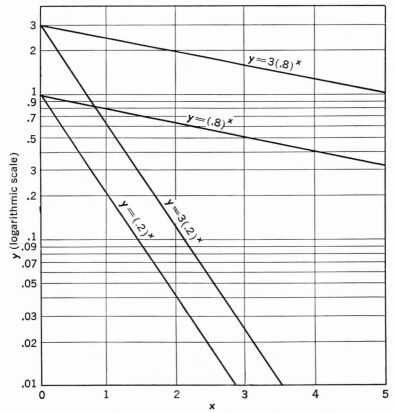

FIG. 8.13   Data of figure 8.11 plotted on semi-log co-ordinates.

logarithms of numbers. In Figure 8.9, the population-growth data are plotted on semi-log paper.

Figures 8.10 and 8.11 present several plots of the type $y = ab^x$ showing the effects of changes in the constants a and b. These same plots are presented on semi-log paper in Figures 8.12 and 8.13.

The exponential may also be of the form:

$$x = ab^y$$

In this case, geometric increases in x lead to arithmetic increases in y. This type of curve is frequently encountered in biology and psychology, where a geometric progression of changes in some aspect of the stimulating environment leads to an arithmetic progression

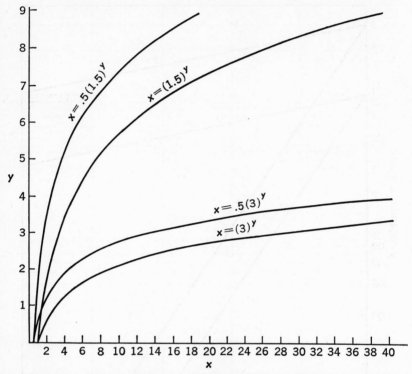

FIG. 8.14 The equation $x = ab^y$ where b is greater than 1, showing effects of changes in a and b.

of changes in the organism. One of the oldest laws in psychology, Fechner's Law, states that

$$S = k \log R$$

where S is the magnitude of a sensation, measured in number of just-noticeable-differences above threshold

R is the magnitude of the stimulus intensity, measured in terms of the absolute threshold

k is some (arbitrary) constant

Geometric changes in the stimulus lead to arithmetic changes in the sensation. Nowadays we measure response instead of trying to get at sensation directly as Fechner did, but we often find that response (magnitude or frequency or some other characteristic) is proportional to (linearly related to) the logarithm of the magnitude of the stimulus.

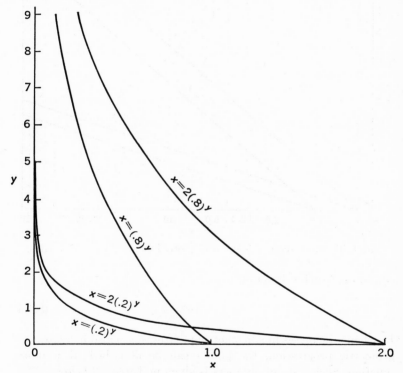

FIG. 8.15   The equation $x = ab^y$ where b is less than 1, showing effects of changes in a and b.

In Figures 8.14 and 8.15, some curves of the form $x = ab^y$ are plotted on arithmetic co-ordinates, and in Figures 8.16 and 8.17 the same points are plotted on semi-log co-ordinates. This time the horizontal axis rather than the vertical axis is logarithmic.

3. **The power function.** When y is proportional to some constant power of x, the equation is called a power function. The general

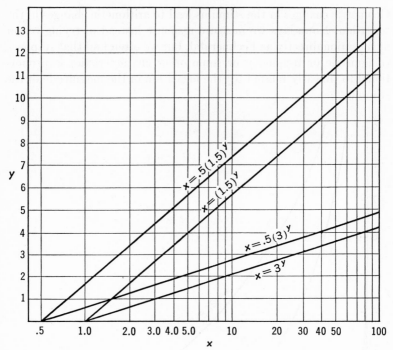

Fig. 8.16   Same data as figure 8.14 plotted on semi-log co-ordinates.

equation of such a function is

$$y = ax^b \qquad (8.1.4)$$

If, when x increases in a geometric progression, y also increases in a geometric progression, the points can be described by a power function. Such a set of numbers is given in Table 8.2 below.

Table 8.2

x	1	2	4	8	16	32
y	1	4	16	64	256	1024

In this table each x is twice the x before it and each y is four times the y before it. Both series therefore form geometric progressions, and are described by the power function $y = x^2$.

The exponent, b, may be either positive or negative, and it may have an absolute value greater than, or less than, 1. Remember that

$$x^{-b} = \frac{1}{x^b} \qquad \text{and} \qquad x^{1/b} = \sqrt[b]{x}$$

Therefore, if the exponent is negative, y will get smaller and smaller as x gets larger and larger. The larger the absolute value of a negative exponent, the faster will y shrink as x grows. If the exponent is

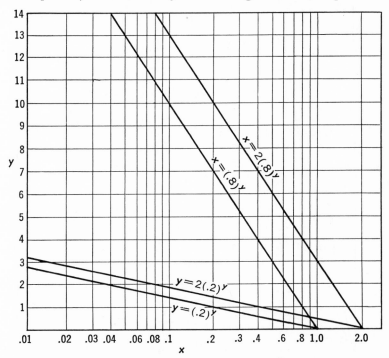

FIG. 8.17 Same data as figure 8.15 plotted on semi-log co-ordinates.

positive but less than 1, y will get larger as x does, but y will not increase as fast as x. The closer the exponent is to 1, the closer will be the rate of growth of y to the rate of growth of x. If the exponent *is* 1, then y grows at the same rate as x and the equation is a straight line. Some of these relationships are shown in Figures 8.18 and 8.19.

Power functions, like exponentials, are likely to be very little fun to compute. Furthermore, it is very difficult to tell by eye alone whether a scattered collection of points can be adequately described by such a function. Again, taking logarithms will help. If

$$y = ax^b \qquad \text{then} \qquad \log y = \log a + b \log x$$

Log a is a constant, but both log x and log y are variables. Again we
have the equation for a straight line with intercept log a and slope b.

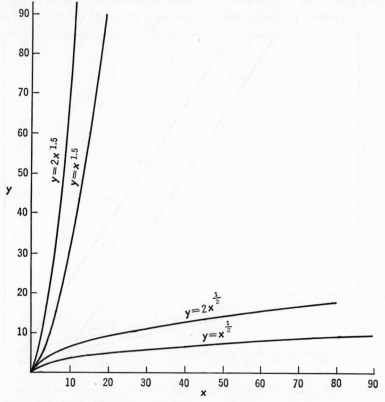

FIG. 8.18　Equations of the form $y = ax^b$ where b is positive, showing
effects of changes in a and b.

This time, however, we plot the logarithm of y against the logarithm
of x. Graph paper that has logarithmic spacing on both axes, called
log-log or double-log paper, can be used for this. The curves of
Figures 8.18 and 8.19 are replotted on log-log paper in Figures 8.20
and 8.21.

Log-log graph paper has another useful function in addition to that of making straight lines out of power functions. If two variables are linearly related to each other over a very wide range of values, it may be physically impossible to show this fact on ordinary graph paper. If, for example, $y = ax$ for all values of x from 0 to 100,000, and we wish to show that the proportionality holds just as well

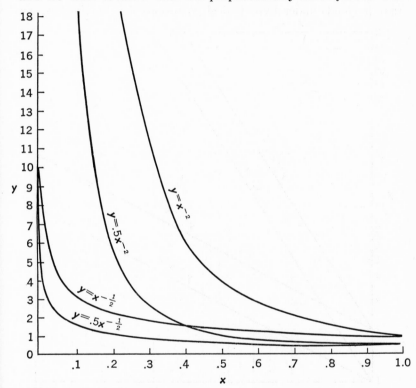

FIG. 8.19 Equations of the form $y = ax^b$ where b is negative, showing effects of changes in a and b.

when x changes between 0 and 1 as when it changes between 10,000 and 100,000, we must use log-log paper. Log-log paper exaggerates the importance of low numbers relative to high ones

4. **Other kinds of equations.** The straight line, the exponential, and the power function are relatively simple kinds of equations. Unfortunately, such simple functions are seldom encountered in practice in the biological and social sciences, since laws and regular-

ities in these sciences usually result from the interactions of many variables. We cannot possibly hope to do more than indicate some of the many different kinds of curves and equations which you may run across in reading reports on these subjects.

We spoke of the growth of a population of organisms and said that it could, under hypothetical conditions, be described by an

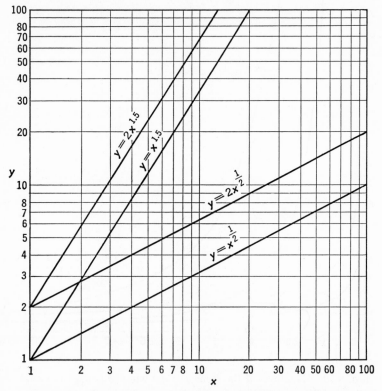

FIG. 8.20   Data of figure 8.18 plotted on log-log co-ordinates.

exponential function. Such an equation would apply, however, only when there was no theoretical limit to growth. When there is a limit—the more usual situation—some equation that specifies the limit must be used. An equation that is frequently applicable is

$$y = a(1 - e^{-cx}) \qquad (8.1.5)$$

A curve of this form is shown in Figure 8.25c. In this equation, a is the limit above which y cannot go. As x gets larger and larger, e^{-cx} which is the same as $\dfrac{1}{e^{cx}}$, gets closer and closer to zero, hence the quantity in the parentheses gets closer and closer to 1, which makes y get closer and closer to a. A value to which a curve gets closer and

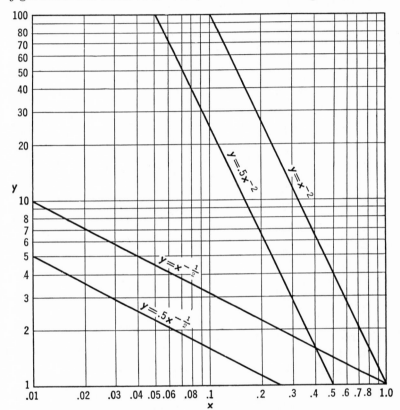

Fig. 8.21   Data of figure 8.19 plotted on log-log co-ordinates.

closer without ever reaching it is called the **asymptote** of the curve. a is the asymptote of the function above. Equations of this form are frequently used to describe learning: in these cases, a is the level of perfect performance. y stands for some measure of performance and x for the number of learning trials. A learning curve described by this equation has been shown in Figure 8.4. An equation of the form of formula 8.1.5 is called a **logistic**.

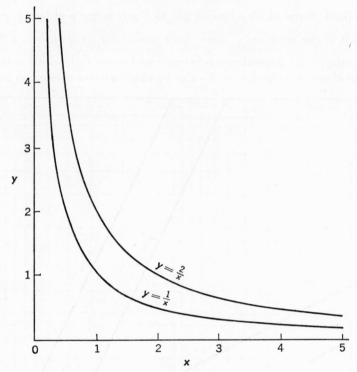

FIG. 8.22   Two simple hyperbolas.

Another fairly simple type of function that you may encounter is the **reciprocal function,** or **hyperbola.** All the equations below describe hyperbolas; equation 8.1.6 is the general form of the equation and can be used to describe any hyperbola.

$$y = \frac{1}{x} \qquad xy = 1 \qquad y = \frac{a}{x} \qquad xy = a$$

$$\frac{x^2}{a^2} - \frac{y^2}{b^2} = 1$$

$$\frac{(x - h)^2}{a^2} - \frac{(y - k)^2}{b^2} = 1 \qquad (8.1.6)$$

Two very simple hyperbolas have been plotted in Figure 8.27 and replotted on hyperbolic graph paper. This graph paper has an x-axis on which the spacing of lines is proportional to the reciprocals of various values of x. If a set of points forms a hyperbola they will appear as a straight line when plotted on this paper. Notice that hyperbolic paper actually includes a point for infinity, indicated by the symbol ∞. The value of y at this point on the x-axis is one asymptote of the hyperbola.

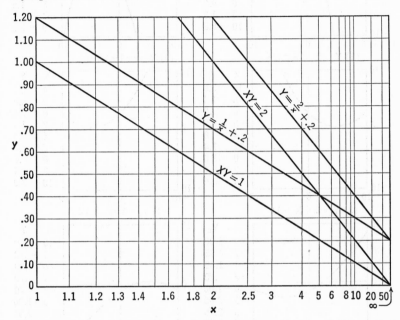

FIG. 8.23   Four hyperbolas, including the two of figure 8.22, plotted on hyperbolic co-ordinates.

The **parabola** is another type of curve that you may occasionally encounter. Its general equation is

$$y = ax^2 + bx + c \qquad (8.1.7)$$

Parts of several parabolas have been plotted in Figure 8.24.

Finally there are S-shaped or *sigmoid curves*, sometimes called **ogives.** You will remember from Chapter 6 that when a normal distribution is plotted as a cumulative percentage graph, the result is an S-shaped curve. (See Figure 6.13 to refresh your memory.) The equation of the cumulative form of the normal distribution is

$$y = \int\limits_{-\infty}^{t} \frac{1}{\sigma\sqrt{2\pi}} e^{-\frac{1}{2}z^2} dz \qquad (8.1.8)$$

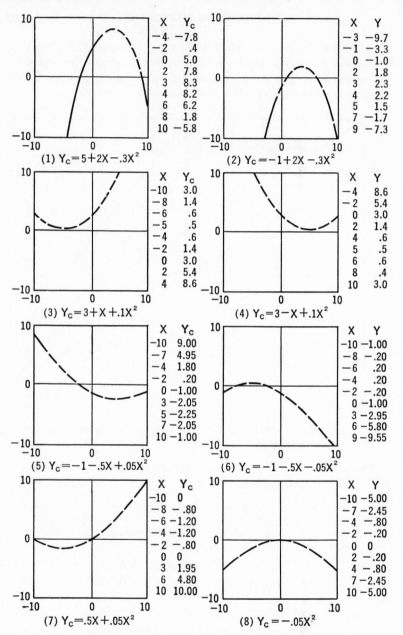

FIG. 8.24 Parts of some parabolas. (From Croxton, F. E., and Cowden, D. J., *Applied General Statistics*, New York, Prentice-Hall, 1955, p. 283; by permission of the authors and publisher.)

There are many other equations which give similar-looking curves but are quite different mathematically from the normal ogive. Some illustrations are given in Figure 8.25 along with the hideous equations that generate them. The main thing of interest about this figure is that the *curves* look very much alike, but the *equations* are very different. If we had a set of data which, when plotted, gave

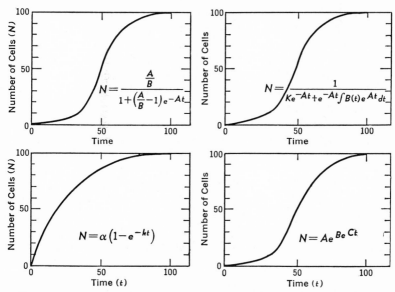

FIG. 8.25 Some curves characteristic of growth. The x axis represents time, and the y axis number of cells or organisms. Note that curves which look very similar may have very different equations. (From Shock, N., Growth Curves, Chap. X in *Handbook of Experimental Psychology*, Stevens, S. S. (ed.), New York, Wiley, 1951, p. 334; by permission of the author and publisher.)

an S-shaped curve, we *could* do a statistical test to see which equation minimized the sums of the squared deviations from the curve, but this would not really be a very good way to tell which equation was most satisfactory. Since the experimental error is usually greater than the small differences between the curves, a statistical test may be quite misleading. Instead, we should try to identify the parameters and predict how they will change when some aspect of the experimental situation is changed. Then we can carry out an experimental test to determine whether or not the parameters do indeed change as predicted.

Questions

1. Formulate each of the scientific laws below (a) as an equation, and (b) as a graph:

    a. Boyle's Law: At a constant temperature the volume of a given quantity of any gas varies inversely as the pressure to which the gas is subjected.

    b. The distance traveled during any period of time by a body falling from rest will be one half the product of the acceleration due to gravity and the square of the time.

    c. Charles's Law: The volumes assumed by a given mass of a gas at different temperatures, the pressure remaining constant, are, within moderate ranges of temperatures, directly proportional to the corresponding absolute temperatures.

    d. Weber's Law: The increment of intensity which must be added to some original stimulating intensity in order for an observer barely to detect a difference is a constant proportion of the original stimulating intensity.

2. Express each of the equations below (a) in words, and (b) as a graph:

    a. The Talbot-Plateau Law for the brightness of an interrupted light:

$$\log S = \log P + K$$

       Where S is the intensity to which a steady light must be adjusted to match the brightness of an interrupted light

          P is the proportion of the light-dark cycle which is illuminated

          K is a constant (actually, the logarithm of the intensity of the interrupted light).

    b. The Roscoe-Bunsen Law: for the threshold intensity of a short pulse of light:

$$I \times t = K$$

Where I is the intensity of the pulse of light, t is the duration of the pulse, and K is the amount of light required for threshold stimulation.

c. The Ferry-Porter Law relating the rate at which a light must be interrupted in order to appear fused (not flickering) to the intensity of the light:

$$n = a \log I + b$$

n is the number of flashes per second required for fusion
I is the intensity of the light

a and b are parameters related to experimental condition

3. Find, in any recent psychological journal, an example of research results which the author is trying to describe by means of an equation. How successful is he? Is the equation rational or empirical? How does the author test the validity of his equation?

4. Browse through some text on experimental psychology and try your hand at interpreting the graphs therein. Some good books for the purpose are:

Murchison, C. A. (ed.), *Handbook of General Experimental Psychology*, 1934.

Osgood, C., *Method and Theory in Experimental Psychology*, 1953.

Stevens, S. S. (ed.), *Handbook of Experimental Psychology*, 1951.

Woodworth, R. S., *Experimental Psychology*, 1938.

Woodworth, R. S., and Scholsberg, H., *Experimental Psychology*, Revised Edition, 1954.

5. If you are interested in giving further thought to the question of what constitutes a good scientific law, the following references will provide thought-provoking reading:

Jerison, H. J., 'Brain to Body Ratios and the Evolution of Intelligence,' *Science*, 121, 1955, 447–9.

Count, E. W., and Jerison, H. J., 'On Brain to Body Ratios and the Evolution of Intelligence,' *Science*, 122, 1955, 647–8 (and exchange of letters).

6. Plot the following equations on linear graph paper:

    a. $y = 3x$
    b. $y = .5x + 4$
    c. $y = -2x - 3$
    d. $y = -4$
    e. $x = 2$
    f. $2y = 3x - 1$

7. Plot the following equations on linear graph paper:

    a. $y = 10^x$ b. $y = 1.5(2)^x$ c. $y = 4(.5)^x$

8. Plot the equations in problem 7 either (a) by taking logarithms of both sides and plotting log y as a function of x, or (b) on semi-log paper.

9. Plot the following equations on linear graph paper:

    a. $x = 3^y$ b. $x = 2(\frac{1}{5})^y$

10. Plot the equations in problem 9 either (a) by taking logarithms of both sides and plotting y as a function of log x, or (b) on semi-log paper.

11. Plot the following equations on linear graph paper:

    a. $y = x^3$ b. $y = \frac{1}{2}(x)^2$ c. $x = 2y^{\frac{1}{2}}$ d. $x = 3y^{-2}$

12. Plot the equations in problem 11 either (a) by taking logarithms of both sides and plotting log y as a function of log x, or (b) on log-log graph paper.

13. Below are several sets of values of X and Y. Plot the points and try to identify the kind of equation they represent. Test your conjectures by using semi-log, log-log, or hyperbolic paper when the plot suggests that the equation is, respectively, an exponential, a power function, or a hyperbola. (Since the points represent hypothetical experimental results, they will not lie exactly along any theoretical curve, but will exhibit typical experimental variability.)

a. X	1	10	20	50	75	100	150			
Y	0	1.43	1.77	2.48	2.66	2.75	3.00			
b. X	0	1	2	3	4	5	6	7	8	9	10
Y	0	1.87	2.62	2.70	2.95	2.98	3.09	2.99	2.98	2.90	3.00

c. X 0   1   2   3   4   5   6

    Y 0   .2   .9   2.4   6.8   11.0   23.1

d. X 0   1   2   3   4   5   6

    Y -2.2 -4.0 -5.0 -7.3 -9.1 -9.6 -11.5

e. X 1   2   3   4   5   6   10

    Y 10.2   7.1   6.2   4.9   4.8   3.8   3.2

f. X 5   10   15   20   25   35   50   100

    Y .4   .7   .9   .9   1.1   1.3   1.4   1.7

g. X .5   1   2   3   4   5   6   7   8   9

    Y 8.5   4.7   3.5   3.3   2.6   2.6   2.4   2.5   2.4   2.3

14. Rule a sheet of semi-log paper and a sheet of log-log paper.

8.2 Frequency Distributions

Numerals from a ratio scale have all the properties of real numbers, and for the first time we are in a position to raise those numerals to

Table 8.3

X	$\log X$	Frequency	Cumulative frequency
20	1.30	1	100
19	1.28	0	99
18	1.26	1	99
17	1.23	1	98
16	1.20	1	97
15	1.18	1	96
14	1.15	1	95
13	1.11	2	94
12	1.08	2	92
11	1.04	3	90
10	1.00	3	87
9	.95	5	84
8	.90	6	79
7	.85	7	73
6	.78	10	66
5	.70	13	56
4	.60	15	43
3	.48	16	28
2	.30	10	12
1	0	2	2

powers, to extract roots, or to take reciprocals or logarithms. If we plot our histogram or frequency polygon in terms of the transformed values of the numerals (that is, in terms of x^2, or $\frac{1}{x}$ or $\log x$) we shall obtain very different results from those obtained by plotting the distribution in terms of x itself. We have already seen some of the

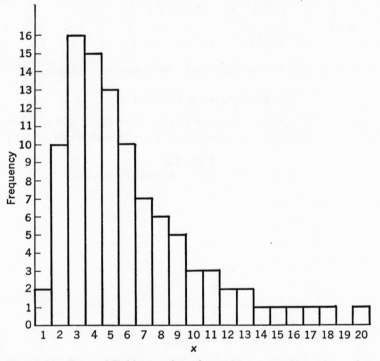

Fig. 8.26 Data of Table 8.3 plotted as a histogram. Note the positive skewness of the distribution.

uses of the normal distribution. Normally distributed data can be analyzed more easily and more fully than data that are not normally distributed. Sometimes, when X is not normally distributed, some transformed value of X, such as $\frac{1}{X}$, may be normally distributed, and, in such a case, we should ordinarily find it convenient to carry out our statistical manipulations with the transformed value. Of all the transformations that *could* be made, the one that has turned out to be most generally useful is the logarithmic transformation.

Consider the data in Table 8.3, p. 311. These data have been plotted as a histogram in Figure 8.26. Obviously the distribution is not normal, but positively skewed. In a burst of inspiration, we decide

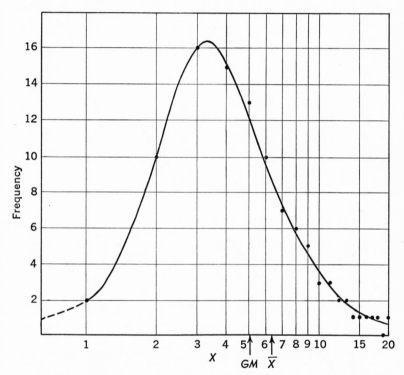

FIG. 8.27 Data of Table 8.3 plotted as a smoothed frequency curve on semi-log co-ordinates. Note the close approximation to a normal curve. Arrows indicate the arithmetic and geometric means, as explained in section 8.3.

to try plotting frequency against the logarithms of the X values instead of against X with the results shown in Figure 8.27. Behold! A normal distribution! Or at least something closely resembling one.

When we wanted to see if an obtained distribution was normal, we plotted the cumulative percentages on normal-probability paper. When a distribution is **log-normal,** that is, when the logarithms of the X values are normally distributed, the cumulative percentages will form a straight line on a special kind of graph paper called *log-probability paper*. On this paper the spaces between adjacent numerals on the x-axis are proportional to the differences between

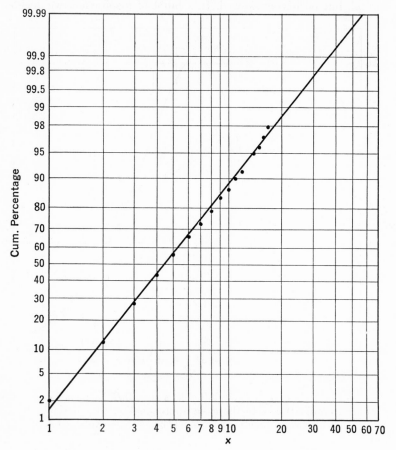

FIG. 8.28   Data of Table 8.3 plotted on log-normal graph paper.

the logarithms of those numerals. The y-axis is ruled like the y-axis of normal-probability paper. In Figure 8.28 the data of Table 8.3 are plotted on log-probability paper, and the result is very nearly a straight line.

Our distribution is not truly log-normal, as shown by Figures 8.27

and 8.28. If it were, there would be several cases having scores of $\frac{1}{2}$, $\frac{1}{4}$, $\frac{1}{8}$, and so on. The logarithms of these scores would be negative and the distribution would stretch as far out to the left as it does to the right. When fractional values of X cannot be measured or recorded, many truly log-normal distributions will appear to be only approximately log-normal.

When a logarithmic transformation of X has been made and the transformed values are found to be normally distributed, we are able to treat the logarithms as a normal distribution, with all the rights and privileges thereunto appertaining. There are many other kinds of transformations we could try if we suspected that our data were regularly but not normally distributed. If X is not normally distributed perhaps X^2 or $\sqrt{X}$ or $\frac{1}{X}$ is. With a ratio scale, many transformations of our variable are possible. If the shape of the distribution of X is not a familiar or useful one, it may be well to investigate the shape of the distribution of some transformed value of X.

8.3 The Minor Means

Three new kinds of average become available to us when our measures have, in addition to a meaningful unit, an absolute zero. These new averages, which have some of the characteristics of the arithmetic mean but not its general usefulness or applicability, are called the *minor means*. Each is used only in special circumstances and for particular purposes. They are the geometric mean, the harmonic mean, and the contraharmonic mean.

8.3.1 The Geometric Mean: The geometric mean, G, is defined as *the Nth root of the product of N scores.*

$$G = \sqrt[N]{X_1 \cdot X_2 \cdot X_3 \cdot \ldots \cdot X_N} \qquad (8.3.1)$$

In the special case where there are only two scores, the geometric mean is the mean proportional between them. For example, the coefficient of correlation, r, is the mean proportional between the two regression coefficients, b_{yx} and b_{xy}. We can write either

$$b_{yx} : r = r : b_{xy} \quad \text{or}$$
$$r = \sqrt{b_{yx} b_{xy}}$$

They mean the same thing. r is the geometric mean of the regression coefficients.

Nobody in his right mind would try to compute the geometric mean from formula 8.3.1 unless there were only two or three scores. A far better way to compute it is by the use of logarithms.

$$\log G = \frac{\log X_1 + \log X_2 + \log X_3 + \ldots + \log X_N}{N} \quad (8.3.2)$$

and

$$G = \text{antilog}\left(\frac{\log X_1 + \log X_2 + \ldots + \log X_N}{N}\right) \quad (8.3.3)$$

When a distribution is log-normal, the geometric mean is a more appropriate measure of central tendency than the arithmetic mean. That makes sense if you stop to think about it. If the logarithms are normally distributed, then the mean of the logarithms should be at the center of the distribution, and converting to an antilog merely takes us back to our original measurements of X. For the data of Table 8.3, the arithmetic mean is 6.4, while the geometric mean is 5.1. Both these points are indicated by arrows on Figure 8.27, and you can see that the geometric mean is much closer to the center of the symmetrical distribution. If the distribution were truly log-normal the geometric mean would be at the exact center of the distribution.

The geometric mean is sometimes used to find the average of a set of ratios. Since rates of change are ratios of amount of change to time within which the change takes place, an average rate usually means the geometric mean of two or more rates.

If any measurement is zero, the geometric mean will also be zero, so it should never be used in such a situation.

8.3.2 The Harmonic Mean: The harmonic mean, $H.M.$, is *the reciprocal of the mean of the reciprocals of the numbers.*

$$H.M. = \frac{1}{\dfrac{\sum \dfrac{1}{X}}{N}} = \frac{N}{\sum \dfrac{1}{X}} \quad (8.3.4)$$

It is a special statistic of very limited application. Its principal use is for the averaging of time rates of change. It should also be used when the reciprocals of the scores rather than the scores themselves

are normally distributed. Like the geometric mean it cannot be
used when any of the scores is zero.

8.3.3 The Contraharmonic Mean:[4] This is a little-known statistic,
but one that has great potential usefulness for special situations.
Let us start with an illustration.

We are interested in determining the average number of children
per family in a group of 50 families. The frequency distribution is
given below:

(X) Children/family	(f) No. of families	fX
4	10	40
3	10	30
2	10	20
1	10	10
0	10	0
	50	100

There are 100 children and 50 families, so we conclude that the
average number of children per family is 2, a perfectly correct conclusion. We may, however, go on to draw the erroneous conclusion
that the average child comes from a two-child family. To see why
that conclusion is erroneous, let us investigate further. Let us ask
each of the 100 children what size family he comes from:

X Children/family	f' No. of children	f'X
4	40	160
3	30	90
2	20	40
1	10	10
0	0	0
	100	300

The mean of *this* distribution is $\frac{300}{100}$, or 3. We must conclude that the
average child comes from a family of three children, though the
average family has only two children. The answer 3 is the contra-

[4] Jaspen, Nathan, An empirical verification of the standard errors of the minor
means. Paper presented at meetings of American Psychological Assn. and the
Psychometric Society, September 6, 1955.

harmonic mean of the original distribution. The formula for it is

$$C.M. = \frac{\Sigma f X^2}{\Sigma f X}$$

Whenever a few individuals contribute disproportionately to the total the contraharmonic mean will be quite different from the arithmetic mean, and may be a more useful statistic. In an industrial plant, for example, a very few workers who are 'accident-prone' may be responsible for almost all the accidents that occur. The arithmetic mean, telling us the average number of accidents per worker, may be quite low. The contraharmonic mean, however, which would tell us that the average accident was one of $C.M.$ contributed by that employee, would be high. Or a social worker might be more interested in knowing that a visit was, on the average, one of so many to a particular family, than in knowing that the average family received so many visits. The ratio of the contraharmonic mean to the arithmetic mean is a measure of the extent to which a few individuals contribute disproportionately to the total.

The contraharmonic mean can be used only when each X is, itself, a frequency, as *number* of children, *number* of accidents, or *number* of visits.

8.4 The Coefficient of Variation

Ordinarily the variance and the standard deviation are used with ratio scales just as they are with interval scales. These statistics have, however, the important limitation that they are expressed in the original units of measurement—inches or pounds or whatever. (By way of contrast, think of $\hat{H}$, which is a pure number. One $\hat{H}$ is equivalent to any other $\hat{H}$, whether the measures are of inches or pounds or colors.)

Furthermore, even when we know that the standard deviation is 3 inches, for example, we interpret this fact in different ways depending upon the circumstances. A standard deviation of 3 inches in a set of 100 telegraph poles would not be alarming, but the same standard deviation in a set of 100 noses would be, quite literally, out of this world! Noses are, in general, shorter than telegraph poles, but the standard deviation doesn't care.

The coefficient of variation, V, does care. It relates the standard deviation to the absolute size of the objects being measured.

$$V = \frac{100s}{\overline{X}} \qquad (8.4.1)$$

The coefficient of variation is 100 *times the ratio of standard deviation to mean.* Like $\hat{H}$ it is a pure number, and one V can be compared to any other V.[5]

8.5 The Relative Position of an Individual

With the advance to a ratio scale as a measuring instrument, a new and powerful method of describing an individual relative to the rest of the group becomes available. Any individual measurement can now be compared directly with any other measurement or with any aggregate of measurements or with any fixed standard in terms of a *ratio* of their magnitudes. To say that one individual took ten minutes longer than another to perform some task may be interesting, but it is not nearly so informative as to say that the second individual took twice as long as the first.

Often a ratio between two measurements is a more meaningful way of describing something than is a statement of the magnitude of either variable alone. Thus, for example, a child's mental age means little if we do not know the age of the child, but the ratio of a child's mental age to his chronological age (intelligence quotient) is meaningful and important. The ratio of brain weight to body weight, in different species of animals, may turn out to be a useful index of the 'intelligence' of the species; and anthropologists have found that in many cases the ratio of one body measurement to another may be a more useful descriptive tool than either measurement alone.

The people who have really made extensive use of ratios are the economists. To say that 'prices are high' means something only if we go on to say that they are high *compared* to what they were at some other time or place. The comparison is made in terms of a ratio called an 'index number.' The construction of good index numbers is more complicated than it sounds; in fact, whole books have been written on the subject. If your work ever requires you to make extensive use of complicated ratios, you might do well to take a look at what the economic statisticians have to say on the subject.

[5] $\dfrac{V^2}{100} + 1 = \dfrac{\text{C.M.}}{\overline{X}}$

8.6 Correlation

Relax! No new statistics—just new ways of using the old ones!

In Chapter 7 we said that the product-moment correlation should be used only when X and Y are linearly related. In the first section of this chapter, we saw that when X and Y are not linearly related, Y may still be linearly related to some transformed value of X, or vice versa. Thus, if the relationship between X and Y is exponential, and

$$Y = ab^X$$

the logarithm of Y is linearly related to X.

$$\log Y = \log a + X \log b$$

While it would not be legitimate or sensible to use the product moment correlation to describe the strength of relationship between X and Y, it is entirely proper to find the product moment correlation between X and the *logarithm of* Y. To find this correlation, we simply substitute '$\log Y$' for 'Y' in the formula for r.

$$r_{X \log Y} = \frac{N\Sigma X \log Y - (\Sigma X)(\Sigma \log Y)}{\sqrt{N\Sigma X^2 - (\Sigma X)^2} \sqrt{N\Sigma(\log Y)^2 - (\Sigma \log Y)^2}}$$

After computing the correlation we can go ahead to find the standard errors of estimate and, perhaps more important, the regression equation of $\log Y$ on X. This regression equation will tell us the appropriate values for the constants a and b in the original exponential equation.[6]

Exactly the same principles apply whenever one variable is linearly related to some transformed value of another. If X is the variable that has been transformed, the transformed values of X are substituted wherever X appears in the original formula. Sometimes, as in the case of a power function where the logarithm of Y is linearly related to the logarithm of X, transformed values of both X and Y must be substituted.

Questions

1. Plot the data below in the form of a cumulative percentage graph, both on linear graph paper and on log-normal paper. (If you

---

[6] However, the values found in this way will not be identical with those found from a least-squares fit to the exponential equation.

do not have log-normal paper, plot the cumulative percentages on normal-probability paper against the logarithms of the X values.) You may consider the X's, as listed, to be the upper real limits of intervals.

X	Cum. f
100	200
90	196
80	195
70	193
60	191
50	187
40	182
30	171
20	151
10	96
5	56
4	44
3	30
2	16
1	4

2. Find the geometric mean of the numbers below:

$$1, 2, 2, 8, 12, 22$$

3. Find the harmonic mean of the numbers below:

$$2, 2, 4, 8, 8$$

4. Below are some hypothetical data on the occurrence of truancy in 1000 school children. Obtain the arithmetic mean and the contraharmonic mean and interpret your results.

NO. OF TRUANCIES	NO. OF CHILDREN
10	2
9	0
8	3
7	6
6	24
5	32
4	52
3	60
2	103
1	225
0	493

5. In a learning experiment, a subject is given 50 trials a day for 5 days, and the time he requires to perform a psychomotor task is measured. Means and standard deviations for each day's results are given below. For each day, compute V, and then plot a graph showing the functional relationship between V and the day of the experiment. Interpret the results.

Day 1	Day 2	Day 3	Day 4	Day 5
$\bar{X}$ = 150 sec.	$\bar{X}$ = 120 sec.	$\bar{X}$ = 100 sec.	$\bar{X}$ = 90 sec.	$\bar{X}$ = 90 sec.
s = 25 sec.	s = 18 sec.	s = 14 sec.	s = 13 sec.	s = 12 sec.

6. From the data in problems 13a and 13f, p. 310, compute the correlation between Y and log X. Obtain the regression equations for $\tilde{Y}$ on log X, and by taking antilogarithms obtain a non-linear regression equation. (For simplicity of calculation, carry logarithms to two places only.)

7. From the data in problem 13e, p. 311, compute the correlation between log Y and log X. Obtain the regression equation for log $\tilde{Y}$ on log X, and by taking antilogarithms, obtain the non-linear regression equation. (Carry logarithms to two places only.)

Summary

When measurements are made on a ratio scale they have all the properties of real numbers. This fact does not add materially to the list of statistics available, but it does add to the number of mathematical techniques that can be used to describe the data.

At its best, a scientific law is a rational equation relating two or more variables. By 'rational equation' we mean an equation in which all the constants either are natural constants like π and e, or are related to identifiable aspects of the experimental situation. Constants that do not fall into either of these categories are called 'arbitrary fitting constants.' The use of arbitrary fitting constants is characteristic of a young science such as psychology or sociology. As a science matures, observations tend to become more closely related to theory, and arbitrary constants tend to be replaced by parameters. Several simple equations have been discussed: the straight line, the exponential, the power function, the logistic, the hyperbola, and the parabola.

In the special case where Y stands for 'frequency' or 'cumulative frequency,' transformed values of X may yield a useful or familiar frequency distribution, such as a normal distribution, where the original values did not.

Three new kinds of average become available for use with data from a ratio scale: the geometric mean, the harmonic mean, and the contraharmonic mean. These measures are applicable only in special circumstances.

One new measure of variability, the coefficient of variation, V, has been introduced. V relates the variability of a distribution to the average magnitude of the variables being measured. It is a pure number, independent of the original units of measurement.

Descriptions of individuals can now be made in terms of ratios.

Correlational techniques can be applied to transformed values of X and Y, when these appear to be linearly related, in the same way that they were applied to X and Y when these were linearly related. Regression equations may be used to determine the values of the constants in the non-linear equations.

References

Much of the material in this chapter is omitted from most books on psychological and educational statistics. Further elaboration of specific measures and techniques can be found in the following sources:

1. Croxton, F. E., and Cowden, D. J. *Applied General Statistics*, Englewood Cliffs, N. J., Prentice-Hall, 1955. This complete book, which is primarily concerned with economic statistics, gives thorough coverage of curve-fitting, non linear frequency distributions, and the geometric and harmonic means.
2. Edwards, A., *Statistical Methods for the Behavioral Sciences*, New York, Rinehart, 1954, pp. 129–41. A section on curve-fitting and on regression equations for logarithmic and exponential equations.
3. Guilford, J. P., *Psychometric Methods*, New York, McGraw-Hill, 1936, pp. 287–326. A discussion of the principles underlying the search for functional relationships. This material is integrated with material on correlation, and statistical techniques for fitting non linear equations are given. Typical functional relationships in psychology are illustrated.
4. Richardson, C. H. *Introduction to Statistical Analysis*, New York, Harcourt, Brace, 1944. This book, which is primarily concerned with economic statistics, has good discussions of curve-fitting and of the geometric and harmonic means.

Answers

Page 308

1. (a) $V = \dfrac{k}{P}$; (b) $D = \frac{1}{2}gt^2$; (c) $V = kT_{abs}$; (d) $\dfrac{\Delta I}{I} = k$.

Page 320

2. 4.51.

3. $\frac{2}{3}$.

4. $\overline{X} = 1.21$, $C.M. = 3.61$,

5. 16.7, 15, 14, 14.4, 13.3.

6. (a) $r = +1.00$, $\tilde{Y} = 1.39 \log X + .01$, $X = (.53)^{\tilde{Y}}$; (f) $r = +.99$.
   $\tilde{Y} = 1.01 \log X - .32$, $X = 2.09(9.8)^{\tilde{Y}}$.

7. $r = -.99$, $\widetilde{\log} \, \tilde{Y} = -.52 \log X + 1.01$, $\tilde{Y} = 10.2X^{-.52}$.

LOOKING BACKWARD

Variability, we said in the beginning, is a fundamental fact of nature. It is the fact that frustrates the scientist in his attempts to give precise descriptions, but also the fact that challenges him. In his attempt to describe and make predictions about a probabilistic universe, he must take account of nature's inherent variability, and he does so by predicting or describing the variability itself. Statistics is the tool he uses.

One of the two main functions of statistics is to describe a group. Before we describe a group we must make measurements of some variable or aspect of the individuals in the group. These measurements constitute our data, and of the data we ask five basic questions:

1. What general picture do the data convey? How many cases fell into this category and how many into that? How many of the animals were dogs, how many cats? How many men were six feet tall and how many six feet one?

2. If we know that an individual is a member of the group, what is our best prediction about him in terms of the measured variable? Is a dog in the group more likely to be a great Dane or a poodle? How tall is a man likely to be? This question is to be answered with some kind of average, or measure of the typical.

3. How bad is that prediction? Some predictions are very accurate, while others stand a good chance of missing the mark widely. We need a measure that will tell us the extent to which our prediction is likely to be in error. The statistics that answer this question are the measures of variability.

4. How much can the prediction be improved by knowledge of another variable? We may stand just an even chance of predicting correctly the sex of an individual in our group, but if we know about another variable—if we know that the individual ordinarily wears a skirt—our prediction can be vastly improved. When knowledge

of one variable improves prediction about another, the two are said to be related, or correlated. Sex and the wearing-of-skirts-or-trousers are two highly correlated variables.

5. How does a particular individual compare with the rest of the group? Is this individual *more* something-or-other than that one? Is this one so many units bigger or heavier or brighter than average? Than his neighbor? Is he twice as big or as heavy? How can individuals be described relative to the group from which they come?

In practice (as you have probably observed with regret) the answering of these questions requires extensive manipulation of numbers. Yet computation is a relatively late step in the application of statistics. Our interest is in describing our world, not in practicing arithmetic, and the world could be described and those same questions answered without ever using a number. Should we want, for example, to get a picture of the height of a typical man in our group, we could line up all the men from tallest to shortest. Then we could ask the two men on the ends of the line to depart, then the two remaining on the ends, and so on, eliminating always the shortest and tallest men remaining. When this process had continued until we had only one man left, we could point to him and say, '*He* is of middling height.' We should have found a median without ever using a number.

But that is decidedly a cumbersome way to do it! If we assign a symbol to each individual and then manipulate the symbols instead of the objects, life is a great deal easier. It is not enough, however, to manipulate the symbols any old way. We want some assurance that the results of manipulating the symbols will be the same as the results of manipulating the objects. The need for that assurance sharply restricts our statistical activities. It means that before we statisticize we must give serious consideration to the nature of our measurement.

Measurement is the assignment of symbols, or numerals, according to rules. We have found that there are four sets of rules by which numerals can be assigned, each set stricter and more rigorous than the set before it.

1. Numerals can be names and nothing more. They can serve merely to distinguish like from unlike, and to group all the likes together. When numerals have been assigned in this way, we say

that the variable (such as color or breed) has been 'measured' on a **nominal scale.**

2. Numerals can describe an order. If one object can be said to have *more* of some variable than another object, and if certain requirements about the ordered relationship are fulfilled, then the variable is said to have been measured on an **ordinal scale.** When we assign numerals on an ordinal scale, we make sure that the order of the numerals corresponds to the order of the objects that have been measured.

3. Numerals can utilize a unit of measurement. If we can say not only that this object is bigger than that but also that it is two *inches* or three *pounds* or twenty *seconds* bigger, then the variable has been measured on an **interval scale.** The numerals on an interval scale are assigned in such a way that when the differences between two pairs of objects are equal, the differences between the pairs of numerals used to represent them are also equal.

4. Numerals can describe an absolute magnitude. If we can say not only that this object is so many units bigger than that one but also that it is so many times as big as that one, the variable has been measured on a **ratio scale.** Besides a unit of measurement the ratio scale has an absolute zero point. The sizes of the numerals on a ratio scale are proportional to the sizes of the objects they represent.

There are very strict limits to the ways in which we can manipulate the numerals assigned on a nominal scale. We cannot order them, we cannot add them, we cannot multiply or divide them. That is because there are no manipulations of the objects that correspond to those manipulations of the numerals. On the other hand, numerals assigned on a ratio scale can be manipulated in any way that real numbers can, because such manipulations do correspond to physical operations that could be carried out on the objects.

Thus as numerals are assigned by stricter and stricter rules, they come to correspond more and more closely to numbers, and we can do with the numerals many more of the things we can do with numbers. The nominal scale is a weak tool, the ratio scale a powerful one. Our questions about our data can be answered in more and better ways when the measuring instrument is strong than when it is weak. It is our intention now to summarize the kinds of answers we can give to our basic questions when the variable has been measured on each of the instruments described above. The different kinds of answers, that is, the statistics available, are summarized in Table 9.1.

To Table 9.1 we must add another, specifically concerned with measures of unpredictability reduction, or correlation. In Table 9.1, the measures of correlation listed for the various scales always require that at least one of the two variables be measured on the kind of scale specified. Sometimes both must be so measured. In Table 9.2 the kinds of correlation measure appropriate for all combinations of two scales are tabulated.

From a study of Tables 9.1 and 9.2 it can be seen that stronger measuring instruments permit the use of a wider variety of statistical tools, and the tools they permit are themselves likely to be stronger than those that are available for weaker scales.

One of the morals of this story is that in gathering data, one should try to use the strongest possible measuring instruments. If measures of a person's performance are to be made, it is usually better to determine, for example, the number of seconds he requires to complete a task than to have another person rate his performance as 'excellent,' 'good,' 'fair,' and soon. The second method yields, at best, an ordinal scale, while the first produces a ratio scale.

Psychology, perhaps more than any other science, is often stuck with poor measuring instruments. Usually such psychological variables as neuroticism, radicalism, sympathy, anti-Semitism, and so on resist any attempt to measure them on other than an ordinal scale. A large body of psychological literature, however, is concerned with attempts to scale sense impressions (the subjective loudness of a tone, the apparent heaviness of a weight, or the brightness of a light) on interval or ratio scales. Sometimes these attempts have been successful, as in the *sone* scale of loudness, where a sone is a unit of loudness just as an inch is a unit of length. Acoustical engineers, as well as psychologists, now express certain of their measurements in sones. Attempts to develop interval scales of attitudes have met with less success, yet the attempts have been valiant, and valiantly they continue. There is no a priori reason why the construction of good measuring instruments for such elusive variables is impossible, and the science of psychology will undoubtedly advance increasingly rapidly as increasingly powerful measuring instruments are developed.

What does all this mean to the practicing research worker? It

Table 9.1

	QUESTION
SCALE	**1. What general picture do the data convey?** Answer: Frequency Distributions
NOMINAL	*Bar graphs:* only the relative heights of the bars have mathematical significance.
ORDINAL	Discrete data: *Bar graphs:* order and heights of bars have mathematical significance. Continuous data: *Histograms:* order and heights of bars have mathematical significance, and adjacent bars must be contiguous. *Frequency polygons:* horizontal distances between points are arbitrary. *Cumulative frequency and cumulative percentage graphs:* horizontal distances between points are arbitrary.
INTERVAL	Discrete data: *Bar graphs:* heights, order, widths, and spacing of bars have mathematical significance. Area inside bars is proportional to number of cases. Continuous data: *Histograms:* as for bar graphs; adjacent bars must be contiguous. *Frequency polygons:* horizontal spacing of points has mathematical significance, and area under curve is proportional to number of cases. *Cumulative frequency and cumulative percentage graphs:* horizontal spacing of points has mathematical significance. The shape of the distribution is meaningful. *Skewness* and *kurtosis* can be described. Theoretical distributions (e.g. normal) can be approximated by obtained data.
RATIO	*Bar graphs* *Histograms* *Frequency polygons* *Cum freq. and cum percentage graphs* } as for interval scale. *Skewness and kurtosis* *Theoretical distributions* *Transformed measurements* can be used to approximate a theoretical distribution from obtained data.

Table 9.1 (Continued)

	QUESTION
SCALE	**2. What is the best prediction?** Answer: Measures of Central Tendency
NOMINAL	*Mode:* the mode is the numeral representing the category with the highest frequency of occurrence. It is the prediction most likely to be right.
ORDINAL	*Mode:* as for nominal scale. Appropriate for discrete data only. *Median:* the point above and below which lie 50 per cent of the cases. It is the prediction that is just as likely to be too high as too low. It is more stable than the mode.
INTERVAL	*Mode:* } as for ordinal scale. *Median:* } as for ordinal scale. The prediction that minimizes average error. *Mean:* $\overline{X} = \dfrac{\Sigma X}{N}$, The prediction that makes the sum of the errors zero, and makes the sum of the squares of the errors a minimum. More stable than the median.
RATIO	*Mode:* *Median:* } as for interval scale. *Mean:* *Geometric mean:* $GM = \sqrt[N]{X_1 \cdot X_2 \ldots \cdot X_N}$ *Harmonic mean:* $HM = \dfrac{N}{\sum \dfrac{1}{X}}$ } Statistics for special situations. *Contraharmonic mean:* $CM = \dfrac{\Sigma f X^2}{\Sigma f X}$

Table 9.1 (Continued)

	QUESTION
SCALE	**3. How bad is that prediction?** Answer: Measures of Variability
NOMINAL	*Uncertainty,* $\hat{H}$. $\hat{H} = -\Sigma p(x) \log_2 p(x)$. The average number of binary decisions required to specify the category of an individual.

ORDINAL	*Uncertainty,* $\hat{H}$: undesirable because it does not utilize ordinal nature of data.
	Interpercentile ranges:
	    Range: $X_{max} - X_{min} + 1$. Unstable.
	    Interquartile range: 75th percentile $-$ 25th percentile.
	    Semi-interquartile range, **Q**. Half of interquartile range.
	    Other interpercentile ranges.

INTERVAL	*Uncertainty,* $\hat{H}$ *Interpercentile ranges* $\Big\}$ as for ordinal scale. *Average deviation: AD:* $AD = \dfrac{\Sigma\lvert x \rvert}{N}$ *Standard deviation,* s, *and variance,* s²: $$s^2 = \frac{\Sigma x^2}{N}$$ More useful in later computations than *AD*.
RATIO	*Uncertainty,* $\hat{H}$ *Interpercentile ranges* *AD* s *and* s² $\Bigg\}$ as for interval scale. *Coefficient of variation,* **V**: $$V = \frac{100s}{\overline{X}}$$ Expresses variability in terms of absolute size of measured objects.

Table 9.1 (Continued)

	QUESTION
SCALE	**4. How much can prediction be improved by knowledge of another variable?** Answer: Measures of Relationship (see also Table 9.2)
NOMINAL	*Uncertainty reduction,* $\hat{T}$: $\hat{T} = \hat{H}(x) - \hat{H}_y(x)$; can also be expressed as a relative measure: $$\hat{T}_{\text{rel}} = \frac{\hat{T}}{\hat{H}(x)} \text{ or } \frac{\hat{T}}{\hat{H}(y)}$$ *Contingency coefficient,* C: serves same function as $\hat{T}$. Not discussed in this text. *Phi coefficient,* ϕ: describes strength of relationship between two dichotomous variables. Not discussed in this text.
ORDINAL	*Uncertainty reduction,* $\hat{T}$ } undesirable because do not utilize ordinal *Contingency coefficient,* C } nature of data. *Phi coefficient,* ϕ: describes direction of relationship as well as strength. *Index of order association,* o: compares excess of 'same' over 'different' pairings with total number of pairings. Describes strength and direction of relationship between two sets of ratings. *Rank-order correlation,* r_o: $r_o = 1 - \dfrac{6\Sigma D^2}{N(N^2 - 1)}$ Describes strength and direction of relationship between two sets of ranks.

INTERVAL	*Uncertainty reduction,* $\hat{T}$
	Contingency coefficient, C } as for ordinal scale.
	Phi coefficient, ϕ
	Index of order association, o
	Rank-order correlation, r_o } do not utilize unit of measurement.
	Correlation ratio, E, *and its square,* E^2:
	$$E^2 = \frac{\text{Betw. Grp. } s^2}{s_y^2} = 1 - \frac{s_w^2}{s_y^2}$$
	Especially useful when x and y are not linearly related.
	Coefficient of correlation, r:
	$$r = \sqrt{1 - \frac{s_{\text{est}y}^2}{s_y^2}} = \sqrt{1 - \frac{s_{\text{est}x}^2}{s_x^2}} = \frac{1}{N}\sum z_x z_y = \frac{\Sigma xy}{N s_x s_y}$$
	Special measures of correlation:
	  Tetrachoric correlation
	  Biserial correlation
	  Partial correlation } statistics for special situations.
	  Multiple correlation

RATIO	*Uncertainty reduction,* $\hat{T}$ *Contingency coefficient,* C *Phi coefficient,* ϕ *Index of order association,* o *Rank order correlation,* r_o } as for interval scale. *Correlation ratio,* E *Coefficient of correlation,* r *Special measures of correlation* r *and special correlation measures for transformed values of* x *or* y *or both.* *Non-linear curve fitting.*

Table 9.1 (Continued)

	QUESTION
SCALE	**5. How does an individual compare with the group?** Answer: Measures of Individual Position
NOMINAL	No comparison possible.
ORDINAL	*Ranks:* number of cases equaled or surpassed by individual. *Percentile ranks:* per cent of cases surpassed by individual.
INTERVAL	*Ranks* $\Big\}$ as for ordinal scale. *Percentile ranks* *Standard scores,* z *and* Z: $\quad z = x/s$ $\quad Z = 10z + 50$ *Normalized scores,* T: T equals the Z-score corresponding to the individual's percentile rank in a normal distribution.
RATIO	*Ranks* *Percentile ranks* *Standard scores,* z *and* Z $\Bigg\}$ as for interval scale. *Normalized scores,* T *Ratios* of individuals' measurements to each other or to some standard. Ratios of measurements on one variable to measurements on another. Index numbers (special kinds of ratios).

Table 9.2. Correlation Measures Available for Different Kinds of Measurement

X Variable

SCALE	NOMINAL	ORDINAL	INTERVAL	RATIO
RATIO	$\hat{T}$, ϕ, C $\mathbf{E_{xy}}$	$\hat{T}$, ϕ, C $\mathbf{E_{xy}}$ o, r_o	$\hat{T}$, ϕ, C $\mathbf{E_{xy}}$, $\mathbf{E_{yx}}$ o, r_o $\mathbf{r}$ $\mathbf{r}$ **when y has been transformed** **special measures of correlation**	$\hat{T}$, ϕ, C $\mathbf{E_{xy}}$, $\mathbf{E_{yx}}$ o, r_o $\mathbf{r}$ $\mathbf{r}$ **when x or y or both have been transformed** **special measures of correlation**
INTERVAL	$\hat{T}$, ϕ, C $\mathbf{E_{xy}}$	$\hat{T}$, ϕ, C $\mathbf{E_{xy}}$ o, r_o	$\hat{T}$, ϕ, C $\mathbf{E_{xy}}$, $\mathbf{E_{yx}}$ o, r_o $\mathbf{r}$ **special measures of correlation**	$\hat{T}$, ϕ, C $\mathbf{E_{xy}}$, $\mathbf{E_{yx}}$ o, r_o $\mathbf{r}$ $\mathbf{r}$ **when x has been transformed** **special measures of correlation**
ORDINAL	$\hat{\mathbf{T}}$, $\boldsymbol{\phi}$, C	$\hat{T}$, ϕ, C o, r_o	$\hat{T}$, ϕ, C o, r_o $\mathbf{E_{yx}}$	$\hat{T}$, ϕ, C o, r_o $\mathbf{E_{yx}}$
NOMINAL	$\hat{\mathbf{T}}$, $\boldsymbol{\phi}$, C	$\hat{\mathbf{T}}$, $\boldsymbol{\phi}$, C	$\hat{T}$, ϕ, C $\mathbf{E_{yx}}$	$\hat{T}$, ϕ, C $\mathbf{E_{yx}}$

Y Variable

The most appropriate or most powerful measures are printed in bold-face type.

means that the first job of the man who wishes to use statistics is to identify the kinds of scales on which his variables have been measured. Until he knows that, he cannot know what statistical tools are available to him. Then he must determine which questions he wishes to ask of his data. When he knows these two things, he can turn to Tables 9.1 and 9.2 to find out what measures are available. From that point on, finding answers is just a matter of carrying out computations and interpreting results.

PROBABILITY

The first part of this book has dealt with the description of data. The groups of measurements we considered were complete groups, and when we used statistical techniques to make 'predictions,' we were predicting only for individual cases already included in the groups. It would be fair to say that we never (well—*hardly* ever!) 'went beyond our data.' The second part of the book will be concerned with how to use the known facts to make predictions about the unknown. If will deal with the techniques of 'going beyond our data' legitimately.

The reason we want to go beyond our data is that it is often impossible, impractical, or too expensive to obtain a complete set of data. To obtain a complete set of data means to make measurements on an entire population, and some populations are infinite, some are unknown, some are unavailable, and in some cases we have to destroy the individuals in the population in order to make measurements on them. Let us consider some examples.

We wish to know whether a coin is biased or not. To say that the coin is biased means that *in the long run* (that is, if the coin is tossed an infinite number of times) it will not land heads and tails equally often. The population of tosses of the coin is *an infinite population* and our set of measurements on it can never be complete, even in theory.

A medical research worker is interested in the physiological characteristics of individuals in the beginning stages of tuberculosis. That population is finite but *unknown*, and merely to identify its members would be a long-term project in itself.

We wish to know how many cavities American males between the ages of 50 and 60 have in their teeth. The population of American males between those ages is finite and known, but *unavailable*. The time and expense involved in making such a survey would be prohibitive.

A dairy farmer suspects a certain hen of laying mostly double-yolked eggs. He can break every egg she lays for the rest of her life and find out exactly what proportion have double yolks, but such scientific exactitude does not lead to a profitable dairy business. In this case, *measurement involves destruction.*

For these and other reasons, we are often required to select a sample from the population and draw conclusions about the population from our knowledge of the sample. Such conclusions always have an element of uncertainty about them. If we toss a coin 50 times and get 50 heads, that does not *prove* that the coin is biased. Perhaps for the rest of our natural lives we could toss the coin and get nothing but tails, or a happy mixture of heads and tails. Nevertheless, if we actually got 50 heads on 50 tosses, we should be quite justified in saying that the coin was *probably* biased. If the dairy farmer broke ten eggs and found nine double yolks, he could safely conclude that the hen was *probably* unusual.

When we make statements about complete groups we can make these statements flatly and unequivocally. If the mean height of 100 men is 5'11", that is what it is and there is no doubt about it. But if we say, on the basis of those measurements, that the mean height of all men is between 5'10" and 6', we must add the word 'probably.' Statements about populations, made on the basis of our knowledge of samples, are *probability statements.* In making them, we shall not be satisfied with saying 'probably'; we shall want, in addition, to specify *how* probably. We shall want not only to say that the hen is probably unusual but to specify that the probability that she is unusual is .95, or .80, or some other figure.

The techniques of statistical inference are designed to enable us to quantify probability statements, to determine exactly the probabilities that certain things are true. For this reason, we start our discussion of statistical inference with a more formal and complete presentation of the principles of probability than was given in Chapter 6.[1]

10.1 Principles of Probability

10.1.1 Definition: In friendly and familiar words, the probability of an outcome can be defined as the proportion of the time that it

---

[1] A review of Chapter 6, particularly pp. 181–90, is highly recommended at this point.

will happen in the long run. The probability of the outcome 'heads' on the toss of a coin is .5 because in the long run the proportion of time that outcome will happen is .5.

More formally: *The probability of an outcome is the limiting relative frequency of its occurrence as the number of events becomes infinite.* The words 'relative frequency' mean approximately the same thing as 'proportion of the time.' They mean the frequency of the outcome—that is, the number of times it occurs—divided by the total number of events. In the case of the coin, the relative frequency of heads is the number of heads divided by the number of tosses. The word 'limiting' requires a little more explanation. If you toss a coin once, the relative frequency of heads is either $\frac{1}{1}$ or $\frac{0}{1}$—it is either 1.00 or 0.00. If you toss twice, the relative frequency of heads may be $\frac{2}{2}$, $\frac{1}{2}$, or $\frac{0}{2}$. If you toss 10 times, the relative frequency of heads may be anything from $\frac{10}{10}$ to $\frac{0}{10}$ but it is not likely to be either of those extreme values. Ordinarily you would expect it to be something like $\frac{7}{10}$, $\frac{6}{10}$, $\frac{5}{10}$, $\frac{4}{10}$, or $\frac{3}{10}$. Those values are closer to .5 than $\frac{10}{10}$ or $\frac{0}{10}$. If you tossed the coin 100 times you might not get exactly 50 heads, but you'd expect that the fraction would be close to $\frac{1}{2}$— closer than it was for 10 tosses. The more you toss the coin, the closer to $\frac{1}{2}$ you expect the relative frequency to be. The *limiting relative frequency* of heads is the relative frequency to which you get closer and closer as the number of tosses gets larger and larger. Of course, when I say that the probability that this penny, which I hold in my hand, will land heads is .50, I do not mean that I have tossed it millions of times and watched the proportion of heads get closer and closer to .50. What I mean is that I am thinking of my penny as an idealized 'honest' penny. It has two sides and I assume that the coin is just as likely to land on one as on the other. If that is the case, then the proportion of heads *will* get closer and closer to .50 as I toss the coin more and more times, and the probability of heads is .50.

If there are k outcomes, it does not automatically follow that they are equally likely. The sum of the numbers rolled on two dice can be anything from 2 to 12, but every dice player knows that some of these outcomes are more likely than others. That is because some totals (2 and 12) can be obtained in only one way, while others, such as 5, 6, 7, and 8, can be obtained in many ways. In this case it would be more logical to think of the 6 faces of one die as one class of outcomes. Those 6 outcomes are equally probable, and from them we can go on to determine the probabilities of the various sums for 2 dice.

Sometimes it is not possible to predict a probability in advance. Suppose that we were to open a book at random and point to a word. What is the probability that the word we point to will be 'sesquipedalian'? To answer this question it is not enough to know that there are umpteen million words in the English language and assume that the probability of 'sesquipedalian' is 1 over umpteen million. To determine the exact probability we should have to count words from books until our eyes gave out and *then* make an estimate.

We shall refer to the possible outcomes of an event as a *set* of outcomes and represent the set as a closed squiggle. Now we shall draw a circle inside the squiggle to represent a particular class of outcomes in the set. If the set consists of draws of a card from a deck, then the squiggle represents all possible cards—52 of them—and the circle may represent, for example, draws of spades. N stands for the number of equally likely outcomes in the set. If we let $n(a)$ stand for the number of outcomes of a particular class, a, and $P(a)$ for the probability that an outcome will be in class a, then:

$$P(a) = \frac{n(a)}{N} \tag{10.1.1}$$

For example, there are 52 possible ways of drawing a card. Thirteen of these are members of the class 'spades.' So the probability of drawing a spade is

$$P \text{ (spades)} = \frac{13}{52} = \frac{1}{4}$$

Since $n(a)$ can never be less than zero or more than N, it follows that $P(a)$ can never be less than zero or greater than 1.

$$0 \leq P(a) \leq 1 \tag{10.1.2}$$

If you compute a probability and find it to be 1.79, you have made a mistake.

Every point inside the closed squiggle of Figure 10.1 is either inside the circle labeled a or outside of it. Every card is either a spade or not a spade. We shall use the symbol a' to mean *not a*, and $Q(a)$ to represent the probability of a'. Then:

$$Q(a) = P(a') = \frac{n(a')}{N} \tag{10.1.3}$$

Since

$$n(a) + n(a') = N$$

and

$$P(a) = \frac{n(a)}{N} \quad \text{and} \quad Q(a) = \frac{n(a')}{N}$$

then

$$P(a) + Q(a) = \frac{n(a)}{N} + \frac{n(a')}{N} = \frac{n(a) + n(a')}{N} = \frac{N}{N} = 1$$

$$P(a) + Q(a) = 1 \tag{10.1.4}$$

10.1.2 Addition of Probabilities of Mutually Exclusive Outcomes:
Classes of outcomes are called **mutually exclusive** if they cannot

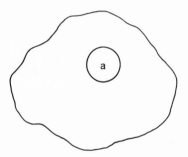

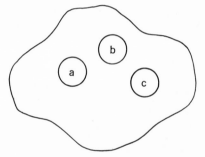

Fig. 10.1 The closed squiggle represents the set of all possible outcomes. The circle a represents all outcomes of class a.

Fig. 10.2 The three non-overlapping circles, a, b, and c, represent three mutually exclusive classes of outcome.

both happen at once. A card cannot be both a spade and a heart, so the outcomes spades and hearts are mutually exclusive. A card can be both a spade and an ace, so the outcomes spades and aces are not mutually exclusive.

If two or more outcomes are mutually exclusive, the probability that either one of them (or any one if there are more than two) will occur is equal to the sum of their individual probabilities.

$$p(a \text{ or } b \text{ or } c) = P(a) + P(b) + P(c) \tag{10.1.5}$$

Mutually exclusive classes are shown diagramatically by non-overlapping circles.

The probability that a card will be either a heart or a spade is equal to the probability that it will be a heart plus the probability that it will be a spade.

$$P \text{ (hearts or spades)} = P \text{ (hearts)} + P \text{ (spades)} = \frac{13}{52} + \frac{13}{52} = \frac{26}{52}$$

Classes of outcomes are called **exhaustive** if every possible outcome in the set is included in one of the classes. The classes spades, hearts, diamonds, and clubs are exhaustive because every card must be one of these. They are also mutually exclusive because no card can belong to two of the classes at once. The classes red cards, diamonds, spades, and clubs are exhaustive but not mutually exclusive because every card must belong to one of these classes, but a card can belong to two.

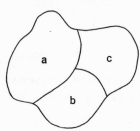

FIG. 10.3   The total set of possible outcomes has been divided into three mutually exclusive, exhaustive classes.

The probability that an outcome will belong to some unspecified one of k mutually exclusive, exhaustive classes is the sum of the probabilities of these classes, which is equal to 1.

If

$$N = n(a) + n(b) + n(c)$$

then

$$P \text{ (a or b or c)} = \frac{n(a)}{N} + \frac{n(b)}{N} + \frac{n(c)}{N} = \frac{n(a) + n(b) + n(c)}{N} = \frac{N}{N}$$
$$= 1 \quad (10.1.6)$$

10.1.3 Conditional Probabilities: The probability that a book taken off the library shelves at random will be written in Russian is very small. It is

$$\frac{\text{number of library books written in Russian}}{\text{number of library books}}$$

But if the book is taken from that section of the library called 'Russian Language and Literature,' the probability that it will be written in Russian is much higher. It is

$$\frac{\text{Number of Russian-language books in Russian Language and}}{\text{Literature section}}$$
$$\overline{\text{Number of books in Russian Language and Literature section}}$$

This second probability requires the fulfillment of a certain condition: that the book come from the Russian section. It is therefore called the **conditional probability** of choosing a book in Russian on the hypothesis (that is, condition) that the book comes from the Russian section.

A conditional probability may be diagrammed as follows:

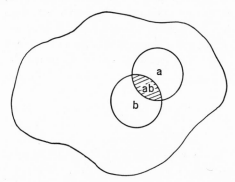

Fig. 10.4   The conditional probability that an outcome will be in class b on the hypothesis that it is in class a is $n(ab)/n(a)$.   In the figure, this probability is the ratio of the shaded area, ab, to the area of circle a.

Notice that we are dealing here with classes that are not mutually exclusive. An outcome can be in both classes at once.

We shall let $n(ab)$ stand for the number of outcomes that belong both to class a and to class b. The notation $P_a(b)$ will mean: the conditional probability that an outcome is in class b on the hypothesis that it is in class a. Then:

$$P_a(b) = \frac{n(ab)}{n(a)} \qquad (10.1.7)$$

If there are 100 books in the Russian section, and 80 of them are written in Russian, then the probability that a book chosen from that section will be written in Russian is $\frac{80}{100}$.

Notice how similar the definition of conditional probability is to the definition of absolute probability. (A probability that is not a conditional probability is called an **absolute probability**.) We have simply to consider one class of outcomes as if it were the total set of possible outcomes and the two definitions become identical.

If and only if the conditional probability of outcome a *on the hypothesis of outcome* b *is the same as the absolute probability of outcome* a, *then the two outcomes are said to be independent.*

a and b are independent if and only if

$$P(a) = P_b(a) \tag{10.1.8}$$

Let us try this out. Suppose the library has 1000 books and 200 of them are written in Russian. Of these 200, 80 are in the Russian section, which has a total of 100 books.

Let $n(a)$ stand for the number of books written in Russian, 200.

$\quad\quad n(b)$ stand for the number of books in the Russian section, 100

$\quad n(ab)$ stand for the number of books in the Russian section that are written in Russian, 80

$\quad\quad\quad N$ stand for the number of books in the library, 1000, then:

$P(a)$, the absolute probability that a library book will be written in Russian, is $\dfrac{n(a)}{N} = \dfrac{200}{1000} = .2$.

$P_b(a)$, the conditional probability that a book will be written in Russian on the hypothesis that it comes from the Russian section, is $\dfrac{n(ab)}{n(b)} = \dfrac{80}{100} = .8$.

Since $.2 \neq .8$, the two classes of outcome—being in the Russian section and being written in Russian—are not independent.

Is the denomination of a playing card independent of the suit of the card? Let $n(a)$ stand for the number of aces, 4, $n(ab)$ for the number of spade aces, 1, $n(b)$ for the number of spades, 13, and N for the number of cards, 52. Then the absolute probability that a card will be an ace, $P(a)$, is $\frac{4}{52}$. The conditional probability that a card will be an ace on the hypothesis that it is a spade, $P_b(a)$, is $\frac{1}{13}$. Since $\frac{4}{52} = \frac{1}{13}$, the two probabilities are the same and we conclude that the two classes of outcome are independent.

10.1.4 Probabilities of Joint Outcomes: By the probability of a joint outcome we mean the probability that an event will fall simultaneously into two classes of outcomes—for example, the probability that a book will be written in Russian *and* will come from the Russian section, or the probability that a card will be both a spade and an ace. The probability that an outcome will be both a member of class a and a member of class b is written $P(ab)$.

$$P(ab) = \frac{n(ab)}{N} \tag{10.1.9}$$

In the diagram, (ab) is represented, as before, by the shaded area where the two circles overlap, while N is represented by the entire area inside the squiggle.

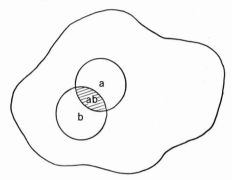

FIG. 10.5 The shaded area, ab, represents outcomes that are in both class a and class b.

The formula for the probability of a joint outcome is

$$P(ab) = P(b) \cdot P_b(a) = P(a) \cdot P_a(b) \tag{10.1.10}$$

This important theorem is easy to prove mathematically:

$$P(b) = \frac{n(b)}{N} \text{ by definition}$$

$$P_b(a) = \frac{n(ab)}{n(b)} \text{ by definition}$$

$$P(b) \cdot P_b(a) = \frac{n(b)}{N} \cdot \frac{n(ab)}{n(b)} \text{ by substitution}$$

The $n(b)$'s cancel and

$$P(b) \cdot P_b(a) = \frac{n(ab)}{N} = P(ab)$$

Let us apply formula 10.1.10 to the probability of drawing at random from the library a Russian book from the Russian section, and also to the probability of drawing the ace of spades at random from the deck.

From the figures given on page 342, we can determine that

$$P(b) = \frac{100}{1000} = .1$$

$$P_b(a) = \frac{80}{100} = .8$$

Then $P(ab) = .1 \times .8 = .08$. We can be sure this answer is correct by going back to the definition formula: $P(ab) = \dfrac{n(ab)}{N}$. In this case, $P(ab) = \frac{80}{1000} = .08$.

The probability of drawing a card that is both an ace and a spade, from formula 10.1.10, is:

$$P(ab) = \frac{13}{52} \times \frac{1}{13} = \frac{1}{52}$$

From these two examples we can draw the conclusion that formula 10.1.10 is applicable whether or not the two classes of outcome are independent.

On the other hand, the two classes of outcome are defined as independent if and only if $P(a) = P_b(a)$, so if they are independent we can substitute $P(a)$ for $P_b(a)$ in formula 10.1.10, and we have, if and only if a and b are independent:

$$P(ab) = P(a) \cdot P(b) \qquad (10.1.11)$$

The probability of drawing a spade ace, found by formula 10.1.11, is

$$\frac{13}{52} \cdot \frac{4}{52} = \frac{1}{52}$$

which is the same answer we obtained before. But the probability of selecting at random a Russian book from the Russian section is found to be:

$$\frac{200}{1000} \times \frac{100}{1000} = .02$$

which is *not* the same answer we got before and is *not* a correct answer. The language in which a book is written is not independent of the section of the library from which it comes, and formula 10.1.11 was therefore wrongly applied.

If two variables are not independent they are said to be related. In the first half of this book we studied many measures of relationship. Directly or indirectly, all of these measures are based on a comparison of conditional with absolute probabilities, or on a comparison of $P(ab)$ as computed from formulas 10.1.10 and 10.1.11. For example, the formula for $\hat{T}$ is: $\hat{T} = \hat{H}(x) - \hat{H}_y(x)$. In this formula, $\hat{H}(x)$ stands for the average logarithm of the *absolute probabilities* of the various x classes. $\hat{H}_y(x)$ stands for the average logarithm of the *conditional probabilities* of the various x classes on the hypotheses of various y classes. If $\hat{H}_y(x)$ is very different from $\hat{H}(x)$, then the conditional probabilities are very different from the absolute probabilities, and x and y are said to be related.

10.1.5 Addition of Probabilities When Outcomes Are Not Mutually Exclusive: We have said that when two or more outcomes are mutually exclusive the probability that one or the other of them will occur, written $P(a \text{ or } b)$, is equal to the sum of the probabilities that each will occur.

$$P(a \text{ or } b) = P(a) + P(b)$$

when a and b are mutually exclusive.

We are now prepared to consider the case where the outcomes are not mutually exclusive.

We wish to determine the probability that either a or b *or both* will occur. Actually any of four things can happen:

a may occur but not b.
b may occur but not a.
Both a and b may occur.
Neither a nor b may occur.

Any of the first three outcomes will be considered a 'success.' What is the probability of a success?

Consider Figure 10.6 below. We wish to find the area inside the heavy outline.

The vertically shaded circle represents the occurrence of outcome a, the horizontally shaded circle the occurrence of outcome b, and the doubly shaded area the joint occurrence of outcomes a and b. If we simply add the areas inside the two circles we actually include the doubly shaded area *twice*, while we want to include it only once.

We would have

$$P(a) + P(b) + 2P(ab)$$

while what we want is

$$P(a) + P(b) + P(ab)$$

Therefore, to obtain the probability that either a or b or both will occur, we must obtain the sum of the probabilities that a and b will occur and then *subtract* the probability that both will occur.

$$P(a \text{ or } b \text{ or both}) = P(a) + P(b) - P(ab) \qquad (10.1.12)$$

Suppose Zilch and Weatherby are each going to fire one shot at a beer bottle. Zilch has a probability of .9 of hitting the bottle, and

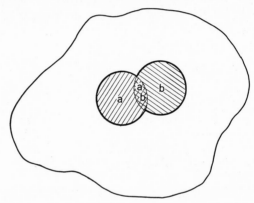

Fig. 10.6 The area inside the heavy outline represents the class of outcomes that are either a or b or both.

Weatherby has a probability of .8. What is the probability that one or the other or both of them will hit the bottle? By formula 10.1.2:

$$P \text{ (Zilch or Weatherby or both)} = P \text{ (Zilch)} + P \text{ (Weatherby)}$$
$$- P \text{ (both)}$$

We shall assume that their results are independent. (If Zilch hits, Weatherby is neither more nor less likely to than usual.) So

$$P \text{ (both)} = .9 \times .8 = .72.$$

Then:

$$P \text{ (Zilch or Weatherby or both)} = .9 + .8 - .72 = .98$$

We could have solved this problem just as easily by going about it in reverse. We could have said, 'What is the probability that both Zilch and Weatherby will *miss* the bottle?' If $Q(a)$ stands for the probability that Zilch will miss, $Q(b)$ for the probability that Weatherby will miss, and $Q(ab)$ for the probability that both will miss, then $Q(ab) = Q(a) \cdot Q(b) = (1 - .9)(1 - .8) = .1 \times .2 = .02$. And we can state as a general formula that

$$P(a \text{ or } b \text{ or both}) = 1 - Q(ab) \qquad (10.1.13)$$

So the probability that one or the other or both will hit the bottle is

$$1 - .02 = .98$$

In complicated problems where there are many possible outcomes instead of just two, formula 10.1.13 is usually much simpler to apply than formula 10.1.12.

10.1.6 The Probability of a Single Event: We have defined probability as a limiting relative frequency, yet in practice we often use the term where this definition would not seem to apply. For example, Mary Millstone has been accepted by Mudville College, but her high-school grades are marginal and she is not sure that she should attend. She consults a statistician, who looks at her high-school grades and her scholastic-aptitude scores and then tells her: 'The probability that you will graduate from Mudville is .6.'

How are we to interpret this statement? Is Mary to enroll at Mudville, flunk out, re-enroll and graduate, re-enroll and graduate again, and so on an infinite number of times with an average proportion of 6 graduations to 10 enrollments? Obviously not. Mary, if she goes to Mudville, will either graduate or not, and in that sense her probability of graduating is either 1 or 0. Which of these it will be cannot be specified in advance. Mary's graduation from Mudville is a single event, and in terms of the definition, a single event cannot have a probability.

What the statistican meant when he gave Mary the figure .6, however, was something else. He could have meant either of two things:

a. Of a very large group of people with grades and test scores similar to Mary's, and attending colleges similar to Mudville, 60 per cent graduated.

or

b. When he predicts that Mary will graduate, the method of prediction that he is using will give correct results 60 per cent of the time.

If he is making his prediction from his knowledge of a large group of similar females, these two meanings work out to be the same thing. More often he will be using a fancy statistical technique such as a regression equation, and he may never have encountered anyone like Miss Millstone before.

In the chapters to come we shall frequently make statements like: 'The probability that the population mean is at least 500 is greater than .95; we therefore predict that the population mean is at least 500.' When we make such statements, we mean that our method will lead to the correct prediction more than 95 per cent of the time.

10.1.7 Summary of Probability Definitions and Theorems: For your convenience we shall now gather all the definitions and theorems together and put them down in one place where you may refer to them readily.

Definitions: *Formula*

$$P(a) = \frac{n(a)}{N} \tag{10.1.1}$$

a' means not a. $Q(a) = P(a') = \dfrac{n(a')}{N}$ (10.1.3)

The conditional probability of outcome b on the hypothesis of outcome a, $P_a(b) = \dfrac{n(ab)}{n(a)}$ (10.1.7)

a and b are independent if and only if $P(a) = P_b(a)$ (10.1.8)

The absolute probability that an outcome will be in both class a and class b, $P(ab) = \dfrac{n(ab)}{N}$ (10.1.9)

Theorems:

$$0 \leq P(a) \leq 1 \tag{10.1.2}$$
$$P(a) + Q(a) = 1 \tag{10.1.4}$$

If a, b, and c are mutually exclusive:
$$P(a \text{ or } b \text{ or } c) = P(a) + P(b) + P(c) \qquad (10.1.5)$$
If a, b, and c are mutually exclusive and exhaustive:
$$P(a \text{ or } b \text{ or } c) = 1 \qquad (10.1.6)$$
$$P(ab) = P(b) \cdot P_b(a) = P(a) \cdot P_a(b) \qquad (10.1.10)$$
If and only if a and b are independent:
$$P(ab) = P(a) \cdot P(b) \qquad (10.1.11)$$
$$P(a \text{ or } b \text{ or both}) = P(a) + P(b) - P(ab) \qquad (10.1.12)$$
$$P(a \text{ or } b \text{ or both}) = 1 - Q(ab) \qquad (10.1.13)$$

Questions

1. From formula 10.1.1 determine:

   a. The probability that a die will land 4.
   b. The probability that a card will be an honor (A, K, Q, J, 10).
   c. The probability that a single digit selected from a table of random numbers will be a 7.
   d. The probability that a member of your statistics class will be a male.

2. If you call each of the probabilities found in the problem above $P(a)$ explain in words, for each example, what is meant by $Q(a)$. Use formula 10.1.4 to determine $Q(a)$ and check your finding from the definition of $Q(a)$.

3. If A stands for getting too little vitamin D in childhood and B for having bow legs, express in symbols:

   a. The probability that a person will have had enough vitamin D.
   b. The probability that a person will have bow legs.
   c. The probability that a person who had too little vitamin D in childhood will have bow legs.
   d. The probability that a person who has bow legs will have had too little vitamin D in childhood.
   e. The probability that a person will have had too little vitamin D in childhood and will have bow legs.
   f. The probability that a person will have had too little vitamin D in childhood or will have bow legs, or both.

4. If a stands for eating college food and b stands for being continually hungry, what is meant by each of the following:

a. $P_a(b)$	c. $Q(b)$	e. $P(ab)$	g. $1 - Q(ab)$
b. $1 - P(a)$	d. $P_b(a)$	f. $P(a$ or b or both$)$	h. $1 - P(ab)$

5. Which of the following do you think are independent and which dependent:

   a. The weather on one day and the weather on the next day.
   b. The sex of a baby born in a hospital and the sex of the next baby born in the same hospital.
   c. The probability that a man will live to be 75 and the probability that his wife will live to be 75.
   d. The probability that a man will be a football star and the probability that he will be an honor student.
   e. The probability that the first card drawn from a deck will be a diamond and the probability that the second card will be a diamond.

6. If a college population includes 300 freshmen, 250 sophomores, 250 juniors, and 200 seniors, what is the probability that a student chosen at random will be a sophomore or a junior or a senior? Use both formulas 10.1.4 and 10.1.5. What happens if you use formula 10.1.12?

7. If this same college has 600 men and 400 women, determine, on the assumption that class and sex are independent, the probability that:

   a. a student will be both a male and a sophomore.
   b. a student will be neither a male nor a sophomore.
   c. a student will be either a male or a sophomore (or both).
   d. a student will be a male but not a sophomore.
   e. a student will be a sophomore but not a male.

8. If you have drawn an ace from a deck of cards, and keep it, what is the probability that you will get another ace on your second draw?

9. What is the probability that a poker hand will contain the following cards:

   a. 2 of hearts, 9 of clubs, J of clubs, 7 of spades, and 4 of diamonds.
   b. The A, K, Q, J, and 10 of spades.

10. What is the probability that the sum of the numbers thrown on two dice will be:

    a. 7
    b. 8
    c. 11

11. Prove that if $P(a) = P_b(a)$ then $P(b) = P_a(b)$.

12. If an urn contains 6 black balls, 3 white balls, and one lavender ball:

    a. If we reach blindly into the urn, draw out a ball, throw it back, then draw again, what is the probability that we shall draw a black ball and a lavender ball?

    b. If we do not throw the first ball back after drawing it, what is the probability of getting a black ball and a lavender ball?

13. Compare the probabilities of rolling a five with one die and rolling a total of five with two dice.

14. If the ratio of male to female children is $1:1$, and the sexes of successive children born in one family are independent, find the probability that, in a family of six children:

    a. All will be of the same sex.

    b. The four youngest children will be boys and the two oldest girls.

    c. Exactly half the children will be boys.

15. If two judges independently rank five subjects from 1–5 on aggressiveness, what is the probability that their rankings will agree perfectly? (Assume that the five subjects are really equally agressive.)

16. If a class of 50 students contains 10 juniors and 40 seniors, what is the probability that the first six names on the roll call will be those of seniors?

17. If your opponents in a bridge game have four spades between them, what is the probability that there will be two in one hand and two in the other? If they have five spades between them, what is the probability that they will be split three in one hand and two in the other?

18. In a poker hand of five cards, what are the probabilities of being dealt:

a. One pair.
b. Two pairs.
c. Three of a kind.
d. A full house (two cards of one denomination and three of another).

19. Determine the probabilities that a poker hand will contain 0, 1, 2, 3, 4, and 5 spades and plot these as a probability distribution.

10.2 Probability Distributions and Probability Density Distributions

One of the most fundamental problems of inferential statistics is to determine the probabilities of certain classes of outcomes. One way to do this is to compute them directly, as we have done in these illustrative problems. Another way is to find them from a probability distribution or a probability density distribution.

Let us consider the binomial distribution for a moment. We found in Chapter 6 that by expanding the binomial $(P + Q)^N$ we could determine the probabilities of 0, 1, 2, . . . N successes out of N trials, and all these probabilities could be plotted as a graph against the number of successes, as was done in Figures 6.1 to 6.5 (pp. 181–8). Such a graph is called a **probability distribution.**

In any probability distribution, all the possible outcomes are plotted on the x-axis in an ordered arrangement and probability is plotted on the y-axis. The variable for which the probabilities are plotted is always a discrete variable.

If the variable is continuous we cannot specify the probability of any particular outcome. This, you remember from our discussion of the normal curve, is because the probability corresponds to the area of a rectangle, but a particular outcome, on a continuous variable, means a *point* on the x-axis. A point has no width, hence no rectangle can be erected above it. For the normal curve and other curves like it, the height of the curve really represents 'probability per unit x-axis.' The 'units' on the x-axis are actually these widthless points that we have just described. To find the probability that a measurement will lie between two points on the x-axis, we measure the distance between those points and multiply it by the probability per unit distance. The correct name for 'probability per unit x-axis' is **probability density.** For a continuous variable, we cannot have a probability distribution, but we have, instead, a

probability density distribution. The normal distribution is an example of a probability density distribution.

Probability distributions and probability density distributions are among the most useful tools of inferential statistics. In the chapters to follow the normal and binomial distributions will turn up again and again, and in addition many new probability and probability density distributions will be encountered.

References

1. Clark, C. E., *An Introduction to Statistics*, New York, Wiley, 1953, pp. 1–92. A detailed treatment of permutations and combinations, probability, and probability distributions.
2. Feller, W., *An Introduction to Probability Theory and Its Applications*, New York, Wiley, 1950. An up-to-date, authoritative reference on probability. Not too difficult for a serious student.
3. Kasner, E., and Newman, J., *Mathematics and the Imagination*, New York, Simon and Schuster, 1940, pp. 223–64. An easy, non-mathematical chapter on probability; also includes a few pages on the statistical view of the universe.
4. Levinson, H. C., *The Science of Chance*, New York, Harcourt, Brace, 1950. A fascinating account of the application of probability theory to games of chance, operations analysis, advertising, and other fields.
5. Nagel, E., Principles of the Theory of Probability, *International Encyclopedia of Unified Science*, Vol. 1, No. 6, Chicago, Univ. of Chicago Press, 1939. A scholarly but readable summary published as a separate monograph.
6. Newman, J. R. (ed.), *The World of Mathematics*, New York, Simon and Schuster, 1956. The section on probability contains the following selections:

    > De Laplace, P. S., 'Concerning Probability,' pp. 1325–33.
    > Pierce, C. S., 'The Red and the Black,' pp. 1334–40.
    > Pierce, C. S., 'The Probability of Induction,' pp. 1341–54.
    > Keynes, J. M., 'The Application of Probability to Conduct,' pp. 1360–73.
    > Poincaré, H., 'Chance,' pp. 1380–94.
    > Nagel, E., 'The Meaning of Probability,' pp. 1398–1414.

Answers

Page 349

1. (a) $\frac{1}{6}$; (b) $\frac{5}{13}$; (c) $\frac{1}{10}$ 2. (a) $\frac{5}{6}$; (b) $\frac{8}{13}$; (c) $\frac{9}{10}$
3. (a) $Q(A)$ or $1 - P(A)$ or $P(A')$; (b) $P(B)$; (c) $P_A(B)$; (d) $P_B(A)$; (e) $P(AB)$; (f) $P(A$ or B or both) or $P(A) + P(B) - P(AB)$ or $1 - Q(AB)$

4. (a) hungry if college food; (b) not eat college food; (c) not hungry; (d) college food if hungry; (e) college food and hungry; (f) college food or hungry or both; (g) same as f; (h) neither college food nor hungry

5. (a) dep.; (b) indep.; (c) dep.; (d) dep.; (e) dep.

6. .7

7. (a) .15; (b) .30; (c) .70; (d) .45; (e) .10

8. $\frac{3}{51}$

9. (a) $1/(52 \times 51 \times 50 \times 49 \times 48)$; (b) same

10. (a) $\frac{1}{6}$; (b) $\frac{5}{36}$; (c) $\frac{1}{18}$ 13. $\frac{1}{6}$ vs. $\frac{1}{9}$

12. (a) .12; (b) .133   14. (a) $2(\frac{1}{2})^6$; (b) $(\frac{1}{2})^6$; (c) $20(\frac{1}{2})^6$

15. $\frac{1}{120}$

16. $\frac{40}{50} \times \frac{39}{49} \times \frac{38}{48} \times \frac{37}{47} \times \frac{36}{46} \times \frac{35}{45}$

17. $\frac{3}{8}$; $\frac{5}{8}$

18. (a) $\frac{3}{51} \times \frac{48}{50} \times \frac{44}{49} \times \frac{40}{48} \times 10$; (b) $\frac{3}{51} \times \frac{48}{50} \times \frac{3}{49} \times \frac{44}{48} \times 30$; (c) $\frac{3}{51} \times \frac{2}{50} \times \frac{48}{49} \times \frac{44}{48} \times 10$; (d) $\frac{3}{51} \times \frac{2}{50} \times \frac{48}{49} \times \frac{3}{48} \times 10$

19. .222; .411; .274; .082; .011; .000

TESTING HYPOTHESES AND ESTABLISHING MARGINS OF ERROR[1]

In Chapter 1, we said that inferential statistics were techniques designed to perform one of two functions: (a) to test hypotheses about populations; and (b) to predict something about a population from our knowledge of a sample and specify a margin of error in that prediction. In this chapter we shall examine in detail the way these functions are carried out.

11.1 Testing Hypotheses

11.1.1 An Illustration: A friend approaches you with a bright and shiny penny clutched tightly in his hand. He offers to sell you the penny for a nickel, and when you ask him why you should make such a ridiculous exchange, he explains: 'Ah, but this is no ordinary penny! This is a biased penny—a loaded penny, which doesn't stand an even chance of coming up heads or tails, but will land one way more often than the other. Think of the bets you can win, the decisions that will be in your favor, when you toss this coin instead of an ordinary one!'

You give some thought to this proposition. Such a coin would

[1] Warning: The material in this chapter is the most abstract and, for most students, the most difficult that will be encountered in elementary statistics. We say this not to scare you but to reassure you when you find the going hard. It isn't that *you* are *stupid*, but that the material is inherently difficult. Keep trying! Most students will have to read this chapter very slowly and go over parts of it many times in order to grasp all the ideas presented. Even then, the concepts tend to be elusive. You may think you have grasped them, then find that they have slipped away again. Throughout the rest of the book the material in this chapter will be utilized again and again with concrete examples, so even if you feel a little hazy when you leave the chapter your difficulties may clear up as you go on. If you will come back to the material after studying Chapters 12–15, you should find your understanding of it vastly increased. One more thing: review questions have been sprinkled liberally throughout the text. Be very sure that you can answer them before you go on to the next section. Writing out your answers, even if the questions are not assigned, is the best way to avoid fooling yourself into thinking that you understand when you really don't. Good luck!

indeed be a valuable thing to own if what your friend says about it is true. 'Is it more likely to land heads or tails?' you ask. Your friend says he doesn't know. The only thing he knows for sure is that the two possibilities aren't equally likely.

You ask if he will let you test the coin by tossing it. He says he will, but points out correctly that even if you toss 'til doomsday you can never *prove* that the coin is biased. Anything that happens *could* happen by chance alone, even to a perfectly fair coin. You snort. 'Yes,' you reply, 'but if I toss it 100 times and get 100 heads, I'll be satisfied that it's biased, even though that could happen by chance. If the coin were unbiased, the probability that it would land heads 100 times in a row is only $(\frac{1}{2})^{100}$, which is a small enough risk for me!' 'Right!' agrees your statistically minded friend, 'but I'm not going to stand around all day watching you flip coins. Where's your gambling spirit? Would you accept a one-in-eight risk, say, of paying for a biased coin and getting an honest one?' You decide that a nickel is not very much to pay and agree to take the one-in-eight risk. Your friend points out that in that case you only need to toss the coin four times. This is because there are five things that can happen. You may get:

0 heads. This will happen an average of 1 time in 16 to an honest coin.
1 head.   "   "   "   "   "   " 4 times in 16 " "   "   "
2 heads. "   "   "   "   "   " 6 times in 16 " "   "   "
3 heads. "   "   "   "   "   " 4 times in 16 " "   "   "
4 heads. "   "   "   "   "   " 1 time in 16 " "   "   "

On the average you will have two chances out of 16, or one in eight of tossing either no heads or four heads if the coin is unbiased.

You toss the coin, get four tails, give your friend the nickel, and receive the penny. Of course, you may have been stung. The penny may have been a perfectly ordinary one that did the one-in-eight thing the one time it really mattered. On the other hand, if it had landed with one or two or three heads out of four tosses and you had accordingly decided not to buy, you would have run a risk too, for the penny might truly have been biased but have landed that way in spite of its bias.

This example contains all the important features of a statistical test of a hypothesis. Let us now break it down step by step and examine these features in detail.

11.1.2 The Steps in Hypothesis Testing:

STEP 1: *State two alternative hypotheses:*

Your friend claims the coin is biased. That means that in the long run the proportion of heads (or tails) will not be $\frac{1}{2}$. The alternative hypothesis is that in the long run the proportion of heads will be $\frac{1}{2}$. We can write these two hypotheses this way:

$$H_0: P(H) = \frac{1}{2}$$

$$H_1: P(H) \neq \frac{1}{2} \qquad \text{(your friend's claim)}$$

One of these hypotheses must be true, and the other cannot be true. H_0 can be tested directly, because if the coin is unbiased you know exactly what to predict for it. H_1 cannot be tested directly, because your friend has refused to make any statement except that the coin is biased. He has not said, for example, that the coin will land heads 80 per cent of the time in the long run. If he had said such a thing, his statement could have been tested directly.

H_0 is called the **null hypothesis.** *The null hypothesis is any hypothesis stated in such a way that the data are given a chance to disprove it.* Your friend's claim can never be proved nor disproved directly because it is not stated explicitly. That is, from the simple statement that the coin is biased, there is no way to predict what it *will* do. From the alternative statement that the coin is not biased, however, we can predict what it *will not* do. It will not, in the long run, yield all heads or all tails on four tosses more than $\frac{1}{8}$ of the time.

You asked your friend whether the coin was more likely to land heads or tails and he said he didn't know. If he had, instead, said 'tails,' then your two alternative hypotheses would have been:

$$H_0: P(H) \geq \frac{1}{2}$$

$$H_1: P(H) < \frac{1}{2} \qquad \text{(your friend's claim)}$$

In this instance, H_1 is called a **one-sided alternative** because the *direction* of the results has been specified. The statistical test of a one-sided alternative is slightly different from the test of a two-sided alternative, and we shall consider the differences as we go along.

Before an experiment has ever been carried out and while it is still in the planning stage, the experimenter should always formulate his two alternative hypotheses. Suppose, for example, an educational psychologist thinks that teaching method A will yield a different amount of learning than will method B, and sets up an experiment to test his notion. His alternative hypotheses are:

H_0 (null hypothesis): The difference in the amount of learning achieved by the two methods is no greater than would be expected by chance alone.

H_1: The difference between the results of the two methods is greater than would be expected by chance alone.

If he specifies not only that there will be a difference but that method B will be better, he has a one-sided alternative, and his hypotheses are:

H_0 (null hypothesis): The learning of children taught by method B will be no better than that of those taught by method A, except for such superiority as might arise by chance alone.

H_1: The children taught by method B will learn more than children taught by method A, and the difference will be greater than would be expected by chance alone.

In every well-designed experiment there are at least two alternative hypotheses: a null hypothesis and one other. The test of a hypothesis is always the test of the null hypothesis, since the alternative hypothesis is seldom one that can be tested directly.

Questions

1. What is a *null hypothesis?*
2. What is a *one-sided alternative?* A *two-sided alternative?*
3. If a salesman tries to sell you a loaded die, telling you that the die will land 4 more often than would an honest die, what are your two alternative hypotheses?
4. A sociologist considers the possibility that juvenile delinquency may be higher among children from broken homes than among children from intact homes. What are his two alternative hypotheses?
5. Explain as well as you can the statement that 'the alternative hypothesis is seldom one that can be tested directly.'

STEP 2: *Decide on the risk that you are willing to take:*

Your friend asked you if you had enough gambling spirit to take a one-in-eight chance of getting stuck with a perfectly ordinary penny, and you said yes. In saying that, you made an important statistical decision: you stated that you were willing to take a one in eight, or $12\frac{1}{2}$ per cent risk of rejecting the null hypothesis if it were really true.

As your friend correctly pointed out, you must always take *some* risk. You can never demand absolute certainty, because as we have said before and will say again, anything *can* happen by chance alone. Even if the coin were perfectly normal, it could land 'heads' 100 times in a row—except that, as you pointed out, the chance that a normal coin would do so is only $(\frac{1}{2})^{100}$—a very slight risk. You can never disprove an hypothesis absolutely, but you can make the risk you take in calling it 'disproven' just as small as you like.

The risk of rejecting a true null hypothesis, expressed as a percentage or a proportion, is called the **level of significance,** and is represented by the Greek letter Alpha, α. You chose the $12\frac{1}{2}$ per cent level of significance for your results. You disproved the null hypothesis at the $12\frac{1}{2}$ per cent level of significance. In your experiment, $\alpha = 12\frac{1}{2}$ per cent.

If the coin is unbiased—that is, if the null hypothesis is true— you have one chance in eight of making a wrong decision, and you have seven chances in eight of making a correct decision. You might say, then, that you are $\frac{7}{8}$ confident of your decision. Your **level of confidence** is $\frac{7}{8}$. *The level of confidence is* $1 - \alpha$, where α is the level of significance.

If before buying the coin, you had demanded that it land either heads or tails 100 times in a row, you would have been demanding a very high degree of confidence in your results. You would have required that $\alpha = 2(\frac{1}{2})^{100}$, and your level of confidence would have been $[1 - 2(\frac{1}{2})^{100}]$.

In practical statistical work the level of significance is usually chosen someplace between 5 per cent and .1 per cent. Few research workers are willing to take the high risk of error that you took when you agreed to one-in-eight odds. One in twenty (5 per cent) is about the biggest risk that most are willing to accept, and one in a thousand (.1 per cent) is about the smallest that most would think of demanding. The practical consequences of the decision may be important in determining the level of significance that one demands. For example, if you make the decision to buy the coin when it is, in fact, unbiased, you are out four cents. That is such a small sum that you can afford to take a fairly big risk. But suppose the government agrees to support a $50,000,000 research program on a certain drug if it can be shown, in a small preliminary experiment, that the drug decreases the mortality from a certain disease. Fifty million dollars is a lot of money, and no one would want to invest it unless he was fairly sure that the drug held some promise. In this case the government might demand that the results of the preliminary experiment be such that they would happen less than one time in one thousand if the drug was really ineffective.

We shall come back to the question of how to choose a level of significance. It is one that has many important consequences and ramifications.

Questions

1. What is meant by *level of significance? level of confidence?*
2. If you get three tails on three tosses of a coin and decide that the coin is biased:

    a. What are your two alternative hypotheses?
    b. What is the level of significance at which you are rejecting the null hypothesis?
    c. What is your level of confidence?

3. If the educational psychologist who is comparing teaching methods A and B says, 'I will adopt whichever method is better if the difference is significant at the 5 per cent level,' what does he mean?

STEP 3: *Determine which classes of results will cause you to accept and which to reject the null hypothesis:*

When you said that you would toss the coin four times and would take a one-in-eight risk of buying a dud, you automatically specified which results would cause you to reject the hypothesis that the coin was unbiased. The coin can do five things. If it is unbiased:

the probability of 0 heads is $\frac{1}{16}$.
    "   "   " 1 head " $\frac{4}{16}$.
    "   "   " 2 heads " $\frac{6}{16}$.
    "   "   " 3 heads " $\frac{4}{16}$.
    "   "   " 4 heads " $\frac{1}{16}$.

The two most unusual things that could happen are no heads and four heads. If the coin is unbiased, the probability that one or the other of them will happen is $(\frac{1}{16} + \frac{1}{16})$ or $\frac{1}{8}$. If either of those things happens, therefore, the null hypothesis can be rejected at the $12\frac{1}{2}$ per cent level of significance.

When you determined the probability of each of the five possible outcomes of the four tosses of a coin, you were constructing what is called a **sampling distribution**. *A sampling distribution is a theoretical probability or probability density distribution. It specifies the probability of obtaining any given value of a statistic in a sample of size*

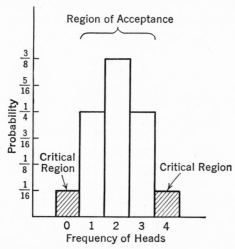

Fig. 11.1 Sampling distribution of frequency of heads on four tosses of an unbiased coin, showing critical regions and region of acceptance for a two-tailed test.

N. In the case of the coin, the statistic under consideration was *frequency of heads*. This statistic could assume the values of 0, 1, 2, 3, and 4 in a sample of four tosses. You determined the probability of each of these outcomes and plotted these probabilities as a theoretical probability distribution.

After constructing the sampling distribution of frequencies of heads, you said, 'Since I am willing to take a one-in-eight risk of buying an honest coin, I want to cut off, from each tail of the sampling distribution, a probability of $\frac{1}{16}$. The probability of 0 heads is $\frac{1}{16}$, and the probability of 4 heads is $\frac{1}{16}$, so if either of these things happens I shall be taking a one-in-eight risk when I reject the null hypothesis.' The outcomes 0 heads and 4 heads constitute what is called the **critical region** of the sampling distribution. *The critical region is the set of values of the sample statistic that will cause you to reject the null hypothesis at the level of significance* α. If your obtained statistic falls in the critical region, you will reject the null hypothesis. If it does not fall in the critical region, it falls in what is called the **region of acceptance,** and you accept the null hypothesis. The probability that one sample statistic will fall in the critical region if the null hypothesis is true is α, and the probability that it

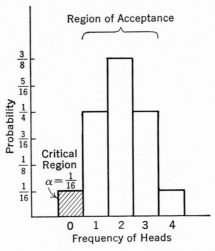

Fig. 11.2 Sampling distribution of frequency of heads on four tosses of an unbiased coin, showing critical region and region of acceptance for a one-tailed test.

will fall in the region of acceptance if the null hypothesis is true is $1 - \alpha$.

If your friend had claimed that the coin was biased in favor of tails, you would not have rejected the null hypothesis if you had gotten four heads. (Null hypothesis: $P(H) \geq \frac{1}{2}$.) You would have demanded an excess of tails—an excess so great that it would happen by chance only one time in eight or less if the coin were unbiased. From Figure 11.1 you can see that the probability of four tails is $\frac{1}{16}$, and the probability of three tails is $\frac{4}{16}$. If the coin lands tails four times you can reject the null hypothesis with one chance in 16 of being wrong; and if the coin lands tails three or more times you can reject the null hypothesis with 5 chances in 16 of being wrong.

Five chances in 16 is too much risk for you, so you decide to buy the coin only if it lands tails four times. Your level of significance is $\frac{1}{16}$ instead of the previous $\frac{1}{8}$. Your critical region, in this case, is the outcome four tails, and your region of acceptance, any smaller number of tails.

When you were testing a two-sided alternative, your critical region included a probability of $\frac{\alpha}{2}$ in each tail of the distribution; when you tested a one-sided alternative, the critical region included a probability of α in one tail of the distribution. The test of a two-sided alternative is therefore called a **two-tailed test,** and the test of a one-sided alternative a **one-tailed test.**

Questions

1. Explain in your own words what is meant by

   a. Sampling distribution
   b. Critical region
   c. Region of acceptance
   d. One-tailed test
   e. Two-tailed test

2. Construct a sampling distribution for five tosses of a coin.

   a. If your two alternative hypotheses are:

   $$H_0: P(H) = \frac{1}{2}$$

   $$H_1: P(H) \neq \frac{1}{2}$$

   and $\alpha = \frac{1}{16}$, what is the critical region? What is the critical region if $\alpha = \frac{3}{8}$?

   b. If your two alternative hypotheses are:

   $$H_0: P(H) \geq \frac{1}{2}$$

   $$H_1: P(H) < \frac{1}{2}$$

   and $\alpha = \frac{1}{32}$, what is the critical region? If $\alpha = \frac{3}{16}$, what is the critical region?

Let us consider some further examples of sampling distributions. Suppose you and your friend decide that you will toss the coin 50 times, and that you will take a risk of 1 in 20 of spending your nickel for an honest coin. Now you wish to construct a sampling distribution for sample size 50, and select a two-tailed critical region for $\alpha = .05$.

You *could* construct this sampling distribution by expanding the binomial $(\frac{1}{2} + \frac{1}{2})^{50}$, but if you remember your study of the normal curve, you will recall that when N becomes quite large, the normal distribution gives a good approximation to the binomial distribution and is certainly a great deal easier to work with. For your sampling distribution, therefore, you will use a normal approximation to the binomial. The mean of this normal distribution will be NP, and the standard deviation, $\sqrt{NPQ}$. In your sample, $N = 50$, and, if the null hypothesis is true, $P = \frac{1}{2}$. So the mean is 25 heads, and the standard deviation is $\frac{1}{2} \sqrt{50} = 3.6$. Your critical region is to include $2\frac{1}{2}$ per cent of the cases in each tail. How many heads or how many tails will you require for the statistic to fall in the critical region?

This problem is exactly like many others you have solved. It requires you to find the two measurements that will make the area between them under the normal distribution equal to .95. Between the mean and each of these measurements there will therefore be an area of .4750. You turn to Table C to find out what z-score corresponds to an area of .4750, and find that for this area, $z = 1.96$, or -1.96.
Since

$$z = \frac{X - \mu}{\sigma}$$

and since you know z, μ, and σ, you can solve for X.

$$1.96 = \frac{X - 25}{3.6}$$
$$X = 32.056$$
$$-1.96 = \frac{X - 25}{3.6}$$
$$X = 17.944$$

Between the measurements 17.944 and 32.056 lies 95 per cent of the area under the normal curve. To put it a different way, the probability of getting some number of heads between 17.944 and 32.056 from 50 tosses of an unbiased coin is .95. If you actually got fewer than 17.944 heads or more than 32.056 heads, something has happened to you that will happen by chance less than 1 time in 20 (5 per cent of the time) if the coin is honest. All values less than 17.944 and greater than 32.056 therefore constitute your critical

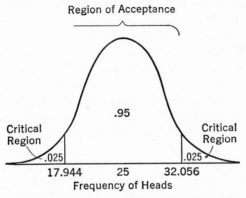

Fig. 11.3   Sampling distribution of frequency of heads on 50 tosses of an unbiased coin. The binomial distribution is well approximated by the normal.

region, and the range of values between these points is your region of acceptance.

Question

Find the critical region for 100 tosses of a coin, with $\alpha = .05$. Do this both for a two-sided alternative and for a one-sided alternative.

A sampling distribution, like any other distribution, has a mean and a standard deviation. *The standard deviation of a sampling distribution is called a* **standard error.** Since the sampling distributions we have been considering have been distributions of theoretical *frequencies*, the standard deviation of one of these distributions is called *the standard error of a frequency*. Its symbol is σ_f We ordinarily use the standard error to locate the critical region, as we did in the last example.

Let us consider one more kind of sampling distribution. Suppose that in some infinite population the mean score made on a certain test is 100. We now draw a sample of 50 cases from that population. Will its mean be 100? Perhaps, but not necessarily. The sample mean may be somewhat larger or somewhat smaller than the population mean. We make our measurements and find that, for this sample, the mean is 99. Now we draw another sample of 50 cases and find its mean to be 101. We draw a third and find it has a mean of 100. We draw 100 more samples and find their means. We plot a frequency distribution of the results we have obtained so far, and keep drawing more samples. When the number of samples we (or our great-grandchildren) have drawn approaches infinity, the frequency distribution of the means of the samples will be the *sampling distribution of the mean for samples of size* 50. This sampling distribution (which is, of course, a purely theoretical construct) will be approximately normal in shape, and its mean will be 100. Its standard deviation is called *the standard error of the mean* and is represented by the symbol $\sigma_{\bar{x}}$.

What we have done for a frequency and for a mean we can do for any other statistic, such as a median, a standard deviation, and so on. Not all of these sampling distributions will be normal is shape, as we see later. The standard deviation of any of these theoretical sampling distributions will be called the standard error. The standard deviation of the sampling distribution of medians is called the standard error of the median, σ_{Mdn}; the standard deviation of the sampling distribution of standard deviations is called the standard error of a standard deviation, σ_s, and so on. Standard errors are used in determining critical regions.

Questions

1. What is meant by the term *standard error?*
2. What is meant by a *sampling distribution of the mean?*
3. What is meant by a *sampling distribution of a standard deviation?*
4. What would be meant by the *standard error of a difference between means?*
5. If the sampling distribution of means is normal with a mean of 50 and a standard deviation of 5, what is the probability of drawing a sample with a mean less than 40 or more than 60?

STEP 4: *Draw a sample from the population:*

Your two alternative hypotheses about the penny were statements about what the penny would do in the long run. They were hypotheses about the population of all tosses of the penny, past and future. Of course, you cannot measure that population, so you draw a sample from it: you toss the penny four times. Those four tosses are your sample, drawn from the population of all tosses. From this sample you will make inferences about the population of all tosses.

It is extremely important that the sample be representative of the population about which inferences are to be made. This fact won't bother you much when you toss the penny—it's hard to toss a penny 'unrepresentatively'—but let's consider some other problems where it would be very easy to draw an unrepresentative sample.

You are interested in describing the dating habits of students in your dormitory. You can't study them all, so you decide to conduct interviews with just ten. Being an early riser you decide to interview the first ten people to appear in the dining room in the morning. There are many good reasons why those ten may not be representative of the rest of the population in their dating habits. They will be the early risers, and they probably will not include either the people who were out late on dates or the people who were up until four o'clock finishing term papers. They may include a great many of the healthy outdoor types, who are not at all representative of the rest of the students in dating patterns.

A much better way of selecting a representative sample is by **random sampling.** *A sample is called random if every member of the population has the same chance of being included in the sample.* For example, you might write each student's name on a slip of paper, put all the slips in a goldfish bowl, shake well, draw out a slip, shake again, draw another slip, and so on until you had drawn ten slips. The names on the slips would tell you which students were to be included in your sample.

Not every laboratory is equipped with a goldfish bowl, and you may have to do your sampling without one. In that case you can use a table of random numbers. Table R in this book is one such table. In it, the digits 0, 1, 2, . . . 9 are printed in a random order. If there were 60 students in your dormitory, you would assign a number to each student. Then you would go to Table R, enter it at some arbitrarily chosen place such as the fourth row and seventh column of the first page, and decide, again arbitrarily, to read across the row. The first ten pairs of digits you would encounter are

$$33 \quad 05 \quad 74 \quad 84 \quad 59 \quad 93 \quad 56 \quad 81 \quad 17 \quad 20$$

Four of these pairs, 74, 84, 93, and 81, are useless to you because your numbers do not run that high. You throw them away and read the next four pairs of digits that are between 01 and 60. These are 35, 15, 37, and 49. The students to whom these numbers have been assigned are the ten to be included in your sample.

What are you to do if two of them refuse to be interviewed on the grounds that they have too much work to do? The answer is that it will now be *impossible* for you to select a random sample of all the students. You can use the remaining eight, but they will be a sample of those members of the dormitory *who are willing to be interviewed.* Since students who are so pressed by schoolwork that they have no time to be interviewed are almost certainly not representative in their dating habits, you cannot generalize from your sample to the population. This general problem plagues all those researchers who must get their data from questionnaires. They cannot tell whether or not those who do not return the questionnaires are unrepresentative of the population, and hence they are always uncertain about what population to generalize to.

When a sample is chosen in such a way that certain classes of individuals have a greater chance of being included in the sample than others, the sample is called **biased.** Before the 1936 Presidential election, a magazine of national circulation conducted a public-opinion poll which showed that Landon, who was the Republican candidate running against Roosevelt, was overwhelmingly the favorite. When the election was held, however, Roosevelt won by a landslide. What had happened? The magazine had chosen its sample by drawing names at random from telephone directories. This meant that any person not listed in the telephone directory had no chance of being chosen for the sample. People in the lowest economic groups characteristically did not have telephones, hence were not listed in the directory, hence were automatically excluded from the sample. Since this election occurred during a great depression, there were many such people. The magazine had sampled only a wealthy minority—a decidedly biased sample.

Bias creeps into samples in the most devious and subtle ways. A survey of householders conducted entirely during normal working hours would include a biased sample, because a household where both adults worked during the day would automatically be excluded. In every investigation where a representative sample is to be drawn, the experimenter must examine and re-examine his sampling procedure to make sure there is no possible way for bias to have crept in. In those cases where bias cannot be avoided (as when one must depend upon volunteers for a psychological experiment, for example) it is important to generalize only to the population that has *actually been sampled* (volunteers), rather than to the population *one wishes one could have sampled.*

Questions

1. Why should a sample be representative of the population?
2. What is a random sample? a biased sample?
3. If you go to a table of random numbers, enter it randomly, and get for your sample the five pairs of digits:

$$01 \quad 11 \quad 21 \quad 31 \quad 41$$

do these constitute a biased sample? (Notice that all pairs end in 1, which is not what you would expect in a random sample.)
4. If you decided to go into the business of conducting public-opinion polls, could you find any more efficient procedure for getting a representative sample of the country's population than random sampling?
5. If a sample is not random, is it necessarily biased?
6. Describe three ways in which you could draw a representative sample of 25 students from your college population. Describe three sampling methods that would give a biased sample.

STEP 5: *Determine whether your sample statistic falls in the critical region or the region of acceptance, and accept or reject the null hypothesis accordingly:*

When you tossed the coin you got four tails. That frequency falls in the critical region and you therefore reject the null hypothesis that the coin is honest. If you had gotten four heads, that result, too, would have fallen in the critical region, and you would again have rejected the null hypothesis. If you had gotten 1, 2, or 3 heads, your result would have fallen in the region of acceptance, you would have accepted the null hypothesis, your friend would have kept his penny, and you your nickel.

11.1.3 The Goodness of Your Decision: When you finally handed over your nickel and got a penny in return, you were well aware that you were taking a risk. In fact, you even knew how great the risk was. You stood one chance in eight of getting an unbiased coin. On the other hand, if the coin had landed heads 1, 2, or 3 times, and you had decided not to buy it, you would have been running a risk of a different kind. The coin might truly have been biased but have fallen as it did by chance. Anything *can* happen by chance.

There are four possible things that can happen in any hypothesis test. These are summarized in the table below:

NULL HYPOTHESIS

	True	False
Reject	Type I Error	Correct Decision
Accept	Correct Decision	Type II Error

1. The null hypothesis may be true and we may reject it. If we do this we are making what is called a Type I Error. If the coin had been honest and you had bought it, you would have been making a Type I error. The probability of making a Type I Error, if the null hypothesis is true, is α.

2. The null hypothesis may be true and we accept it. This is a correct decision. If the null hypothesis is true, the probability of making this decision is $1 - \alpha$.

3. The null hypothesis may be false and we reject it. This is a correct decision. If the null hypothesis is false, the probability of making this decision is $1 - \beta$.

4. The null hypothesis may be false and we may accept it. If this happens, we are making a Type II error. If the null hypothesis is false, the probability of making a Type II error is β. If the coin had been biased but landed 1, 2, or 3 heads, you would have decided not to buy it, and you would have been making a Type II error.

Obviously we want to make a correct decision if we can. We want to make the probability of an error as small as possible. We can make the probability of a Type I error as small as we like, since we ourselves decide what value α is to take. But if we make α very small, we run a great risk of making a Type II error. Do you remember that you first proposed tossing that famous coin 100 times and buying it only if you got 100 heads or 100 tails? If you did that, your risk of making a Type I error would be very small, but even

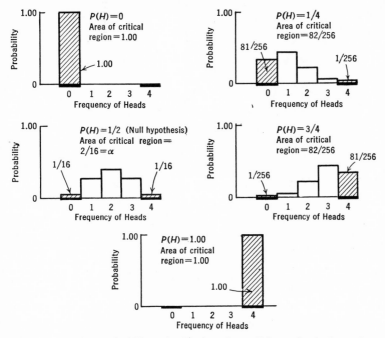

FIG. 11.4   The probability of rejecting the null hypothesis depends on the actual value of $P(H)$. Critical region 0 heads or 4 heads.

if the coin were very biased indeed you might easily have gotten 99 heads and 1 tail, or 98 heads and 2 tails, and accepted the null hypothesis. In that case you would be making a Type II error. The smaller we make the probability of making a Type I error if the null hypothesis is true, the greater becomes the probability of making a Type II error if the null hypothesis is false. The smaller we make α, the greater β becomes. Our problem is to make β as small as possible for any given value of α.

When we make β small, we increase *the probability of rejecting the null hypothesis if it is false.* This probability is called the **power of a test.** The power of a test depends upon many factors.

1. The power of a test depends upon the condition that actually holds when the null hypothesis is false. In the case of the coin, this means that the power of the test depends upon the actual probability of the coin's landing heads. Let us compute the probability

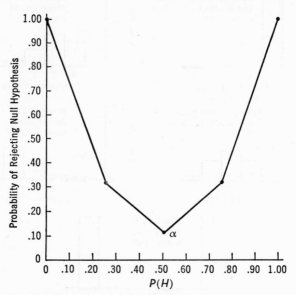

FIG. 11.5   Power function for test of $H_0: P(H) \leq \frac{1}{2}$ with four tosses of a coin and $\alpha = \frac{1}{8}$.

of rejecting the null hypothesis when the probability of the coin's landing heads is 0, $\frac{1}{4}$, $\frac{1}{2}$, $\frac{3}{4}$, and 1.

For each $P(H)$, we can expand the binomial $(P + Q)^4$, and thus determine the probabilities of getting 0, 1, 2, 3, or 4 heads. We shall reject the null hypothesis if we get either 0 or 4 heads, so the probability of either of those events (that is, the sum of their probabilities) for a given $P(H)$ is the probability of rejecting the null hypothesis for that $P(H)$. These probabilities have been computed, and the distributions are plotted in Figure 11.4.

From this figure you can see that the probability of rejecting the null hypothesis when $P(H)$ is

0 is 1.00.

$\dfrac{1}{4}$ is $\dfrac{82}{256}$ or .32.

$\dfrac{1}{2}$ is $\dfrac{1}{8}$, α.

$\dfrac{3}{4}$ is $\dfrac{82}{256}$, or .32.

1 is 1.00.

We can plot these results in a graph. A graph showing how the probability of rejecting the null hypothesis varies with the actual value of the population parameter (the actual $P(H)$ in this case) is called a **power function**. Figure 11.5 is the power function whose values have just been calculated. What it says, very simply, is that the more biased the coin actually is, the more likely we are to reject the null hypothesis that the coin is unbiased.

2. The power of a test depends upon the size of α. The greater α is, the more powerful is the test. Suppose you had (very foolishly) agreed to accept odds of five chances in eight of being wrong when you bought the coin. With $\alpha = \frac{5}{8}$, you would have bought the coin if you had gotten 0, 1, 3, or 4 heads, as you can see from an examination of Figure 11.1. Now let us compute the probability of rejecting the null hypothesis for $P(H)$ equal to 0, $\frac{1}{4}$, $\frac{1}{2}$, $\frac{3}{4}$, and 1.

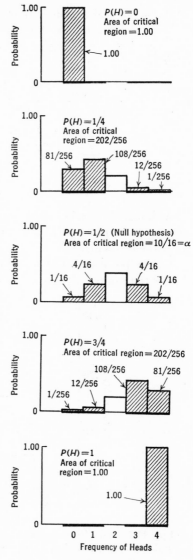

FIG. 11.6 Probability of rejecting the null hypothesis with a critical region of 0, 1, 3, or 4 heads.

The binomial expansions are the same as in the previous example;

only the critical region is different. These distributions, with the new critical region, are shown in Figure 11.6. From this figure you can see that the probability of rejecting the null hypothesis when $P(H)$ is

0 is 1.00.

$\frac{1}{4}$ is $\frac{202}{256}$ or .789.

$\frac{1}{2}$ is $\frac{5}{8}$, α.

$\frac{3}{4}$ is $\frac{202}{256}$ or .789.

1 is 1.00.

Although increasing α increases the power of the test, it also increases the probability of a Type I error, so it is not a good idea to make α too big.

3. The power of a test depends upon the size of the sample. The larger the sample, the more powerful the test.

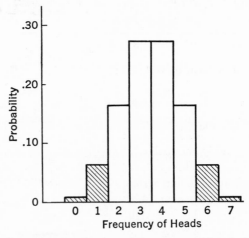

FIG. 11.7   Sampling distribution of frequency of heads for 7 tosses of an unbiased coin. With $\alpha = \frac{1}{8}$, the critical region includes 0, 1, 6, or 7 heads.

To demonstrate this fact, we shall suppose that you and your friend agree to toss the coin 7 times instead of 4. You agree to take the same risk of falsely rejecting a true null hypothesis—$\frac{1}{8}$. The sampling distribution of frequencies, computed by expanding the binomial $(\frac{1}{2} + \frac{1}{2})^7$, is shown in Figure 11.7. From it, you can see that the critical region includes the occurrences 0, 1, 7, and 8 heads. Any number of heads from 2 to 6 will fall in the region of acceptance.

Now, to compute the probability of rejecting the null hypothesis when $P(H) = 0$, $\frac{1}{4}$, $\frac{1}{2}$, $\frac{3}{4}$, and 1, we expand the binomial $(P + Q)^7$, substituting the appropriate values for P and Q. This has been done and the results have been plotted in Figure 11.8. From this figure you can see that the probability of rejecting the null hypothesis, when $P(H)$ is

0 is 1.00.

$\frac{1}{4}$ is .44. Compare this with .32, the probability with $N = 4$.

$\frac{1}{2}$ is $\frac{1}{8}$, α.

$\frac{3}{4}$ is .44. Compare this, too, with .32.

1 is 1.00.

Increasing the sizes of the sample increases the power of the test without increasing the risk of a Type I error. This important fact is one that should always be kept in mind when one is deciding on the number of subjects or observations to be included in an experiment.

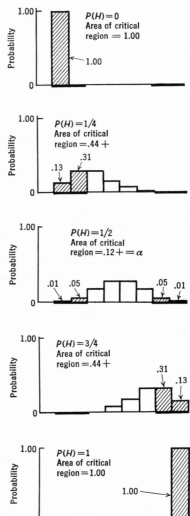

FIG. 11.8 Probability of rejecting null hypothesis on 7 tosses of a coin. $\alpha = \frac{1}{8}$.

4. The power of a test depends upon whether we are testing a

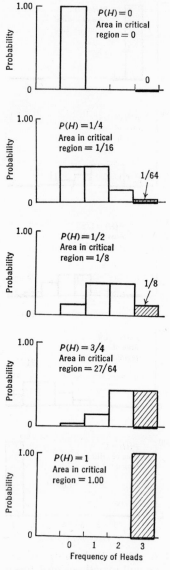

FIG. 11.9 Probability of rejecting the null hypothesis on three tosses of a coin. One-tailed test, $\alpha = \frac{1}{8}$.

one-sided or a two-sided alternative. A test for a one-sided alternative is more powerful than a test for a two-sided alternative.

Unfortunately we cannot demonstrate this fact with an N of 4 and an α of $\frac{1}{8}$, because there is no class of possible discrete alternatives in one tail of the sampling distribution that has a probability of $\frac{1}{8}$. (You can see this from an examination of Figure 11.1.) Instead, we shall use the same value of α, $\frac{1}{8}$, and a sample of size 3. The two alternative hypotheses may be:

$$H_0: P(H) \leq \frac{1}{2}$$

$$H_1: P(H) > \frac{1}{2}$$

We want to take a one-in-eight risk of rejecting H_0 if, in fact, $P(H)$ is less than or equal to $\frac{1}{2}$. We first determine the form of the sampling distribution. If $P(H) \leq \frac{1}{2}$, the probability of getting

0 heads is equal to or greater than $\frac{1}{8}$.

1 head is equal to or greater than $\frac{3}{8}$.

2 heads is less than or equal to $\frac{3}{8}$.

3 heads is less than or equal to $\frac{1}{8}$.

We shall reject the null hypothesis, therefore, only if we get three heads on three tosses of the coin.

Now we can determine the probability of rejecting the null hypothesis for $P(H)$ equal, as before, to 0, $\frac{1}{4}$, $\frac{1}{2}$, $\frac{3}{4}$, and 1, by expanding the binomial $(P + Q)^3$. The resulting distributions are shown in Figure 11.9. From this figure, you can see that the probability of rejecting the null hypothesis if $P(H)$ is

0 is 0.

$\frac{1}{4}$ is $\frac{1}{64}$. This would be an erroneous rejection of the null hypothesis.

$\frac{1}{2}$ is $\frac{1}{8}$, α.

$\frac{3}{4}$ is $\frac{27}{64}$, or .42. Compare this with .32, the probability with $N = 4$.

1 is 1.00.

The value of interest here is $P(H) = \frac{3}{4}$, where the power of the test is greater, with an N of 3, than it was for a test of a two-sided alternative with an N of 4.

5. In general, the power of a test depends upon the amount of available information the test uses. A test that uses a great deal of the available information is usually more powerful than one that uses little of that information.

This statement will make more sense to you if you think back to the first half of this book. There we introduced several statistics to answer each of five basic questions, but we saw that if we applied nominal scale statistics to interval scales we were throwing away information. If our data come from an interval scale, s is a better measure of unpredictability than the range or Q or $\hat{H}$, because it uses more of the available information. In the chapters to follow, we shall see that there are often many ways of testing the same null hypothesis. Some of these tests will require that a great many conditions be fulfilled before they are appropriate, while others will involve no such requirements. In general (though not without exception) the test that requires a great deal will be more powerful than the test that requires little. Tests that can be used with ordinally scaled data will be less powerful than tests that require interval scaling. To put it in nice practical terms, most of the tests that you will study in Chapter 13 will be more powerful than those described in Chapter 12, and those in Chapters 14 and 15 will be more powerful than those in Chapter 13.

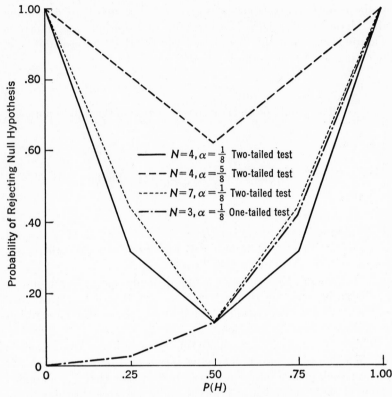

FIG. 11.10   The comparative powers of different kinds of tests.

Questions

1. Construct the power function for a test of the hypothesis $P(H) = .5$, with $\alpha = \frac{1}{16}$ and $N = 5$, for $P(H) = 0, \frac{1}{5}, \frac{2}{5}, \frac{1}{2}, \frac{3}{5}, \frac{4}{5}$, and 1. Do the same for the hypothesis $P(H) \leq .5$, $\alpha = \frac{1}{32}$ and $N = 5$ for the same values of $P(H)$.

2. Identify or define:

    a. α

    b. β

    c. $1 - \alpha$

    d. $1 - \beta$

    e. Type I error

    f. Type II error

g. Power of a test

h. Power function

3. Insert the word 'increase' or 'decrease' in the blank in each of the following sentences:

a. As the condition that actually holds becomes less and less like the condition described by the null hypothesis, the power of a test will _____.

b. As the size of the sample is decreased, the power of a test will _____.

c. As the probability of making a Type I error is increased, the power of a test will _____.

d. As the size of the critical region is decreased, the power of a test will _____.

e. As the level of confidence is increased, the power of a test will _____.

f. Changing from a one-sided to a two-sided alternative will _____ the power of the test.

11.2 Estimation

The second function of inferential statistics is to predict something about a population from our knowledge of a sample, and to specify the margin of error in that prediction. This general process is called **estimation.**

11.2.1 Statistics, Parameters, and Estimators: When we compute a sample mean, a sample standard deviation, a sample proportion, we are finding **statistics.** These same measures for a population are called **parameters.** (This is a slightly different use of the word parameter from that given in Chapter 8.) Statistics are generally distinguished from parameters by using Roman letters for the former, Greek for the latter. Sometimes other conventions are used instead. Thus

$\overline{X}$ is a sample mean, a statistic. μ is a population mean, a parameter.

s is a sample standard deviation, a statistic. σ is a population standard deviation, a parameter.

p is a sample proportion, a statistic. P is a population proportion (or a probability), a parameter.

$\hat{H}$ is the uncertainty in a sample, a statistic. H is the uncertainty in a population, a parameter.

We can seldom if ever find parameters by computation. We must make an **estimate** of a parameter from an obtained sample statistic.

Frequently our best estimate of a parameter is that it is the same as the sample statistic. For example, if we have obtained the mean of a sample, our best guess about the population mean is that it is the same as the sample mean. When our best guess about a parameter is that it is the same as the sample statistic, the statistic is called an **unbiased estimator of the parameter.** An unbiased estimate is not necessarily correct, but it has no consistent tendency to be either too large or too small. The mean and the median are examples of unbiased estimators. When we want to show that some value of a parameter is obtained by estimation from a sample, we write the symbol for the parameter with a squiggle over it. Thus the equation

$$\tilde{\mu} = \overline{X}$$

is to be interpreted: the estimated value of the population mean is the same as the obtained sample mean.

There are other instances where the sample statistic is consistently larger or consistently smaller than the corresponding population parameter. Such statistics are called **biased estimators.** $\hat{H}$, $\hat{T}$, and s^2 are biased estimators of their population counterparts. $\hat{H}$ and s^2 tend to be somewhat smaller than H and σ^2, while $\hat{T}$ tends to be larger than T. Mathematical statisticians have derived formulas that enable us to correct for the bias and get an unbiased estimate of the parameter. For example, $\tilde{\sigma}^2$ is estimated from s^2 by the formula:

$$\tilde{\sigma}^2 = s^2 \left(\frac{N}{N-1} \right)$$

There are other formulas available to enable us to use biased estimators to make unbiased estimates.

When we estimate a parameter, giving as our estimate some single number, we are making what is called a **point estimate.** If our sample mean is found to be 100, we estimate the population mean to be exactly 100—a single point, or value. You can easily see that a point estimate is almost certain to be a little bit off. A sample with a mean of 100 could easily have come from a population with a mean of 99 or of 101, though it is not likely to have come from a population with a mean of 10 or of 200. There is a margin of error in point estimates, and our next job is to specify it.

11.2.2 Interval Estimates: When we make what is called an **interval estimate,** we specify that a parameter probably lies someplace between two values, that is, that it is within some designated interval. The interval so designated is called a **confidence interval.** If, for example, we say that the population mean probably lies between 90 and 110, we are making an interval estimate and our confidence interval is the range of values from 90 to 110. The values 90 and 110 are called **confidence limits.** We make the statement more definite by saying, 'The probability that the population mean lies between 90 and 110 is .95.' In this statement, the values 90 and 110 were pulled out of a hat and mean nothing. Let us see, next, exactly how to find the limits of a confidence interval.

Our first step is to decide how confident we want to be. Do we want to say that the probability that the parameter lies within the interval is .95? Then our level of confidence is .95. Choosing it is the first step in making an interval estimate. Next, we draw a representative sample and determine the value of the statistic from which we are going to estimate the parameter. We have drawn a sample, with a mean of 100. Let us assume that the sample had a standard deviation of 30 and an N of 101. Next we ask: '*If* the population parameter is such and such, how likely is it that we have chosen a sample with the obtained statistic?' For example, *if* the population mean is 80, how likely is it that we have chosen a sample with a mean of 100? To answer this question, we construct a theoretical sampling distribution. In this case, we construct a sampling distribution of the mean, with a population mean of 80, for samples of size 101. By techniques that you have not yet learned, we estimate that the standard deviation of this sampling distribution is 3. (This is estimated from the sample standard deviation and the sample N, and you will learn the how and why of the procedure in a later chapter.) The sampling distribution of the mean will be approximately normal, then, with a mean of 80 and a standard deviation of 3. In that case, our obtained sample mean of 100 is 20 points, or $\frac{20}{3}$ standard deviations, away from the mean. Without even looking that value up in a table, you can see that it will be way out in the upper tail of the distribution. A sample mean of 100 is very improbable if the population mean is 80. We could continue to test various possible values of the population mean in this way until we came to one that is not highly improbable, but since we have chosen our level of confidence in advance, we can use a more efficient method. We can determine the two values of z that will make the area between them under the normal curve equal to .95. These values are -1.96 and $+1.96$. Then, since we know the sample mean and we

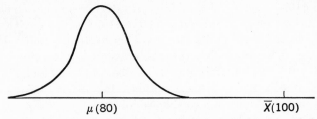

FIG. 11.11   If the population mean is 80, it is highly improbable that we would select, at random, a sample with a mean of 100. Therefore, we reject the hypothesis that the population mean is 80.

have a good estimate of the standard deviation of the distribution, we can solve for the population mean.

$$-1.96 = \frac{100 - \tilde{\mu}}{3}$$
$$\tilde{\mu} = 94.12$$
$$1.96 = \frac{100 - \tilde{\mu}}{3}$$
$$\tilde{\mu} = 105.88$$

Now we can say that *if* the population mean were less than 94.12, the probability that we would draw a sample with a mean *as high* as 100 is .025 or less; *if* the population mean were more than 105.88, the probability that we would draw a sample with a mean *as low* as 100 is .025 or less. Therefore, if the population mean lies outside of the limits 94.12 − 105.88, the probability of getting a sample mean of 100 is .05 or less. We translate this into the statement that 'We are 95 per cent confident that the population mean lies within those limits.'

We can summarize the steps theoretically involved in finding confidence limits:

1. Choose a level of confidence. In our example it was .95. This is one of the values that is frequently chosen.

2. Draw a representative sample and calculate the sample statistic. In our example the statistic was the mean, but it might have been a proportion, a standard deviation, a correlation coefficient, or any other statistic.

3. Construct a sampling distribution for some value of the parameter lower than the sample value. Determine the probability of obtaining the sample statistic from that sampling distribution. If

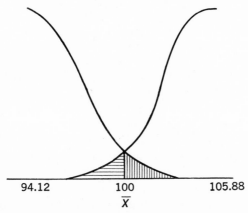

FIG. 11.12   If the true mean were 94.12, a sample mean would have $2\frac{1}{2}$ chances in 100 of falling in the range of values under the vertically shaded area. If the true mean were 105.88, a sample mean would have $2\frac{1}{2}$ chances in 100 of falling in the range of values under the horizontally shaded area.

the probability is less than .025 [that is, less than $\frac{1}{2}(1 - .95)$] reject the hypothesis that the statistic could have come from a population with the parameter you are trying out. If the probability is greater than that, accept the hypothesis.

4. Repeat the process with another parameter value, less extreme or more extreme than the one you just tried, depending upon your previous results. Continue this process until you find the parameter value that will yield a probability of exactly .025 of obtaining the sample statistic. That is your lower confidence limit.

5. Repeat steps 3 and 4 for values of the parameter higher than the sample value, and thus establish the upper confidence limit.

In practice, steps 3, 4, and 5 are greatly simplified. If the sampling distribution is normal, as it frequently is, we can go directly from step 2 to the determination of the z-scores that will give the appropriate probabilities and then solve for the parameter by substituting in the formula for z. When the sampling distribution is not normal, other tables are provided to make the trial-and-error process unnecessary.

11.3 Comparison of Estimation and Hypothesis Testing

The establishment of interval estimates and the testing of hypotheses are very similar processes, both in principal and in practice. Let us examine the similarities and differences between them. Both processes require that we choose a level of significance or level of confidence. Both require that we draw a representative sample and determine the value of the sample statistic. Both require that we construct sampling distributions, but here there is a difference. When we test hypotheses, we need construct only one sampling distribution—that one based on the assumption that the null hypothesis is true. When we establish interval limits, we must construct many sampling distribution, one for each hypothesized value of the parameter.

Both processes require that we determine the probability of our obtained results from our theoretical sampling distributions. We need do this only once when we are testing a null hypothesis; we must do it many times when we are testing a variety of hypothesis. Both processes conclude with the accepting of one or more hypotheses and the rejection of others. The confidence interval corresponds to the region of acceptance in hypothesis testing; all values outside the confidence limits correspond to the critical region.

For example, we determined that we could be 95 per cent confident that the population from which our sample was drawn had a mean not lower than 94.12 or higher than 105.88. Suppose, then, we wished to test at the 5 per cent level of significance the null hypothesis that the population mean was 90. That value falls outside the confidence limits; hence the probability of getting our sample mean from a population with a mean of 90 is less than $\frac{\alpha}{2}$, and we can reject the null hypothesis without further ado. Any null hypothesis that specifies that a parameter is outside of the confidence limits can be immediately rejected.

Questions

1. You toss your newly acquired coin 100 times and get 60 heads. By fancy statistical techniques you are able to estimate that on future sets of 100 tosses the probability is .95 that you will get not fewer than 49 or more than 70 heads (i.e. that the real $P(H)$ is between .49 and .70). Which of the following hypotheses can you reject at a level of significance of .05 or less:

a. $P(H) = .5$ d. $P(H) = .7$

b. $.4 < P(H) < .7$ e. $P(H) < .49$

c. $P(H) = .8$

2. You have drawn a sample with a mean of 100. The confidence limits of the mean are 95 and 105. (Level of confidence is .95.) Test the null hypothesis that the population mean is 106. That the population mean is 103.

3. You prepare to test the null hypothesis that a coin is unbiased. You decide to reject the hypothesis if, on 6 tosses, you get no heads or 6 heads.

a. What is your level of significance? Your level of confidence?

b. You toss the coin and get exactly 3 heads. What do you estimate $P(H)$ to be? What are the confidence limits of your estimate if you choose the same level of confidence you used in testing the null hypothesis?

4. Just on the basis of common sense, do you think you could do a better job in estimating from a sample to a population:

a. With a large sample or a small one?

b. With a sample with a large variance or a sample with a small variance?

If you answered those two questions, explain what you meant by 'a better job.'

5. Vocabulary test: identify or define each of the following terms. If you can, express any relations that exist between terms.

a. Null hypothesis
b. Level of significance
c. Level of confidence
d. α
e. Sampling distribution
f. Standard error
g. Critical region
h. Region of acceptance
i. Type I error
j. Type II error
k. β
l. $1 - \beta$
m. Probability of rejecting null hypothesis

n. Power of a test
o. Confidence limits
p. Biased estimator
q. Unbiased estimator
r. Parameter
s. Statistic
t. Point estimate
u. Interval estimate
v. One-sided alternative
w. Two-sided alternative
x. One-tailed test
y. Two-tailed test
z. Confidence interval

Summary

Inferential statistics are techniques designed to test hypotheses about populations and to make estimates of population parameters. The steps involved in testing a hypothesis are:

1. State two alternative hypotheses, a null hypothesis and one other. The hypotheses may be either one-sided or two-sided.

2. Choose a level of significance, α. This is the probability of rejecting the null hypothesis if it is true. The probability of *accepting* the null hypothesis if it is true is $1 - \alpha$, and is called the level of confidence.

3. Construct a sampling distribution showing the probability of obtaining each class of sample outcome on the assumption that the null hypothesis is true.

4. Draw a representative sample, and determine whether the outcome falls in the critical region of the sampling distribution or in the region of acceptance.

5. Accept or reject the null hypothesis.

In accepting or rejecting a null hypothesis, one runs two risks of error. One may reject the null hypothesis when it is true, a Type I error, or may accept it when it is false, a Type II error. The probability of a Type I error, if the null hypothesis is true, is α, the level of significance. The probability of a Type II error, if the null hypothesis is false, is called β. The probability of correctly rejecting a false null hypothesis, $1 - \beta$, is called the power of a test. Other things being equal, a test is most powerful when: (1) the actual population parameter is very different from that stipulated in the null hypothesis: (2) the level of significance is high (i.e. α is large); (3) the sample is large; (4) a one-sided alternative is being tested; and (5) the statistical test uses all of the available information.

Population values—means, standard deviations, and so on—are called parameters, while those same measures in samples are called statistics. Parameters are estimated from statistics. If we estimate a single value for a parameter, we are making a point estimate. An interval estimate, in which we specify our degree of confidence that a parameter lies within some interval, is usually more useful. An interval estimate is made by determining the probability of the obtained sample statistic on the hypotheses of various parameter values. Finally two parameter values are found, such that the probability of the obtained statistic, if the parameter lies outside of those values, is less than the level of significance. Those two values are the confidence limits. Once confidence limits have been established, we can immediately reject any null hypothesis that states that the parameter lies outside those limits. Thus the establishment of confidence limits and the testing of hypotheses are really very similar procedures.

References

1. Fisher, R. A., *The Design of Experiments*, Edinburgh, Oliver and Boyd, 1951, pp. 11–25. A classic description of a psycho-physical experiment and an exposition of the principles of experimental design and hypothesis testing. Not difficult.
2. Kish, L., Selection of the Sample, in *Research Methods in the Behavioral Sciences*, Festinger, L., and Katz, D. (eds.), New York, Dryden, 1953, pp. 175–239. A short treatment of the theoretical and practical problems of selecting a sample.
3. Hansen, M. H., Hurwitz, W. N., and Madow, W. G., *Sample Survey Methods and Theory*, Vol. I., New York, Wiley, 1953. Very thorough coverage of many methods of sampling from finite populations.
4. Mosteller, F., and Bush, R. R., Selected Quantitative Techniques, in *Handbook of Social Psychology*, Lindzey, G. (ed.), Cambridge, Mass.,

Addison-Wesley, 1954, pp. 289–334. The first 14 pages contain a technical but very clear discussion of the powers of various statistical tests.

5. Newman, J. R., *The World of Mathematics*, New York, Simon & Schuster, 1956. Contains the selection above from Fisher (pp. 1512–21) and the selection below from Tippett (pp. 1459–86).

6. Tippett, L. H. C., *Statistics*, London, Oxford Univ. Press, 1943, pp. 77–93. A very elementary discussion of sampling and the standard error.

Answers

Page 358

3. $H_0: P(4) \leq \frac{1}{6}$, $H_1: P(4) > \frac{1}{6}$

Page 360

2. (a) $H_0: P(H) = \frac{1}{2}$, $H_1: P(H) \neq \frac{1}{2}$; (b) $\frac{1}{4}$, (c) .75

Page 363

2. (a) 0 heads, 5 heads; 0 or 1 heads and 4 or 5 heads
   (b) 0 heads; 0 or 1 head

Page 365

Less than 40.2 and more than 59.8 heads
Either less than 41.775 heads, or more than 58.225 heads, depending upon
   alternative

Page 366

5. .0456

Page 378

1. 1.00, $\frac{41}{125}$, $\frac{11}{125}$, $\frac{1}{16}$, $\frac{11}{125}$, $\frac{41}{125}$, 1.00; 0, $\frac{1}{3125}$, $\frac{32}{3125}$, $\frac{1}{32}$, $\frac{243}{3125}$, $\frac{1024}{3125}$, 1.00
3. (a) increase; (b) decrease; (c) increase; (d, e, and f) decrease

Page 385

1. Reject c and e
2. Reject, accept

3. (a) $\frac{1}{32}$, $\frac{31}{32}$; (b) .5, $\frac{1}{6}$ to $\frac{5}{6}$
4. (a) large; (b) small

INFERENCES FROM NOMINALLY SCALED DATA

In this chapter and the four that follow it, we shall consider specific techniques for establishing interval estimates and for testing hypotheses. As we have pointed out in the last few pages however, there is really no very rigid distinction between these two procedures, so they will not always be rigidly separated in the text. In general, our procedure will be to consider, for each kind of scale, the methods of making point or interval estimates of the parameters appropriate with that scale, then go on to consider tests of hypotheses. Where logic or convenience suggests a change from this organization, the change will be made.

We start with the nominal scale. The categories of a nominal scale are just names—which means that the statistics appropriate to that scale are all based on *counts* of the numbers of cases in the various categories, or, as we have generally called them, *frequencies*. Frequencies can be converted into percentages or proportions, and these, of course, can readily be converted into frequencies. Whether we work with frequencies or with proportions is simply a matter of convenience. Some of the formulas in this chapter will be given in one form, some in the other. By dividing or multiplying by N, you can always change the formula to suit your particular need.

12.1 Estimating Parameters

12.1.1 Estimating a Population Proportion: In a random sample of 100 college men it is observed that 25 are in need of haircuts. Of course, we cannot conclude from that finding that 25 per cent of *all* college men need haircuts—the true percentage might actually be somewhat higher or somewhat lower. In fact it *could* be any value between almost 0 and almost 100.

A sample proportion, p, *is an unbiased estimator of the population proportion* P. That means that our best estimate of the population proportion is that it is the same as the sample proportion. In this example, therefore, we estimate that 25 per cent of all college men need to visit their barbers.

Next we should like to specify with some known degree of confidence that the population proportion lies within a stated range. In theory, our procedure in establishing confidence limits should be, first, to choose a level of confidence and, second, to determine the probability of finding 25 men out of 100 in need of haircuts when the proportion in the population is .01, .02, .03, . . . and so on. Fortunately, if we are willing to accept a confidence level of 95 per cent, we can simply read the confidence limits out of Table D. In that table, the sample proportion, p, is given on the x-axis, and the population proportion, P, on the y-axis. In the table are a series of curved lines. Each line corresponds to a different sample size, and for each sample size there are two lines. Our sample size is 100, so the two lines labeled 100 will be the ones of interest to us. Our procedure for establishing confidence limits is this:

1. We locate our sample proportion, p, on the x-axis. In this example, $p = .25$. We find .25 on the x-axis.

2. We look *up* along the line for $p = .25$ until we come to the curved line labeled 100.

3. We determine the value of P (on the y-axis) at which the vertical line for p intersects the curved line for N. In our example, these two lines intersect where P is higher than .15 and lower than .20. We can estimate the intersection to be at a P of .17. *This is the lower confidence limit.* What it says is that if the proportion of all college men needing haircuts were less than .17, our chances of finding 25 unshorn men in a sample of 100 would be less than $\frac{25}{1000}$, or .025. We conclude that the population proportion is probably *at least* .17.

4. Now we go back to the vertical line for p and continue reading up until we come to the second curved line for N. In our example, we continue up the line for $p = .25$ until we come to the upper curved line labeled 100.

5. We determine the P value of this second intersection. In our example, it is almost exactly .35. *This is the upper confidence limit.* If the proportion of all college men needing haircuts were greater than .35, the probability that we should draw a random sample of 100 men and find 25 needing haircuts would be less than .025. We conclude that the population proportion is probably *at most* .35.

Putting these two results together, we can state that we are 95 per cent confident that the population proportion lies between .17 and .35. It also follows that if we were to draw many more samples from the same population, we should expect 95 per cent of them to contain between 17 and 35 men in need of haircuts.

Note that the upper confidence limit differs more from the sample proportion than does the lower confidence limit. We could more easily have drawn our sample from a population with a higher proportion of men needing haircuts than from a population with a lower proportion. If we had worked with the proportion of well-clipped men, .75, instead of with the proportion of unclipped ones, we should have obtained confidence limits of .65 and .83. When p is greater than .5, the lower confidence limit is closer to the sample value than the upper confidence limit. When p is exactly .5, the two confidence limits are equally different from p.

If our sample size does not happen to be one of those listed in Table D, it will be necessary to interpolate between the lines on that table, and it may also be necessary to interpolate between the listed values of p and of P. The table provides a sufficiently close approximation for most purposes, however.

12.1.2 An Unbiased Estimate of H:[1] $\hat{H}$ is a biased estimator of H. The uncertainty in a sample, $\hat{H}$, tends to be less than the uncertainty in the parent population, H. To see why this should be so, let us consider a simple example.

An urn contains an infinite number of balls, half black and half white, so our uncertainty about the color of a ball drawn from the urn is 1 bit. We do not know that fact, however, and must estimate the population uncertainty from a sample of balls drawn from the urn. We draw four balls. We can, of course, draw any number of black balls from 0 to 4. The probability of drawing any particular proportion can be determined by expanding the binomial $(\frac{1}{2} + \frac{1}{2})^4$. By doing this, we learn that:

The probability of a sample proportion of 1.00 or 0 is $\frac{1}{8}$. In this case, the sample uncertainty is 0.

The probability of a sample proportion of $\frac{1}{4}$ or $\frac{3}{4}$ is .50. In this case, the sample uncertainty is .8113 bits. (You can check this by adding $.25 \log_2 .25$ and $.75 \log_2 .75$.)

---

[1] Miller, G. A., Note on the Bias of Information Estimates, in: *Information Theory in Psychology*, H. Quastler (ed.), Glencoe, Ill., The Free Press, 1955, pp. 95–100.

The probability of a sample proportion of $\frac{1}{2}$ is .375. In this case, the sample uncertainty is 1 bit.

On the average, therefore, the sample uncertainty will be (.125 × 0) + (.50 × .8113) + (.375 × 1), or .78065 bits, even though the population uncertainty is 1 bit.

To put the reason for the discrepancy very simply, there are more ways to divide four things *unevenly* than there are to divide them *evenly*. Only an even distribution will result in an $\hat{H}$ of 1. Any uneven distribution will give a lower $\hat{H}$. So, on the average, the sample $\hat{H}$ will tend to be lower than the population H.

The size of the bias of $\hat{H}$ depends upon two things: the number of categories into which the cases are divided and the number of cases in the sample. The more categories there are, the worse the bias is likely to be. If, for example, we had an urn containing red, yellow, blue, and green balls in equal proportions, the population uncertainty would be two bits. But to get a sample of four cases with an uncertainty of two bits, we should have to pull out one ball of each color, and the probability that we would do so is only $\frac{24}{256}$, as you can determine by applying your knowledge of probability. Any other choice of balls would lead to a smaller uncertainty. If there were fewer cases in the sample than there were categories, it would be *impossible* to draw a sample with an uncertainty as large as that in the population.

As the number of cases in the sample becomes larger, the bias of $\hat{H}$ becomes less. For example, it is easier to get a nearly equal division of 1000 cases than it is of 4 cases. If you tossed a coin four times, you would not be too surprised to get no heads or no tails, but if you tossed it a thousand times, you would be very surprised indeed to get either of those results.

If there are k categories into which the cases in the sample can be classified, and there are N cases in the sample, then we can get an unbiased estimate of the population H from the formula:

$$\tilde{H} = \hat{H} + \frac{(k-1)}{1.3863N} \tag{12.1.1}$$

(The 1.3863 is not a mystic number. It is $\frac{1}{2} \log_2 e$.)

For example, we found in our sample of 100 college men that the proportion needing haircuts was .25. The uncertainty about whether or not a man needs a haircut, then, is

$$.25 \log_2 .25 + .75 \log_2 .75 = .5000 + .3113 = .8113$$

for the sample of 100 cases. Now we can estimate the uncertainty in the population by the use of formula 12.1.1. There are two categories—shorn or unshorn—so $k = 2$. There are 100 men in the sample, so $N = 100$.

$$\tilde{H} = .8113 + \frac{1.00}{138.63}$$
$$\tilde{H} = .8113 + .0072$$
$$\tilde{H} = .8185$$

In this example, the correction made little difference because the number of categories was small and the number of cases large. If there are only a few cases classified into a large number of categories, the unbiased estimate of the population uncertainty will be considerably larger than the sample uncertainty.

If the number of cases in the sample is less than the number of categories into which these cases may be divided, formula 12.1.1 should not be used because it *overcorrects*—that is, it causes us to *overestimate* the population uncertainty. In fact, if N is less than k, it is probably a good idea not to use the uncertainty measure at all.

We should often like to be able to obtain an interval estimate of H, but it is a relatively new statistic, and the form of the sampling distribution of $\hat{H}$ is not known, except for certain special cases.[2] Therefore, we cannot compute confidence limits or obtain an interval estimate.

12.1.3 An Unbiased Estimate of T: $\hat{T}$ is the difference between two estimates of uncertainty.

$$\hat{T} = \hat{H}(y) - \hat{H}_x(y)$$

We have seen that the sample uncertainty is a biased estimator of the population uncertainty, so both $\hat{H}(y)$ and $\hat{H}_x(y)$ will be biased. The amount of the bias depends upon the number of categories and the number of cases in the sample. In computing $\hat{H}_x(y)$, which, you

---

[2] Rogers, M. S., and Green, B. F., The Moments of Sample Information When the Alternatives Are Equally Likely, in *Information Theory in Psychology*, H. Quastler (ed.), Glencoe, Ill., The Free Press, pp. 101–8; and Augenstine, L., *The Use of Illiac in Determining Distributions for Information Functionals*, op. cit., pp. 109–15.

remember, is the average uncertainty of the subgroups, the number of cases will always be smaller than it is when we compute $\hat{H}(y)$, the uncertainty of the total group. Therefore, $\hat{H}_x(y)$ will always be *more biased* than $\hat{H}(y)$. $\hat{H}(y)$ will be slightly smaller than it should be, but $\hat{H}_x(y)$ will be *much* smaller than *it* should be, so $\hat{T}$ will therefore be *larger* than *it* should be. $\hat{T}$, therefore, is a biased estimator of T. The sample uncertainty reduction tends to *overestimate* the population uncertainty reduction. Formula 12.1.2 enables us to make an unbiased estimate of T from a sample value of $\hat{T}$

$$\tilde{T} = \hat{T} - \frac{(r-1)(k-1)}{1.3863N} \tag{12.1.2}$$

where r is the number of categories into which the x variable may be divided, k is the number of categories into which the y variable may be divided, and N is the number of cases in the sample.

Suppose, for example, we have used $\hat{T}$ to find out how well subjects can judge emotion from photographs. Twenty-five subjects have classified four photographs according to whether these represented anger, fear, happiness, or grief. By the usual computational techniques, we find that our uncertainty is reduced by .9279 bits.

We wish now to get an unbiased estimate of the true uncertainty reduction by applying formula 12.1.2. There are four x categories and four y categories, so $r = 4$ and $k = 4$. Although there are only 25 subjects, each subject judged 4 pictures, so the total number of judgements is 100.

$$\tilde{T} = .9279 - \frac{(4-1)(4-1)}{1.3863 \times 100}$$
$$\tilde{T} = .9279 - .0649$$
$$\tilde{T} = .8630$$

We estimate that in the total population, uncertainty is reduced by .8630 bits.

Formula 12.1.2 will give us a correction that is somewhat too large in certain circumstances. In particular, if N is less than $5rk$ or if the uncertainty is reduced almost to zero, formula 12.1.2, by overcorrecting, may cause us to underestimate the actual reduction of uncertainty in the population. Unfortunately, we do not yet have any very good way of getting an unbiased estimate under these conditions.

Questions

1. A random sample of 100 first-grade children shows that 35 per cent need glasses. Find the 95 per cent confidence limits for the population proportion and interpret your results.

2. Of 15 rats inoculated with a certain disease, 10 die. What are the 95 per cent confidence limits for the mortality rate of the disease?

3. Of 1000 randomly selected voters, 500 say they are going to vote for candidate Witherspoon. What can you predict about the results of the election?

4. Find the 95 per cent confidence limits for the following proportions:

   a. $p = .62$ $N = 75$
   b. $p = .10$ $N = 500$
   c. $p = .50$ $N = 12$

5. See question 11, p. 87. Assume that the percentages found for item A were obtained on a sample of 50 cases and those on item B on a sample of 100 cases. Make an unbiased estimate of H for both items and interpret your results.

6. 50 subjects are tested on their preferences for four different foods. They are then given a course on the nutritional value of the foods and retested. During the experiment, 25 of the subjects drop out, so the final test is made on only 25 subjects. Use $\hat{H}$ to interpret the results below, correcting it to get an unbiased estimate of the population H.

PREFERENCES BEFORE
Food A: 10 Food B: 15
Food C: 20 Food D: 5

PREFERENCES AFTER
Food A: 4 Food B: 7
Food C: 11 Food D: 3

7. Apply formula 12.1.2 to the value of $\hat{T}$ you obtained in problem 3, p. 98, to get an unbiased estimate of the uncertainty reduction in the population.

8. In an experiment on extrasensory perception a subject is asked to divide 100 cards into 5 categories according to the design he thinks is on each one. (He does not see the cards, of course.) The uncertainty about the design on a card is reduced by .1158 bits by a knowledge of what the subject called. Use formula 12.1.2 to interpret this result.

12.2 Testing Hypotheses

12.2.1 The Hypothesis That a Sample was Drawn from a Population with a Known P:
Suppose that a college has observed that over the years 25 per cent of its students apply for scholarship aid. Of the most recent freshman class of 300 students, 105, or 35 per cent, request such aid. The college would like to know whether students are getting poorer or whether 35 per cent is close enough to 25 per cent that it could conclude that this freshman class is really drawn from the same population as previous classes.

We could approach this problem in the same way we approached the problem of the unshorn men. We could look up a p of .35, N of 300, in Table D and determine what population values of P would give us such a sample result. By interpolating between the lines on the table, we should conclude that P must (that is, must with 95 per cent confidence) lie between .30 and .40, and we should therefore conclude that this year's freshman class was *not* drawn from the same population as previous classes.

We are now prepared, however, to see how Table D was made up, and to approach this problem more directly. We start by stating our two alternative hypotheses:

$$H_0: P = .25$$
$$H_1: P \neq .25$$

We decide that we are willing to take a 5 per cent risk of rejecting the null hypothesis if it is false. $\alpha = .05$. Our next step is to determine, on the assumption that the null hypothesis is true (that is, that $P = .25$), the probabilities of various classes of outcome.

We know from previous studies that with such a large sample as 300, the probabilities of various proportions will be distributed normally. The mean of the sampling distribution of proportions will be P. (This may sound unfamiliar to you, but that is only because we have stopped talking about frequencies and started talking about proportions. If we were talking about frequencies the mean of the sampling distribution would be NP. To convert to proportions, we divide by N, so the mean is now simply P.) The standard deviation of the sampling distribution of *frequencies*, we know, is $\sqrt{NPQ}$. To obtain the standard deviation of the sampling distribution of proportions, we divide that value by N.

$$\sigma_p = \frac{\sqrt{NPQ}}{N} = \sqrt{\frac{PQ}{N}} \qquad (12.2.1)$$

We substitute the appropriate values in that formula:

$$\sigma_p = \sqrt{\frac{.25 \times .75}{300}} = .025$$

We can now plot our sampling distribution of proportions. It is a normal distribution, with a mean of .25 and a standard deviation of .025, as shown in Figure 12.1. Our critical region will include part of each tail of this distribution, and the area under the curve in the two parts of the critical region will be α, .05. That means that

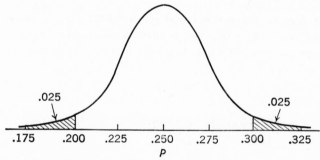

.025

.025

| .175 | .200 | .225 | .250 | .275 | .300 | .325 |

P

Fig. 12.1 The sampling distribution of p for $P = .25$, $N = 300$. The two-tailed critical region, with $\alpha = .05$, has been cross-hatched.

the area in one tail in the critical region will be .025. Now we refer to a normal curve table to determine what value z must have to include an area of (.5000 − .0250) or .4750 between itself and the mean. This z (and you should memorize it, because you will need it frequently) is +1.96 or −1.96.

An obtained proportion must differ from P, .25, by 1.96 standard errors before we reject the null hypothesis that it was drawn from a population with a proportion, P. A standard error, in this instance, is .025.

Now we examine our sample. The sample proportion is .35. That differs from the population proportion by (.35 − .25) or .10. The standard error is .025, so the sample proportion differs from the population proportion by

$$\frac{.10}{.025} = 4$$

or 4 standard errors. That is more than 1.96 standard errors, so the obtained result falls in the critical region. We reject the null hypothesis that $P = .25$ in the population from which these freshman were drawn.

This whole procedure may be reduced to a very few simple steps. To test the null hypothesis that the population from which a sample was drawn has some specified value of P:

1. Determine the difference between the sample p and the population P.

2. Determine the standard error of the sampling distribution by the formula $\sigma_p = \sqrt{\dfrac{PQ}{N}}$.

3. Divide the difference found in step 1 by the standard error found in step 2. This is z, the number of standard errors by which the sample proportion differs from the population proportion.

$$z = \frac{p - P}{\sqrt{PQ/N}} \tag{12.2.2}$$

4. If $\alpha = .05$, reject the null hypothesis if z is greater than 1.96 or less than -1.96.

This procedure will have to be modified slightly if a one-sided alternative is being tested.

12.2.2 The Hypothesis That the Difference between Two Proportions Is Zero:

We now encounter for the first time that most important and most frequently tested of all null hypotheses: the hypothesis that a difference is zero. We suspect, for example, that a certain crooner will have a different appeal to junior-high-school girls and to high-school girls. To test that notion, we restate it in the form of the null hypothesis that there is *no difference* between the two groups of girls with respect to their opinion of the crooner.

Why is this general kind of hypothesis so important and so frequently tested? Because so many of our hunches tell us that something will 'make a difference.' We suspect that the amount of security an infant receives will make a difference in his later adjustment. We suspect that the method of teaching reading will make a difference in pupils' later enjoyment of reading. We suspect that the color of a light will make a difference in people's ability to see details under it. When we really suspect that something will make a difference, we set up our experiment in such a way that the data are given a chance to disprove the null hypothesis that that something makes *no* difference. A more formal way of saying this is to say that two groups which have been treated differently in some way are really 'random samples of the same population.'

If we have one population and we draw two random samples from it we shall not expect those two samples to be identical. If you toss a penny 50 times and get 26 heads, you are not surprised when on the next 50 tosses you only get 24 heads. You do not conclude that the penny has changed. You are perfectly willing to admit that such a difference could occur by chance. You have drawn two samples of 50 cases each from the total population of tosses of the penny and you have found a small difference, yet you are not willing to reject the null hypothesis that those two samples were drawn from the same population. If you were to make successive tests, tossing the penny 50 times, counting the number of heads, then tossing another 50 times and determining the second number of heads, and then finding the difference between the two numbers, you would expect to get some differences in one direction and some in the other, a few large differences and many small differences. If you actually conducted that experiment, you would be constructing *a sampling distribution of differences between frequencies*. You would expect the mean of that distribution to be zero.

That is what we will do, in theory at least, in the paragraphs to follow. We shall assume that there is an infinite number of *pairs* of samples of size N, and that between the samples in each pair there is a difference (which may be zero). Our null hypothesis states that the mean of the sampling distribution of differences is zero. The sampling distributions of differences of frequencies, percentages, and proportions are normal. All we need to know, then, is the standard error of our difference. Then, since the mean of the sampling distribution is assumed to be zero, we have only to divide the obtained difference by its standard error. If the result is greater than 1.96 or less than -1.96, we shall conclude that we should have had fewer than 5 chances in 100 of drawing a pair of samples with that large a difference from the same population. We shall therefore reject the null hypothesis that the samples were drawn at random from the same population, and conclude that there is a difference.

All we need are the formulas for the standard errors, and

$$z = \frac{\text{Difference} - 0}{\text{Standard error of difference}}$$

There are many different techniques available for testing the hypothesis that the difference between two proportions is zero. The choice of a technique depends on the particular circumstances under which the difference was obtained. We shall consider only one technique in detail and then outline the conditions that call for other methods.

When the two proportions come from two independent samples, the standard error of their difference is

$$\sigma_{D_p} = \sqrt{p_a q_a \left(\frac{1}{N_1} + \frac{1}{N_2} \right)} \tag{12.2.3}$$

where p_a is the weighted average of the two proportions, obtained as follows:

$$p_a = \frac{N_1 p_1 + N_2 p_2}{N_1 + N_2}$$

N_1 is the number of cases in one sample, and N_2 the number in the other and q_a is $(1 - p_a)$

For example, we may be interested in determining the effectiveness of fluoridation in preventing tooth decay. We suspect that floridation will prevent decay, and hence that 'fluoridated children' will have fewer cavities than 'unfluoridated children.' Since we specify not only that there will be a difference but also the direction of the difference, we are, in this case, testing a one-sided alternative. Our hypotheses are:

H_0: At least as many fluoridated children as unfluoridated children will have cavities.

H_1: Fewer fluoridated than unfluoridated children will have cavities.

If $\alpha = .05$, we shall not require that $z = 1.96$. Instead, we must find the z-score that will put 5 per cent of the cases in *one* tail of the distribution. From the normal curve table, we determine that the desired z is 1.645. We must, to reject the null hypothesis, find a difference at least 1.645 times as great as its standard error, and the difference must favor the fluoridated children.

It is found that in a sample of 200 children from towns with treated water supplies, 12 per cent have had two or more cavities during the past year. In a sample of 500 children with towns from untreated water supplies, 20 per cent have had two or more cavities in the past year. The difference is 8 per cent in favor of the fluoridated children. Would a difference this great, and in this direction, occur more than 5 times in 100 if fluoridation really made no difference? We start by finding the standard error of the difference:

$$p_a = \frac{200 \times .12 + 500 \times .20}{700} = .177$$

$$q_a = 1.000 - .177 = .823$$

$$\sigma_{D_P} = \sqrt{.177 \times .823 \left(\frac{1}{200} + \frac{1}{500} \right)} = .032$$

The standard error of the difference is .032. Next, we compute z.

$$z = \frac{.20 - .12}{.032} = 2.50$$

This value is much greater than the 1.645 required for rejection of the null hypothesis. We therefore reject the null hypothesis that the proportion of fluoridated children having two or more cavities is the same as or larger than the comparable proportion for un-fluoridated children. We conclude that fluoridation reduces tooth decay.

The method just illustrated applies *only* when the two proportions come from two independent samples. Other situations require other methods. If the two proportions come from *the same sample*, as when we observe that 10 per cent of 100 children are underweight and 12 per cent are overweight and wish to test the significance of this difference, another formula for the standard error of the difference must be used. Still another formula is required when the proportions come from *correlated samples*. By correlated samples we ordinarily mean samples in which the same individuals have been studied under different conditions, as when we determine the proportion of a class passing test item A, and the proportion of the same class passing item B. The necessary formulas may be found in advanced statistics texts.

Questions

1. A school teacher discovers that 18 of the children in her class of 30 have intelligence-test scores below the median for that school. She complains to the principal that she is being discriminated against. He says it was just bad luck. Use your newly acquired knowledge to settle their argument.

2. A certain disease is known to have a mortality rate of 50 per cent. In a group of 50 patients treated with a new drug, 32 live and 18 die. Test the hypothesis that the drug really improves a patient's chances. (Will this be a one-tailed or a two-tailed test?)

3. On a sample of 72 rolls, a die lands '4' 20 times. Test the hypothesis that the die is loaded.

4. Out of 125 women who attend a certain movie, 75 say they like it. Out of 240 men who attend the same movie, 160 say they like it. Does sex really have an effect on attitudes toward the movie?

5. It is hypothesized that a certain brain operation will interfere with an animal's ability to acquire a certain conditioned response. Of 20 normal animals, 18 acquire the response. Of 18 operated animals, 14 acquire the response. Does the operation really interfere?

12.2.3 Other Tests of the Hypothesis That Two Groups Are Drawn from the Same Population: In certain circumstances, the **run test** and the **sign test,** which are described in detail in Chapter 13, can be applied to data from nominal scales to test the null hypothesis that two samples were drawn at random from the same population.

12.2.4 Testing the Hypothesis That Obtained Frequencies Are the Same As Expected Frequencies: In the last section, we saw how to test the null hypothesis that there was no difference between proportions, and in the section before that, how to test the hypothesis that an obtained proportion was the same as some theoretical (population) proportion. These tests, however, would be cumbersome to use if there were many categories into which our data could be classified instead of just two or three. For this purpose, we shall use an important test called the chi-square (χ^2) test. The purpose of the chi-square test is to test the null hypothesis that a set of obtained frequencies differs no more from a set of expected frequencies than would be expected by chance alone. Chi-square is defined as:

$$\chi^2 = \sum_{}^{k} \frac{(f_o - f_e)^2}{f_e} \qquad (12.2.4)$$

f_o stands for one obtained frequency

f_e stands for one expected frequency

k stands for the number of categories over which the summation is made

Let us apply this formula to a very simple problem—a problem so simple that in practice a χ^2 would never be used for it—and see how the result comes to be interpreted as it is.

We shall test the null hypothesis that a class of students is drawn from a population equally divided with respect to sex. The class has 100 members, so if our null hypothesis were true, we should expect 50 of them to be men and 50 women. Actually 40 are men and 60 women. Applying the χ^2 formula we have:

Men: $\quad f_e = 50; \quad f_o = 40; \quad (f_o - f_e) = -10; \quad (f_o - f_e)^2 = 100;$

$$\frac{(f_o - f_e)^2}{f_e} = 2$$

Women: $\quad f_e = 50; \quad f_o = 60; \quad \dfrac{(f_o - f_e)^2}{f_e} = 2$

$$\chi^2 = 2 + 2 = 4$$

To interpret this result we turn to Table E, a chi-square table. This table gives the probability of obtaining various values of χ^2. It is a table of the sampling distribution of χ^2. At the tops of the columns are listed the probabilities of obtaining the tabled values of χ^2, or any larger values, if the null hypothesis is true. On the extreme left is a column labeled 'd.f.' Those letters stand for 'degrees of freedom.' We shall explain that term fully in just a page or two, but for the moment please accept on faith the fact that in our example, d.f. = 1. We therefore look for our value of χ^2 in the top row of the table. We do not find the value '4,' but we do find, in the column headed .05, the entry '3.841.' That entry means that the probability of obtaining a χ^2 as high as 3.841, or higher, if the null hypothesis is true, is .05 or less. If we have chosen $\alpha = .05$, therefore, we *reject* the null hypothesis because *our* χ^2 is *larger* than the one given in the table. Any value of χ^2 higher than 3.841 falls into the critical region when $\alpha = .05$.

There is another way of tackling this same problem. That is to use formula 12.2.2 and test the null hypothesis that the proportion of men is .50.

$$\sigma_P = \sqrt{\frac{PQ}{N}} = \sqrt{\frac{.5 \times .5}{100}} = .05$$

The obtained proportion of men is .40.

$$z = \frac{p - P}{\sigma_P} = \frac{.40 - .50}{05} = 2$$

The obtained proportion is thus two standard errors lower than the hypothesized population proportion. To find out how often we should expect that small a proportion of men if the population proportion were .50, we look up a z of 2.00 in a normal curve table. There we find that between the mean and a z of 2.00 lie 47.725 per cent of the cases, so only 2.28 per cent of the time should we expect to have such a small number of men. We must also consider, now, the possibility of a deviation as large as two standard errors in the other direction—too many men. In other words, we must consider *both* tails of the normal distribution. If we consider both tails, we see that the probability of getting a split as great as 60-40, *in either direction*, is .228 + .228, or .456. Our answer is 'almost 5 per cent,' which is what we obtained by the use of χ^2.

We neglected the women in this second treatment of the problem because if there were 100 students and 40 of them were men, the other 60 would simply *have* to be women! We learn nothing new when we add what information we have about the women, and it would be 'cheating' to count them twice.

Not only does the chi-square test give the same results as the treatment in terms of number of standard errors from the mean, but it is basically the same principle. In fact when there is only one category to be considered independently (one degree of freedom) then:

$$\chi^2 = z^2$$

The probability of obtaining any given value of χ^2 is the same as the probability of obtaining a z-score of $\sqrt{\chi^2}$.

Chi-square is seldom used for a comparison of two groups, as was done above, because the z-score method is more convenient. Chi-square becomes valuable when there are many different possible outcomes of an event and we wish to consider them all at once. For example, a cafeteria serves three main dishes, hash, beans, and spaghetti. It wishes to test the hypothesis that they are equally popular. Of the first 150 dinners sold one night, 65 are hash, 45 beans, and 40 spaghetti, while if the three had been equally popular, 50 meals of each kind would have been ordered. How likely is it that the differences between the observed and expected frequencies would have occurred by chance alone? Chi-square permits us to solve this problem easily:

$$\chi^2 = \frac{(65 - 50)^2}{50} + \frac{(45 - 50)^2}{50} + \frac{(40 - 50)^2}{50} = 7$$

Is this value of 7 one that is likely to occur by chance if the true frequencies are 50, 50, 50? To answer that question, we must look up our result in the χ^2 table. But to look it up, we must know which row of the table to consult, and to do that we must understand what is meant by 'degrees of freedom.' Instead of looking up our chi-square now, we shall digress for a bit and consider this new concept; then we shall return to the interpretation of a χ^2 of 7.

Degrees of freedom:

Suppose one is given the problem:

$$v + w + x + y + z = 125$$

There might be many solutions to that problem. Each of the five variables might assume any one of a large range of values. But notice this—if we specify that

$$v = 10$$
$$w = 25$$
$$x = 45$$
$$y = 7$$

there is only one thing that z can be: 125 minus the sum of all the other numbers, or 38. Four of the five numbers have been selected freely, but, since we know the sum of the numbers, the fifth is determined. Because four of the numbers can be chosen freely, we say that there are four degrees of freedom in the equation.

Suppose that in addition to specifying the sum of the numbers we also specify the sum of their squares.

$$v + w + x + y + z = 125$$
$$v^2 + w^2 + x^2 + y^2 + z^2 = 4375$$

Now we shall find that only *three* of the numbers can be chosen freely. Suppose we select, as before:

$$v = 10$$
$$w = 25$$
$$x = 45$$

Then

$$y + z = 125 - 10 - 25 - 45 = 45, \quad \text{and}$$
$$y^2 + z^2 = 4375 - 100 - 625 - 2025 = 1625$$

We now have two equations with two unknowns, and by solving them simultaneously we find that the roots must be $y = 40$, $z = 5$ (or vice versa). Only three of the numbers can now be chosen freely. We have only three degrees of freedom in our choice of the numbers.

Every time an additional condition or restriction is added, the number of degrees of freedom is reduced by one.

Let us consider the number of degrees of freedom in a bivariate frequency distribution. We know the marginal totals in advance but we do not know the frequencies in the cells. How many of these can be chosen freely and how many are determined by restrictions on the data?

		45*
		55
30*	70	100*

There are four cells to be filled in. The first restriction is imposed when we say that N must be 100. The number 100 has been starred to indicate that it imposes a restriction. When we specify that the number of cases in the top row must be 45, that imposes an additional restriction, so it, too, has been starred. But no *new* restriction is added when we specify that the number of cases in the bottom row must be 55, because if the total is 100 and the number of cases in the top row is 45, the number of cases in the bottom row *must be* 55. Similarly, one of the column totals imposes an additional restriction, but the second one does not. So there are three restrictions imposed upon the way we choose four numbers, and therefore only one of those numbers can be chosen freely. Suppose we choose a number at random—say, 25—and put it in the upper left-hand cell. Then there is only one way the rest of the table can be filled in:

25**	20	45
5	50	55
30	70	100

The number 25 has been marked because it was chosen freely.

This two-by-two table has just one degree of freedom.

One more example. Consider a larger table such as the 3×4 table below.

				25*
				20*
				30
16*	10*	24*	30	70*

Each total that imposes an independent restriction has been starred.

There is one star for the grand total, and one star for every row but one, and one star for every column but one. The number of restrictions is

$$1 + (r - 1) + (k - 1)$$

There are rk cells to be filled in, so the number that can be chosen freely is

$$d.f. = rk - (1 + r - 1 + k - 1) = rk - r - k + 1$$

and that in turn is equal to

$$d.f. = (r - 1)(k - 1) \qquad (12.2.5)$$

In the case of the table above, with three rows and four columns, the number of degrees of freedom is $(3 - 1)(4 - 1) = 2 \times 3 = 6$. If you try filling the table in, you will find that you can choose 6 numbers—two in each column and three in each row—freely, but the remaining six are chosen for you by the marginal totals.

The chi-square distribution: The probability of obtaining any specified value of chi-square depends only upon the number of degrees of freedom. There is a different sampling distribution of χ^2 for each number of degrees of freedom and the mean of each χ^2 distribution is approximately equal to the number of degrees of freedom. Some typical sampling distributions of χ^2 are shown in Figure 12.2. Since

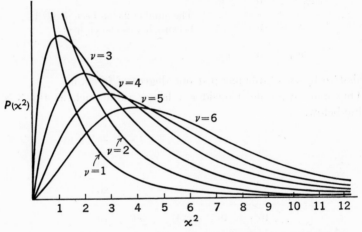

Fig. 12.2 Sampling distributions of χ^2 for 1, 2, 3, 4, 5, and 6 degrees of freedom. (From Hoel, P. G., *Introduction to Mathematical Statistics*, New York, Wiley, 1954; by permission of the publisher.)

we want to know what value of χ^2 will make the area in the right-hand tail equal to .05, we must know which of these distributions to use, and to find that out, we determine the number of degrees of freedom available in our frequency table.

Whenever a χ^2 test is used, *the sum of the obtained frequencies must equal the sum of the expected frequencies*. That is an exceedingly important restriction on our data, and in the examples we have considered it is the only restriction. In the cafeteria example, therefore, since we 'expected' that 50 meals of each kind would be eaten, the total number of meals actually eaten (sum of the obtained frequencies) must be 150. We have three numbers and one restriction. Two of those numbers can be chosen freely. We have two degrees of freedom. Now, to interpret our obtained χ^2 of 7, we turn to Table E and look in the row labeled $d.f. = 2$. Here we find that the probability of obtaining a χ^2 as large as 7, if the null hypothesis is true, is between .05 and .02. (A chi-square of 5.991 is required for rejection of the null hypothesis when $\alpha = .05$, and a χ^2 of 7.824 when $\alpha = .02$.) We can therefore *reject* the null hypothesis, with an α less than .05 but greater than .02. We can be more than 95 per cent confident, though less than 98 per cent confident, that the differences between obtained and expected frequencies did not arise by chance. Apparently people really like hash better than beans or spaghetti.

Let us consider for the cafeteria example how the probability of a χ^2 value is arrived at. If we can see where χ^2 comes from, we shall be better able to recognize those situations where the use of χ^2 is appropriate and those where it is inappropriate.

When there is only one degree of freedom, we have seen that $\chi^2 = z^2$. When there is more than one degree of freedom, the situation becomes more complicated. If we wished to tackle the cafeteria example by testing hypotheses about proportions, we might start this way: one-third of the people are assumed, on the basis of the null hypothesis, to like hash, but more than that ($\frac{65}{150}$) choose hash. Is this difference significant? We can tell by using formula 12.2.2. The result will give us a z-score, which has a probability that can be determined from the normal curve table, and which we shall call $P(z_1)$.

Now we think about beans. There are 85 people left who do not choose hash, and our null hypothesis states that half of this remainder will choose beans. Actually, 45 people, instead of the expected $42\frac{1}{2}$, choose beans. We test the significance of this discrepancy by getting a z-score from formula 12.2.2 and determining its probability. We shall call this probability $P(z_2)$.

Finally our attention focuses on spaghetti, but not for long. There are 40 people left. Our null hypothesis states that 40 of them will choose spaghetti, and 40 of them do. Forty of them must, because they have no other choice. The number 40 is a restricted number, not chosen freely, so it does not contribute to our estimate. In other words, for the last category, z must always be zero.

The probability of the hash z was $P(z_1)$ and the probability of the beans z was $P(z_2)$. If the people choosing beans made their choices *independently* of the people choosing hash, then the probability of getting *both* those values of z is

$$P(z_1 z_2) = P(z_1) \times P(z_2)$$

and that is approximately the probability of getting the obtained value of χ^2. We say 'approximately' because, in fact, the chi-square distribution is only a mathematical approximation to the probabilities calculated in this way.

There are two important assumptions involved in calculating the probability of a χ^2 value in the manner described above. First, our estimates of the probabilities of the z-scores are derived from the normal curve table. But the normal curve itself is a good approximation to binomial probabilities only when N is large and P is not too small. We have stated as a rule of thumb that NP should be at least 5 before the normal approximation to the binomial is used. The same restriction applies to chi-square. If we want our probabilities to be exact, we cannot use χ^2 if more than one or two of the expected frequencies are less than 5. If we are satisfied (as we often are) with approximate probabilities, slightly smaller expected frequencies are acceptable, particularly if there are not too many of them.

The second assumption is that the people choosing beans make their choices independently of the people choosing hash. The outcomes in the various classes of a distribution must be independent. In practice, that means that every *unit* in the table from which χ^2 is computed must be contributed by a different individual. We could not have used χ^2 for the cafeteria example if we had counted the food choices of 3 men on 50 nights, because all the entries would then not have come from different individuals.

Finding the expected frequencies:

One of the reasons that χ^2 is such a useful statistic is that there are many ways of determining the expected frequencies. We may 'expect' that the frequencies will be the same in each of k categories, as we did in the cafeteria example. We may 'expect' that the frequencies will be distributed now as they have been in the past. We often 'expect' that the frequencies will be distributed in accordance with some theoretical distribution, such as the binomial or normal distribution. When a chi-square is used to determine whether or not this expectation is fulfilled, we are testing 'the goodness of fit' of the theoretical distribution to the obtained data. One very important use of χ^2 in genetics is to determine whether certain biological characteristics occur in the frequencies predicted from Mendelian ratios. In short, when:

a. The sum of the expected frequencies equals the sum of the obtained frequencies,

and

b. The expected frequencies are not too small—no more than one or two less than 5,

and

c. The entries in the table are all independent of each other—

chi-square can be used to test the deviation of any set of obtained frequencies from a set of theoretically expected frequencies.

Questions

1. How many degrees of freedom are there in each of the following equations:

a. $a + b + c + d + e + f = 247$

b. $\sum_{1}^{6} X_i = 247$

c. $\sum^{N} X = 247$ and $N = 6$

d. $a + b + c + d + e + f = 247$, and $a^2 + b^2 + c^2 + d^2 + e^2 + f^2 = 1099$

e. $\sum_{1}^{6} X_i = 247$ and $\sum_{1}^{6} X_i^2 = 1099$

f. $\sum^{N} X = 247$, $\sum^{N} X^2 = 1099$, and $N = 6$

2. If we know that the mean of a sample of 100 cases is 30, how many degrees of freedom are there?

3. If we know that the mean of a sample of 100 cases is 30, and the standard deviation of the sample is 5, how many degrees of freedom are there?

4. How many degrees of freedom are there in a:

    a. 2 × 2 table
    b. 7 × 9 table
    c. 20 × 2 table
    d. 3 × 3 × 3 table (This will take a little thought.)

5. Determine from the χ^2 table the probability of obtaining a χ^2 as large as or larger than each of the ones listed below:

d.f.	χ^2
1	.46
1	5.4
1	5.0
1	5.2
6	12.6
6	12.7
20	8.26
16	10.0

6. For each of the values of χ^2 listed below, decide whether you would accept or reject the null hypothesis that the obtained frequencies are the same as the expected frequencies. Test each value at $\alpha = .05$, $\alpha = .02$, and $\alpha = .01$.

	d.f.	χ^2
a.	1	3.9
b.	2	8.2
c.	2	20.4
d.	4	.19
e.	10	22.0

7. If the obtained frequencies are all *exactly* equal to the expected frequencies, what will χ^2 be? What will you say about the null hypothesis? What will happen to χ^2 when the obtained and expected frequencies become increasingly different? Explain in simple words what a large χ^2 means.

8. Use χ^2 to test the null hypothesis that the obtained frequencies do not differ from the expected frequencies for the data below:

						Total
f_e	20	20	20	20	20	100
f_o	16	18	24	24	18	100

9. A geneticist crosses two plants with hybrid Mendelian characteristics and determines the numbers of offspring which are pure dominant (DD), pure recessive (RR), and hybrid (DR). The ex-

pected ratios are $1:1:2$. Determine whether the obtained frequencies are in accord with the expectation. He obtains: 28 DD plants; 20 RR plants; 66 DR plants.

10. In a coin-tossing experiment in which four coins were tossed 80 times, the following results were obtained:

No heads 6 times	2 heads 35 times
1 head 22 times	3 heads 16 times
	4 heads 1 time

Determine by expanding the binomial what the expected frequencies would have been and use χ^2 to test the hypothesis that obtained and expected frequencies show only chance differences.

11. If exactly the same proportions of heads were obtained on 160 tosses, what would χ^2 be, and how would it be interpreted?

12.2.5 Testing the Hypothesis of Independence: If we are given a bivariate frequency distribution, there are three kinds of questions we can ask about it:

1. How strong is the relationship between the variables in this sample? When the data come from nominal scales, the statistic that answers this question is $\hat{T}$. If the data come from stronger scales, there are other measures of correlation which provide an answer to the question.

2. How strong is the relationship between the variables in the population from which this sample was drawn? When we apply a correction to $\hat{T}$ to get an unbiased estimate of the population value of T, we are answering this question. In later chapters we shall learn to obtain interval estimates for other measures of correlation. These will enable us to say that we are 95 per cent (or some other per cent) confident that in the population from which the sample was drawn the correlation was at least so much and not more than so much.

3. Are the two variables independent? This is really a much more fundamental question than either of the ones above. If two variables are independent, they are uncorrelated—that is, the strength of the correlation between them is zero.[4] If we answer yes to the

[4] Oddly enough, the converse does not *necessarily* follow: zero correlation does not necessarily imply independence, though in most practical situations it does. Mathematically, independence is a stronger assertion than zero correlation. See Cramér, H., *Mathematical Methods of Statistics*, Princeton, N. J., Princeton U. Press, 1946, p. 279.

question: 'are the variables independent?' we shall have no further interest in the strength of their relationship; it will be assumed to be zero. If we answer no to this question, we shall go on to the logical next step of asking how strongly the variables are related.

Independence, you will remember, has a very rigorous mathe-mathical definition. Outcomes a and b are defined as independent if and only if

$$P(a) = P_b(a).$$

Notice that in this definition we use a capital P, meaning a popu-lation proportion, or a probability. Since sample proportions are not always identical with the proportions in the population from which the samples were drawn, it will sometimes happen that in a sample $p(a) \neq p_b(a)$ even though in the population the conditional and absolute probabilities *are* equal. When we test the null hy-pothesis of independence, we shall test the hypothesis that two un-equal sample proportions, $p(a)$ and $p_b(a)$, could have been drawn from a population in which the corresponding population propor-tions were equal.

The statistic that we shall use for this test is χ^2. Chi-square is designed to test the null hypothesis that obtained and expected frequencies are equal, and it has been pointed out that there are many ways of establishing the expected frequencies. One way, not yet mentioned, is to determine the expected frequencies *on the hy-pothesis of independence*. We shall start with an example.

One thousand respondents to a public-opinion poll are classified according to the amount of education they have had. Three cate-gories are used: no high school, some high school but no college, and some college. All are asked the question: 'Should college students who are doing well in their studies be exempt from the draft?' Answers permitted are: 'yes,' 'no,' and 'not sure.' The null hy-pothesis to be tested is: Answers to this question are independent of the educational level of the respondent. Translated into more formal terms: the absolute probability of any response is equal to the conditional probability of that response on the hypothesis of a particular level of education. For example, if $P(a)$ stands for the probability of answering the question 'yes' and $P_b(a)$ stands for the probability of answering the question 'yes' on the hypothesis of having had only a high-school education, we shall test the hypothesis that $P(a) = P_b(a)$. And of course we shall also test comparable hypotheses for every combination of educational level and response.

Finding the expected frequencies: A 3×3 table is prepared for the presentation of the data. The three educational levels are listed in one dimension and the three answers in the other. Marginal totals are filled in from the obtained data.

| | | ANSWER | | | |
		Yes	No	Not sure	Total
EDUCA- TION	No H.S.				500
	H.S.				300
	College				200
	Total	450	350	200	1000

Our next step is to fill in the expected frequencies. From our study of probability, we know that, if a and b are independent,

$$P(ab) = P(a)P(b)$$

and in the sample, $p(ab) = p(a)p(b)$. It is from this formula that we shall compute the expected frequencies. For example, the proportion of respondents having no high-school training is $\frac{500}{1000}$, or .50. The proportion of respondents answering 'yes' is $\frac{450}{1000}$, or .45. Therefore, if response is independent of education, the proportion of respondents having no high-school training *and* answering 'yes' should be (.50) (.45), or .225. Since there were 1000 respondents, we should expect .225 × 1000, or 225, of them to fall into this category. That number is the expected frequency for the cell in the upper left corner of the table.

We can simplify this calculation a little bit. Let i stand for any particular educational level and j for any particular response. Then the expected proportion in any one cell is

$$p(i)p(j)$$

and the expected frequency in that cell is

$$Np(i)p(j)$$

But $p(i) = \dfrac{n(i)}{N}$, and $p(j) = \dfrac{n(j)}{N}$, so

$$Np(i)p(j) = \frac{Nn(i)}{N} \cdot \frac{n(j)}{N} = \frac{n(i)n(j)}{N} \tag{12.2.6}$$

From this formula the various expected frequencies can be calculated directly, as illustrated in the table below:

		ANSWER			
		Yes	No	Not sure	Total
EDUCA-TION	No H.S.	$\dfrac{500 \times 450}{1000}$	$\dfrac{500 \times 350}{1000}$	$\dfrac{500 \times 200}{1000}$	500
	H.S.	$\dfrac{300 \times 450}{1000}$	$\dfrac{300 \times 350}{1000}$	$\dfrac{300 \times 200}{1000}$	300
	College	$\dfrac{200 \times 450}{1000}$	$\dfrac{200 \times 350}{1000}$	$\dfrac{200 \times 200}{1000}$	200
	Total	450	350	200	1000

and the table, complete with the calculated expected frequencies, is:

		ANSWER			
		Yes	No	Not sure	Total
EDUCA-TION	No H.S.	225	175	100	500
	H.S.	135	105	60	300
	College	90	70	40	200
	Total	450	350	200	1000

Now we are ready to look at our original data to see what frequencies were actually obtained for each of the cells in the table. The data are given in the table below.

		ANSWER			
		Yes	No	Not sure	Total
EDUCA-TION	No H.S.	100	250	150	500
	H.S.	180	80	40	300
	College	170	20	10	200
	Total	450	350	200	1000

Now that we have the obtained frequencies and the expected frequencies we can compute χ^2 by the regular formula. It will be easier to list our frequencies in columns than to work with them in the original tabular form. The computation follows.

Educ.	Answ.	f_e	f_o	$f_o - f_e$	$(f_o - f_e)^2$	$\dfrac{(f_o - f_e)^2}{f_e}$
No H.S.	Y	225	100	-125	15,625	72.2
No H.S.	N	175	250	75	5,625	32.2
No H.S.	N.S.	100	150	50	2,500	25.0
H.S.	Y	135	180	45	2,025	15.0
H.S.	N	105	80	-25	625	6.0
H.S.	N.S.	60	40	-20	400	6.7
College	Y	90	170	80	6,400	7.1
College	N	70	20	-50	2,500	35.6
College	N.S.	40	10	-30	900	22.5
		1000	1000	0		222.3

$$\chi^2 = \sum^{k} \frac{(f_o - f_e)^2}{f_e} = 222.3$$

Our table has three rows and three columns, so d.f. $= (3 - 1)(3 - 1) = 4$. We enter the χ^2 table with d.f. $= 4$, and find there that we should need a χ^2 as large as 13.3 to be able to reject the null hypothesis at the 1 per cent level of significance, and a χ^2 of 18.5 to reject it at the .1 per cent level. Since our obtained χ^2 is so much higher than that we can feel very confident indeed in rejecting the null hypothesis. We *reject* the null hypothesis of *independence*, and conclude that *response depends upon education*. Let us be even more specific about what hypothesis we are rejecting. Chi-square compares the discrepancies between obtained and expected frequencies with the discrepancies to be expected by chance if there were no real population difference. The expected frequencies, in turn, are obtained by assuming (a) that the variables are independent, *and* (b) that the marginal frequencies correspond exactly to population proportions. Thus it is assumed in the example above that *exactly* half the persons in the population from which the sample was drawn have had no high-school education. Our conclusion in rejecting the null hypothesis must therefore be limited to a population in which the proportions are the same as those in the margins of our table.

Chi-square for a 2 × 2 table: When a χ^2 is computed for a 2 × 2 table, there are two additional factors that must be taken into consideration. One of these simplifies our calculations; the other complicates them.

First, as you can verify from the example below, every $(f_o - f_e)^2$ has the same numerical value as every other. This fact permits a simplified computational formula.

	R	S	Total
P	12 (a)	28 (b)	40 (p)
Q	8 (d)	52 (c)	60 (q)
Total	20 (r)	80 (s)	100 (N)

Now, if we calculate the expected frequencies in the usual way, we have for cells a, b, c, and d:

	f_e	$f_o - f_e$	$(f_o - f_e)^2$
a:	$\dfrac{40 \times 20}{100} = 8$	$12 - 8 = \quad 4$	16
b:	$\dfrac{40 \times 80}{100} = 32$	$28 - 32 = -4$	16
c:	$\dfrac{60 \times 80}{100} = 48$	$52 - 48 = \quad 4$	16
d:	$\dfrac{60 \times 20}{100} = 12$	$8 - 12 = -4$	16

The second factor is a little more complicated. The theoretical sampling distribution of χ^2 is based on the assumption that χ^2 is a continuous variable. But when we use frequencies to calculate χ^2, we can obtain only a set of discrete values. This fact means that ordinary formulas give values for χ^2 that are slightly too high. Unfortunately, there is ordinarily no known way to correct for this bias. However, when we compute χ^2 with one degree of freedom, as in a 2 × 2 table, a correction is available. For any calculation with one degree of freedom, we make a **correction for continuity** by using the following rule:

Reduce the absolute value of each $(f_o - f_e)$ *by .5 before squaring it.* (Every once in a while it will happen that $(f_o - f_e)$ has an absolute value less than .25. In this case, applying the correction would increase χ^2, and the correction should not be used.)

One proper formula for χ^2 when there is only one degree of freedom is therefore

$$\chi^2 = \sum_{}^{k} \frac{(|f_o - f_e| - .5)^2}{f_e} \tag{12.2.7}$$

This formula does not, however, take into account the simplification resulting from the fact that in a 2×2 table all the $(f_o - f_e)$'s have the same absolute value. When this fact is taken into account, the new, simplified formula for χ^2 computed from a 2×2 table is

$$\chi^2 = \frac{N(|bd - ac| - N/2)^2}{pqrs} \tag{12.2.8}$$

a, b, c, d, p, q, r, and s refer to cell frequencies or marginal totals as labeled in the preceding 2×2 table.

Applying this formula to the data in the 2×2 table above, we have:

$$\chi^2 = \frac{100(|28 \times 8 - 12 \times 52| - 50)^2}{40 \times 60 \times 20 \times 80}$$

$$\chi^2 = \frac{100(|-400| - 50)^2}{40 \times 60 \times 20 \times 80}$$

$$\chi^2 = \frac{100(-350)^2}{40 \times 60 \times 20 \times 80}$$

$$\chi^2 = 3.19$$

The hypothesis that T = 0; the likelihood-ratio chi-square: Chi-square is used to test the hypothesis that two variables are independent. If they are independent, then knowledge of one will effect no reduction in our uncertainty about the other, and we should expect T to be zero. Conversely, if $T = 0$, the variables are independent. Thus a test of the null hypothesis that $T = 0$ is really the same kind of test as a chi-square test of independence.

We have seen that $\hat{T}$ is a biased estimator of T, tending to overestimate the latter. The smaller the sample, the greater the bias. For any given sample size, however, the greater the uncertainty reduction, $\hat{T}$, the greater will be a χ^2 computed from the same data, and the more confidence we may have in rejecting the null hypothesis of independence.

There is a statistic, λ, called the **likelihood-ratio,** which, like χ^2

and $\hat{T}$, is computed from cell frequencies and marginal totals.[5] It has been shown that if x and y are independent, $-2 \log_e \lambda$ will have a χ^2 sampling distribution with $(r - 1)(k - 1)$ degrees of freedom. It can *also* be shown that $-2 \log_e \lambda$ is mathematically identical with $1.3863N\hat{T}$. Therefore, if x and y are independent, $1.3863N\hat{T}$ will have a χ^2 distribution.

Therefore, to test the null hypothesis that $T = 0$, we have only to multiply our obtained value of $\hat{T}$ by $1.3863N$, and we can look the result up in a χ^2 table with $(r - 1)$ $(k - 1)$ degrees of freedom and accept or reject the hypothesis. A χ^2 computed in this manner is called a **likelihood-ratio chi-square.**

A likelihood-ratio chi-square will not necessarily be numerically equal to a χ^2 computed from the same data by the usual techniques. The actual numerical answers may be quite different, but the probabilities of obtaining those answers as found from the χ^2 table, will be almost identical. The choice of computational technique is simply a matter of convenience.

Requirements for the use of a chi-square test: Chi-square is an easy technique to apply and a very useful one. It is altogether too easy, however, to assume that whenever one has some obtained frequencies and can list some expected frequencies the χ^2 test is appropriate. The sampling distributions for χ^2 are derived on the assumption that certain conditions have been fulfilled, and if these assumptions are not met by the data the application of χ^2 will give wrong and misleading results. To prevent the misuse of χ^2 we shall repeat, in the form of a list, the requirements that must be met by the data before the use of χ^2 is justified.

1. *The sum of the expected frequencies must equal the sum of the obtained frequencies.*

An example of a situation where this restriction is violated is the following: Each of 5 students tosses 100 coins and the number of heads is counted by each. Chi-square is used to test the hypothesis that the obtained results are not out of line with the expectation

$$5\,\lambda = \frac{\displaystyle\prod_{i=1}^{i=r} n(i)^{n(i)} \prod_{j=1}^{j=k} n(j)^{n(i)}}{N^N \displaystyle\prod_{ij} n(ij)^{n(ij)}}$$

that the average number of heads per 100 tosses is 50. The results are:

STUDENT:	A	B	C	D	E	TOTAL
Heads obtained:	44	58	52	53	49	244
Heads expected:	50	50	50	50	50	250

Here the sum of the obtained frequencies is 244, while the sum of the expected frequencies is 250. To use a χ^2 test upon the data as they stand would violate an important assumption underlying its use.

To make the results amenable to treatment, what we must do is include the frequencies of tails in the table as well as the frequencies of heads. Thus the correct table from which to operate is:

STUDENT:	A	B	C	D	E	TOTAL
Heads obtained:	44	58	52	53	49	244
Heads expected:	50	50	50	50	50	250
Tails obtained:	56	42	48	47	51	256
Tails expected:	50	50	50	50	50	250
Total obtained:	100	100	100	100	100	500
Total expected:	100	100	100	100	100	500

Now the sum of the obtained frequencies is equal to the sum of the expected frequencies, and the application of χ^2 is appropriate and proper. Thus a specific application of the general warning about obtained and expected frequencies is that the frequencies of *nonoccurrence of an outcome* (as frequencies of nonoccurrence of heads in the example above,) as well as frequencies of occurrence, must be included in the table from which χ^2 is calculated.

2. *Chi-square applies only to frequencies.*

The probability of any given value of χ^2 depends upon the size of the sample. If χ^2 were computed from percentages, the result would be equivalent to a χ^2 based on an N of 100. If data are given in the form of percentages or proportions, they must be converted to frequencies before χ^2 can be used. If this cannot be done (because N is not known) χ^2 cannot be used.

3. *The entries must be independent.*

This assumption underlies the calculation of the probabilities of different values of χ^2. In practice, it means that every unit in the table from which χ^2 is calculated must be contributed by a different individual.

4. *No expected frequency should be too small.*

A very safe rule to follow is that no expected frequency should be less than 5; however, if we are satisfied with approximate probabilities and there are more than two degrees of freedom in the table, some of the expected frequencies may be as low as 2.

5. *When there is only one degree of freedom, a correction for continuity should be used.*

This correction consists of subtracting .5 from the absolute value of each $(f_o - f_e)$ before squaring it. If the correction would increase the value of χ^2, it should not be used.

Questions

1. Below are four problems which, as they stand, cannot properly be solved by the use of the χ^2 test. Explain why not and state how, if at all, they could be modified so that χ^2 would be applicable.

    a. A social psychologist wishes to test the null hypothesis that the ability of a group to solve a problem is independent of the size of the group. Two groups, one large and one small, are given eight problems to solve. The results are:

		GROUP SIZE		
		Small	Large	Total
RESULTS	Solved	2	7	9
	Unsolved	6	1	7
	Total	8	8	16

    b. On a public-opinion survey it is found that:
    44 per cent of the respondents with no high-school education are in favor of interracial housing projects, 10 per cent had no opinion, and 46 per cent are opposed.

Of those with only high-school education, **30** per cent are in favor, 8 per cent had no opinion, and 62 per cent are opposed. Of those with some college education, **63** per cent are in favor, 6 per cent had no opinion, and 31 per cent are opposed.

The researcher wishes to test the hypothesis that response is independent of education.

c. A modified thematic apperception test of ten cards is given to 50 subjects. The developer of the test wishes to determine whether the responses of the subjects are more likely to refer to sexual problems when the main figure on the card is of the same sex as the subject or of the opposite sex. The results are:

		SEX OF MAIN FIGURE	
		Same	Opposite
RESPONSE	Sex Response	307	79
	No Sex Response	193	421

d. Four different methods were used to administer questionnaires to each of 400 subjects. It has been found in the past that 60 per cent of such questionnaires are ordinarily returned. The problem is to determine whether the different methods of administration yield significantly different proportions of returned ballots. The results are:

Method	Expected Frequency	Obtained Frequency
Interview	60	84
Meeting	60	78
Questionnaire	60	63
Request for letter	60	36

2. In a study of dial designs, 120 subjects are asked for their preferences among 4 different designs. Their actual performance on these dials is also measured. Use χ^2 to determine whether there is a significant relationship between performance and preference. Use $\hat{T}$ to measure the strength of the relationship, and estimate T. Calculate the likelihood-ratio χ^2.

DIAL PREFERRED

		A	B	C	D	Total
	D	2	5	1	9	17
BEST	C	1	6	20	13	40
PERFORMANCE	B	3	20	13	5	41
	A	9	4	6	3	22
	Total	15	35	40	30	120

3. Use the likelihood-ratio χ^2 to test the null hypothesis that sex and major subject are independent for the data of problem 2, p. 85.
4. Thirty pupils were rated by their teachers as above average or below average in intelligence. An objective test was then given. Test the hypothesis of independence.

TEACHERS RATINGS

		Below	Above	Total
	Above	4	10	14
TEST	Below	7	9	16
	TOTAL	11	19	30

Summary

A sample proportion is an unbiased estimator of a population proportion. Confidence limits of a proportion are obtained from Table D. $\hat{H}$ tends to underestimate H, and $\hat{T}$ to overestimate T. Correction formulas enable us to make unbiased estimates of these population parameters.

To test the null hypothesis that a sample with a proportion p was drawn from a population with a proportion P, the difference between obtained and expected proportions is divided by its standard error, and the result referred to a normal curve table. The same principle applies in testing the significance of a difference between two proportions, where the expected difference is ordinarily taken to be zero.

The statistic χ^2 is used to test the hypothesis that the obtained frequencies are the same as expected frequencies. Chi-square has its own sampling distribution, which depends upon the number of degrees of freedom. An important application of chi-square is to test the hypothesis that two variables are independent. When T is zero, the statistic $1.3863N\hat{T}$ has a chi-square distribution. Several requirements must be fulfilled before the use of the chi-square test is appropriate.

Answers

Page 395

1. .26–.45. 2. .31–.89.
3. Chances are 95 out of 100 that he will get 47 per cent–53 per cent of vote.
4. (a) .49–.74; (b) .07–.14; (c) .20–.80.
5. $\tilde{H}_A = 2.3797$, $\tilde{H}_B = 1.7715$.
6. Before: $\tilde{H} = 1.8898$; after: $\tilde{H} = 1.9121$.
7. $\tilde{T} = .4675$. 8. $\tilde{T} = 0$.

Page 402

1. Principal is right. 3. $z = 2.53$. 5. $z = 1.03$.
2. $z = 1.98$. 4. $z = 1.27$.

Page 411

1. (a) 5; (b) 5; (c) 5; (d) 4; (e) 4; (f) 4.
2. 99. 3. 98. 4. (a) 1; (b) 48; (c) 19; (d) 8.
5. .50, .02, .025, less than .025, .05, less than .05, .99, less than .90.
6. (a) R, A, A; (b) R, R, A; (c) R, R, R; (d) A, A, A; (e) R, R, A.
7. 0, accept, χ^2 will increase. 8. $\chi^2 = 2.8$.
9. $\chi^2 = 3.97$. 10. $\chi^2 = 5.23$. 11. $\chi^2 = 10.47$.

Page 422

2. $\chi^2 = 44.84$, $\hat{T} = .2536$, $\tilde{T} = .1995$; likelihood-ratio $\chi^2 = 42.18$.
3. $\chi^2 = 266.9$. 4. $\chi^2 = .23$.

INFERENCES FROM ORDINALLY SCALED DATA

In Chapter 4 we learned that the principal statistics available to describe a group that had been measured on an ordinal scale were histograms and cumulative frequency or cumulative percentage curves, percentiles and interpercentile ranges, and, for the measurement of relatedness, the index of order association and the rank-order correlation. Now we are ready to go back to these statistics in order to estimate their values in the population and to test hypotheses about them.

13.1 Estimation

13.1.1 Estimation of the Population Median and Other Percentiles:
Suppose we have ten measurements drawn at random from a population. These measurements, arranged in increasing order of size, are

$$2, 8, 14, 15, 16, 21, 23, 28, 29, 30$$

The median of these measurements is halfway between 16 and 21, or 18.5. *This sample median is an unbiased estimator of the population median.* Our best guess about the population median is that it, too, is 18.5.

Of course the population median could be higher or lower than that, and our next step is to determine its confidence limits. An examination of our sample measurements strongly suggests that the population median is neither less than 2 nor more than 30. Why? *Because a statement about the population median is a statement about probability.* If we say, for example, that the population median is 31, that means that the probability of selecting at random from the population a measurement less than 31 is .5. And by the application of the probability principle that $P(ab) = P(a)P(b)$ when a and b are independent, we can see that if the population median were greater than 30 the probability of selecting at random ten measurements less than 30 would be $(\frac{1}{2})^{10}$, a very very low probability. So the population median is probably less than 30 and, by the same line of reasoning, greater than 2. We can also feel fairly confident (though less so) that it is higher than 8 and lower than 29, for if it were outside of those limits it is very unlikely that we should have picked the particular values we have. On the other hand, we do not feel nearly so confident that the population median lies between 16 and 21, for that is a very narrow range, and the median could easily lie outside of that range and still give the obtained measurements a fairly high proportion of the time.

We wish to find limits such that, if the population median lay outside of them, our obtained results would occur by chance less than 1 per cent, or 5 per cent, or some other arbitrarily chosen per cent of the time. To do this we need know only the number of observations or measurements in our sample, and we can then use Table F to get a direct answer to our question. Let us look in this table for $N = 10$, with $\alpha = .05$. Here we find that the entry for 'largest k' is 2. This means that if we want to be at least 95 per cent confident that the population median will lie within the stated limits, we can say that it lies between the second observation from the bottom and the second observation from the top. In our illustration, this means that the population median lies between 8 and 29. The value listed in the column labeled $\alpha < .05$, .021, gives us the *exact* probability of obtaining our measurements if the population median really lies outside of those limits. In this case, we may be more than 95 per cent confident; we may be $(100 - 2.1)$ or 97.9 per cent confident that the population median lies within the stated limits. If we wish to be 99 per cent sure, we use the column headed $\alpha = .01$.

Table F is useful when the size of the sample is 65 or less. When N is greater than 65 we can make direct use of the normal approximation to the binomial. The proportion of scores lower than the median is .5, and the proportion of scores higher than the median is likewise .5. The standard error of a proportion is $\sqrt{\dfrac{PQ}{N}}$, hence, $\dfrac{.5}{\sqrt{N}}$. To happen less than 5 per cent of the time, a proportion must differ from the population proportion by 1.96 standard errors in either direction, and to happen less than 1 per cent of the time it must differ by more than 2.58 standard errors. (The figures

1.96 and 2.58 are obtained from the normal curve table. They should be fairly familiar to you by now.) Therefore, to happen less than 5 per cent of the time, a proportion must differ from .5 by

$$1.96 \left(\frac{.5}{\sqrt{N}} \right) \quad \text{or} \quad \frac{.98}{\sqrt{N}}$$

For $\alpha = .01$, the figure is

$$2.58 \left(\frac{.5}{\sqrt{N}} \right) \quad \text{or} \quad \frac{1.29}{\sqrt{N}}$$

These are the formulas for proportions. Our interest is in frequencies, so we multiply these results by N.

$$N \left(\frac{.98}{\sqrt{N}} \right) = .98 \sqrt{N} \tag{13.1.1}$$

$$N \left(\frac{1.29}{\sqrt{N}} \right) = 1.29 \sqrt{N} \tag{13.1.2}$$

The results of formulas 13.1.1 and 13.1.2 are the number of cases on either side of the sample median that must be included in our interval estimate of the population median. For example, suppose we have a sample of 81 cases. The sample median is the value of the 41st measurement. If we wish to be 95 per cent confident that the population median lies within certain limits, we find .98 $\sqrt{81} = 8.82$. We count off 9 measurements on either side of the median. This takes us to the 32nd and 50th measurements. We can be 95 per cent confident that the population median is not higher than the 50th measurement or lower than the 32nd measurement.

Since we want to be *at least* 95 per cent confident or 99 per cent confident, we must always include in our interval estimate *at least* as many cases as specified by formula 13.1.1 or 13.1.2. That means that if those formulas give fractional numbers, we always round to the next largest number. If we had 85 scores, for example, we should find that .98 $\sqrt{85} = 9.02$. So we include *ten* cases on either side of the median, and we can be *more than* 95 per cent confident of our results.

This method of establishing confidence limits for a median has only one requirement, which may sometimes be difficult to meet in practice. The test requires that the variable on which the measurements have been made be a continuous variable. This, in turn, means that no two measurements will be *exactly* the same. If the variable is actually discrete and there are tied measurements, it will occasionally happen that the cth score away from the median is the same as the $(c + 1)$th score away. Thus, though our confidence interval *should* include, say, the 9 observations on either side of the sample median it will actually include 9 on one side and 10 on the other. If this happens, we can be *even more* confident that our population median lies within the interval than if we had actually included only 9 on either side.

The same general techniques used to establish confidence limits for a median can also be used to establish confidence limits for other percentiles. A binomial expansion, or the normal approximation to it, is used, and P is taken as equal to whatever percentile is having its confidence limits established. For example, if we wished to establish the confidence limits of the 25th percentile, in a sample of 100 cases we should obtain, for 95 per cent confidence limits, $1.96 \sqrt{\frac{1}{4}(\frac{3}{4})100} = 8.33$. The confidence interval would include 9 scores below the 25th percentile and 9 scores above it. We could be 95 per cent confident that in the population the 25th percentile was not lower than the 17th score or higher than the 34th score.

13.1.2 Confidence Limits of a Cumulative Percentage Curve: Since it is possible to obtain confidence limits for a single percentile, it is possible also to establish limits for an entire set of percentiles. The logic and derivation of the procedure is too complicated to explain here, but the actual technique is simple.

First, we obtain a cumulative percentage distribution. It is not necessary to group the data in step intervals; each measurement may be considered separately. Then we plot a cumulative percentage histogram. By a histogram, we mean that instead of connecting the points with straight lines, we connect them with two lines, a horizontal one drawn to the right of one point and a vertical dropped from the next point.

Suppose, for example, we start with 15 scores on a medical-aptitude test. These scores, which are drawn supposedly at random from a large population of such scores, are

114, 119, 120, 128, 131, 142, 143, 144, 145, 148, 155, 156, 161, 162, 169

The cumulative percentage histogram for these data is shown in Figure 13.1.

Next we decide on our level of confidence. For convenience we decide that we want to be 95 per cent confident.

Now we turn to Table G and look for the column headed '.95.' We read down that column until we come to $N = 15$. In this table,

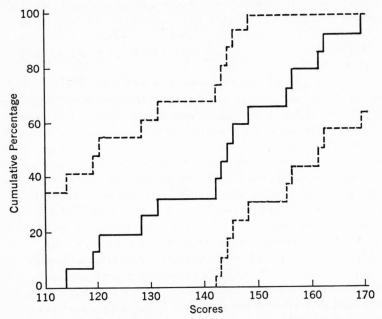

Fig. 13.1   Kolmogorov-Smirnov confidence band. We can be 95 per cent confident that the cumulative percentage graph for the population lies inside the broken lines.

we can find $N = 10$ and $N = 20$, but no $N = 15$, so we must interpolate. Linear interpolation in the table gives us a value halfway between .29 and .41, or .35.

Now we go back to our cumulative percentage histogram and we draw two new histograms, one 35 percentage points above the old and one 35 percentage points below the old. These are shown by the dotted lines in Figure 13.1.

We are 95 per cent confident that the cumulative percentage histogram for the population lies between these two new histograms. Had we wished to be 99 per cent confident, we should have used the column labeled .99, and for any other level of confidence we should, of course, have chosen the column appropriate to that level.

Between the two new histograms lies a *band* of values. Such a band is called a **confidence band.** A confidence band is to a set of values what a confidence interval is to a single value. This particular confidence band is called the **Kolmogorov-Smirnov Confidence Band,** after the two gentlemen who derived the method for obtaining it.

Questions

1. For the 40 measurements given below, find the median. Determine its confidence limits with a level of confidence of 95 per cent and also with a level of confidence of 99 per cent. Interpret your results.

15	33	42	56
16	34	43	58
18	36	44	71
18	37	46	73
19	37	46	74
23	38	50	85
23	39	51	85
24	40	52	86
30	40	54	87
31	40	54	88

2. For the data in Chapter 4, p. 116, problem 9 find confidence limits for Q_1, Mdn., and Q_3 with $\alpha = .05$ and $\alpha = .01$.

3. For the data in problem 1 above, plot a cumulative percentage histogram and find its confidence limits. ($\alpha = .05$.)

13.2 Testing Hypotheses

13.2.1 The Hypothesis That Two Groups Are Random Samples of the Same Population: In Chapter 12 we saw that the null hypothesis that there is no difference between two groups is an extremely important one to test. It is important because so many of our hunches suggest that something *will* make a difference, and to verify these hunches we must reject the null hypothesis that that something makes *no* difference. In formal terms, we must reject the null hypothesis that two groups are random samples of the same population.

In this chapter we shall study four ways of testing this null hypothesis for data from an ordinal scale.

a. The Run Test: A psychologist has a 'hunch' that if children are frustrated, their behavior after the frustrating experience will be more aggressive than the behavior of children who have not been frustrated. He therefore conducts an experiment with 20 children. These children are divided at random into two groups of 10, an experimental group (E), and a control group (C). The 10 children in the experimental group are subjected to mildly frustrating experiences, such as being interrupted in their play, having their toys taken away from them, being shown candy they cannot have, and so forth. The children in the control group are treated in a way that is identical to the treatment of the experimental-group children, except that they are not subjected to the frustrating experiences. All 20 children are then released in a large playroom to play together. An impartial observer ranks the children in the amount of aggressive behavior shown. Let us consider some of the kinds of rankings that might occur.

It could happen that the 10 experimental children are the most aggressive. If E stands for any child in the experimental group, and C for any child in the control group, the order in which the ranks are assigned would then be

RANK: 1 2 3 4 5 6 7 8 9 10 11 12 13 14 15 16 17 18 19 20
CHILD: C C C C C C C C C C E E E E E E E E E E

Another possible result would be that some children would be made aggressive by the frustrating experience, while others became frightened, withdrawn, and submissive. If every child reacted either one way or the other, and to an extreme degree, then the ranks from one to 20 would be assigned as follows:

RANK: 1 2 3 4 5 6 7 8 9 10 11 12 13 14 15 16 17 18 19 20
CHILD: E E E E C C C C C C C C C C E E E E

Perhaps a frustrating experience makes no difference in the amount of aggressive behavior shown. In that case we should not expect to find any particular regularity in the way the ranks are assigned. They might, for example, fall into a pattern something like the one below:

RANK: 1 2 3 4 5 6 7 8 9 10 11 12 13 14 15 16 17 18 19 20
CHILD: C E E C C E E C E C E E E C C E C C E

—a pattern that could be called 'well-mixed.'

It is the characteristic of 'well-mixedness' that distinguishes the third result, where frustration did not affect aggressiveness, from the other two. In the first two instances, many ranks in succession were assigned to members of one group, and then many ranks in succession to members of the other group. In the third case, few ranks in succession were assigned to children from one group. The ranks were mixed with respect to the groups from which the children came.

Any succession of items, objects, or measurements that are of the same kind is called a *run*. Thus, in the first set of ranks there are two runs: one run of 10 E's and one run of 10 C's. In the second set there are three runs: a run of 5 E's followed by a run of 10 C's followed by another run of 5 E's. In the third set there are 12 runs. (Count 'em!)

If there are N items in a list, m of one kind and n of another, then there cannot be fewer than 2 or more than N runs. To get as few as 2 runs, all the items of each kind would have to occur together, while the only sequence that would give N runs would be a regular alternation, $ABABAB$, et cetera. (This could occur, of course, only if m and n were equal, or differed only by 1.) Neither of these things is very likely to happen by chance. Therefore, if we find that the number of runs is either very large or very small, we should suspect that something other than chance is operating. When we use the run test to evaluate the null hypothesis that two groups are drawn at random from the same population, we shall not be concerned with getting too many runs, but only with getting too few.

To find out how many runs are 'too few' we turn to Table H. In this table, m is the number of items of one kind and n is the number of items of the other kind. Any number of runs less than or equal to that given in the body of the table would happen by chance less than 2.5 per cent of the time, if there were really no difference between the two kinds of items.

In the case of the frustration experiment, there were 10 children from group E and 10 from group C, so we look under $m = n = 10$. We find that the critical number of runs is 6. The first and second sets of results that we considered had 2 and 3 runs, respectively.

For both of those examples, we can therefore reject the null hypothesis that the two groups are random samples of the same population at a level of confidence of 97.5 per cent. In the third set of ranks however, there are 12 runs; 12 is more than 6, so we cannot reject the null hypothesis.

The table gives critical numbers of runs for sequences where both m and n are 20 or less. For numbers larger than these, the sampling distribution of the number of runs is normal with a mean of

$$M_r = \frac{2mn}{m+n} + 1 \qquad (13.2.1)$$

and a standard deviation of

$$\sigma_r = \sqrt{\frac{2mn(2mn - m - n)}{(m+n)^2(m+n-1)}} \qquad (13.2.2)$$

Suppose, for example, we had 100 items, 40 of one kind and 60 of another. When these 100 items are arranged in sequence it is found that there are 39 runs. Can we reject the null hypothesis that the two kinds of items are drawn at random from the same population?

The mean of the sampling distribution is

$$M_r = \frac{(2)(60)(40)}{60+40} + 1 = 49$$

The standard deviation of the sampling distribution is

$$\sigma_r = \sqrt{\frac{2(60)(40)[(2)(60)(40) - 60 - 40]}{(60+40)^2(60+40-1)}} = 4.77$$

Now we are ready to compute z.

$$z = \frac{\text{Obt. number of runs} - M_r}{\sigma_r} = \frac{39 - 49}{4.77} = -2.10$$

If our level of confidence is 95 per cent, we must determine whether this z is greater than the z required to cut off 5 per cent in one tail of the distribution. The required z for a one-tailed test is 1.645, and our obtained z is considerably larger than that, so we can reject the null hypothesis that the two kinds of items are random samples of the same population.

With the run test, this one-tailed versus two-tailed business gets confusing. Let us try to straighten it out by stating in more formal terms exactly what it is that we are doing.

Our original 'hunch' is usually that two groups will differ.

We restate this in the form of a null hypothesis: 'The two groups are random samples of the same population.'

We make a deduction from the null hypothesis. We say: *if* the two groups are random samples from the same population, *then* the number of runs in the population from which this sample was drawn will be M_r *or more*. The actual hypothesis we test, H_0, is

$$M_r \geq \left(\frac{2mn}{m + n} \right) + 1.$$

We then make a deduction from H_0. If H_0 is true, then 95 per cent of the time z will be less than 1.645.

Thus the run test, used to test the hypothesis that two groups are random samples from the same population, is always a *one-tailed test about the number of runs;* but it is always a *two-tailed test about the difference between the groups.*

Notice that the run test is used to evaluate the hypothesis that two samples are from the *same population.* In the second example of what might happen to the frustrated children, we suggested that the children might show the same *average* degree of aggressiveness, yet the run test would tell us to reject the null hypothesis. *The two samples must be alike in variability, as well as in central tendency*, before the null hypothesis can be accepted. This characteristic of the run test makes it sometimes very desirable, sometimes undesirable. We shall consider other tests where the null hypothesis can be accepted if the central tendencies of the samples are alike even though their variabilities differ.

The run test has many applications besides the one presented here. It can be used to test hypotheses about the population median, or about the randomness with which a series of events occurs.

b. The Median Test: This is a very simple test of the hypothesis that two samples were drawn at random from populations with the same median.

Suppose we wish to determine the effect of class hour on performance. Two classes are selected at random; one class is scheduled to
meet regularly at 8:00 A.M. and the other at 11:00 A.M. At the end
of the year, both classes are given the same final examination. The
median grade for the two classes, combined into a single distribution,
is obtained. The results are given in the four-celled table below.

		MEETING HOUR		
		8:00	11:00	Total
	Above median	5	15	20
GRADES	Not above median	11	9	20
	Total	16	24	40

A chi-square test of independence is then computed in the usual
manner for a four-celled table.

$$\chi^2 = \frac{N(|bd - ac| - N/2)^2}{pqrs}$$

$$\chi^2 = \frac{40(|165 - 45| - 20)}{20 \times 20 \times 16 \times 24} = 2.60$$

a	b	p
d	c	q
r	s	

The result, 2.60, is less than that required for significance at the
95 per cent level of confidence with one degree of freedom; we cannot reject the null hypothesis that there is no difference between
classes.

If N is odd, one of the observations will fall exactly at the median.
That is a nuisance, because it means that we must compute two
chi-squares instead of just one. First, we divide the observations
into the categories 'above the median' and 'not above the median.'
The median observation falls, of course, in the second category.
We compute a χ^2 from that table. Then we set up another table
with the categories 'below the median' and 'not below the median,'
and compute a χ^2 from that table. These two tables will usually
give slightly different values of χ^2; if N is small the results may be
quite different. The smaller (less significant) value of χ^2 is the one
to use. If, however, the first value of χ^2 is much greater or much less

than that required for significance, the second one need not be computed.

The median test requires that the variable on which the median is obtained be continuous, which, in turn, means that there will be no tied scores. If several scores are all tied for the median value, the two χ^2's computed from the 'above–not above' and 'below–not below' tables may be quite different. In that case the median test should not be used.

The median test is a χ^2 test, which means that all the restrictions previously described for the use of χ^2 apply to this new test.

As we shall see later, the median test can also be used when we wish to test the null hypothesis that *many* samples come from populations with the same median.

c. The Rank-Sums Test: This test starts off the same way as the run test but uses more of the information available in the data. Like the median test, it is a test of the hypothesis that two groups have been drawn at random from populations with the same median.

Two groups of individuals, which have been treated differently, are to be compared. For example, in a medical experiment a vitamin compound is given to one group of 9 subjects and is not given to another 8. (One of the control subjects is drafted during the experiment, and results for him are not available.) In all other respects the two groups are alike. We wish to determine whether the treated group has better 'general health' than the untreated group.

TREATED GROUP	UNTREATED GROUP
Anderson	Jones
Adams	Jenkins
Arden	James
Abel	Johnson
Adelman	Jackson
Abrams	Jennings
Andover	Jastrow
Anstruther	Jordan
Arnold	

Members of both groups are then combined into one group and are ranked in general health, with ranks ranging from one to 17. The ranks assigned to the various individuals, with 1 being the most healthy and 17 the least healthy, are:

Rank	Name	Ranks rec'd by Treated Subjects	Ranks rec'd by Untreated Subjects
1	Adams	1	
2	Anstruther	2	
3	Jastrow		3
4	Arden	4	
5.5	Johnson		5.5
5.5	Abrams	5.5	
7	Jordan		7
8	Jenkins		8
9	Andover	9	
10	Abel	10	
11	Anderson	11	
12	Jones		12
13.5	Jennings		13.5
13.5	Jackson		13.5
15	Abel	15	
16	James		16
17	Arnold	17	

$$T_1 = 74.5 \qquad T_2 = 78.5$$

The ranks for the treated group alone are then summed, and the ranks for the untreated group are summed separately, as in the table above. Each rank total will be called T_i. In this case T_1 is one of the two T_i's and T_2 the other; $T_1 = 74.5$ and $T_2 = 78.5$. As a check on the accuracy of our computation so far we make sure that:

$$T_1 + T_2 = \frac{N(N+1)}{2}$$

Where N stands for the number of individuals being ranked.

$$74.5 + 78.5 = \frac{17(18)}{2} = 153$$

(Whenever N objects are being ranked, the sum of the ranks is always $\frac{N(N+1)}{2}$. $T_1 + T_2$ is the sum of the N ranks.)

Next, we want to determine the significance of our result. We compute the statistic:

$$z = \frac{2T_i - N_i(N + 1)}{\sqrt{\frac{N_1 N_2 (N + 1)}{3}}} \qquad (13.2.3)$$

Where T_i stands for *either* of the rank totals, and N_i for the number of individuals in the group from which T_i was obtained.

$$z = \frac{2 \times 74.5 - 9(18)}{\sqrt{\frac{8 \times 9 \times 18}{3}}} = -.62 \qquad \text{or} \qquad z = \frac{2 \times 78.5 - 8(18)}{\sqrt{\frac{8 \times 9 \times 18}{3}}}$$
$$= +.62$$

If the number of cases in each of the two samples is 8 or larger, then the statistic we have computed from formula 13.2.3 will be normally distributed with a mean of zero and a standard deviation of 1. In other words, our result of $-.62$ is actually a z-score and is to be interpreted by reference to normal curve tables. The obtained result is .62 standard deviations below the expected mean of zero. Even without looking this up, we know that it is not large enough to cause us to reject the null hypothesis, so we conclude that vitamin pills did not have any significant effect on the health of those who took them.

If one or both of the samples are too small to make the test above applicable, Tables I and J may be used instead. It is not necessary to compute formula 13.2.3. We simply go to the table, look in the column that corresponds to the size of the smaller sample and the row that corresponds to the size of the larger sample, and find in the table the maximum permissible size for the smaller of the two rank totals. For example, in our case we look in the column labeled 8 and the row labeled 9, and find from the table that only if we get a rank total as small as 51 can we reject the null hypothesis of 'no difference' at the 5 per cent level of significance. Our smaller rank total cannot be larger than 45 if we wish to reject the null hypothesis at the 1 per cent level.

The basic logic underlying this test, though not its details, should be easy to see. To make it easier, let us consider a *really* small sample —two men in each group. That gives us four men to rank. We know from previous chapters that there are 4! ways those four ranks can be arranged, or 24 ways. Now suppose the two men from the experimental group got the two best ranks, 1 and 2, and the two men from the control group got ranks 3 and 4. How many ways can the four ranks be arranged with the ranks divided that way? There are two ways the two men from the experimental group can get ranks 1 and 2, and for each of these there are 2 ways the two men from the control group can get ranks 3 and 4, so there are four arrangements altogether that will give the experimental subjects the best ranks and the control subjects the worst. The probability of that result is therefore $\frac{4}{24}$, or $\frac{1}{6}$. If our significance level were $\frac{1}{6}$, for a one-tailed test, we could reject the null hypothesis.

In the rank-sums test the sum of one set of ranks is used as an index of the unevenness of division of the ranks between the two groups. If N objects are ranked, the sum of the ranks is $\frac{N(N+1)}{2}$. We now proceed to break this sum into two parts, one from one group, the other from the second group. If the two groups are very much alike, the sums of the ranks for the two will be proportional to the sizes of the groups, while if the two groups are very different one group will have a rank total that is disproportionately small. This test simply evaluates the probability of getting a rank total as small as or smaller than some fixed value.

Comparison of the Run Test, the Median Test, and the Rank-sums Test: We have now discussed three tests of the null hypothesis that two samples are drawn at random from the same population or from populations with the same median. Let us consider the relative merits and demerits of these tests.

The *run test*, in the application described here, has the outstanding characteristic that it will detect differences in variability between the samples as well as differences in central tendency. If the null hypothesis to be tested is that the samples are drawn at random from the *same* population, the run test provides a better test than either of the others. If the hypothesis is that the samples are drawn from populations having the *same median*, the run test is a poor test, because this null hypothesis will be erroneously rejected if the variabilities, but not the medians, of the samples differ widely. For this test, the probability of a Type I error is high. Furthermore, since the run test does not make use of information about difference between medians, it is not a very powerful test of hypotheses about difference between medians, and the probability of a Type II error is also high.

The *median test* and the *rank-sums test* both provide good checks on the null hypothesis that two samples were drawn at random from populations having the same median. The rank-sums test uses more available information than the median test (ranks, instead of just a two-part division) and is therefore a more powerful test. If the median test requires us to reject the null hypothesis we can be pretty sure than the rank-sums test will, too, but not vice versa. If the median test gives results of borderline significance (allowing us, say, to reject the null hypothesis at $\alpha = .08$) then it is a good idea to go ahead and try the rank-sums test.

Paired observations: The three tests discussed above are all for the purpose of comparing *independently selected* samples. Often we are interested in comparing the same individuals 'before and after' or matched individuals treated in different ways. If we do this, we speak of having 'paired observations.' When our experiment is of this kind, we must use different statistics to evaluate the results. For ordinally scaled data, the *sign test* is the appropriate test to use.

d. The Sign Test: An experiment is performed upon 15 pairs of identical twins (one-egg twins). One member of each pair is breast-fed for the first eight months of its life, while the other twin is bottle-fed from the second week of life on. The various pairs of twins differ in general health, socio-economic status of parents, size at birth, and in many other ways. As each pair of twins reaches the age of five years, standardized ratings of adjustment are made by raters who do not know about the twins' previous histories. The null hypothesis to be tested is that there is no superiority in adjustment of breast-fed over bottle-fed babies except one that would occur by chance if they had been treated alike.

If the breast-fed baby is the better adjusted we shall assign a plus sign to the pair, while if the bottle-fed baby does better, we shall assign the pair a minus sign. It is found that in 4 of the 15 pairs the bottle-fed baby is better adjusted than his twin, while in the other 11 pairs the breast-fed baby does better. There are 4 minus signs and 11 plus signs.

With this information we turn to Table K. In this table, we look up the critical numbers for an N of 15 (the number of pairs). In the body of the table, we find the numbers 2, 3, 3, and 4 listed under the 1 per cent, 5 per cent, 10 per cent, and 25 per cent levels of significance respectively. That means that not more than 2, 3, 3, or 4 differences can be of one kind if we are to reject the null hypothesis at the stated probability levels for a two-tailed test. The figures permit the differences to be in either direction (too few plus or too few minus signs). Often, as in the example above, we are interested only in a difference in one direction. We did not even entertain the possibility that the bottle-fed twins would be better adjusted. If they had been, we should have accepted our original null hypothesis immediately. To use the table for a one-tailed test, we divide the listed probability by 2.

We obtained 4 differences in favor of bottle feeding. The number 4 appears in the table under the 25 per cent level. Since we wish to make a one-tailed test, we divide that probability by two and conclude that 11 out of the 15 pairs of twins would have shown a difference in the expected direction less than $12\frac{1}{2}$ per cent of the time by chance if there were really no difference, or a difference in the other direction. That is about as likely as a coin is to land heads three times in a row. By our usual criterion, therefore, we cannot reject the null hypothesis.

That conclusion may seem like an affront to common sense. The results certainly suggest that, as we expected, breast-fed babies come off better, and the 4:11 ratio sounds as if it should be significant. Yet consider what the sign test ignores. It may be that in the 11 pairs where the breast-fed baby was superior, the differences between the twins were enormous, while among the other four pairs, the differences in adjustment may have been so slight as almost to defy detection. The sign test doesn't care. A difference is a difference, and big ones and little ones are treated alike. That means that the test throws away a great deal of information, and that, in turn, means that it is not a very powerful test. The sign test is a fine labor-saving device when differences are great, and a very useful technique for getting an approximation of 'the way the wind blows.' When more powerful tests are appropriate, however—that is, when it is possible at least to rank the differences—these tests should ordinarily be used in preference to the sign test.[2]

The sign test is based upon essentially the same principles as those involved in testing the null hypothesis that $P = .5$, as described in Chapter 12.

[2] See 'Wilcoxon's Test for Paired Replicates' on p. 489. This test usually requires that the original measurements be made on an interval scale.

To sum up the procedure for using the test:

1. The test requires a series of paired observations. These pairs may be obtained under widely differing conditions, but the results for one pair must be independent of the results for any other pair.

2. The two observations in each pair are compared. If the difference is in one direction the pair is assigned a plus sign; if in the other, a minus sign. If there are a few pairs in which ties occur, these pairs are eliminated and N reduced accordingly. If there are many such pairs, the test should not be used.

3. If there are more plus signs than minus signs, the number of minus signs is counted. The number of minus signs is called 'r.' If there are more minus than plus signs, the number of plus signs is called 'r.'

4. The result, r is evaluated by reference to Table K. This table gives the probabilities of getting r's as small as the ones listed. The probabilities are for a two-tailed test. For a one-tailed test, the probabilities are divided by 2.

5. If N is larger than 90, the required values of r may be found by the use of the formula at the bottom of the table.

Questions

1. Below is a list of 'hunches.' Restate each in the form of a null hypothesis, decide how you would test the hypothesis, and explain your decision.

    a. A certain drug will stimulate lethargic schizophrenic patients and calm excited ones.

    b. A year in nursery school will help shy children become more sociable.

    c. Patients with organic brain damage will be less able to handle abstract problems than will normal persons.

    d. Intelligence-test scores of Northern Negroes will be higher than those of Southern Negroes.

    e. Rigid persons will have fewer insights into difficult problems than non-rigid persons.

    f. College seniors will have more extreme scores on vocational-aptitude tests than college freshmen.

    g. Leaders will be less submissive personalities than non-leaders.

2. A group of 30 persons is divided into 'neurotic' (A), and 'normal' (N). They are then ranked in the strength of their religious feelings. The subjects, from least religious to most religious, are

A N N A A N N N N N N N N N N N N N A N N N N N A A N N A A A

Test the null hypothesis that, with respect to intensity of religious feeling, the two groups are random samples of the same population.
3. The order in which 60 students leave an examination room is tabulated. Later, when the examination has been graded, each student's grade is classified as above (A) or below (B) the median. Find out from the data below whether there is any difference between the 'good' and 'poor' students in their order of leaving the room. The first letter in the list applies to the first student to leave the room, and the last letter applies to the last student.

B B B B A B B B A A B B B A B B B B A B A A A A A A A B A A A A
B A A A A A B B A A A B B B B B A A A B B B B B B A B

4. An Air Force officer divides the men under him into two equal groups: 'more efficient than average' and 'less efficient than average.' These same men are then asked whether they plan to re-enlist in the Air Force. Test the null hypothesis that there is no significant difference between the efficiencies of the men who plan to re-enlist and those who do not.

| | OFFICER'S RATING | | |
	Below	Above	Total
Re-enlist	21	4	25
Not re-enlist	11	28	39
Total	32	32	

5. Six pupils are taught reading by one method, and seven by another, supposedly better method. The subjects are then given a test of reading comprehension. Their scores are given below. Test the null hypothesis that the old method is at least as good as the new.

OLD	NEW
114	133
137	191
108	141
125	138
119	129
122	142
	142

6. Sixteen animals who have received one pellet of food reward at the end of a maze are compared to 16 who have received three pellets. Running times are recorded for each animal. Use both the median test and the rank-sums test to evaluate the null hypothesis that the smaller reward is at least as effective as the larger one in speeding running. Compare the results of the two tests and explain any differences.

1 PELLET	3 PELLETS
59 seconds	83 seconds
48	84
73	95
109	86
211	102
602	98
81	75
94	74
99	73
121	47
78	34
85	39
92	41
47	63
192	65
235	80

7. A new type of steering mechanism is designed for automobiles. Of the first 25 people who try the new device, 18 prefer it, 5 prefer the old, and 2 are undecided. Test the null hypothesis that the new mechanism is liked no better than the old.

8. Two dial designs are being compared. Eighteen subjects make 100 readings on each dial and the number of reading errors is tabulated.

The results are given below. Test the null hypothesis that the two dials are equally difficult to read correctly.

SUBJECT	ERRORS, DIAL A	ERRORS, DIAL B
1	0	1
2	0	3
3	2	4
4	1	2
5	6	2
6	3	5
7	1	10
8	0	4
9	1	2
10	4	0
11	3	1
12	0	5
13	0	0
14	1	2
15	8	6
16	2	3
17	0	2
18	0	2

13.2.2 The Hypothesis That Several Groups Are Random Samples of the Same Population:
All the tests in the last section are designed to test one of two null hypotheses: (a) that the two groups are drawn at random from the same population, or (b) that two groups are drawn at random from populations with the same median. It frequently happens that we are interested in testing the second of these hypotheses with *several* groups instead of just two. There are three techniques available for making the test when the data come from an ordinal scale.

a. The Median Test: The median test can be used to evaluate the significance of differences among several groups just as it was used to compare two groups. The null hypothesis to be tested is that all the groups were drawn at random from populations with the same median.

Four groups of children, coming from homes of different economic levels, are given a test of 'honesty in handling money.' A high score on the test indicates a high degree of honesty, while a low score indicates the opposite. The scores are given below:

ECONOMIC STATUS			
Very Poor	Poor	Average	Well-to-do
14	19	33	69
44	54	21	65
27	51	16	59
25	25	17	22
33	38	66	40
48	40	67	49
21	47	52	54
20		53	60
		43	

Now the median for the total group is obtained. In this example there are 32 scores, so the median lies halfway between the 16th and 17th scores, which are 40 and 43 respectively. The median is therefore halfway between 40 and 43, or 41.5.

Next, the number of scores above and below the median is determined separately for each group and a new table is made up:

	ECONOMIC STATUS				
Very Poor	Poor	Average	Well-to-do	Total	
2	3	5	6	16	Above Median
6	4	4	2	16	Below Median
8	7	9	8	32	Total

For each cell, the expected frequency is then determined and a χ^2 computed. The expected frequency is always half the number of cases in the group. The remainder of the χ^2 calculations are carried out below:

f_o	f_e	$(f_o - f_e)^2$	$\dfrac{(f_o - f_e)^2}{f_e}$
2	4	4	1.00
6	4	4	1.00
3	3.5	.25	.07
4	3.5	.25	.07
5	4.5	.25	.07
4	4.5	.25	.07
6	4	4	1.00
2	4	4	1.00
			4.28

χ^2 is found to be 4.28. There are four groups, hence three degrees of freedom. By reference to a χ^2 table, we find that this value is not significant at the 5 per cent level of confidence and we fail to reject the null hypothesis.

As in the median test for two samples, it sometimes happens that N is odd and one score falls on the median. If N is large, the score that falls on the median may be omitted without doing much violence to the data. If N is small, two chi-squares should be computed and the less significant of the results used.

b. The Kruskal-Wallis Test: This test is very similar to the rank-sums test for comparing two samples, but is enlarged so that we may consider any number of samples instead of just two. Like the rank-sums test, it is based on a comparison of the sums of the ranks for several samples. The data above will also be used to illustrate this technique.

STEP 1: All the scores are ranked as members of one group. Thus, in the illustration, ranks from 1 to 32 will be assigned.

ECONOMIC STATUS

| VERY POOR | | POOR | | AVERAGE | | WELL-TO-DO | |
Score	Rank	Score	Rank	Score	Rank	Score	Rank
14	1	19	4	33	12.5	69	32
44	18	54	25.5	21	6.5	65	29
27	11	51	22	16	2	59	27
25	9.5	25	9.5	17	3	22	8
33	12.5	38	14	66	30	40	15.5
48	20	40	15.5	67	31	49	21
21	6.5	47	19	52	23	54	25.5
20	5			53	24	60	28
				43	17		
$T_i =$	83.5		109.5		149.0		186.0
$N_i =$	8		7		9		8

STEP 2: The sum of the ranks is determined for each group and is called T_i. The number of cases in each group is called N_i.

STEP 3: Check on the correctness of the ranking and summing by ascertaining that $\sum\limits^{k} T_i = \dfrac{N(N+1)}{2}$, and that $\sum\limits^{k} N_i = N$.

$$83.5 + 109.5 + 149.0 + 186.0 = 528.0 \qquad \frac{(32 \times 33)}{2} = 528.0$$

$$8 + 7 + 9 + 8 = 32$$

STEP 4: Obtain the statistic h as defined below. (The letter H is usually used, but since we have already used up that letter we shall use the lower-case h instead.)

$$h = \frac{12}{N(N+1)} \sum_{}^{k} \frac{T_i^2}{N_i} - 3(N+1) \qquad (13.2.4)$$

a. Square each T_i and divide the result by the corresponding N_i. Sum the results.

$$\frac{(83.5)^2}{8} = 872.8$$

$$\frac{(109.5)^2}{7} = 1712.9$$

$$\frac{(149.0)^2}{9} = 2466.8$$

$$\frac{(186.0)^2}{8} = 4324.5$$

$$\sum^{k} \frac{T_i^2}{N_i} = 9377.0$$

b. Substitute in the formula for h:

$$h = \frac{12}{32(33)} (9377.0) - 3(33) = 7.8$$

STEP 5:[3] The statistic h has a χ^2 distribution with $k - 1$ degrees of freedom, where k is the number of groups. That means that we evaluate h by reference to a χ^2 table, in this case looking under 3 degrees of freedom. We find that a χ^2 of 7.8 is required for significance with $\alpha = .05$. That is exactly the value we obtained, so we

[3] If there are several sets of tied ranks and the obtained h is of borderline significance, it should be multiplied by a correction term, c, which is:

$$c = 1 - \frac{\Sigma T}{N(N^2 - 1)}$$

where t is the number of ranks in one set of ties, and $T = (t - 1)t(t + 1)$ for that set.

conclude that our results are significant and reject the null hypothesis at the 95 per cent level of confidence. There are only five chances in 100 that these four groups are random samples from the same population or from populations with the same median.

Notice that the Kruskal-Wallis Test permitted us to reject the null hypothesis while the median test did not. In both tests, the probability of making a Type I error was the same, .05, but for the median test the probability of making a Type II error is greater than it is for the Kruskal-Wallis Test. The Kruskal-Wallis Test, since it uses more information (ranks, instead of just a two-part division) is a more powerful test than the median test.

c. The Friedman Test: When we wished to test the hypothesis that two samples were drawn at random from populations with the same median, we had available two kinds of tests: tests appropriate when the two samples were drawn independently, and tests for use when the measurements were obtained from paired observations. Thus, when we compared the adjustments of breast-fed and bottle-fed twins, we used the sign test instead of, for example, the ranksums test, because the babies were identical twins reared differently. It was thus possible to compare each breast-fed baby with his bottle-fed twin and determine the direction of the difference between them.

Exactly the same principles apply when we are testing hypotheses about several samples. Suppose each of eight subjects has been tested in five different problem situations. Our interest is in whether the problems differ significantly in difficulty. We have five scores for each of the eight subjects, and these five scores can be ranked. This is quite a different situation from the one with which we should be faced if 40 subjects had been used, and eight assigned at random to solve each problem, for in this second situation, it might happen that all the bright subjects were given problem A and all the dullards problem D. That would make it look as if problem A were easy and problem D hard, while actually the differences between subjects, rather than between problems, could account for the results. When each subject gets every problem, the finding that one problem is solved consistently better than the others means that the problem is easier; it cannot be due to the fact that different and brighter subjects have tackled it. Therefore, the Kruskal-Wallis Test would throw away useful information, and increase the probability that we should erroneously accept the null hypothesis. The Friedman Test is the appropriate one to apply. The procedure for its use is as follows:

			PROBLEM		
SUBJECT	A	B	C	D	E
Brown	69 (3)	75 (2)	81 (1)	58 (5)	60 (4)
Conley	47 (3)	52 (2)	53 (1)	36 (4)	35 (5)
Doakes	51 (2)	49 (3)	62 (1)	45 (5)	47 (4)
Earl	49 (3)	53 (2)	55 (1)	40 (4)	39 (5)
Farmer	32 (3)	46 (1)	43 (2)	29 (4)	22 (5)
Garth	56 (1)	55 (2)	54 (3)	44 (5)	47 (4)
Howe	55 (3)	57 (2)	61 (1)	42 (4)	30 (5)
Ivers	38 (2)	41 (1)	40 (3)	35 (5)	37 (4)
	20	15	13	36	36

STEP 1: Set up a table like that above. In that table, every subject's score on every problem is listed. In the table, each row is a subject, and each column a problem. There are r rows and k columns. In our example, there are 8 rows and 5 columns.

STEP 2: Rank the k entries in each row from 1 to k. Notice that the ranks 1 . . . k are used over and over again, once for each row.

STEP 3: Sum the ranks for each column. Each column sum will be called T_i.

STEP 4: As a check on the accuracy of step 3, obtain $\sum\limits^{k} T_i$. It should be equal to $\dfrac{rk(k + 1)}{2}$.

$$20 + 15 + 13 + 36 + 36 = \frac{40 \times 6}{2} = 120$$

STEP 5: If there really were no difference in problem difficulty, we should expect the various values of T_i to be quite similar. When some are very high and some are very low, we may suspect that there are real differences in the problems. To measure the relative magnitudes of these differences, we obtain the sum of the squares the T_i's.

$$\sum\limits^{k} T_i^2 = 20^2 + 15^2 + 13^2 + 36^2 + 36^2 = 3386$$

STEP 6: Substitute in the formula for χ_r^2 below:

$$\chi_r^2 = \frac{12}{rk(k+1)} \sum T_i^2 - 3r(k+1) \qquad (13.2.5)$$

$$\chi_r^2 = \frac{12}{8 \times 5(5+1)} (3386) - 3 \times 8(5+1)$$

$$\chi_r^2 = 25.3$$

STEP 7: The statistic χ_r^2 is distributed approximately as χ^2 with $k-1$ degrees of freedom, provided r and k are large enough. To interpret a result for a large r and k, we therefore turn to the χ^2 table and look under $k-1$ degrees of freedom. When k is 3 and r is less than 10, or when k is 4 and r is less than 5, the results should be interpreted by reference to Table L, which gives the values of χ^2 required for significance at $\alpha = .05$ and $\alpha = .01$.

In our example, r and k are large enough to permit us to use the χ^2 table. We find that the value we obtained for χ_r^2 is much higher than any of the values listed there, so we feel very confident in rejecting the null hypothesis. We conclude that the problems really differ in difficulty.

Comparison of the Median Test, the Kruskal-Wallis Test, and the Friedman Test: These three tests all evaluate the null hypothesis that several groups were drawn at random from the same population or from populations with the same median. The median test and the Kruskal-Wallis Test are both used when different, independently chosen individuals make up the various samples. Of these two, the Kruskal-Wallis Test is the more powerful and is normally to be preferred. The Friedman Test is the *only* appropriate test when the *same* individuals have been treated in different ways and our interest is in comparing the effects of the treatments.

Questions

1. In a large university, the elementary-psychology course was divided at random into five sections. Each section was taught by a different method. The five methods were lecture, lecture and discussion, discussion and laboratory, individual projects, and individual projects combined with laboratories. At the end of the year, the same final examination was given to all students. How would you test the null hypothesis that all methods were equally effective

in preparing students for the final? What would be the principal objection to the use of the Kruskal-Wallis Test?

2. A dog trainer is interested in comparing the hunting abilities of different breeds of dogs. He selects 8 puppies of each of three breeds and 7 puppies of a fourth breed and gives all puppies the same training. He puts the puppies through field trials, scoring each on field performance. Test the null hypothesis that all breeds perform equally well.

SETTERS	SPANIELS	HOUNDS	POINTERS
14	12	11	13
19	14	13	26
28	15	19	25
20	16	21	24
17	16	28	19
17	25	29	10
18	23	11	30
22	18		18

3. A large mail-order house is interested in the relative effectiveness of black-and-white, two-color, and four-color representations of merchandise. It prepares 15 pictures of different items, 5 in each manner, and determines the number of orders placed for each of the 15 items. From the results below, determine whether the use of color affects the sales appeal of a picture significantly.

BLACK-AND-WHITE	TWO-COLOR	FOUR-COLOR
11,143	10,955	7,291
4,002	9,612	9,405
5,888	2,490	5,409
3,156	4,087	5,882
785	1,010	1,224

4. The advertising manager of the mail-order house above suddenly realizes that the 15 items that were pictured in the experiment above may not be equally attractive to customers. He therefore plans another test. Five different items—socks, fabrics, furniture, china, and jewelry—are chosen for study. In three different editions of the catalogue, these items are pictured by the three different reproduction processes. The same number of catalogues of each edition are distributed, and sales are tabulated for the five items. From the data below, test the null hypothesis that the color process used in picturing an item has no effect on sales.

	BLACK-AND-WHITE	TWO-COLOR	FOUR-COLOR
Socks	11,393	11,291	14,604
Fabrics	2,112	2,304	6,928
Furniture	4,033	7,938	7,941
China	2,040	3,121	4,642
Jewelry	922	1,130	1,024

5. Six different kinds of ear plugs are being compared. Different subjects use each kind, and their immediate hearing losses after two hours of exposure to a very loud noise are measured. Do the ear plugs differ significantly?

HEARING LOSSES IN DECIBELS

PLUG A	B	C	D	E	F
20.5	17.3	18.4	21.2	3.2	13.6
17.2	14.1	6.5	23.0	5.0	13.5
18.4	13.1	8.8	19.8	4.1	14.2
20.1	16.4	10.1	19.9	6.9	15.1
21.3	18.0	11.7	20.0	7.7	23.0
22.4	12.5	9.7		6.5	19.6
	12.5				

6. The Army Quartermaster Corps is trying to develop new kinds of winter underwear. Each of 10 subjects wears, under controlled conditions, a union suit made of cotton and wool (CW), a suit made of nylon and wool (NW), a suit made of nylon pile (N), and a suit made of orlon pile (O). Each subject then ranks the four suits in order of preference. The orders are given below, with the subject's first choice listed first. Test the null hypothesis that the four kinds of underwear are equally acceptable to the subjects.

SUBJECT	PREFERENCES	SUBJECT	PREFERENCES
A	O, N, NW, CW	F	NW, O, N, CW
B	O, NW, N, CW	G	N, NW, CW, O
C	N, O, NW, CW	H	O, N, CW, NW
D	N, O, NW, CW	I	O, CW, N, NW
E	N, O, CW, NW	J	O, N, NW, CW

7. Class Project:

Purpose: to determine empirically the form of the sampling distribution of h, with two d.f., when the null hypothesis is true.

Method: Each member of the class prepares from the table of random numbers from three to ten lists (depending upon the size of the class) of the digits 1, 2, and 3. Each list should contain 18 digits. These lists then serve as the basis for dividing the ranks 1–18 into three groups. For each set of 18 ranks, h is computed. The frequency of occurrence of each value of h, is then determined for the whole class, and a frequency distribution plotted. The distribution, if the number of samples is large enough, should resemble a χ^2 distribution with two d.f. (See Figure 12.2.)

13.2.3 The Use of Ordinal Scale Tests with Interval Scale Data:
The seven tests we have discussed in this section are all most appropriately used with data from ordinal scales. It has been one of our basic principles in statistical work that tests and statistics that can be used with a 'weaker' scale do not do full justice to the data when they are applied to a 'stronger' scale. As we shall see in Chapter 14, however, many of the tests of hypotheses that can be used with data from an interval scale demand in addition that the samples be large (greater than 30) or that the variables being measured be distributed normally in the population, or both. When these additional demands cannot be met, the tests described in the last section are the only ones that can appropriately be used, even though they do not make use of the unit of measurement that the interval scale provides.

13.2.4 The Hypothesis That Variables Are Independent:
A null hypothesis that is frequently tested is the hypothesis that two variables are independent, or that the correlation between them is zero. In Chapter 12, we saw how chi-square could be used to test these hypotheses for nominally scaled data. In this chapter we shall consider three new tests of the hypotheses of independence and zero correlation.

a. The null hypothesis that the index of order association in the population, ω, is zero: The index of order association, o, you will remember (?), is a statistic that results from the comparison of every individual with every other. When one individual is higher than the other on both variables, the result of the comparison is called 'same,' while if one individual is higher on one variable but lower on the other, the result of the comparison is called 'different.' If S stands for 'number of "same" comparisons,' and D for 'number of "different" comparisons,' then

$$o = \frac{S - D}{S + D} \quad \text{or} \quad \frac{S}{S + D} - \frac{D}{S + D}$$

The hypothesis that ω equals zero is really the hypothesis that $S = D$, or that the proportion of 'same' comparisons is $\frac{1}{2}$. When $P(S) = \frac{1}{2}$, the sampling distribution will be normal with a standard error of $\dfrac{1}{\sqrt{S + D}}$. To test our null hypothesis, we obtain a z-score and interpret it by reference to normal curve tables.

$$z = \frac{o}{1/\sqrt{S + D}} = o\,\sqrt{S + D} \qquad (13.2.6)$$

If z is equal to or greater than 1.96, we can reject the null hypothesis with $\alpha = .05$, and if z is equal to or greater than 2.58, we can reject the null hypothesis with $\alpha = .01$. All of these values are for a two-tailed test—that is, one which does not specify the direction of the relationship.

b. The null hypothesis that the rank-order correlation in the population, ϱ_o, is zero: Suppose that in a sample of three cases, we obtain a rank-order correlation of $+1.00$. This might mean that the X and Y variables are strongly related, but even if there were no relationship we might have gotten this result because we just happened to select those three cases. How likely is it?

For a sample of 3, there are just 3! or 6 equally likely ways the three pairs of ranks can be arranged. These arrangements or **permutations** are listed below, along with the ensuing r_o. We obtain the surprising result that it is *impossible* to obtain a sample correlation of zero, and by chance alone we can expect a sample correlation of $+1.00$ one sixth of the time. When N is only three, therefore, we can *never* reject the null hypothesis at the 95 per cent level of confidence.

RANKS ON X		POSSIBLE RANKS ON Y				
1	1	1	2	2	3	3
2	2	3	1	3	1	2
3	3	2	3	1	2	1
r_o	$+1.00$	$+.50$	$+.50$	$-.50$	$-.50$	-1.00

When N is 4, there are 4! or 24 possible arrangements of the pairs of ranks. Only one of these will give an r_o of $+1.00$, so the probability of getting that result by chance if ρ_0 is zero is $\frac{1}{24}$, or approximately .04. This result would therefore permit us to reject the null hypothesis with $\alpha = .04$ by a one-tailed test. When N is 5 or higher, correlations lower than 1.00 will permit the rejection of the null hypothesis. To evaluate the significance of a sample rank-order correlation, we simply determine, by the technique illustrated above, what proportion of the $N!$ arrangements would give correlations as high as or higher than the one obtained. When that proportion is less than α, the null hypothesis is rejected.

Be of good cheer! You will not have to do this work yourself. It has been done for you for values of N up to 10, and the results are printed in Table M. To test the null hypothesis that ρ_o is zero, we look under the appropriate N, and find there all values of r_o that have probabilities of less than .10 on the assumption of the null hypothesis. The tabled probabilities are for a two-tailed test—that is, a test that does not specify the sign of the correlation. For a one-tailed test, we divide the values of α in the table by 2. For example, with $N = 10$, $\alpha = .05$, and the sign of the correlation specified, a rank-order correlation would have to be greater than .442 and in the correct direction to permit rejection of the null hypothesis.

When N is greater than 10, r_o behaves pretty much like the product-moment correlation, and a rough approximation of the probability of any sample r_o, on the assumption that ρ_o is zero, can be obtained by treating the rank-order correlation as if it were a product-moment correlation. The techniques are described on pp. 491, and 520. The use of this kind of approximation, however, is only as valid as the assumption that differences between successive ranks correspond approximately to equal differences in the variable under investigation.

c. The contingency test of association: Chi-square can be used to test the null hypothesis that two ordinally scaled variables are independently distributed. Suppose, for example, 160 people take a mechanical-aptitude test and a mathematical-aptitude test. We wish to test the null hypothesis that score on one test is independent of score on the other. To use the contingency test, we make a four-celled table as follows:

SCORES ON MECHANICAL TEST

		BELOW MEDIAN	ABOVE MEDIAN	
SCORES ON MATHEMATICAL APTITUDE	ABOVE MEDIAN	25 (a)	55 (b)	80 (p)
	BELOW MEDIAN	55 (d)	25 (c)	80 (q)
		80 (s)	80 (r)	

Now we simply compute χ^2 by the usual formula for a four-celled table:

$$\chi^2 = \frac{N\left(|bd - ac| - \dfrac{N}{2}\right)^2}{pqrs} = \frac{160(|55 \times 55 - 25 \times 25| - 80)^2}{80 \times 80 \times 80 \times 80}$$
$$= 21.025$$

This χ^2 greatly exceeds that required for significance with $\alpha = .01$, so we reject the null hypothesis of independence. We conclude that there is a real tendency for people who are above the median on one test to be above the median in the other test also.

Questions

1. Two judges have rated 30 subjects on their leadership potentialities, and the coefficient of order association between their ratings is found to be $+.15$. The judges have made a total of 144 interindividual comparisons. Test the null hypothesis that the agreement between the judges is due to chance alone.

2. For each of the rank-order correlations below, test the null hypothesis that $\rho_o = 0$. Use both $\alpha = .05$ and $\alpha = .01$.

     a. $N = 6$ $r_o = +.67$
     b. $N = 8$ $r_o = -.25$
     c. $N = 9$ $r_o = +.62$
     d. $N = 5$ $r_o = -.41$

3. For each of the rank-order correlations below, test the null hypothesis that $\rho_o \leq 0$. Use both $\alpha = .05$ and $\alpha = .01$.

     a. $N = 6$ $r_o = -1.00$
     b. $N = 4$ $r_o = +1.00$
     c. $N = 7$ $r_o = -.64$
     d. $N = 10$ $r_o = +.58$
     e. $N = 10$ $r_o = +.66$
     f. $N = 5$ $r_o = +.51$

4. Use the method illustrated in the text to list the 24 ways that ranks on Y can be arranged to match the ranks 1, 2, 3, and 4 on X. For each arrangement, compute r_o and plot as a cumulative percentage curve the theoretical sampling distribution of r_o.

5. Of 30 students who have grades above the median in French, 21 have grades above the median in English. Test the null hypothesis that grades in the two subjects are independent.

Summary

Confidence limits can be established for a median or for any other percentile, and a confidence band for an entire cumulative frequency distribution can be obtained.

Several techniques are available to test the null hypothesis that two samples are drawn from the same population or from populations with the same median. When the samples have been independently selected we can use:

The *run test*, which evaluates the hypothesis that the samples are from the *same* population. It is sensitive to differences in variability, as well as in central tendency, between the samples.

The *median test*, which is a special application of the χ^2 test. It evaluates the hypothesis that the samples came from populations with the same median.

The *rank-sums test*, which evaluates the same hypothesis as the median test, but uses more of the information available in the data.

When the two samples have not been chosen independently, but in such a way that each measure in one sample 'goes with' some particular measure in the other sample, the *sign test* is used to evaluate the hypothesis that the two samples were drawn from the same population.

To test the null hypothesis that several samples were drawn at random from the same population, we can use the *median test* or the *Kruskal-Wallis Test*. This latter makes use of information about ranks and is ordinarily more powerful than the median test.

When the same individuals have been subjected to several different treatments, the null hypothesis that there are no differences among the treatments should be tested by the *Friedman Test*.

All of these tests can also be used with data from interval or ratio scales. When the assumptions underlying stronger tests cannot be fulfilled, the tests described here may be the best ones to use instead.

· To test the null hypothesis of independence, or the hypothesis of zero correlation, the contingency test of association, which is a variant of the chi-square test, may be used, or the hypothesis that the index of order association or the rank-order correlation is zero may be tested.

Reference

Siegel, S., *Nonparametric Statistics*, New York, McGraw-Hill, 1956. A clear and simple presentation of the techniques described in this chapter and others appropriate for ordinally scaled data. Siegel classifies the techniques according to the scale of measurement with which they should be used.

Many recent textbooks on statistics contain chapters on nonparametric statistics, distribution-free statistics, or order statistics. Most of the methods described in these chapters are appropriate for ordinally scaled data.

Answers

Page 431

1. $\alpha = .05$: Median $= 36.5$–50.5;
   $\alpha = .01$: Median $= 34.5$–53.5.
2. $\alpha = .05$; $Q_1 = 2.05$–4.15, Median $= 4.75$–5.65, $Q_3 = 6.05$–7.45;
   $\alpha = .01$: $Q_1 = 1.75$–4.55, Median $= 4.55$–5.85, $Q_3 = 5.85$–7.85.

Page 443

2. $z = -2.05$.   3. $z = -2.60$.   4. $\chi^2 = 16.8$.
5. reject at $\alpha = .025$, but not at $\alpha = .005$.
6. $\chi^2 = 1.125$, $z = 2.19$.   7. reject at $\alpha = .025$.
8. reject at $\alpha = .05$.

Page 452

2. $h = 1.47$.   3. $h = .18$.   4. $\chi_r^2 = 6.4$.
5. $h = 27.1$.   6. $\chi_r^2 = 12.96$.

Page 458

1. $z = 1.80$.
2. (a) accept, accept; (b) accept, accept; (c) reject, accept; (d) accept, accept;
3. (a) accept, accept; (b) reject, accept; (c) accept, accept; (d) reject, accept; (e) reject, reject; (f) accept, accept.
5. $\chi^2 = 8.07$.

INFERENTIAL STATISTICS FOR DATA FROM
INTERVAL AND RATIO SCALES. PART I

14

When our data come from interval and ratio scales, some very powerful techniques are available to enable us to generalize from sample to population. We need no longer depend on ranks and percentile ranks, but can use the measurements themselves. Furthermore it is now possible to specify something about the form of the sample distribution and to draw reasonable inferences about the distribution of the population from which the sample was drawn. Many of the techniques to be described in this chapter, however, not only use these inferences but depend upon them. When we cannot make reasonable inferences about the form of the population distribution, some of these techniques cannot be used.

A goodly proportion of the space devoted to each technique will be concerned with the *assumptions* or *requirements* that must be fulfilled before that technique can be used appropriately. One important assumption that frequently turns up is the assumption that the data are drawn from a normally distributed population. How to evaluate that assumption is, therefore, the first topic that we shall consider.

14.1 The Assumption of Normality

In Chapter 6 we considered at length the conditions that brought forth a normal distribution and the conditions that prevented its occurrence. It would be a good idea to go back and reread those pages now, but you probably won't, so we shall remind you that when NP or NQ is low—less than 5 has been our rule of thumb—or when an upper or lower limit is imposed on the distribution, or when a selective factor is operating, or when results from several widely disparate subgroups are combined, a normal distribution is *not* likely to result. Variables that are *not* normally distributed include, for example, incomes, reaction times, and response latencies.

In Chapter 6 we saw, too, how to evaluate the normality of a sample distribution by plotting the cumulative percentage graph on normal-probability paper. If the points lay on a fairly straight line, it was reasonable to conclude that the sample distribution was normal. At that time you may have wondered how straight a line had to be to be considered straight. Now, whether you know it or not, you have learned two techniques of inferential statistics that will enable you to test the hypothesis of normality.

14.1.1 The Chi-Square Test: Chi-square, you remember, is used to test the hypothesis that obtained and expected frequencies are the same. We said that there were many ways of arriving at the expected frequencies. One of these is to determine what the frequencies in various step intervals would be if the data were normally distributed. The exact method of applying the technique is described in many books and we shall not repeat the details here. The principles are simple:

1. Compute the mean and standard deviation from the obtained data.

2. The lower real limit of each step interval lies so-many standard deviations away from the mean, and the upper real limit lies so-many standard deviations away. These distances are calculated.

3. From normal curve tables, the area under the normal curve between those two points, expressed as z-scores, is found. This is done for every step interval.

4. The areas are converted to frequencies by multiplying by N. The results are the expected frequencies for the various step intervals.

5. Since the expected frequencies in the tails of the distribution are usually less than 5, the two or three step intervals in each tail of the distribution are usually lumped into one.

6. The obtained frequencies are the actual frequencies in the various step intervals. The differences between obtained and expected frequencies are easily determined, and a chi-square is calculated.

7. One degree of freedom is lost because the sum of the obtained and expected frequencies must be equal, one is lost because the means of the obtained and expected distributions are set equal, and one because the standard deviations have been set equal. The number of degrees of freedom is therefore three less than the number of step intervals used in calculating chi-square.

If chi-square is low, we conclude that the obtained and expected frequencies do not differ significantly, and hence that the obtained distribution could easily have come from a normally distributed population.

14.1.2 The Kolmogorov-Smirnov Test: The Kolmogorov-Smirnov confidence band, described in the last chapter, allowed us to establish confidence limits for an entire cumulative percentage distribution. It can be used to test the hypothesis of normality. The procedure is:

1. Compute the mean and standard deviation of the obtained distribution.

2. Plot the cumulative normal distribution with this mean and standard deviation. (An easy way to determine its shape is to plot it first on normal-probability paper, then read the cumulative percentages off the graph for plotting on linear paper.)

3. Refer to Table G, looking under the appropriate value of N, and determine the width of the confidence band.

4. Plot two new cumulative normal distributions the specified number of percentage points above and below the old.

5. Now, on the same graph, plot the original obtained distribution. If it lies entirely within the confidence band, the hypothesis of normality can be accepted.

If the original sample is small, neither of these techniques is very powerful. It is easy to conclude falsely that the data do come from a normally distributed population when they really don't. If the original sample is very small—say 5 or 6 cases—the data must show really wild deviations from normality before we can reject that hypothesis by a statistical test. For that reason, common sense can sometimes be a more powerful tool than fancy statistical techniques. If you must decide whether you can use tests appropriate only for data from normal populations—think! Is there any reason why the variable should not be normally distributed? Go back to Chapter 6 and reread the list of factors that make for non-normality. Do any of these apply in your case? Do you have any information from other sources about the form of the population distribution? What do your obtained data look like, and how close to a straight line do they fall on normal-probability paper? If you conclude that the population distribution is probably not normal, or if you are in serious doubt about its normality, don't use techniques that require a normal population. The techniques described in Chapter 13 are appropriate for non-normal data, and furthermore, they are usually a good deal easier to compute than the ones you'll meet in this chapter. They should be used, therefore, whenever you are in grave doubt about the hypothesis of normality.

14.2 Tchebychev's Inequality

There is one statistical test that is applicable in a great many different situations and that makes no assumptions about the form of the population distribution. This test is called Tchebychev's Inequality.

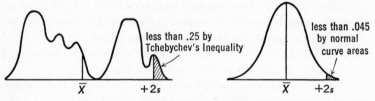

Fig. 14.1   Comparison of Tchebychev's inequality and normal curve tests.

This famous inequality states that *the area under that portion of any distribution which is more than* k *standard deviations away from the mean is less than* $\frac{1}{k^2}$.

Thus, for example, the area which is more than two standard deviations away from the mean under any distribution curve is less than $\frac{1}{2^2}$, or $\frac{1}{4}$, as shown in Figure 14.1.

That is a very weak statement. If we know that the distribution is normal, then we can be much more exact and much stronger in our statement. The area under a normal curve (in one tail) which is more than two standard deviations away from the mean is .045, as compared to the figure of .25 given by Tchebychev's Inequality. But we can use the information about the normal curve area only when we know that we *have* a normal curve, whereas the inequality can be used anytime.

Tchebychev's Inequality can be applied just as well to sampling distributions as to distributions of original measurements. If we can determine the standard error of a statistic (i.e. the standard deviation of its sampling distribution) we can apply the inequality even though we do not know anything about the form of the sampling distribution. As a last resort, therefore, Tchebychev's Inequality can always be used to establish confidence limits and test hypotheses.

14.3 Point and Interval Estimates

14.3.1 The Variance and Standard Deviation: The variance of a sample, s^2, is a biased estimator of its population counterpart, σ^2. s^2 tends to be smaller than σ^2. This fact may seem surprising at first, but consider how the statistic and the parameter would be computed.

To find σ^2, we should obtain $\Sigma(X - \mu)^2$
To find s^2, we should obtain $\Sigma(X - \overline{X})^2$

But if $\overline{X}$, the mean of the sample, is different from μ, the mean of the population, then:

$$X - \mu = (X - \overline{X}) + (\overline{X} - \mu)$$

and σ^2 is found from $\Sigma[(X - \overline{X}) + (\overline{X} - \mu)]^2$.

Therefore, only when the sample mean is identical with the population mean, and hence $(\overline{X} - \mu) = 0$, will the sample variance be an unbiased estimator of the population variance. In other cases the quantity $(\overline{X} - \mu)$ is ignored when computing s^2 but would be needed if we were to compute σ^2. Since, in the formula, it is always squared, it is always positive, and to ignore it is to make s^2 smaller than σ^2. As the samples get larger and larger, their means tend to be less and less different from the population mean, hence $(\overline{X} - \mu)$ gets smaller and smaller, and s^2 gets closer and closer to σ^2. The population variance is estimated by the use of the following formula:[1]

$$\tilde{\sigma}^2 = s^2 \left(\frac{N}{N - 1} \right) \tag{14.3.1}$$

[1] In some textbooks, the formula for s^2 is given as

$$s^2 = \frac{\Sigma x^2}{N - 1}.$$

This is simply a device for estimating the population variance *directly* from the original data. The 'sample variance' thus computed is actually an unbiased estimator of the population variance, and in our symbolism we should write:

$$\tilde{\sigma}^2 = \frac{\Sigma x^2}{N - 1}.$$

You can easily see from formula 14.3.1 that when N becomes very large the bias of s^2 as an estimator of σ^2 is very small, since $\dfrac{N}{N-1}$ is practically 1. For very large samples, therefore, s^2 is sometimes used as an unbiased estimator.

Occasionally you will be called upon to make an interval estimate of $\tilde{\sigma}$ or $\tilde{\sigma}^2$. An interval estimate can ordinarily be made only when the sample is drawn from a normal population, and the technique of making the estimate depends upon the size of the sample.

When small samples are drawn from a normal population, the statistic, $\dfrac{Ns^2}{\sigma^2}$ *has a chi-square distribution with* N − 1 *degrees of freedom.*

For example, to find the confidence limits of σ^2 from a sample variance of 5 with $N = 10$ and $\alpha = .05$, we first look up in the chi-square table $\chi^2_{.025}$ and $\chi^2_{.975}$ for 9 degrees of freedom. There are 95 chances out of 100 that

$$\frac{Ns^2}{\chi^2_{.025}} > \sigma^2 > \frac{Ns^2}{\chi^2_{.975}} \tag{14.3.2}$$

With 9 degrees of freedom, $\chi^2_{.025}$ is 2.7 and $\chi^2_{.975}$ is 19.0, so we can be 95 per cent confident that

$$\frac{10 \times 5}{2.7} > \sigma^2 > \frac{10 \times 5}{19.0}$$
$$20.8 > \sigma^2 > 2.6$$

We can be 95 per cent confident that the population variance lies between 2.6 and 20.8.

When the number of degrees of freedom is very large, the chi-square distribution becomes very much like the normal distribution. This means that *when large samples are drawn from a normal distribution, the standard deviations of the samples will form a distribution that is approximately normal.* The mean of this sampling distribution will be $s\sqrt{\dfrac{N}{N-1}}$ and its standard deviation will be

$$\tilde{\sigma}_s = \frac{s}{\sqrt{2(N-1)}} \tag{14.3.3}$$

14.3.2 The Mean and the Median: By 'sampling distribution of the mean' we refer, of course, to the theoretical frequency distribution of the means of an infinite number of samples of size N. Two very important statements about this sampling distribution can be made.

1. *If the population from which the samples are drawn is normal, the sampling distribution of means will be normal. The mean of the sampling distribution will be μ, the population mean, and the standard deviation of the sampling distribution will be* $\dfrac{\sigma}{\sqrt{N}}$.

2. *If the population from which the samples are drawn is not normal, the sampling distribution of the mean will become more and more normal as the number of cases in the sample gets larger and larger. The mean of the sampling distribution will μ, and its standard deviation will be* $\dfrac{\sigma}{\sqrt{N}}$.

Notice that whether or not the sampling distribution is normal, its mean is μ. Therefore, a sample mean is an unbiased estimator of a population mean. Our best guess about a population mean is that it is the same as the sample mean.

The standard error of the mean is always $\dfrac{\sigma}{\sqrt{N}}$, but this formula involves the population standard deviation, σ, which is ordinarily known only to God. We poor mortals must estimate[2] it from our knowledge of the sample standard deviation by formula 14.3.4.

$$\tilde{\sigma} = s \sqrt{\frac{N}{(N-1)}} \qquad (14.3.4)$$

and

$$\sigma_{\bar{X}} = \frac{\sigma}{\sqrt{N}}$$

so, substituting the estimated $\tilde{\sigma}$ for the true σ, we have

$$\tilde{\sigma}_{\bar{X}} = \frac{\tilde{\sigma}}{\sqrt{N}} = \frac{s}{1} \cdot \frac{\sqrt{N}}{\sqrt{N-1}} \cdot \frac{1}{\sqrt{N}} = \frac{s}{\sqrt{N-1}}$$

$$\tilde{\sigma}_{\bar{X}} = \frac{s}{\sqrt{N-1}} \qquad (14.3.5)$$

[2] Formula 14.3.4 does not provide an unbiased estimate of the population standard deviation, even though its square provides an unbiased estimate of the population variance. That is so because the mean of square roots is not equal to the square root of the mean. See Dixon, W. J. and Massey, F. J. Jr., *Introduction to Statistical Analysis*, 1st ed., New York, McGraw-Hill, 1951, p. 72.

Statements 1 and 2 tell us that the ratio: $\dfrac{\overline{X} - \mu}{\sigma_{\overline{X}}}$ is normally distributed when small samples are drawn from normal populations, or when large samples are drawn from any populations. It would be easy to jump to the conclusion that when $\dfrac{\overline{X} - \mu}{\sigma_{\overline{X}}}$ is normally distributed, $\dfrac{\overline{X} - \mu}{\tilde{\sigma}_{\overline{X}}}$ is, too, but that conclusion is valid only for large samples.

When samples are small, the sampling distribution of s is not normal. We have seen that the statistic $\dfrac{Ns^2}{\sigma^2}$ has a chi-square distribution, and the sampling distribution of s itself is positively skewed. This means that when we use $\dfrac{s}{\sqrt{N-1}}$ to calculate $\tilde{\sigma}_{\overline{X}}$, we are more likely to choose a very small s than a very large one; hence $\tilde{\sigma}_{\overline{X}}$ is more likely to be too small than too large. So the ratio $\dfrac{\overline{X} - \mu}{\tilde{\sigma}_{\overline{X}}}$ will more often be too large than too small. We can use the letter z for the ratio $\dfrac{\overline{X} - \mu}{\sigma_{\overline{X}}}$ because it has a normal distribution with a mean of 0 and a standard deviation of 1.

$$z = \frac{\overline{X} - \mu}{\sigma_{\overline{X}}} = \frac{\overline{X} - \mu}{\sigma/\sqrt{N}} \tag{14.3.6}$$

But the ratio $\dfrac{\overline{X} - \mu}{\tilde{\sigma}_{\overline{X}}}$ must have another symbol to show that its distribution is not normal. It is called t.

$$t = \frac{\overline{X} - \mu}{\tilde{\sigma}_{\overline{X}}} = \frac{\overline{X} - \mu}{s/\sqrt{N-1}} \tag{14.3.7}$$

The statistic t has its own distribution, which is called the t-**distribution,** or sometimes **Student's distribution** after the British statistician, Student, who derived it. The t-distribution is more leptokurtic than the normal distribution, which means that more of the area under the curve is in the tails of the distribution. That is another way of saying that extreme values of t are more probable than are extreme values of z.

As the size of the sample increases, the sampling distribution of s becomes less and less skewed and more and more normal. If s is normally distributed, then the *t*-ratio is the ratio of a normally distributed numerator, $\overline{X} - \mu$, to a normally distributed denominator, $\dfrac{s}{\sqrt{N-1}}$. Such a ratio will itself be normally distributed. So as samples get bigger and bigger, the sampling distribution of *t* becomes more and more like a normal distribution. That means that there is not one *t*-distribution, but many, for different sample sizes. When the size of the sample becomes 'infinite' (which is, of

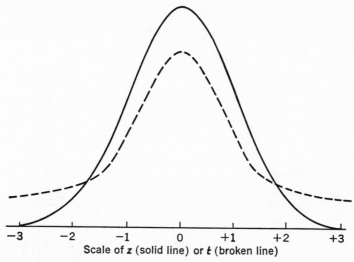

Scale of *z* (solid line) or *t* (broken line)

Fig. 14.2 Comparison of normal and *t*-distributions. The solid line is the normal distribution, the broken line the *t*-distribution, for one degree of freedom. In the *t*-distribution less of the area is under the central portion of the curve and more is under the tails.

course, a purely theoretical notion) then the *t*-distribution becomes identical with the normal distribution.

Table N is a *t*-table. Look first at its last line, for d.f. = ∞. You will see some familiar numbers there—1.645, 1.96, and 2.58. You should remember that those numbers are the values of *z* that cut off 5 per cent, $2\frac{1}{2}$ per cent, and 1 per cent of the area under one tail of the normal distribution. When $N = \infty$, those are also the values of *t* that cut off the same areas of the *t*-distribution. But if *N* is smaller, the value of *t* must be larger to cut off the same area. Thus, for example, if $N = 5$, then d.f. = 4, and the *t* required to cut off

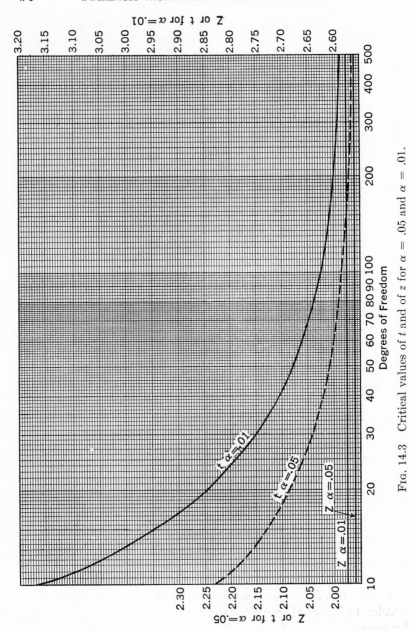

Fig. 14.3   Critical values of t and of z for $\alpha = .05$ and $\alpha = .01$.

$2\frac{1}{2}$ per cent of the area under one tail of the t-distribution is, from Table N, 2.78.[3]

In Figure 14.3, the relation between size of the sample and the t's required to cut off 5 per cent and 1 per cent of the area under the curve, is shown graphically. As N gets larger and larger the required value of t gets closer and closer to the value that would be required if the distribution were normal. The change is a gradual one. This figure shows, too, that the t-values and the normal curve values differ more for the 1 per cent level of significance than they do for the 5 per cent level.

Since the change from the t-distribution to the normal distribution is a gradual one, there is no point at which we can say that one sample is large, suggesting the use of normal curve tables, and another small, suggesting the use of t-tables. Often $N = 30$ is taken as a dividing point, with samples larger than that being called 'large.' Whenever the population variance must be estimated from the sample, the t distribution is appropriate, and it is just as easy to use a t-table as a normal curve table, so we shall do so for all samples, regardless of their sizes. For sample sizes not listed in Table N, the required value of t can be read from Figure 14.3.

The use of the t-distribution in establishing confidence limits for the mean: A carefully conducted market-research investigation has shown that for 26 boys at Coney Island for the day, the mean number of ice-cream cones eaten is 8, with a standard deviation of 1.5. We wish to establish interval limits for the true number of ice-cream cones eaten, on the average, by such urchins. We proceed in much the same manner as we would with a normal distribution problem, except that we refer to the t-distribution instead of the normal distribution.

$$t = \frac{\overline{X} - \mu}{s/\sqrt{N-1}} \qquad \overline{X} = 8, \; s = 1.5, \; \text{and} \; N = 26$$

By reference to the table of the t-distribution, we find that when $N = 26$, and hence d.f. = 25, we can be 95 per cent confident that t will lie between -2.060 and $+2.060$. We can substitute those values in the equation above, and solve for our unknown parameter, μ.

---

[3] The 'd.f.' in the t-table refers to the number of degrees of freedom available in getting an interval estimate of σ^2 from the chi-square distribution.

$$-2.060 = \frac{8 - \mu}{1.5/\sqrt{25}} = \frac{8 - \mu}{.3}$$

$$\mu = 8.618$$

$$+2.060 = \frac{8 - \mu}{.3}$$

$$\mu = 7.382$$

We can be 95 per cent confident that the average number of ice-cream cones eaten by boys at Coney Island lies between 7.382 and 8.618.

The t-distribution does not apply to small samples drawn from a nonnormal distribution. The only way to establish confidence limits for the mean in this unhappy situation is to apply Tchebychev's Inequality.

All this complicated theory can be reduced to two very simple recipes.

When the sample is large, or the population distribution is assumed to be normal, or both, the statistic

$$t = \frac{\overline{X} - \mu}{s/\sqrt{N - 1}}$$

has a t-distribution with $N - 1$ degrees of freedom. The t-table is used in place of the normal curve table for establishing confidence limits and testing hypotheses.

2. If the sample is small and the population nonnormal, Tchebychev's Inequality is used in establishing confidence limits.

The general principles involved in establishing confidence limits for the median are the same as those in establishing confidence limits for the mean. The formula for the standard error of the median is

$$\tilde{\sigma}_{\text{Mdn}} = \frac{1.253 \; s}{\sqrt{N - 1}} \qquad (14.3.8)$$

Two points are worthy of note. The standard error of the median is about 25 per cent larger than the standard error of the mean. That was what we meant, many pages ago, when we said that the mean is a more *stable* measure of central tendency than the median. Sample medians will differ more from sample to sample than will sample means.

The other point is that we give here a formula for the standard error of the median, while in Chapter 13 we gave a method for establishing confidence limits for the median in terms of sample percentiles. When a unit of measurement has not been established, the concept of a standard error is meaningless because a standard error is expressed in the original units of measurement. When such units do exist, then and only then is it meaningful to say that the probability is .95 that the population median lies within so-many standard errors of the sample median. When small samples are drawn from nonnormal populations, the methods described in Chapter 13 may be more powerful than Tchebychev's Inequality, even though the latter can be used.

Questions

1. For each sample s given below, obtain a point estimate of $\tilde{\sigma}$ and of $\tilde{\sigma}^2$.

a. $s =$	4	$N = 100$
b. $s =$	3.5	$N = 25$
c. $s =$	.19	$N = 12$
d. $s = 21$		$N = 500$

2. Use the appropriate technique to establish the 95 per cent confidence limits for the mean in each of the examples given below.

	$\bar{X}$	s	N	POPULATION
a.	50	5	101	Normal
b.	100	14	50	Nonnormal
c.	73	9	82	Unknown
d.	365	24	65	Normal
e.	365	24	17	Normal
f.	365	24	17	Skewed
g.	121	3	10	Normal
h.	121	3	10	Unknown

3. A school studies attendance records of some of its students and finds that, for 25 students, the frequency distribution of days lost due to sickness is as given below. What conclusions can be drawn about the mean number of days lost due to sickness in the school population?

DAYS LOST	NUMBER OF STUDENTS
0	12
1	6
2	3
3	1
4	0
5	1
9	1
14	1

4. Last year Joe Zilch spent an average of 60 minutes a day studying French. Joe kept time records for ten days of this year, and found that he spent the following amounts of time each day on that subject:

DAY	TIME (MIN.)
1	75
2	70
3	65
4	80
5	50
6	95
7	65
8	70
9	75
10	70

Have Joe's study habits changed significantly?

5. In a sample of 200 college students, the mean number of items answered correctly on a test is 169, the median number is 152, and the standard deviation is 15. What can you say about the mean and median in the college population?

14.3.3 The Product-Moment Correlation: Just as the mean of a sample may be smaller or larger than the mean of the population from which the sample was drawn, so the coefficient of correlation, r, obtained from a sample of size N may be smaller or larger than the actual correlation in the population, ρ. We frequently wish, therefore, to find the confidence limits of ρ or to test the null hypothesis that $\rho = 0$.

Unfortunately, the form of the sampling distribution of r depends upon the size of the sample and also upon the true value of ρ. Furthermore, the distribution is very complex except under one or two special circumstances. If ρ is anything but zero, the sampling distribution of r is skewed. To see why this should be so, consider samples drawn from a population in which two variables, X and Y, are actually correlated with a ρ of $+.95$. If we draw successive samples of size 10 from this population and compute r for each sample, these values of r will form a sampling distribution.

Since the population value of ρ is $+.95$, it is theoretically possible to obtain sample correlations as much as 1.95 points *below* the population value, and occasionally this will happen. It is not possible to obtain sample correlations more than .05 points *above* the population value. We should expect that the sampling distribution of r would therefore be negatively skewed, with a long tail running into the negative values of r and a great clumping of samples in the region around $+.95$. The smaller the sample, the more skewed is the sampling distribution.

Others have done the laborious and difficult job of determining the form of this sampling distribution for various values of ρ and of N, and have published their results in tables where befuddled students and practicing research workers can use them easily. All the methods described depend, however, upon the assumption of a **normal bivariate frequency distribution.**

That is not so bad as it sounds. Let us think about the concrete situation of a correlation between height and weight. Heights are normally distributed in the population, and so are weights. The distributions of height and of weight are *normal univariate frequency distributions*, since each distribution is only for a single variable. A univariate frequency distribution can be thought of, geometrically, as a *plane*, where probability is proportional to the *area* under the curve.

But each individual has both a height and a weight, and when we plot a scatter diagram, we use both dimensions of a plane just to represent the two variables. We need a third dimension, therefore, to represent the density of cases at any particular point on the plane. Imagine, then, a solid, whose height at any point represents the probability density of cases having the values of height and weight indicated by the X and Y co-ordinates of that point. The *volume* under the solid, erected over any square on its base, represents the probability that a case will have X and Y values within that square.

Now if the correlation between two variables is zero, and both are normally distributed, the *normal bivariate frequency distribution* will look rather like the castles that children build out of sand. It will have a circular base, and its profile from any angle will look just like a normal curve.

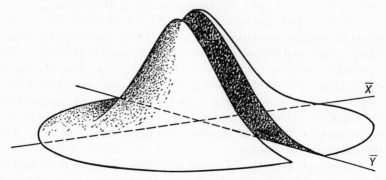

FIG. 14.4 Bivariate normal distribution for uncorrelated variables. A slice has been removed to show the normality of the cut faces.

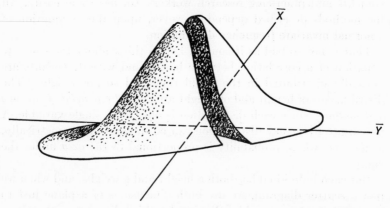

FIG. 14.5 Bivariate normal distribution for correlated variables. A slice has been removed to show the normality of the cut faces.

When a correlation is much greater than zero, the bivariate normal distribution will have an elliptical rather than a circular base, and a shape somewhat like that of a cocked hat. And if you slice the cocked hat in any place and at any angle, provided the cut is perpendicular to the base, the exposed surfaces will have the form of normal distributions.

If both X and Y can be assumed to be normally distributed and if they are linearly related, then their joint distribution is normal bivariate. In this case the techniques to be described are appropriate. A slight departure from this condition will not completely invalidate the techniques.

a. Tables giving confidence limits of ρ.

In Table O, the 95 per cent confidence limits of the coefficient of correlation are given. The procedure for using this table is identical with that for using Table D, which gives the confidence limits of a proportion. We shall illustrate it by considering a sample r of $-.80$ with a sample size of 10.

1. Look up the sample r on the x-axis.
2. Read up the vertical line corresponding to r until the curved line corresponding to a sample size of 10 is reached.
3. For the intersection of the vertical and curved lines, find the value of ρ on the y-axis. In this example, it is $-.94$. That is the lower confidence limit of ρ.
4. Continue up the vertical line until the second curved line for a sample size of 10 is reached. Determine the value of ρ corresponding to this second intersection. In this case, it is $-.325$. This is the upper confidence limit of ρ. We may be 95 per cent confident that the population correlation lies between $-.94$ and $-.325$.

b. Fisher's z_r transformation.

A second method of establishing confidence limits for r is to use what is known as 'Fisher's z transformation.' Since the letter z, as used here, is not our old familiar friend, the normal deviate, we shall follow Walker and Lev[4] in using, instead, the symbol z_r.

Fisher discovered that the statistic z_r as defined below, is distributed normally, even for small samples. The standard error of z_r depends only upon the size of the sample.

$$z_r = 1.1513 \, \log_{10} \frac{1 + r}{1 - r} \tag{14.3.9}$$

$$\sigma_{z_r} = \frac{1}{\sqrt{N - 3}} \tag{14.3.10}$$

We shall use the z_r transformation to establish confidence limits for

[4] *Statistical Inference*, New York, Holt, 1953.

a sample correlation of $-.80$ with an N of 10. Our level of confidence will be taken equal to 95 per cent.

1. Find z_r:

$$z_r = 1.1513 \log_{10} \frac{1 + (-.80)}{1 - (-.80)}$$
$$= 1.1513 \log_{10} \frac{.20}{1.80}$$
$$= 1.1513(\log_{10} 1 - \log_{10} 9)$$
$$= 1.1513(-.9542)$$
$$= -1.10$$

2. Find the standard error of z_r.

$$\sigma_{z_r} = \frac{1}{\sqrt{N - 3}} = \frac{1}{\sqrt{7}} = .38$$

3. Then 95 per cent of the time, the population value of z_r will lie between

$$-1.10 + 1.96(.38) \text{ and } -1.10 - 1.96(.38)$$

The confidence limits of z_r are -1.84 and $-.36$.

4. By the use of antilogarithms, these values of z_r are transformed back to values of r. The obtained values are $-.95$ and $-.35$. These values are close to, but not identical with, those found from Table O, which was developed by a different method.

Questions

1. Find the 95 per cent and 99 per cent confidence limits for ρ for each of the following samples:

	N	r
a.	25	$-.40$
b.	200	$+.69$
c.	400	$-.80$
d.	100	$+.65$
e.	10	$+.10$
f.	50	$-.17$
g.	20	$-.60$

2. The population correlation between two variables is known to be $+.50$. In a sample of 50 cases the correlation is found to be

$+.35$. Do you think the sample was randomly drawn from the population on which the correlation was determined?

3. In a sample of 10 cases the correlation between two variables is $-.40$. Is it reasonable to suppose that the variables might be positively related in the population from which the sample was drawn?

14.4 Testing Hypotheses

In this chapter we shall consider only hypotheses about differences between two groups, and about population product-moment correlations. In Chapter 15 we shall consider the somewhat more complicated techniques for testing the significance of the correlation ratio and for testing the null hypothesis that several samples were drawn from the same population.

14.4.1 The Hypothesis That Two Samples Were Drawn from Populations with the Same Variance: It is sometimes said that in many kinds of performance males are more variable than females even though the averages may be the same for the two sexes. Suppose that 50 elementary-school boys and 25 elementary-school girls took a spelling test. For both sexes the number of errors was normally distributed with a mean of 20, but the standard deviation for the boys was 4, while for the girls it was only 2. Does this difference of 2 points in the standard deviation represent a real difference between the sexes, or could it have been due to sampling fluctuations?

Our first step is to obtain, from each sample variance, an unbiased estimate of the population variance. We do this by the use of formula 14.3.1: $\bar{\sigma}^2 = s^2 \left(\dfrac{N}{N-1} \right)$.

For the boys, $\qquad \bar{\sigma}_b^2 = 16 \left(\dfrac{50}{49} \right) = 16.3$

For the girls, $\qquad \bar{\sigma}_g^2 = 4 \left(\dfrac{25}{24} \right) = 4.2$

Those are two independent estimates of the population variance. If we were to draw pairs of random samples from a single normal population, how often would we get two with such different variances as that? To answer this question, we compare the variance estimates by expressing them as a ratio, which is called the F ratio.

$$F = \frac{\bar{\sigma}_1^2}{\bar{\sigma}_2^2}$$

$$F = \frac{16.3}{4.2} = 3.88$$

(14.4.1)

The sampling distribution of F for samples from normal populations has been computed, and parts of it are tabulated in Table P. Actually, just as there are many different t-distributions for different sample sizes, so there are many different F distributions. To interpret any given F, therefore, we must look up the appropriate sample sizes, or degrees of freedom. For the kind of problem we are now discussing, d.f. $= N - 1$.

Along the top of the F table are listed various numbers of degrees of freedom for the greater variance—i.e. the d.f. associated in this example with the numerator of the F ratio. We cannot find 49, but 40 is close enough. Now we read down the 40 columns until we come to the rows labeled 24, which is the d.f. associated with the smaller variance. There we find the numbers 1.89, 2.15, 2.49, and 2.77. These are the critical values of F for the 5 per cent, 2.5 per cent, 1 per cent, and .5 per cent levels of significance, by the use of a one-tailed test.

When we computed our F ratio, we put the larger variance in the numerator of the ratio and the smaller variance in the denominator. We might have done it the other way, in which case F would have been .26. That small a value of F is just as unlikely as a value as large as 3.88, but for convenience only half the F distribution has been recorded in the table. There are only 5 chances in 100 that the numerator of the ratio will be 1.89 times as large as the denominator, but there are also 5 chances that the denominator will be 1.89 times as large as the numerator, so there are 10 chances in 100 that *either* variance will be 1.89 times as large as the other. If our original null hypothesis was: $\sigma_B^2 = \sigma_G^2$, we should require an F of 2.15 to reject it at the 5 per cent level of significance, and an F of 2.77 to reject it at the 1 per cent level. If our original null hypothesis was that $\sigma_B^2 \le \sigma_G^2$, we require an F of 1.89 to reject that null hypothesis at the 5 per cent level and an F of 2.49 to reject it at the 1 per cent level. Our obtained F of 3.88 permits us to reject the hypothesis that $\sigma_B^2 = \sigma_G^2$ at better than the 1 per cent level of significance.

14.4.2 The Hypothesis That Two Independent Samples Were Drawn from Populations with the Same Mean: We have now seen repeatedly that this kind of null hypothesis is one of the most important and frequently tested ones, regardless of the kind of scale from which the data come. 'Testing the significance of a difference' is one of the main jobs of a practicing statistician. For this reason we shall consider in some detail the many situations that require such a test.

When we test the significance of a difference, what we actually do is to determine the probability that our obtained difference was drawn from a sampling distribution of differences whose mean is zero. If, for example, we wish to test the significance of a difference between the mean reading speeds of two groups of children taught by different methods, we first hypothesize an infinite population of reading children. Now, if we selected two samples at random from this population and determined the mean speed for each sample, we should not expect these two means to be identical, though we should expect them to be fairly similar. If we repeated the process many times, we should expect that sometimes the difference between the means would be large, sometimes small, and sometimes zero. Sometimes the mean of the first sample would be greater than that of the second, and sometimes smaller. These differences between means could be collected into a frequency distribution which would be called the sampling distribution of the differences between means. We should expect the mean of this sampling distribution to be zero. If we knew its standard deviation, we could determine the probability of obtaining a difference of any given size. If the difference between the means of the two differently-taught groups of children were so large that it would occur very rarely in a sampling distribution of differences with a mean of zero, we should reject the null hypothesis that the two samples were drawn at random from the same population. We should say, in statistical jargon, that 'the difference is statistically significant.' The form of the sampling distribution of differences between means depends upon the size of the samples, and upon the population from which they were drawn.

a. Large samples or small samples from normal populations with the same variance:

When pairs of small samples are drawn at random from normal populations with means μ_1, and μ_2, and with the same standard deviation, σ, the ratio $\dfrac{(\overline{X}_1 - \overline{X}_2)}{\tilde{\sigma}_{\overline{X}_1 - \overline{X}_2}}$ will have a t-distribution for $N_1 + N_2 - 2$ degrees of freedom. The same thing is true for all pairs of large samples. The mean of the t-distribution will be $\mu_1 - \mu_2$, and its standard deviation will be

$$\tilde{\sigma}_{\overline{X}_1 - \overline{X}_2} = \tilde{\sigma}\sqrt{\frac{1}{N_1} + \frac{1}{N_2}} \qquad (14.4.2)$$

Our best estimate of the population standard deviation, $\tilde{\sigma}$, comes from a kind of weighted average of the sample standard deviations.

$$\tilde{\sigma} = \sqrt{\frac{\Sigma x_1^2 + \Sigma x_2^2}{N_1 + N_2 - 2}} \qquad (14.4.3)$$

The final formula for the estimated standard error of the sampling distribution of differences is therefore

$$\tilde{\sigma}_{\overline{X}_1 - \overline{X}_2} = \sqrt{\frac{\Sigma x_1^2 + \Sigma x_2^2}{N_1 + N_2 - 2}} \sqrt{\frac{1}{N_1} + \frac{1}{N_2}} = \sqrt{\frac{(N_1 + N_2)(\Sigma x_1^2 + \Sigma x_2^2)}{N_1 N_2 (N_1 + N_2 - 2)}} \qquad (14.4.4)$$

Let us try a problem.

Six chimpanzees have had portions of their brains removed by a surgical operation, while a control group of 10 chimpanzees has been left untreated. After the operated chimpanzees have recovered, all 16 are tested on a simple learning task, and the number of trials required to master it perfectly is determined. The results are:

OPERATED	CONTROLS
$\overline{X} = 25$	$\overline{X} = 22$
$s = 4$	$s = 3.8$
$N = 6$	$N = 10$

Since our samples are definitely small, we must ask whether the distribution of trials required to learn the assigned task is likely to be normal. This is not a question that can be answered with a simple 'yes' or 'no.' The frequency distributions of the samples themselves may give us a clue; in addition we may consider the fundamental nature of the learning task. For some tasks we might expect a normal distribution, while for others the distribution might be skewed. Let us assume that we have considered all the relevant factors and decided that we should expect a normal distribution of trials in the population.

Next, we must ask whether the variabilities are the same for the operated and control chimps. A comparison of the standard deviations of the samples suggests that they are quite similar and might easily have come from populations with the same standard deviations. Just to be on the safe side, however, we shall test that assumption by computing an F ratio.

$$\tilde{\sigma}^2 = s^2 \left(\frac{N}{N-1} \right) \qquad \tilde{\sigma}_o^2 = 16 \left(\frac{6}{5} \right) = 19.2$$

$$\tilde{\sigma}_c^2 = 14.8 \left(\frac{10}{9} \right) = 16.4$$

$$F = \frac{19.2}{16.4} = 1.17$$

We find by reference to Table P that this value of F is one that might easily have arisen by chance if the two samples had come from populations with the same variance. We can therefore feel reasonably safe about that assumption and continue with our t-test.

Now we are ready to compute $\tilde{\sigma}_{\bar{X}_1 - \bar{X}_2}$ by formula 14.4.4.

$$Ns^2 = \Sigma x^2$$
$$\Sigma x_1^2 = N_1 s_1^2 = 6 \cdot (4)^2 = 96$$
$$\Sigma x_2^2 = N_2 s_2^2 = 10(3.8)^2 = 144.4$$
$$\tilde{\sigma}_{\bar{X}_1 - \bar{X}_2} = \sqrt{\frac{(6+10)(96+144.4)}{6 \cdot 10(6+10-2)}} = \sqrt{4.58}$$
$$\tilde{\sigma}_{\bar{X}_1 - \bar{X}_2} = 2.14$$
$$t = \frac{(\bar{X}_1 - \bar{X}_2) - 0}{\tilde{\sigma}_{\bar{X}_1 - \bar{X}_2}} = \frac{25 - 22}{2.14} = 1.40$$

We look up our result in a t-table with $N_1 + N_2 - 2 = 14$ degrees of freedom. Our t is smaller than $t_{.025}$, hence we cannot reject the null hypothesis ($\alpha = .05$, two-tailed test) that the two groups of chimps are really random samples of the same population. The effect of the brain operation on learning is not 'statistically significant.'

b. Small samples from nonnormal populations or from populations with different variances.

If small samples are drawn from populations that cannot be assumed to have the same variance or that cannot be assumed to be normal, the technique above is not applicable. In that situation, the best way to test the significance of a difference is to use the rank-sums test described in Chapter 13.

Questions

1. For each of the samples given below, test (1) the hypothesis that $\sigma_1^2 = \sigma_2^2$, with $\alpha = .05$ and $\alpha = .01$; and (2) the hypothesis that $\sigma_1^2 \geq \sigma_2^2$ with $\alpha = .05$ and $\alpha = .01$. Assume that the samples are drawn from normal populations.

	s_1	N_1	s_2	N_2
a.	3	4	3.6	10
b.	9	20	12	20
c.	6	100	8	200
d.	2.5	25	2.5	100
e.	10	150	16	5

2. Test each of the hypotheses below. Check for equality of population variances wherever necessary, and do not continue the test if the necessary assumptions are not fulfilled. Assume that all samples are drawn from normal populations.

	H_0	α	$\bar{X}_1$	N_1	s_1	$\bar{X}_2$	N_2	s_2
a.	$\mu_1 = \mu_2$	.05	25	145	6	30	65	8
b.	$\mu_1 \leq \mu_2$	.01	134	10	4	130	17	5
c.	$\mu_1 = \mu_2$	.05	175	1000	20	172	1000	22
d.	$\mu_1 \leq \mu_2$	.05	36.4	26	2.4	31.3	17	6.9
e.	$\mu_1 = \mu_2$	.01	100	65	8	104	82	9

3. The mean incomes of two groups of college graduates ten years out of college are compared. One group consists of graduates who majored in the humanities; the other of graduates who majored in the sciences. Determine whether the difference between the mean incomes for the two groups is statistically significant.

SCIENCE MAJORS	HUMANITIES MAJORS
$\bar{X} = \$6544$	$\bar{X} = \$5865$
$s = \$241$	$s = \$227$
$N = 42$	$N = 40$

4. Two groups of rats with identical mean weights are fed on different diets and their weights are measured at the end of six weeks. The weights are normally distributed for each group, with the means and standard deviations given below. Determine whether diet really affects weight.

DIET A	DIET B
$\overline{X} = 265$ gm.	$\overline{X} = 281$ gm.
$s = 14$	$s = 15$
$N = 12$	$N = 11$

5. Whether or not the null hypothesis $\mu_1 = \mu_2$ will be rejected depends, among other things, on the size of the difference between sample means, on the sizes of the samples, and on the variabilities of the samples. Discuss the effect of each of these factors; explain, in common-sense language, why each is important; and show how each is taken account of in the statistical test.

6. From your reading find several examples of the use of a t-test to evaluate the significance of a difference between means of independent samples.

7. Design an experiment requiring a test of the significance of a difference between means. Make some assumptions about sample sizes, population distributions and variances, and explain which test you would use, and why.

14.4.3 The Hypothesis That Correlated Samples Were Drawn from Populations with the Same Mean:

In the last section, we considered tests of the null hypothesis that two random and independently selected samples were drawn from the same population. Now we must consider the situation in which the two samples are *not* chosen independently but represent pairs of measurements on the same individuals, or measurements on matched pairs of individuals. We encountered this same kind of situation in Chapter 13, where we used the sign test to compare the adjustment of breast-fed and bottle-fed babies, where each baby was one of a pair of identical twins treated differently. The crucial difference between this situation and that treated in the last section is that when we have matched pairs we can obtain, by simple subtraction, a *difference score* for each pair of measurements. Thus, if we had been comparing the weights of the babies instead of their adjustments, we could have obtained, for each pair of twins, a measure of the difference in weight between the bottle-fed and the breast-fed babies. Our null hypothesis will be that these differences are drawn from a population of differences that has a mean of zero. How we test that hypothesis will depend upon the nature of our sample.

a. Large samples, or small samples with normally distributed differences.

Difference scores can be treated exactly like any other kind of measurements. If, therefore, the samples are large, or if the difference scores can be assumed to have come from a normally distributed population of differences, with a mean of zero, *the sampling distribution of the means of the differences will be normal with a mean of zero and a standard deviation of* $\dfrac{\sigma}{\sqrt{N}}$.

In short, we are simply testing the hypothesis that a mean is zero. That the mean happens to be computed from difference scores instead of from original measurements does not affect our procedure in the slightest.

Since σ must be estimated from the standard deviation of the sample differences $\left(\tilde{\sigma} = \dfrac{s}{\sqrt{N-1}}\right)$, we shall use the t-distribution, rather than the normal distribution to evaluate our results. In summary:

$$t = \frac{\overline{D} - 0}{s_D/\sqrt{N-1}} = \frac{\overline{D}}{s_D/\sqrt{N-1}} \qquad (14.4.5)$$

where $\overline{D}$ is the mean of the difference scores, and S_D is the standard deviation of the difference scores. The t of formula 14.4.5 has a t-distribution with $N - 1$ degrees of freedom.

For example, we may be interested in the crucial biological and sociological problem of whether students gain weight, lose weight, or remain unchanged in weight during their freshman year in college. We select a random sample of 15 freshmen and measure their weights as they arrive, fresh and plump, and as they end their first year, worn and haggard. For each individual we can compute the weight *change* during the year. Our null hypothesis is that the mean weight change is zero, or could have come from a population of changes with a mean of zero, and we shall take $\alpha = .05$. The results are given on the next page:

INDIVIDUAL	X_i ENTERING WEIGHT	Y_i TERMINAL WEIGHT	D_i DIFFERENCE (GAIN OR LOSS)
A	125	133	8
B	189	190	1
C	164	176	12
D	110	115	5
E	175	169	−6
F	168	167	−1
G	151	153	2
H	132	136	4
I	120	118	−2
J	182	185	3
K	157	161	4
L	155	164	9
M	143	150	7
N	133	133	0
O	165	175	10
	$\bar{X} = 151.27$	$\bar{Y} = 155.00$	$\bar{D} = +3.73$

Before proceding further, we must examine our assumptions. Our sample is small, which means that unless the differences come from a normal population we cannot proceed with a t-test. A plot of the sample differences shows, however, that their distribution is very close to normal, and there is no a priori reason to suppose that these differences would not be normally distributed in the population.

We therefore proceed to compute the standard deviation of the differences, and from it we estimate the standard error of the mean difference.

$$\Sigma D_i = 56$$
$$\Sigma D_i^2 = 550$$
$$N = 15$$

where $\bar{D}_i$ is the change in weight of a given individual during the year.

By computations not shown here the mean of the difference column, $\bar{D}_i$ is found to be $+3.73$, and the standard deviation, s_D, is found to be 4.78.

$$\tilde{\sigma}_{\bar{D}} = \frac{s_D}{\sqrt{N-1}} = \frac{4.78}{\sqrt{14}} = 1.28$$

and

$$t = \frac{\bar{D}}{\tilde{\sigma}_{\bar{D}}} = \frac{3.73}{1.28} = 2.92$$

Turning to the t-table and entering it with $N - 1$ or 14 degrees of freedom, we find that our obtained t is large enough to permit us to reject the null hypothesis with $\alpha = .05$. We conclude that if people really had no tendency to gain or lose weight during their freshman year, we should find an average change as large as 3.73 pounds less than 5 per cent of the time. That is unlikely enough for us to conclude that, in spite of the hardships of college food and other perils, freshman gain weight.

When the sample is very large the calculation of the difference between each pair of measurements can become very laborious. Subtraction is not an operation that lends itself efficiently to machine computation. When samples are very large and a good calculating machine is available there is a more efficient way of arriving at exactly the same result. It can be shown that the mean of the differences is equal to the difference between the means:

$$\bar{D} = \bar{X}_1 - \bar{X}_2$$

In our example, the mean weight of the entering students was 151.27, and of the departing students, 155.00. The difference between the means, $155.00 - 151.27$, is $+3.73$, which is exactly what we found the mean change to be.

Instead of computing each difference and finding the mean of the differences, therefore, we compute the mean of each sample and find the difference between the means. And instead of computing the standard deviation of the differences, and estimating from it the standard error of the mean difference, we can estimate the standard error of the difference between means from the formula:

$$\tilde{\sigma}_{\bar{X}_1 - \bar{X}_2} = \sqrt{\tilde{\sigma}_{\bar{X}_1}^2 + \tilde{\sigma}_{\bar{X}_2}^2 - 2r_{12}\tilde{\sigma}_{\bar{X}_1}\tilde{\sigma}_{\bar{X}_2}} \qquad (14.4.6)$$

Where $\tilde{\sigma}_{\bar{X}_1}$ is the estimated standard error of the first mean.

$\tilde{\sigma}_{\bar{X}_2}$ is the estimated standard error of the second mean.

r_{12} is the correlation between the two sets of measurements.

Then the t-ratio is obtained from the formula

$$t = \frac{\overline{X}_1 - \overline{X}_2}{\tilde{\sigma}_{\overline{X}_1 - \overline{X}_2}}$$

and is evaluated in exactly the same way as in the previous calculation.

For purposes of illustration, we shall apply this second method of calculation to these same data on student weights to show that the value of t is the same as that obtained in the more direct way.

Let X_i stand for the weight of an entering student, and Y_i for the weight of the same student at the end of his freshman year. Then, by machine calculation, it is found that:

$\Sigma X_i = 2269$	$\overline{X} = 151.27$	$\tilde{\sigma}_{\overline{X}} = 6.08$
$\Sigma Y_i = 2325$	$\overline{Y} = 155.00$	$\tilde{\sigma}_{\overline{Y}} = 6.08$
$\Sigma X^2 = 350{,}977$	$s_X = 22.74$	$r_{XY} = .978$
$\Sigma Y^2 = 368{,}125$	$s_Y = 22.73$	
$\Sigma XY = 359{,}276$	$\overline{X} - \overline{Y} = +3.73$	

$$\tilde{\sigma}_{\overline{X} - \overline{Y}} = \sqrt{\tilde{\sigma}_{\overline{X}}^2 + \tilde{\sigma}_{\overline{Y}}^2 - 2r_{XY}\tilde{\sigma}_{\overline{X}}\tilde{\sigma}_{\overline{Y}}}$$

$$\tilde{\sigma}_{\overline{X} - \overline{Y}} = \sqrt{(6.08)^2 + (6.08)^2 - 2(.978)(6.08)(6.08)}$$

$$\tilde{\sigma}_{\overline{X} - \overline{Y}} = 1.28$$

$$t = \frac{3.73}{1.28}$$

$$t = 2.92$$

b. Small samples when the difference scores do not come from a normally distributed population.

If the samples are small, and we cannot assume that the difference scores come from a normally distributed population, we must use an entirely different procedure to evaluate the significance of the differences. The procedure to be employed in this case is called **Wilcoxon's Test for Paired Replicates.** It is a simple test to use, and it can also be used with very little loss of power when differences are distributed normally. To illustrate its application, we shall use the same data on student weights. The steps in carrying out the paired replicates test are:

1. Find, just as we did in computing t, the difference between each measurement and the other measurement of the pair. The

algebraic sign of the difference ($+$ or $-$) is retained, just as it was in computing t.

2. Rank the differences, assigning the rank 1 to the smallest non-zero difference and the rank N to the largest. In ranking, the algebraic sign of the difference is ignored, and only its absolute size is taken into account. Differences of zero are ignored, and N is reduced accordingly.

3. The algebraic sign of each difference is now assigned to the rank corresponding to that difference.

4. Obtain the sum of the positive ranks and the sum of the negative ranks. The smaller of the two sums is called T.

All these calculations have been carried out below for the student weights:

INDIVIDUAL	ENTERING WEIGHT	TERMINAL WEIGHT	DIFFERENCE (GAIN OR LOSS)	RANK OF DIFFERENCE	
A	125	133	8	11	
B	189	190	1	1.5	Sum of positive
C	164	176	12	14	ranks: 91
D	110	115	5	8	Sum of negative
E	175	169	-6	-9	ranks: 14
F	168	167	-1	-1.5	$T = 14$
G	151	153	2	3.5	
H	132	136	4	6.5	
I	120	118	-2	-3.5	
J	182	185	3	5	
K	157	161	4	6.5	
L	155	164	9	12	
M	143	150	7	10	
N	133	133	0	—	
O	165	175	10	13	

5. T is evaluated by reference to Table Q if N is 25 or less.

Since our example N is 14, we can use the table. This table gives the *highest* values of T which will permit rejection of the null hypothesis at various levels of significance with the use of a two-tailed test. From the table we see that T must be less than 21 if we are to reject at the 5 per cent level, less than 16 if we are to reject at the 2 per cent level, and less than 13 if we are to reject at the 1 per cent level. We can reject our null hypothesis, therefore, at the 2 per cent level of significance but not at the 1 per cent level. That is exactly the result that we obtained from the t-test for matched pairs.

6. If the sample includes more than 25 cases, the required values of T for $\alpha = .05$, $\alpha = .02$, and $\alpha = .01$ are given by the formulas below:

$$T_{.05} = \frac{N(N + 1)}{4} - 1.96 \sqrt{\frac{(2N + 1)N(N + 1)}{24}} \qquad (14.4.7(a))$$

$$T_{.02} = \frac{N(N + 1)}{4} - 2.33 \sqrt{\frac{(2N + 1)N(N + 1)}{24}} \qquad (14.4.7(b))$$

$$T_{.01} = \frac{N(N + 1)}{4} - 2.58 \sqrt{\frac{(2N + 1)N(N + 1)}{24}} \qquad (14.4.7(c))$$

The logic of the Wilcoxon Test for Paired Replicates is fairly easy to see. If there is really no difference between the two sets of measurements, the differences should be fairly well balanced between positive and negative. Big positive differences should be matched by big negative differences, and small positive differences by small negative differences. When this doesn't happen, we may suspect that something other than chance is causing the imbalance. The statistic T is simply a convenient way of expressing the unevenness with which the signs of the differences are distributed.

14.4.4 The Hypothesis That ρ Is Zero: When the correlation, ρ, in a normal bivariate population is zero, the sample correlations will have a t-distribution for $N - 2$ degrees of freedom and a standard error of

$$\sigma_r = \sqrt{\frac{1 - r^2}{N - 2}} \qquad (14.4.8)$$

Therefore, to test the null hypothesis that $\rho = 0$, we compute the t-ratio

$$t = \frac{r}{\sigma_r} = \frac{r \sqrt{N - 2}}{\sqrt{1 - r^2}} \qquad (14.4.9)$$

and evaluate it by reference to a t-table with N-2 degrees of freedom. The logic of this test is explained on page 520.

When N is very large, and $\rho = 0$, the sampling distribution of r is approximately normal with a standard error of

$$\sigma_r = \frac{1}{\sqrt{N - 1}} \qquad (14.4.10)$$

Therefore, if the sample r is greater than $\dfrac{1.96}{\sqrt{N-1}}$, the null hypothesis may be rejected at the 5 per cent level of significance by a two-tailed test.

14.4.5 Other Null Hypotheses: We have by no means covered the whole subject of hypothesis tests for data from interval and ratio scales, however exhausted you may feel. We have not discussed, for example, any test of the hypothesis that several samples were drawn from the same population. That hypothesis, and others related to it, will be taken up in Chapter 15. But there are many other possible null hypotheses that simply cannot be covered in an elementary text—for example, the hypothesis that the difference between two correlations is zero, or the hypothesis that two correlated samples have the same variance. Life is only so long, and however much it may pain you, you will simply have to struggle on for the time being without knowing how to test these hypotheses. The important thing to realize is that they can be tested, and there are many books that will tell you how to do it.

Questions

1. Fifteen rats learn a maze. They are then subjected to electric-shock treatments, and three days later they relearn the maze to the same criterion. Determine whether the savings (i.e. the decrease in trials required for the second learning) is significantly greater than zero.

RAT	FIRST LEARNING	SECOND LEARNING
1	10	8
2	12	13
3	15	9
4	19	12
5	14	14
6	18	14
7	16	10
8	20	16
9	11	9
10	10	11
11	15	12
12	22	11
13	19	9
14	10	12
15	15	10

2. One member of each of 9 pairs of identical twins is given special training in motor co-ordination. Both members of the pair are then tested on a motor co-ordination task, and the time required to complete the task is determined. Use the appropriate test to decide whether training improves performance significantly.

UNTRAINED TWINS	TRAINED TWINS
161	42
219	104
99	101
108	105
147	140
195	185
154	170
85	81
108	108

3. Fifty students take two forms of the same test. The results are given below. Are the two forms of the test equal in difficulty?

FORM A	FORM B
$\bar{X} = 101.3$	$\bar{X} = 102.9$
$s = 10.5$	$s = 11.2$

$$r_{AB} = +.89$$

4. Twenty-five students take a test. The mean score for the group is 150. They then receive special training and later take the same test again. Each student's score is exactly one point higher on the second testing than it was on the first.

   a. What is the mean score on the second test?
   b. What is $\tilde{\sigma}_{\bar{D}}$?
   c. What is r_{12}?
   d. Is the change significant?

5. What happens to formula 14.4.8 when r_{12} is $+1.00$? When r_{12} is -1.00? When r_{12} is 0?
6. Prove algebraically that $\bar{D} = \bar{X}_1 - \bar{X}_2$.
7. What information is used by the t-test for matched pairs but is ignored by the Wilcoxon Test for Paired Replicates?
8. What information is used by the Wilcoxon Test but is ignored by the sign test?
9. When all the assumptions required for a t-test for matched pairs are fulfilled, the t-test is more powerful than the Wilcoxon Test,

and the Wilcoxon Test is more powerful than the sign test. From your answers to questions 7 and 8, which difference in power would you expect to be greater: that between the t-test and the Wilcoxon Test, or that between the Wilcoxon Test and the sign test?

10. Find from your reading several situations requiring the use of a test of significance for the difference between the means of two correlated samples. What test was used? What other tests (if any) could have been used?

10. For each sample below, test the null hypothesis that $\rho \leq 0$. Use $\alpha = .05$ and $\alpha = .01$. Assume normal bivariate distributions.

	N	r
a.	9	$+.14$
b.	29	$+.32$
c.	200	$+.15$
d.	300	$-.90$
e.	20	$+.20$
f.	250	$+.18$

Summary

In this chapter, we have discussed some of the many techniques for drawing inferences from sample to population when the data come from interval or ratio scales. Only two of these, Tchebychev's Inequality and Wilcoxon's Test for Paired Replicates, make no assumptions about sample size or population distribution. All the others, whether for the establishment of confidence limits or for the testing of null hypotheses, require either that the sample be large or that the population be normal, and in some cases make additional assumptions.

We have encountered two important new sampling distributions: the t-distribution and the F distribution. The t-distribution is similar to the normal distribution, and, in fact, when the number of degrees of freedom becomes infinite the two are identical. Many sample statistics, including means and differences between means, have t-distributions. The F distribution is a distribution of variance ratios. For samples drawn from a single normal population, its mean is 1.00, and the critical values for the upper tail are given in the F table.

Although many of the new techniques introduced in this chapter may seem complicated, they all follow a standard pattern. We ask about the form of the sampling distribution of the statistic. If the sampling distribution is normal or t, then we must know the proper formula for its standard deviation. Knowing the mean and standard deviation of the sampling distribution, we can express our statistic in the form of a z or a t and determine the probability of obtaining that statistic. If the sampling distribution is asymmetrical, as are the chi-square and F distributions, we refer our obtained statistic directly to the table of the sampling distribution to determine its probability. In this way, confidence limits are established or null hypotheses tested.

References

The material in this chapter is covered thoroughly in most general statistics textbooks. Tables or nomographs for the transformation from r to z_r and from z_r to r can be found in many books including:

McNemar, Q., *Psychological Statistics*, New York, Wiley, 1955.
Snedecor, G. W., *Statistical Methods*, Ames, Iowa, Iowa State Col. Press, 1956.
Walker, H. M., and Lev, J., *Statistical Inference*, New York, Holt, 1953.
Arkin, H., and Colton, R. R., *Tables for Statisticians*, College Outline Series, No. 75, New York, Barnes & Noble, 1950.

Answers

Page 473

1. (a) 4.02, 16.16; (b) 3.57, 12.76; (c) .198, .039; (d) 21.02, 441.88.
2. (a) 49.01–50.99; (b) 95.98–104.02; (c) 71.01–74.99; (d) 359.00–371.00; (e) 352.28–377.72; (f) 327.08–402.92; (g) 118.74–123.26; (h) 114.68–127.32.
3. The mean lies between 0 and 5.83 days.
4. $t = 3.14$; yes.
5. limits of μ are 166.91–171.09; limits of population median: 149.39–154.61 $(\alpha = .05)$.

Page 478

1. (a) −.69 to −.01, −.75 to +.13; (b) .61 to .76, .58 to .77; (c) −.83 to −.76, −.75 to −.84; (d) .52 to .75, .47 to .78; (e) −.56 to .69, −.70 to .79; (f) −.43 to .11, −.50 to .20; (g) −.82 to −.22, −.87 to −.07.
2. +.35 is within 95 per cent confidence interval.
3. Upper limit of 95 per cent confidence interval is +.31.

Page 484

1. (a) $F = 1.20$, accept, accept, accept, accept; (b) $F = 1.78$, accept, accept, accept, accept; (c) $F = 1.77$, reject, reject, reject, reject; (d) $F = 1.03$, accept, accept, accept, accept; (e) $F = 3.18$, accept, accept, accept, accept.
2. (a) $t = 5.00$, reject; (b) $t = 2.07$, accept; (c) $t = 3.19$, reject; (d) no test possible with information given. (e) $t = 2.80$, reject.
3. $t = 13.0$, reject.   4. $t = 2.53$, reject.

Page 492

1. $t = 3.70$, $T = 7$, reject.   2. $T = 7$, accept.
3. $t = 2.18$ reject.
4. (a) 151; (b) 0; (c) $+1.00$; (d) yes.
10. (a) accept, accept; (b) reject, accept; (c) reject, accept; (d) accept, accept; (e) accept, accept; (f) reject, reject.

INFERENTIAL STATISTICS FOR DATA FROM
INTERVAL AND RATIO SCALES. PART II:
The Analysis of Variance

In this chapter we shall consider one of the most important and powerful tools available to the research worker—the analysis of variance. The development of this technique has revolutionized our approach to research and our entire concept of experimental design. In its simplest form, the analysis of variance is a technique for testing the null hypothesis that several samples were drawn at random from the same population.

15.1 The Analysis of Variance

An experimenter has divided 40 rats into four groups of 10 rats each. One group served as a control group, while the other three groups were treated with different drugs, a, b, and c. For each group, the mean number of trials required to learn a maze is determined, as well as the variance of the group about its own mean. What the experimenter would like to know is: do different drugs have different effects on learning? Rephrased as a testable null hypothesis, this question becomes: with respect to trials required to learn the maze, the four groups are random samples of the same population. If the investigator can reject that null hypothesis he can conclude (if his experiment has been properly designed and conducted) that the drugs have different effects on learning. His results are given below.

GROUP	n_i	$\sum\limits^{n_i} X$	$\sum\limits^{n_i} X^2$	$\bar{X}_i$	s_i^2	
A	10	390	15550	39	34	Grand mean: $\bar{X}_t = 37$
B	10	360	13240	36	28	Average variance:
C	10	310	9820	31	21	$\bar{s}_i^2 = 27$
D (control)	10	420	17890	42	25	$N = 40$
Total	40	1480	56500			

15.1.1 Assumptions and Requirements: The experimenter would like to use an analysis of variance to test his null hypothesis. He can do so provided his data meet two requirements:[1]

a. Normality. It must be reasonable to assume that the data come from a normally distributed population of measurements, or from several normally distributed populations. In Chapter 14 we discussed methods of testing this assumption. We shall assume that our experimenter has made one of the tests described there, or has concluded on other grounds that the assumption is satisfied by his data.

b. Homogeneity of variance. It must be reasonable to assume that the populations from which the different samples are drawn have the same variance, σ^2, even though their means may differ. In order to use the analysis of variance technique, we must first be able to *accept* the null hypothesis that

$$\sigma_1^2 = \sigma_2^2 = \sigma_3^2 = \ldots = \sigma_k^2$$

There are several ways of testing this hypothesis, of which we shall consider only the most general, Bartlett's Test. This test can be used even when the samples are of different sizes, and in our illustrative computation we shall not take advantage of the fact that our samples are all of size 10, but shall proceed in the more general, rather than the simpler, fashion. The logic of the test is too involved to go into here. We shall simply describe the way the test is carried out.

Bartlett showed that if k independently selected samples are drawn at random from populations with the same variance, the hideous-looking statistic below has a chi-square distribution with $k - 1$ degrees of freedom.

$$\frac{\log_e 10 \left\{ \sum^k m_i \left(\log_{10} \sum^k m_i s_i^2 - \log_{10} \sum^k m_i \right) - \sum^k m_i \log_{10} s_i^2 \right\}}{1 + \frac{1}{3(k-1)} \left\{ \sum^k \frac{1}{m_i} - \frac{1}{\sum^k m_i} \right\}} \qquad (15.1.1)$$

m_i is $(n_i - 1)$ where n_i is the number of cases in each sample.

[1] Failure to fulfill these requirements, however, apparently results in relatively minor deviations from theoretical probability levels. See Lindquist (ref. 5) pp. 78–90.

Bartlett's Test, therefore, consists of calculating the monstrosity above and interpreting it by reference to a chi-square table. For the maze-learning data, the computation proceeds as follows:

STEP 1: Prepare a table like that shown below. The columns in the table give: (a) number of cases in each sample, n_i; (b) degrees of freedom for each sample, m_i; (c) variance of each sample, s_i^2; (d) product of columns b and c, $m_i s_i^2$; (e) the common logarithm of the variance, $\log_{10} s_i^2$; (f) the product of columns b and e, $m_i \log_{10} s_i^2$; (g) the reciprocal of column b, $\dfrac{1}{m_i}$.

COLUMN: (a)	(b)	(c)	(d)	(e)	(f)	(g)
SAMPLE $\quad n_i$	m_i	s_i^2	$m_i s_i^2$	$\log_{10} s_i^2$	$m_i \log_{10} s_i^2$	$\dfrac{1}{m_i}$
a $\quad$ 10	9	34	306	1.5315	13.7835	.1111
b $\quad$ 10	9	28	252	1.4472	13.0248	.1111
c $\quad$ 10	9	21	189	1.3222	11.9898	.1111
d $\quad$ 10	9	25	225	1.3979	12.5811	.1111
	36		972	5.6988	51.3792	.4444

STEP 2: Total all columns except (a) and (c).

STEP 3: Obtain the logarithm of the sum of column d.

$$\log_{10} \sum_{i}^{k} m_i s_i^2 = \log_{10} 972 = 2.9877$$

STEP 4: Obtain the logarithm of the sum of column b.

$$\log_{10} \sum_{i}^{k} m_i = \log_{10} 36 = 1.5563$$

STEP 5: Subtract the result of step 4 from the result of step 3.

$$\log_{10} \sum_{i}^{k} m_i s_i^2 - \log_{10} \sum_{i}^{k} m_i = 2.9877 - 1.5563 = 1.4314$$

STEP 6: Multiply the result of step 5 by the sum of column b.

$$\sum_{i}^{k} m_i \left(\log_{10} \sum_{i}^{k} m_i s_i^2 - \log_{10} \sum_{i}^{k} m_i \right) = 36(1.4314) = 51.5304$$

STEP 7: From the result of step 6, subtract the sum of column f.

$$\sum^{k} m_i(\log_{10} \sum^{k} m_i s_i^2 - \log_{10} \sum^{k} m_i) - \sum^{k} m_i \log_{10} s_i^2 =$$
$$51.5304 - 51.3792 = .1512.$$

STEP 8: Multiply the result of step 7 by $\log_e 10$, which is 2.3026.

The result is the numerator of the statistic we are computing.

$$\log_e 10 \left\{ \sum^{k} m_i \left(\log_{10} \sum^{k} m_i s_i^2 - \log_{10} \sum^{k} m_i\right) - \sum^{k} m_i \log_{10} s_i^2 \right\}$$
$$= 2.3026(.1512) = .3482$$

STEP 9: Stop! Hold everything! Your labors may be at an end! Turn to a chi-square table and look under $k - 1$ degrees of freedom. If the result of step 8 is less than $\chi^2_{.900}$, you will not need to compute the denominator of the fraction. The denominator is always positive and greater than 1, which means that dividing by it always makes the whole fraction smaller. If the numerator by itself is small enough to permit acceptance of the null hypothesis, it is not necessary to compute the denominator.

With 3 degrees of freedom, we find that $\chi^2_{.900}$ is 6.3. Our result of .3482 is much smaller than that, so we can *accept* the null hypothesis that

$$\sigma_a^2 = \sigma_b^2 = \sigma_c^2 = \sigma_d^2$$

For illustrative purposes, however, we shall continue as if this were not so.

STEP 10: Obtain the reciprocal of the sum of column b.

$$\frac{1}{\sum^{k} m_i} = \frac{1}{36} = .0278.$$

STEP 11: Subtract the result of step 10 from the sum of column g.

$$\sum^{k} \frac{1}{m_i} - \frac{1}{\sum^{k} m_i} = .4444 - .0278 = .4166$$

STEP 12: Divide the result of step 11 by $3(k - 1)$, where k is the number of samples. $\dfrac{1}{3(k - 1)} \left(\displaystyle\sum^{k} \dfrac{1}{m_i} - \dfrac{1}{\displaystyle\sum^{k} m_i} \right) = \dfrac{1}{9} (.4166) = .0463$

STEP 13: Add 1 to the result of step 12.

$$1 + \dfrac{1}{3(k - 1)} \left\{ \sum^{k} \dfrac{1}{m_i} - \dfrac{1}{\displaystyle\sum^{k} m_i} \right\} = 1 + .0463 = 1.0463$$

This is the denominator of the fraction.

STEP 14: Divide the result of step 13 into the result of step 8. This is the statistic we are seeking.

$$\dfrac{\log_e 10 \left\{ \displaystyle\sum^{k} m_i \left(\log_{10} \sum^{k} m_i s_i^2 - \log_{10} \sum^{k} m_i \right) - \sum^{k} m_i \log_{10} s_i^2 \right\}}{1 + \dfrac{1}{3(k - 1)} \left\{ \displaystyle\sum^{k} \dfrac{1}{m_i} - \dfrac{1}{\displaystyle\sum^{k} m_i} \right\}}$$

$$= \dfrac{.3482}{1.0463} = .3328$$

STEP 15: Evaluate the statistic of step 14 by reference to a chi-square table with $k - 1$ degrees of freedom. If it is less than $\chi^2_{.900}$, you may accept the hypothesis that $\sigma_1^2 = \sigma_2^2 = \ldots = \sigma_k^2$ and proceed with the analysis of variance.

There is some evidence that moderate violations of the assumptions of normality and homogeneity of variance will not seriously affect the results of an analysis of variance, but if the distributions are wildly nonnormal or the variances widely different, some other statistical technique should ordinarily be used instead. The Kruskal-Wallis test may be a good one for this purpose.

15.1.2 The Basic Principle of Analysis of Variance: The logic of analysis of variance is simple and beautiful. We are going to start by assuming that our k samples are drawn at random from one population, and we are going to estimate the variance of that population in two different ways. The first of those variance estimates comes from the variation of the individuals in the subgroups about the subgroup means and is called the **within-groups variance estimate.** The second comes from the variation of the subgroup means around the grand mean and is called the **between-groups variance estimate.** Then we are going to compare those estimates in the form of an F ratio and see whether they could reasonably be considered two estimates of the same variance. If they could not, we shall reject our null hypothesis.

a. The within-groups variance estimate. We have seen that the variance of a sample, s^2, is a biased estimator of the variance of the population, σ^2. We obtain $\tilde{\sigma}^2$ from s^2 by the formula:

$$\tilde{\sigma}^2 = s^2 \left(\frac{N}{N-1} \right)$$

When we have several samples to consider we want to use all of them in estimating $\tilde{\sigma}^2$, so we take an average. For the rat experiment, the average sample variance is 27, so

$$\tilde{\sigma}^2 = \frac{n_i \bar{s}_i^2}{n_i - 1} = \frac{10 \cdot 27}{9} = 30$$

That is one estimate of the population variance.

b. The between-groups variance estimate. We have seen that if we draw an infinite number of samples of size n from one population, the means of the samples will make up a distribution that is called the sampling distribution of the mean. The standard deviation of that distribution is called the standard error of the mean, and its formula is

$$\sigma_{\bar{X}} = \frac{\sigma}{\sqrt{N}}$$

If we only knew the standard error of the mean, we could use it to estimate the standard deviation of the population.

Of course, we don't know $\sigma_{\bar{X}}$, because it is the standard deviation of a distribution containing an *infinite* number of samples. But we have k samples, and we can actually compute the variance of our set of four means, $s_{\bar{X}}^2$. Since the grand mean is 37, the variance of the set of sample means is

$$\frac{(39-37)^2 + (36-37)^2 + (31-37)^2 + (42-37)^2}{4} = \frac{66}{4}$$

$s_{\bar{X}}^2$ is the *computed* variance of the distribution of means. For the same reason that s^2 underestimates σ^2, $s_{\bar{X}}^2$ underestimates $\sigma_{\bar{X}}^2$. We correct for the bias in exactly the same way.

$$\tilde{\sigma}_{\bar{X}}^2 = s_{\bar{X}}^2 \left(\frac{k}{k-1}\right) = \frac{66}{4} \cdot \frac{4}{3} = \frac{66}{3} = 22$$

Now, having an unbiased estimate of $\tilde{\sigma}_{\bar{X}}^2$, we can estimate the population variance by the formula:

$$\tilde{\sigma}^2 = N\tilde{\sigma}_{\bar{X}}^2$$

n_i is 10, so $\qquad n_i\tilde{\sigma}_{\bar{X}}^2 = 10 \cdot 22 = 220$

That is our second estimate of the population variance, the between-groups variance estimate.

c. Comparing the variance estimates. We now have two independent estimates of the population variance, 30 and 220. Those seem like rather different estimates if they do indeed estimate the same thing. Do they? We find out by computing an F ratio and evaluating it by reference to Table Q.

$$F = \frac{\tilde{\sigma}_{\text{Between-groups}}^2}{\tilde{\sigma}_{\text{Within-groups}}^2} = \frac{220}{30} = 7.33 \qquad (15.1.2)$$

The degrees of freedom associated with the numerator is $k - 1$, or 3. For the denominator, d.f. is $(N - k)$ or 36. We find by reference to Table Q that to reject the null hypothesis with $\alpha = .01$, by a one-tailed test, the required F is 4.38. Since our F is larger than that, we can reject the null hypothesis that the groups are random samples of the same population and conclude that different drugs have different effects on learning.

Notice that the F ratio is written with $\tilde{\sigma}_{\text{B.G.}}^2$ in the numerator. If we are to conclude that our samples are not drawn from one population, their means must differ. That means that the variance estimate based on the differences between group means must be *larger* than the estimate based on variation within the groups. When we use the F ratio in the analysis of variance, we always make a one-tailed test. If F is less than 1, the null hypothesis can be *accepted* without reference to the table.

Questions

1. If we have three samples of size 5, with variances of 30, 40 and 50, what is our unbiased estimate of the variance of the population from which the three samples were drawn?

2. If, in a sample of size 13, $\Sigma x^2 = 144$, what is our unbiased estimate of the population variance?

3. Prove algebraically that $\tilde{\sigma}^2 = \dfrac{\sum\limits_{1}^{n} x^2}{n-1}$.

4. Prove algebraically that for three samples

$$\tilde{\sigma}^2 = \frac{\Sigma x_1^2 + \Sigma x_2^2 + \Sigma x_3^2}{n_1 + n_2 + n_3 - 3}$$

5. If the means of three samples of size 10 are 8, 10, and 12, find (a) $s_{\bar{X}}^2$; (b) $\tilde{\sigma}_{\bar{X}}^2$ (c) $\tilde{\sigma}^2$.

6. For each of the sets of samples below, compute $\tilde{\sigma}^2$.

	n_i	$\bar{X}_1$	$\bar{X}_2$	$\bar{X}_3$	$\bar{X}_4$	$\bar{X}_5$	$\bar{X}_6$
a.	20	10	11	12			
b.	15	134	121	163	100	112	
c.	8	64	72	91	53		
d.	1	6	9	4	8	3	6
e.	n	114	114	114	114	114	114

7. If the five measurements in a sample are 27, 27, 27, 27, and 27, (a) what will s^2 be? (b) what will $\tilde{\sigma}^2$ be?

8. State a generalization relating the size of the within-groups variance estimate and the homogeneity of the samples.

9. Under what condition will the between-groups variance estimate be zero? State a generalization relating the size of the between-groups variance estimate and the differences among the sample means.

10. Win a free trip to the planet Mars by finishing the sentence below in less than 25 words:

In general, the F ratio will be high when the _____ are large relative to the _____ groups.

11. Without doing any computation, decide from which set of data

you would be more likely to obtain a significant F ratio. Why? Sketch two graphs showing frequency distributions for the three subgroups in the two sets of data.

	SET I				SET II	
	n_i	s_i^2	$\bar{X}_i$		n_i	s_i^2	$\bar{X}_i$
a.	10	68	101.6	a.	10	16	159
b.	10	91	102.8	b.	10	24	172
c.	10	73	104.3	c.	10	19	195

12. Assume that the requirements of normality and homogeneity of variance have been satisfied and perform an analysis of variance on the following data. Interpret your results.

SUBGROUP	n_i	s_i^2	$\bar{X}_i$
A	8	16	105
B	8	21	111
C	8	18	124
D	8	27	103
E	8	33	132

13. For the set of data below, test the null hypothesis that

$$\sigma_A^2 = \sigma_B^2 = \sigma_C^2$$

GROUP	n_i	s_i^2
A	12	36
B	11	91
C	10	8

15.1.3 Computational Formulas: The procedure we followed in section 15.1.2 was a good one for demonstrating the principles of the analysis of variance, but it involves several unnecessary computational steps. If we start with raw scores, there are two steps involved in obtaining the F ratio.

a. Break the *total sum of squares* into the component sums of squares.

Back in Chapter 7 (pp. 233–235) we saw that the deviation of any score from the grand mean was composed of two parts: the deviation of the score from the mean of its own subgroup, and the deviation of the subgroup mean from the grand mean.

$$(X - \bar{X}_t) = (X - \bar{X}_i) + (\bar{X}_i - \bar{X}_t)$$

We proved there that

$$\sum_{k}^{k} \sum_{k}^{n_i} (X - \overline{X}_t)^2 = \sum_{k}^{k} \sum_{k}^{n_i} (X - \overline{X}_i)^2 + \sum_{k}^{k} n_i(\overline{X}_i - \overline{X}_t)^2$$

or, in words: the total sum of squares is the sum of the within-groups sum of squares and the between-groups sum of squares. In computing an analysis of variance, our first step is to obtain the three sums of squares. The raw-score formulas are:

Total SS:
$$\sum_{k}^{k} \sum_{k}^{n_i} (X - \overline{X}_t)^2 = \sum_{k}^{k} \sum_{k}^{n_i} X^2 - \frac{\left(\sum_{k}^{k} \sum_{k}^{n_i} X \right)^2}{N} \tag{15.1.3}$$

Within SS:
$$\sum_{k}^{k} \sum_{k}^{n_i} (X - \overline{X}_i)^2 = \sum_{k}^{k} \sum_{k}^{n_i} X^2 - \sum_{k}^{k} \left[\frac{\left(\sum_{k}^{n_i} X \right)^2}{n_i} \right] \tag{15.1.4}$$

Between SS:
$$\sum_{k}^{k} n_i(\overline{X}_i - \overline{X}_t)^2 = \sum_{k}^{k} \frac{\left(\sum_{k}^{n_i} X \right)^2}{n_i} - \frac{\left(\sum_{k}^{k} \sum_{k}^{n_i} X \right)^2}{N} \tag{15.1.5}$$

Formulas 15.1.3 to 15.1.5 give *weighted* sums of squares—that is, they make allowance for the fact that subgroups may be of different sizes. There are even more efficient formulas available when the subgroups are all the same size, but we shall consider only the general ones here. If we substitute the data from the table on page 497, we have:

$$\text{Total SS} = 56500 - \frac{(1480)^2}{40} = 1740$$

$$\text{Within SS} = 56500 - \left[\frac{(390)^2}{10} + \frac{(360)^2}{10} + \frac{(310)^2}{10} + \frac{(420)^2}{10} \right]$$
$$= 1080$$

$$\text{Between SS} = \left[\frac{(390)^2}{10} + \frac{(360)^2}{10} + \frac{(310)^2}{10} + \frac{(420)^2}{10} \right] - \frac{(1480)^2}{40}$$
$$= 660$$

b. Divide each sum of squares by the number of degrees of freedom associated with it. This step provides a direct estimate of the population variance. There are $N - 1$ degrees of freedom associated with the total sum of squares, and

$$\text{d.f. for Within SS} = N - k \qquad (15.1.6)$$

$$\text{d.f. for Between SS} = k - 1 \qquad (15.1.7)$$

It is conventional to present the results of an analysis of variance in a table of the form given below. The data are from the same experiment.

SOURCE	SUM OF SQUARES	d.f.	VARIANCE ESTIMATE	F	p
Between-groups	660	3	220	7.33	$< .01$
Within-groups	1080	36	30		
Total	1740	39			

15.1.4 After Analysis of Variance, What? When an F ratio has been computed and interpreted, we can state with some specified degree of confidence that our subgroups are, or are not, random samples of the same population. That may be all we want to know, or we may wish to make further more detailed comparisons.

Let us consider first the situation in which the F test allows us to accept the null hypothesis that the subgroups are drawn from the same population. The investigator may notice that the two most unlike subgroups really have quite different means and may be tempted to test the significance of this difference by a t-test. And the t-test is very likely to allow him to *reject* the null hypothesis that those two samples were drawn at random from the same population. Thus the F test says 'accept' and the t-test says 'reject.' This sounds like a contradiction, but it really is not.

A significant t-ratio says that *the probability is less than α* that these two samples were drawn *at random* from the same population. There are two key concepts here. One is implied by the words 'at random.' If we pick the two most different subgroups to compare, we are picking them *because they are different* and not 'at random,' so a t-test is not really appropriate. The other key concept is the notion of a probability. A significant t does not say that such a difference will *never* occur in samples from one population, but rather that it will occur only infrequently. But the event that has a probability of .05 may be expected to occur if we give it 20 opportunities, and it may be expected to occur 5 times if we provide 100 opportunities. Thus, if we make 20 comparisons between means, we should not be surprised or elated if one of them turns out to be significant at the 5 per cent level. That *should* happen by chance alone. If there were 7 subgroups in an analysis, and every subgroup were compared with every other, there would be 21 comparisons (7!/2! 5!), hence one might be expected to be significant at the 5 per cent level by chance alone.

In general, if we are unable to reject the null hypothesis that several samples were drawn at random from one population, we cannot later reject the null hypothesis that one carefully chosen pair was drawn at random from one population. If the analysis of variance yields an insignificant F ratio, differences between pairs of groups should not be treated as significant. Of course, there is no law that prohibits further research designed specifically to investigate the 'suspicious' difference.

If the F ratio allows us to reject the null hypothesis, further comparisons of the subgroups may be in order. For example, the investigator in the rat experiment knows that differently treated groups behave differently, and he may now wish to determine, if he can, which particular drugs are causing the differences. His general method in doing this will be to carry out a further breakdown of the between-groups sum of squares, followed by more F tests.

You remember that the total sum of squares was broken down into two parts, one coming from within-groups variation and the other from between-groups variation. With each sum of squares is associated a specified number of degrees of freedom. Just as the total sum of squares was broken down, so the between-groups sum of squares can be broken down further. It can be decomposed into as many components as there are degrees of freedom associated with it. Each of the resulting variance estimates can then be compared with the within-groups variance estimate by means of an F ratio. In the drug investigation, since there are three degrees of freedom associated with the between-groups sum of squares, three independent variance estimates can be made by the appropriate breakdowns.

For example, the investigator probably wants to know whether the three treated groups differ, on the average, from the control group. He now thinks of the rats as simply 'treated' (Groups A, B, and C) or 'untreated' (Group D.) He calculates a sum of squares for 'treated vs. untreated,' using formula 15.1.5.

Tr. vs. Untr. SS: $\dfrac{(390 + 360 + 310)^2}{30} + \dfrac{(420)^2}{10} - \dfrac{(1480)^2}{40} = 333$

To obtain a variance estimate this sum of squares is divided by the number of degrees of freedom associated with it—one. The variance estimate is 333. This estimate is compared with the within-groups variance estimate previously obtained, 30.

$$F = \frac{333}{30} = 11.1$$

For 1 and 36 degrees of freedom an F of 7.39 is required to reject the null hypothesis with $\alpha = .01$, so the investigator concludes that the treated groups differ significantly from the untreated.

Since two degrees of freedom are still unaccounted for, two further comparisons can be made. The experimenter decides to compare Group C with the average of the other two, and Group A with Group B. His computations are:

C with the average of A and B:

$$\frac{(390 + 360)^2}{20} + \frac{(310)^2}{10} - \frac{(390 + 360 + 310)^2}{30} = 282$$

$$\frac{282}{1} = 282$$

$$\frac{282}{30} = 9.4$$

Since this F is significant at better than the 1 per cent level, the conclusion is reached that Group C differs from the other two treated groups.

Group A is now compared with Group B:

$$\frac{(390)^2}{10} + \frac{(360)^2}{10} - \frac{(390 + 360)^2}{20} = 45$$

$$\frac{45}{1} = 45$$

$$F = \frac{45}{30} = 1.5$$

This F is not significant, so it is concluded that Group A does not differ from Group B.

Note that the three separate sums of squares add up to the sum of squares between groups:

$$333 + 282 + 45 = 660$$

This will always be the case when a sum of squares is broken into its independent components.

The particular comparisons made by an experimenter are chosen with two considerations in mind. First, they should be reasonable ones from the point of view of what the experiment is designed to study. Thus in the rat experiment it is more logical to compare the three treated groups with the control group than, for example, to compare the average of Groups A, B, and D with Group C. Theoretically, all the comparisons should be planned in advance even before the experiment is conducted.

The second consideration is that the comparisons should be mutually independent or **orthogonal.** Only if they are will the probabilities obtained from the F table be exact. How to tell whether all the comparisons in a set are mutually orthogonal is a bit complicated. Let us start with some examples of sets of orthogonal and non-orthogonal comparisons.

ORTHOGONAL	NON-ORTHOGONAL	
Ex. I:	Ex. III:	Ex. V:
1. A vs. BCD	1. A vs. D	1. AB vs. CD
2. BC vs. D	2. B vs. D	2. B vs. C
3. B vs. C	3. C vs. D	3. A vs. D
Ex. II:	Ex. IV:	Ex. VI:
1. AB vs. CD	1. A vs. BCD	1. AB vs. C
2. A vs. B	2. BC vs. D	2. AB vs. D
3. C vs. D	3. C vs. D	3. A vs. B

Now we shall define two terms (for purposes of this discussion only). By a *sum* we shall mean anything that is to be compared with anything else. Thus A is a sum, and BCD is a sum. Every comparison is the comparison of two sums. We shall speak of the sum A as having only one *component*. The same is true of the sum B, the sum C, and the sum D. The sum BCD, however, can be broken into its components in several different ways; B is one of its components, and so are C, D, BC, BD, and CD components.

Now for the two rules that must be fulfilled for two comparisons to be orthogonal:

1. *A sum may appear in only one comparison.* If the same sum appears in two comparisons, the comparisons are not orthogonal. This rule is violated in example III, where D appears three times; in example IV, where D appears twice; and in example VI, where AB appears twice.

2. *A component may be compared only with other components of the same sum.* This rule is violated in example IV, where C, a component of BC, is compared with D; it is also violated in example V where B, one component of AB, is compared with C, and A, the other component of AB, is compared with D. If you study the differences between example II and example V, you will see exactly how rule 2 works.

If none of the comparisons in a set violates either of these rules, the comparisons will be mutually orthogonal, the sums of squares from the comparisons will add up to the between-groups sum of squares, and the probabilities associated with the resulting F ratios will be exact and independent.

It sometimes happens that the experimenter wants a kind of information that he cannot get from a set of orthogonal comparisons. For example, the investigator conducting the drug experiment might be interested only in the comparison of each treated group with the control group, as in example III above. He can make these comparisons, but the probabilities obtained are not independent, hence not exact. Suppose, for example, that the F ratios say that the probability is .1 that A and D were drawn from the same population, and .1 that B and D were drawn from the same population. One of these is an absolute probability, and it is exact. The other *should* be a conditional probability—the probability of such and such a difference between B and D, *on the hypothesis* of such and such a difference between A and B; but the probability given in the table is an absolute probability and hence not exact in this case. If we consider the third comparison, C and D, the trouble becomes painfully obvious. Knowing A–D, B–D, and the grand mean, we can predict C–D exactly. It can be only one thing. Hence the probability of that difference, on the hypothesis of the other two, is 1.00, *not* the value read from the table. In spite of his important drawback, non-orthogonal comparisons can sometimes be useful in suggesting directions for future research.

15.1.5 Extensions of the Analysis of Variance: The analysis of variance as described so far appears to be a fairly simple technique for testing the hypothesis that several samples were drawn at random from one population. That's very nice, but why all the fuss about it?

The kind of analysis that has been described and illustrated is what is technically called a 'simple analysis of variance' or 'one-way analysis.' There are more complicated kinds of analysis, and we shall merely describe them, without going into either the mathematical details or the computational procedures.

Consider our rat psychologist again. He has tried four different kinds of drugs (including 'no drug') and found that they have different effects on maze-learning performance. Perhaps, however, he has a sneaking suspicion that the result was somehow related to the difficulty of the particular maze he used. He therefore redesigns his experiment as follows:

As before, three groups are to be treated with drugs a, b, and c, and a fourth is to be left untreated. This time, however, he will use three mazes, I, II, and III, of which maze I is the easiest and maze III the hardest. There are 12 groups of rats, one for each combination of maze and drug. For practical reasons, he uses 5 rats to a group instead of 10. His design can be summarized in the following table.

| | DRUG | | | | |
Maze	a	b	c	d (Control)	All Drugs
I	5 rats	5 rats	5 rats	5 rats	20 rats
II	5 rats	5 rats	5 rats	5 rats	20 rats
III	5 rats	5 rats	5 rats	5 rats	20 rats
All Mazes	15 rats	15 rats	15 rats	15 rats	60 rats

He runs his rats and collects his data, with the results shown in Figure 15.1. (Since the ordinate of the graph is 'trials required to learn,' quick learning goes with low points on the graph, and slow learning with high ones.) Each point on the graph is the mean number of trials required by the five rats of a subgroup. Let us interpret the graph verbally.

In general, Maze I requires the fewest trials, Maze III the most, and Maze II an intermediate number. That is what we expected. Second, we notice that on the whole the control group performs the worst, the group treated with drug a is 'second worst,' while between groups b and c it is hard to see, at a glance, which way the difference lies.

Now we notice more of the details of the graph. On Maze I, groups a, b, and d all performed equally well. Drugs a and b may help, but they don't help on very simple mazes. Drug c, however, helps equally on all mazes. In short, the effect of a drug depends on the

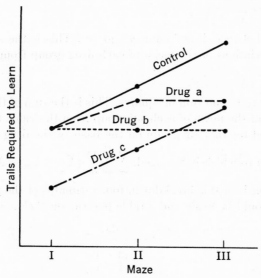

FIG. 15.1   Hypothetical results of maze-learning experiment.

difficulty of the maze. There is an *interaction* between the difficulty of the maze to be learned and the effect of the drug on learning.

An analysis of variance of these data could tell us three things. It could tell us whether the mazes were significantly different in difficulty, whether the drugs were significantly different in effect, and whether the effect of the drugs depended significantly upon the difficulty of the maze.

We call each group of five rats treated in one particular way a 'subgroup.' We shall call each group of 20 rats tested on a single maze a 'maze group' (which includes four subgroups), and each group of 15 rats treated with a particular drug a 'drug group' (which includes three subgroups). The analysis of variance starts by breaking the total sum of squares down into *four* components.

1. The within-groups sum of squares. This is the sum of the squared deviations of each rat's score from the mean of his subgroup, $\sum\limits_{1}^{m} \sum\limits_{1}^{d} \sum\limits_{1}^{n_i} (X - \overline{X}_i)^2$.

2. The 'between-mazes' sum of squares. This is the sum of the squared deviations of the mean of each maze group from the grand mean, $\sum\limits_{}^{m} \sum\limits_{}^{n_i} (\overline{X}_m - \overline{X}_t)^2$.

3. The 'between-drugs' sum of squares. This is the sum of the squared deviations of the mean of each drug group from the grand mean, $\sum\limits_{}^{d} \sum\limits_{}^{n_i} (\overline{X}_d - \overline{X}_t)^2$.

4. The interaction sum of squares. This is the sum of the squared deviations of the mean of each subgroup from the value that would be predicted for that subgroup on the basis of the drug group and maze group to which it belonged, $\sum\limits_{}^{d} \sum\limits_{}^{m} \sum\limits_{}^{n_i} (\overline{X}_i - \overline{X}_m - \overline{X}_d + \overline{X}_t)^2$.

On the basis of this breakdown, four estimates of the population variance would be made and a table like the one below prepared.

SOURCE	SUM OF SQUARES	d.f.	VARIANCE EST.	F	p
Between mazes		$(3 - 1)$			
Between drugs		$(4 - 1)$			
Interaction		$(3 - 1)(4 - 1)$			
Within groups		$3 \cdot 4(5 - 1)$			
Total		$(3 \cdot 4 \cdot 5) - 1$			

From the four variance estimates, three F ratios would be computed —one for 'between mazes,' one for 'between drugs,' and one for interaction. Three significant F ratios would enable the experimenter to conclude that mazes differ in difficulty, that drugs differ in their effects, and that the effectiveness of a drug depends upon the difficulty of the maze.

The analysis of variance that has just been described is called a 'double-classification analysis,' 'two-way,' or 'two-dimensional' analysis of variance, because just two variables, drugs and maze difficulty, are being manipulated. Theoretically there is no limit to the number of variables that can be manipulated and, correspondingly, to the number of dimensions that can be analyzed. For example, our investigator might suspect that the age of the tested rats was a relevant variable and might conduct his experiment with a group of young rats and again with a group of elderly rats. His experimental design would then be described by Figure 15.2. His

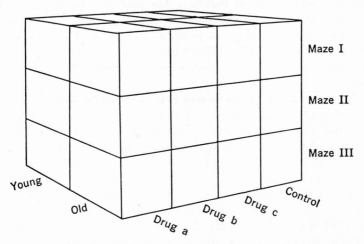

Fig. 15.2 Experimental design for three-variable learning experiment.

table of results would be quite complicated, and would list the following sources of sums of squares:

> Between mazes
> Between drugs
> Between ages
> Interaction between mazes and drugs
> Interaction between mazes and ages
> Interaction between drugs and ages
> Interaction among mazes, drugs, and ages
> Within groups

Mazes, drugs, and ages are known as the **main variables.** They are the variables which the experimenter manipulates or controls. The first three interactions, since they are between two variables, are called **double interactions,** or **first-order interactions.** The fourth interaction term is called a **triple interaction,** or **second-order interaction.** Can you visualize the kind of results that would lead to a significant triple interaction?

With an increase in the availability of automatic computing equipment, research workers are doing longer and more complicated data analyses, and it is not unusual today to run across reports of five- and six-way analyses of variance. The principles involved in such analyses are basically the same as those enunciated here. More variables mean more interactions, and some of the higher-order interactions may be quite difficult to interpret, but a series of graphs and some words of explanation from the author will usually make them understandable.

15.1.6 Analysis of Variance and Experimental Design: Beginning science students are usually told that the only way to conduct an experiment is to manipulate the independent variable and see how the dependent variable changes. In actual practice, experiments are almost never conducted that way. In most investigations, three, four, or even six or seven variables are manipulated at once. The reason for this is that the effect of one variable, such as drugs, may depend upon the state of another—such as maze difficulty. If only one kind of maze is used, the dependence can never be recognized.

Before the analysis of variance was developed, there was no way to determine from a single experiment whether the effects of one variable depended upon the state of another. Complex analysis of variance, by permitting us to test the significance of interactions, enables us to do so. Thus analysis of variance allows us to conduct much more complex experiments than we were previously able to undertake, and to analyze our results in a precise and meaningful way. That is why we have called it an important and powerful tool.

Questions

1. In a study of the effect of incentives on industrial productivity, 30 factory workers are divided at random into 5 groups. The groups are paid as follows: (A) straight salary; (B) salary plus incentive; (C) straight piecework; (D) scaled piecework; and (E) salary based on weekly group output. The average number of pieces per worker per day over a four-week period are given on the next page.

	A	B	C	D	E	
	14	45	54	16	57	
	26	24	32	31	46	
	34	51	60	25	35	
	20	40	53	28	41	
	25	42	55	19	44	
	28	32	43	23	29	
ΣX	147	234	297	142	252	1072
ΣX^2	3837	9590	15223	3516	11048	43214

a. Compute and interpret E^2.

b. Evaluate the assumption of homogeneity of variance.

c. If the assumption of homogeneity can be accepted, carry out an analysis of variance and interpret the results.

d. If the null hypothesis is rejected, make the following set of orthogonal comparisons: ABE vs. CD, AB vs. E, A vs. B, C vs. D.

e. Explain why each of the three sets of comparisons listed below is non-orthogonal:

    (1) A vs. BCDE, BC vs. DE, BCD vs. E, B vs. C.

    (2) ABC vs. DE, A vs. B, A vs. C, D vs. E.

    (3) AE vs. BCD, BC vs. A, D vs. E, B vs. CD.

f. Make up two additional sets of orthogonal comparisons.

2. Prove algebraically that when there are only two subgroups, $F = t^2$.

3. Design an experiment for which the data should be analyzed by a double analysis of variance. Explain what a significant interaction might mean.

4. From your reading, find several examples of the use of analysis of variance in research. Do the examples seem to follow the model described here? If not, wherein do the differences lie? Interpret the results of these analyses.

15.2 Correlation, Regression, and the F Ratio

15.2.1 The Significance of the Correlation Ratio: In Chapter 7, we saw that E^2, the square of the correlation ratio, could be written as

$$E^2 = \frac{\text{Between-groups sum of squares}}{\text{Total sum of squares}}$$

It is easy to show that

$$1 - E^2 = \frac{\text{Within-groups sum of squares}}{\text{Total sum of squares}}$$

The ratio of E^2 to $1 - E^2$ is therefore the ratio of the between-groups sum of squares to the within-groups sum of squares.

$$\frac{E^2}{1 - E^2} = \frac{\text{Between-groups sum of squares}}{\text{Within-groups sum of squares}}$$

These are the same sums of squares that are used in estimating the population variance when we obtain an F ratio. To obtain $\tilde{\sigma}^2$, we divide each sum of squares by the appropriate number of degrees of freedom. To test the null hypothesis that the correlation ratio is zero, therefore, we can use these sums of squares, divide each by its appropriate d.f., compute an F ratio, and interpret it just as we would in an analysis of variance.

$$F = \frac{\dfrac{\text{Between } SS}{k - 1}}{\dfrac{\text{Within } SS}{N - k}} = \frac{(N - k)(\text{Between } SS)}{(k - 1)(\text{Within } SS)} = \frac{(N - k)}{(k - 1)} \cdot \frac{E^2}{1 - E^2}$$

$$(15.2.1)$$

The essential *similarity* between a correlation ratio and an analysis of variance is that both utilize the breakdown of the total sum of squares into a component coming from within-group variability and a component coming from differences between groups. The essential *difference* between them is that the correlation ratio simply compares directly the between-groups sum of squares and the total sum of squares and is a measure of the strength of relationship, while analysis of variance uses the two components of the total sum of squares to obtain estimates of the population variance. In making the estimates, the number and sizes of the subgroups are taken into account, and the probability of the previously obtained relationship, on the assumption of the null hypothesis, can be determined.

15.2.2 A Test for Linearity of Regression: In Chapter 7 we said that when a correlation ratio and a correlation coefficient, r, were calculated from the same set of data, the correlation ratio would always be at least as high as r and usually higher. Only if the subgroup means lie exactly on the regression line will the two be the same. We added, however, with a vague wave of the hand that if the difference between E and r was 'too big,' there was ground for suspecting that the relationship between X and Y was not linear. Now we are prepared to be a little more specific about the meaning of 'too big.'

The deviation of any Y-score from the mean of the Y-scores can be broken down into three parts: (1) the deviation of the score from the mean of its own subgroup $(Y - \overline{Y}_i)$; (2) the deviation of the subgroup mean from the regression line $(\overline{Y}_i - \tilde{Y})$; and (3) the deviation of the regression line, for a particular value of X, from the mean of the Y-scores, $(\tilde{Y} - \overline{Y}_t)$.

$$(Y - \overline{Y}_t) = (Y - \overline{Y}_i) + (\overline{Y}_i - \tilde{Y}) + (\tilde{Y} - \overline{Y}_t)$$

These three components of a deviation enable us to obtain several separate sums of squares, and from these, several estimates of the population variance. Two of these are already familiar: $\Sigma(Y - \overline{Y}_i)^2$ is the sum of squares from which the within-groups variance is estimated; $\Sigma(\overline{Y}_i - \overline{Y}_t)^2$ (which is the same thing as $\Sigma[(\overline{Y}_i - \tilde{Y}) + (\tilde{Y} - \overline{Y}_t)]^2$) is the sum from which the between-groups variance is estimated. The third, $\Sigma(\overline{Y}_i - \tilde{Y})^2$, is a sum of squares which will be zero if the subgroup means lie exactly on the regression line, and hence $E = r$, but will be large if there are major deviations of subgroup means from the regression line. In fact, it can (easily) be shown that $\Sigma(\overline{Y}_i - \tilde{Y})^2 = E^2 - r^2$. By comparing the variance estimate from this third sum of squares with the within-groups variance estimate, in the form of an F ratio, we can test the null hypothesis that $\eta = \rho$.

Since two constants are used in specifying the regression line, two degrees of freedom are lost, and $k - 2$ degrees of freedom are available for estimating the population variance from $\Sigma(\overline{Y}_i - \tilde{Y})^2$. For the within-groups variance, $N - k$ are available as before. So:

$$F = \frac{\dfrac{E^2 - r^2}{k - 2}}{\dfrac{1 - E^2}{N - k}} = \frac{(N - k)}{(k - 2)} \cdot \frac{(E^2 - r^2)}{1 - E^2} \qquad (15.2.2)$$

If the F so obtained is significantly large, we must reject the hypothesis that $\eta = \rho$, and conclude that a straight line does not adequately describe the regression of Y on X.

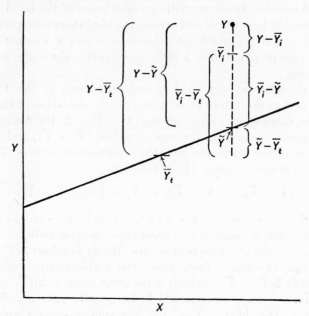

FIG. 15.3   Relations among components of $Y - \overline{Y}_t$.

$$Y - \overline{Y}_t = (Y - \overline{Y}_i) + (\overline{Y}_i - \tilde{Y}) + (\tilde{Y} - \overline{Y}_t)$$
$$Y - \tilde{Y} = (Y - \overline{Y}_i) + (\overline{Y}_i - \tilde{Y})$$
$$\overline{Y}_s - \overline{Y}_t = (\overline{Y}_i - \tilde{Y}) + (\tilde{Y} - \overline{Y}_t)$$

15.2.3 The Significance of the Correlation Coefficient:

Using the same breakdown of $(Y - \overline{Y}_t)$, we can write

$$r^2 = \frac{\Sigma(\tilde{Y} - \overline{Y}_t)^2}{\Sigma(Y - \overline{Y}_t)^2} \quad \text{and} \quad 1 - r^2 = \frac{\Sigma(Y - \tilde{Y})^2}{\Sigma(Y - \overline{Y}_t)^2}$$

hence

$$\frac{r^2}{1 - r^2} = \frac{\Sigma(\tilde{Y} - \overline{Y}_t)^2}{\Sigma(Y - \tilde{Y})^2}$$

$\tilde{Y}$ is entirely determined by the regression equation of Y on X, which has two constants, the slope and the intercept. One of these may be chosen 'freely,' but the other is determined by the fact that the regression line must pass through $\overline{Y}$ at $\overline{X}$, so an estimate of the population variance from $\Sigma(\tilde{Y} - \overline{Y}_t)^2$ has only one degree of freedom associated with it. In estimating the population variance from $\Sigma(Y - \tilde{Y})^2$, two degrees of freedom are lost from the original N for the two constants of the regression line, so $\tilde{\sigma}^2 = \dfrac{\Sigma(Y - \tilde{Y})^2}{N - 2}$. Hence $F = \dfrac{\Sigma(\tilde{Y} - \overline{Y}_t)^2}{1}$ divided by $\dfrac{\Sigma(Y - \tilde{Y})^2}{N - 2}$, and

$$F = \frac{r^2}{1 - r^2} \cdot \frac{N - 2}{1} = \frac{(N - 2)r^2}{1 - r^2} \qquad (15.2.3)[1]$$

Summary

The analysis of variance is a technique for testing the hypothesis that several samples were drawn at random from one population. Two estimates of the population variance are obtained: one based on the variation within the subgroups and one based on differences among the means of the subgroups. These two are compared in the form of an F ratio. Since the F distribution is derived on the assumption of homogeneous variances and normal distributions in the populations from which the subgroups were drawn, these assumptions must be fulfilled before the use of the F ratio is appropriate. Extensions of the analysis of variance permit an experimenter to manipulate several variables in one experiment, and to test the significance not only of their separate effects but also of their interactions. It is therefore an exceedingly powerful research tool.

The F ratio can also be used to test the hypothesis that $\eta = 0$, that $\eta = \rho$, and that $\rho = 0$.

Question

1. In a study of the Müller-Lyer Illusion, one subject makes 10 settings of the 'feathered' end of the line under each of six different experimental conditions, trying always to make the 'feathered' end match in length the end between the arrow heads. The actual length

---

[1] Formula 14.4.9 states that $\dfrac{r\sqrt{N - 2}}{\sqrt{1 - r^2}} = t$. When there is only one degree of freedom associated with the numerator, $F = t^2$; so formula 15.2.3 is really identical with 14.4.9.

of the line between the arrow heads is 200 mm. The six different experimental conditions consist of different angular adjustments of the feathers and arrow heads. The angle made by one feather with the horizontal line describes the condition. Results given below are the settings made by the subject in mm.

ANGLE:	15°	30°	45°	60°	75°	90°
	259	234	234	218	221	200
	251	249	231	230	206	212
	251	242	235	225	210	192
	250	243	237	221	213	201
	249	244	237	234	220	197
	242	245	239	226	215	200
	243	246	238	224	213	198
	250	246	241	226	214	206
	249	239	242	229	215	195
	256	252	236	227	213	199

a. Compute E^2 and E and evaluate the null hypothesis that $\eta = 0$.

b. Plot the mean settings for the various conditions as a function of angle. Do the points lie along a straight line?

c. From the raw data (not the mean settings), compute r and r^2 between angle and setting.

d. Test the null hypothesis that $\rho = \eta$.

e. Look up the cosines of the angles given, and compute the correlation coefficient between the cosine of the angle and the setting made by the subject. Plot the mean settings as a function of the cosine of the angle.

f. Apply the test for linearity to this new correlation.

g. Derive a regression equation for the regression of setting on the cosine of the angle.

h. Derive a general formula relating percentage error made by the subject and cosine of angle.

References

1. Cochran, W. G., and Cox, Gertrude M., *Experimental Designs*, New York, Wiley, 1950, pp. 55–72. A technical treatment of the breakdown of sums of squares.

2. Edwards, A. L., *Experimental Design in Psychological Research*, New York, Rinehart, 1950. A relatively simple treatment of experimental

design, analysis of variance under several different kinds of conditions, and analysis of covariance.

3. Fisher, R. A., *The Design of Experiments*, Edinburgh, Oliver and Boyd, 1951. This reference and the next one are the classic treatments of experimental design and the analysis of variance.
4. Fisher, R. A., and Yates, F., *Statistical Methods for Research Workers*, Edinburgh, Oliver and Boyd, 1948.
5. Lindquist, E. F., *Design and Analysis of Experiments in Psychology and Education*, New York, Houghton Mifflin, 1953. At a level suitable for research workers but simple enough for the intermediate student, this book covers the application of analysis of variance techniques to many different experimental designs. Contains a section on assumptions underlying the techniques and the results of failure to fulfill these assumptions.

Answers

Page 504

1. 50.   2. 12.   5. (a) $\frac{8}{3}$; (b) 4; (c) 40.
6. (a) 20; (b) 8737.5; (c) 2053.3; (d) 5.2; (e) 0.
7. (a) 0; (b) 0.   11. Set II.   12. $F = 47.91$.
13. Bartlett's statistic = 11.08. Reject.

Page 516

1. (a) $E^2 = .625$; (b) num. of B's stat. = 2.5, accept; (c) $F = 10.42$;
   (d) $F < 1, F = 5.71, F = 8.57, F = 27.20$.

Page 521

1. (a) $E^2 = .938$, $E = .968$, $F = 163.4$; (c) $r = -.957$, $r^2 = .916$;
   (d) $F = 4.9$, reject; (e) $r = .968$, $r^2 = .937$; (f) $F = .217$, accept;
   (g) $Y = 51 \cos X + 200$; (h) percentage error $= 25 \cos x$.

AN OVER-ALL VIEW OF INFERENTIAL STATISTICS | 16

Inferential statistics is a body of techniques which enable us to use our knowledge of samples to make inferences about the populations from which the samples were drawn. We compute statistics; we make inferences about parameters. The inference may be a point estimate of a parameter, as when we say that our best estimate of the population mean is that it is the same as the sample mean. Or the inference may take the form of an interval estimate, made with some specified degree of confidence, as when we say that we are 95 per cent confident that the population correlation is not lower than some value or higher than some other value. Or, finally, inferences may enable us to accept or reject some hypothesis about a parameter value, as when we say that there are fewer than five chances in 100 that the mean of the differences is zero in the population. In the last analysis, testing hypotheses turns out to be merely a different aspect of the process of establishing confidence intervals, for once the interval has been established, we can instantly reject, at the same level of confidence, any hypothesis that states that the parameter lies outside of the confidence interval.

The most important theoretical step in establishing confidence intervals or testing hypotheses is to determine the form of the sampling distribution of some statistic, on the hypothesis of one or several values of a parameter. That job is done by mathematical statisticians, who make their results available to consumers of statistics in the form of tables or formulas. When it has been done, we are in a position to ask the question: '*If* the parameter were such and such, how likely would we be to get a statistic whose value is so and so?' When the answer is 'Very unlikely:' we go on to reason: 'But the value of the statistic *is* so and so, and therefore the parameter is probably *not* such and such.' If we are testing a null hypothesis we have to do this only once, because the hypothesis specifies a particular parameter value. If we are establishing a confidence interval, we may, in theory at least, have to repeat the process many times for different parameter values.

One important difference between interval estimation and hypothesis testing—a difference that we didn't mention in Chapter 11 because you wouldn't have understood it then—is that interval estimates are usually estimates of a parameter which is itself a useful descriptive measure, such as the mean or variance or correlation coefficient; while in hypothesis testing we may utilize what might be called an 'artificial statistic.' By 'artificial statistic' we mean a statistic which is of no particular interest in its own right, but which is 'invented' solely for the purpose of testing a hypothesis. Examples are chi-square, the h of the Kruskal-Wallis Test, the T of Wilcoxon's Test, and Bartlett's Statistic. These statistics have no use as descriptive measures, and our interest in them is over when the test has been completed. They have been invented because the forms of their sampling distributions could be determined, on the assumption of the null hypothesis, and thus they permit us to make exact or approximate tests of the validity of the hypothesis.

Tables 16.1 and 16.2 summarize the methods of making point and interval estimates of parameters and of testing hypotheses, in so far as these methods have been covered in this text. Neither table is complete, and occasionally the blank spaces represent real blank spaces in statistical knowledge. More often, however, there are techniques available to make the indicated estimate or test. A good way to keep your knowledge of statistics growing would be to collect new methods as you encounter them in your reading or research, and continue to fill in the blanks and expand the entries in the summary tables.

Table 16.1. Point and Interval Estimates of Parameters

KIND OF MEASURE

SCALE	Frequency distributions or parts thereof	Central Tendency	Variability	Correlation
NOMINAL	$\tilde{P} = p$ $\sigma_p = \sqrt{PQ/N}$ $\dfrac{p-P}{\sigma_p}$ is normally distributed when $NP \geq 5$. Confidence bands for estimating P from p. Chi-square test for correspondence of obtained and expected frequency distributions.		$\tilde{H} = \hat{H} + 1.3863N$	$\tilde{T} = \hat{T} - \dfrac{(r-1)(k-1)}{1.3863N}$
ORDINAL	Confidence interval for any population percentile made in terms of sample percentiles. Kolmogorov-Smirnov confidence band for entire cumulative percentage histogram.	$\widetilde{Mdn}_{pop} = Mdn.$ Confidence intervals in terms of sample percentiles.	Confidence intervals for Q_1 and Q_3 in terms of sample percentiles.	Confidence limits of ω can be established from confidence limits of $\dfrac{S}{S+D}$. [Method not discussed here.]
INTERVAL and RATIO	Chi-square and Kolmogorov-Smirnov tests can be used to determine goodness of fit of any theoretical distribution —e.g. normal.	$\tilde{\mu} = \bar{X}, \tilde{\sigma}_{\bar{X}} = s/\sqrt{N-1}$ $\dfrac{\bar{X} - \mu}{\tilde{\sigma}_{\bar{X}}}$ has t-distribution for samples from normal populations. For small samples from nonnormal populations, use Tchebychev's Inequality. Same principles for Mdn., but $\tilde{\sigma}_{Mdn} = 1.253\,\tilde{\sigma}_{\bar{X}}$.	$\tilde{\sigma}^2 = s^2\left(\dfrac{N}{N-1}\right)$ For samples from normal populations, Ns^2 has chi-square distribution with $N - 1$ degrees of freedom.	Confidence bands for estimating ρ from r. $z_r = 1.1513\log_{10}\dfrac{1+r}{1-r}$ $(z_r - z_\rho)(\sqrt{N-3})$ has unit normal distribution if population is normal bivariate.

Table 16.2. Tests of Hypotheses

HYPOTHESIS

SCALE	Two independent samples have:		Two correlated samples have:	k independent samples have:		k correlated samples have:	Two variables are:	
	Equal variability	Same central tendency or proportion	Same central tendency	Equal variabilities	Same central tendency	Same central tendency	Uncorrelated or independent	Linearly related
NOMINAL		$p_1 - p_2$ is normally distributed with $$\sigma_{D_p} = \sqrt{p_a q_a \left(\frac{1}{N_1} + \frac{1}{N_2}\right)}$$			Chi-square test for equality of several sample proportions.		Chi-square test of independence. Likelihood-ratio chi-square. If $T = 0$, $1.3863 N\hat{T}$ has chi-square distribution with $(r-1)(k-1)$ degrees of freedom.	
ORDINAL		Run test (also sensitive to differences in variability). Median test. Rank-sums test.	Sign test		Median test Kruskal-Wallis test	Friedman test (sometimes called 'analysis of variance by ranks').	Contingency test of association. Test of hypothesis that $\omega = 0$. Test of hypothesis that $\rho_0 = 0$	
INTERVAL AND RATIO	F test. Assumes normality of populations.	$$\bar{\sigma}_{\bar{X}_1 - \bar{X}_2} = \hat{\sigma}\sqrt{\frac{1}{N_1} + \frac{1}{N_2}}$$ $\dfrac{\bar{X}_1 - \bar{X}_2}{\hat{\sigma}_{\bar{X}_1 - \bar{X}_2}}$ has t-distribution with $N_1 + N_2 - 2$ degrees of freedom when samples are from normal populations with equal variances.	Wilcoxon Test for Paired Replicates. For large samples, or small samples from normal populations $$\frac{D}{s_D/\sqrt{N-1}}$$ has a t-distribution with $N - 1$ degrees of freedom.	Bartlett's Test for Homogeneity of Variance.	Analysis of variance. $\dfrac{\hat{\sigma}_B^2}{\hat{\sigma}_W^2}$ has F distribution if samples are from normal populations with equal variances.	Analysis of variance (two dimensional). Assumes normality and homogeneity of variance.	Test hypothesis that $\eta = 0$ by use of F ratio. Test hypothesis that $\rho = 0$ by use of F ratio or t-test.	Test hypothesis that $\rho = \eta$ by use of F ratio.

APPENDIX

LIST OF TABLES

Table A*

$-p(i)$ log$_2$ $p(i)$ for values of $p(i)$ from .000 to .999

How to use this table:

Example: to find the value of $-p(i)$ log$_2$ $p(i)$ when $p(i)$ = .376

1. Look up the first two digits of $p(i)$ in the first column of the table. Find .37 in column 1.

2. Find the last entry in column 2, in this case 0.5. This is the first digit of the required $-p(i)$ log$_2$ $p(i)$.

3. Read across the row starting with .37 until the column headed by the third digit of $p(i)$, in this case 6, is reached. The entry in the table, 306, gives the second, third, and fourth digits of of the required $-p(i)$ log$_2$ $p(i)$. The $-p(i)$ log$_2$ $p(i)$ corresponding to a $p(i)$ of .376 is .5306.

4. When the table entries are in italics, the first digit of the $-p(i)$ log$_2$ $p(i)$ is to be read from the line below the one in which the $p(i)$ is located. For example, the $-p(i)$ log$_2$ $p(i)$ corresponding to a $p(i)$ of .145 is .4040.

---

* From Newman, E. B. Computational methods useful in analyzing series of binary data, *Amer. J. Psychol.*, 54, 1951, 252–62. By permission of the author and editor.

Table A (Continued)
$-p(i) \log_2 p(i)$ for values of $p(i)$ from 0.000 to 0.999

p		0	1	2	3	4	5	6	7	8	9
.00	0.0	000	100	179	251	319	382	443	501	557	612
.01		664	716	766	814	862	909	955	999	043	086
.02	0.1	129	170	211	252	291	330	369	407	444	481
.03		518	554	589	624	659	693	727	760	793	825
.04		858	889	921	952	983	013	043	073	103	132
.05	0.2	161	190	218	246	274	301	329	356	383	409
.06		435	461	487	513	538	563	588	613	637	662
.07		686	709	733	756	780	803	826	848	871	893
.08		915	937	959	980	002	023	044	065	086	106
.09	0.3	127	147	167	187	207	226	246	265	284	303
.10		322	341	359	378	396	414	432	450	468	485
.11		503	520	537	555	571	588	605	622	638	654
.12		671	687	703	719	734	750	766	781	796	811
.13		826	841	856	871	886	900	915	929	943	957
.14		971	985	999	012	006	040	053	066	079	092
.15	0.4	105	118	131	144	156	169	181	194	206	218
.16		230	242	254	266	278	289	301	312	323	335
.17		346	357	368	379	390	401	411	422	432	443
.18		453	463	474	484	494	504	514	523	533	543
.19		552	562	571	581	590	599	608	617	626	635
.20		644	653	661	670	678	687	695	704	712	720
.21		728	736	744	752	760	768	776	783	791	798
.22		806	813	821	828	835	842	849	856	863	870
.23		877	883	890	897	903	910	916	923	929	935
.24		941	948	954	960	966	971	977	983	989	994
.25	0.5	000	006	011	017	022	027	032	038	043	048
.26		053	058	063	068	073	077	082	087	091	096
.27		100	105	109	113	118	122	126	130	134	138
.28		142	146	150	154	158	161	165	169	172	176
.29		179	183	186	189	192	196	199	202	205	208
.30		211	214	217	220	222	225	228	230	233	235
.31		238	240	243	245	248	250	252	254	256	258
.32		260	262	264	266	268	270	272	273	275	277
.33		278	280	281	283	284	286	287	288	289	291
.34		292	293	294	295	296	297	298	299	300	300
.35		301	302	302	303	304	304	305	305	306	306
.36		306	306	307	307	307	307	307	307	307	307
.37		307	307	307	307	307	306	306	306	305	305
.38		305	304	304	303	302	302	301	300	300	299
.39		298	297	296	295	294	293	292	291	290	289
.40		288	287	285	284	283	281	280	278	277	276
.41		274	272	271	269	267	266	264	262	260	258
.42		257	255	253	251	249	247	244	242	240	238
.43		236	233	231	229	226	224	222	219	217	214
.44		212	209	206	204	201	198	195	193	190	187
.45		184	181	178	175	172	169	166	163	160	157
.46		153	150	147	144	140	137	133	130	127	123
.47		120	116	112	108	105	102	098	094	090	086
.48		083	079	075	071	067	063	059	055	051	047
.49		043	039	034	030	026	022	018	013	009	004

Values of $-p(i) \log_2 p(i)$ *(Continued)*

p		0	1	2	3	4	5	6	7	8	9
.50	0.5	000	996	991	987	982	978	973	968	964	959
.51	0.4	954	950	945	940	935	930	926	921	916	911
.52		906	901	896	891	886	880	875	870	865	860
.53		854	849	844	839	833	828	823	817	812	806
.54		801	795	789	784	778	772	767	761	755	750
.55		744	738	732	726	720	714	709	702	697	691
.56		684	678	672	666	660	654	648	641	635	629
.57		623	616	610	604	597	591	584	578	571	565
.58		558	551	545	538	532	515	518	511	505	498
.59		491	484	477	471	464	457	450	443	436	429
.60		422	415	408	401	393	386	379	372	365	357
.61		350	343	335	328	321	313	306	298	291	283
.62		276	268	261	253	246	238	230	223	215	207
.63		200	192	184	176	168	160	152	145	137	129
.64		121	113	105	097	089	081	072	064	056	048
.65		040	032	023	015	007	998	990	982	973	965
.66	0.3	957	948	940	931	923	914	906	897	888	880
.67		871	862	854	845	836	828	819	810	801	792
.68		783	774	766	757	748	739	730	721	712	703
.69		694	685	675	666	657	648	639	630	621	611
.70		602	593	583	574	565	556	546	537	527	718
.71		508	499	489	480	470	461	451	441	432	422
.72		412	403	393	383	373	364	354	344	334	324
.73		315	305	295	285	275	265	255	245	235	225
.74		215	204	194	184	174	164	154	144	133	123
.75		113	102	092	082	072	061	051	040	030	020
.76		009	999	988	978	967	957	946	935	925	914
.77	0.2	903	893	882	872	861	850	839	828	818	807
.78		796	785	774	764	752	742	731	720	708	697
.79		686	676	665	654	642	631	620	609	598	587
.80		576	564	553	542	530	519	508	497	485	474
.81		462	451	440	428	417	405	394	383	371	359
.82		348	336	325	313	301	290	278	266	255	243
.83		231	219	208	196	184	172	160	148	137	125
.84		113	101	089	077	065	053	041	029	017	005
.85	0.1	993	981	969	957	944	932	920	908	896	884
.86		871	859	847	834	822	810	798	785	773	760
.87		748	735	723	712	698	686	673	661	648	635
.88		623	610	598	585	573	560	547	534	522	509
.89		496	484	471	458	445	432	420	407	394	381
.90		368	355	342	329	316	303	290	277	264	251
.91		238	225	212	199	186	173	159	146	133	120
.92		107	094	080	067	054	040	027	014	000	987
.93	0.0	974	960	947	934	920	907	893	880	866	853
.94		839	826	812	799	785	771	758	744	730	717
.95		703	689	675	662	648	635	621	607	593	579
.96		565	552	538	524	510	496	482	468	454	441
.97		426	412	398	384	370	356	342	328	314	300
.98		285	271	257	243	229	215	200	186	172	158
.99		144	129	115	101	086	072	058	043	029	014

Table B
Pascal's Triangle of Binomial Coefficients

N														
0							1							
1						1		1						
2					1		2		1					
3				1		3		3		1				
4			1		4		6		4		1			
5		1		5		10		10		5		1		
6	1		6		15		20		15		6		1	
7		7		21		35		35		21		7		1
8	8		28		56		70		56		28		8	1
9	9	36		84		126		126		84		36	9	1
10	10	45	120		210		252		210		120	45	10	1
11	11	55	165	330		462		462		330	165	55	11	1
12	12	66	220	495	792		924		792	495	220	66	12	1

Table C*
Areas Under the Normal Curve

z	.00	.01	.02	.03	.04	.05	.06	.07	.08	.09
0.0	.0000	.0040	.0080	.0120	.0160	.0199	.0239	.0279	.0319	.0359
0.1	.0398	.0438	.0478	.0517	.0557	.0596	.0636	.0675	.0714	.0753
0.2	.0793	.0832	.0871	.0910	.0948	.0987	.1026	.1064	.1103	.1141
0.3	.1179	.1217	.1255	.1293	.1331	.1368	.1406	.1443	.1480	.1517
0.4	.1554	.1591	.1628	.1664	.1700	.1736	.1772	.1808	.1844	.1879
0.5	.1915	.1950	.1985	.2019	.2054	.2088	.2123	.2157	.2190	.2224
0.6	.2257	.2291	.2324	.2357	.2389	.2422	.2454	.2486	.2517	.2549
0.7	.2580	.2611	.2642	.2673	.2704	.2734	.2764	.2794	.2823	.2852
0.8	.2881	.2910	.2939	.2967	.2995	.3023	.3051	.3078	.3106	.3133
0.9	.3159	.3186	.3212	.3238	.3264	.3289	.3315	.3340	.3365	.3389
1.0	.3413	.3438	.3461	.3485	.3508	.3531	.3554	.3577	.3599	.3621
1.1	.3643	.3665	.3686	.3708	.3729	.3749	.3770	.3790	.3810	.3830
1.2	.3849	.3869	.3888	.3907	.3925	.3944	.3962	.3980	.3997	.4015
1.3	.4032	.4049	.4066	.4082	.4099	.4115	.4131	.4147	.4162	.4177
1.4	.4192	.4207	.4222	.4236	.4251	.4265	.4279	.4292	.4306	.4319
1.5	.4332	.4345	.4357	.4370	.4382	.4394	.4406	.4418	.4429	.4441
1.6	.4452	.4463	.4474	.4484	.4495	.4505	.4515	.4525	.4535	.4545
1.7	.4554	.4564	.4573	.4582	.4591	.4599	.4608	.4616	.4625	.4633
1.8	.4641	.4649	.4656	.4664	.4671	.4678	.4686	.4693	.4699	.4706
1.9	.4713	.4719	.4726	.4732	.4738	.4744	.4750	.4756	.4761	.4767
2.0	.4772	.4778	.4783	.4788	.4793	.4798	.4803	.4808	.4812	.4817
2.1	.4821	.4826	.4830	.4834	.4838	.4842	.4846	.4850	.4854	.4857
2.2	.4861	.4864	.4868	.4871	.4875	.4878	.4881	.4884	.4887	.4890
2.3	.4893	.4896	.4898	.4901	.4904	.4906	.4909	.4911	.4913	.4916
2.4	.4918	.4920	.4922	.4925	.4927	.4929	.4931	.4932	.4934	.4936
2.5	.4938	.4940	.4941	.4943	.4945	.4946	.4948	.4949	.4951	.4952
2.6	.4953	.4955	.4956	.4957	.4959	.4960	.4961	.4962	.4963	.4964
2.7	.4965	.4966	.4967	.4968	.4969	.4970	.4971	.4972	.4973	.4974
2.8	.4974	.4975	.4976	.4977	.4977	.4978	.4979	.4979	.4980	.4981
2.9	.4981	.4982	.4982	.4983	.4984	.4984	.4985	.4985	.4986	.4986
3.0	.4987	.4987	.4987	.4988	.4988	.4989	.4989	.4989	.4990	.4990

* From Neyman, J. *First Course in Probability and Statistics*, New York, Holt, 1954. By permission of the author and publisher.

Table D*

95% Confidence Limits for Proportions

Interval Estimate of Population Proportion P with $\alpha = .05$
for $N = 10, 15, 20, 30, 50, 100, 250,$ and 1000.

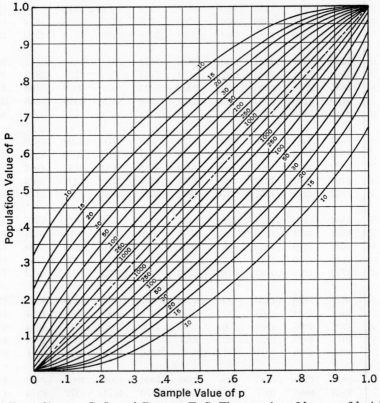

* From Clopper, C. J., and Pearson, E. S. The use of confidence or fiducial limits illustrated in the case of the binomial, *Biometrika*, 26, 1943, 404–13. By permission of the authors and editor.

Table E*
Distribution of χ^2

d.f.					Probability of a χ^2 at least as large as tabled value									d.f.
	.005	.010	.025	.050	.100	.250	.500	.750	.900	.950	.975	.990	.995	
1	7.9	6.6	5.0	3.8	2.7	1.3	.46	.10	.02				—	1
2	10.6	9.2	7.4	6.0	4.6	2.8	1.4	.58	.21	.10	.05	.02	.01	2
3	12.8	11.3	9.4	7.8	6.3	4.1	2.4	1.21	.58	.35	.22	.11	.07	3
4	14.9	13.3	11.1	9.5	7.8	5.4	3.4	1.92	1.1	.71	.48	.30	.21	4
5	16.7	15.1	12.8	11.1	9.2	6.6	4.4	2.7	1.6	1.1	.83	.55	.41	5
6	18.5	16.8	14.4	12.6	10.6	7.8	5.4	3.5	2.2	1.6	1.2	.87	.68	6
7	20.3	18.5	16.0	14.1	12.0	9.0	6.4	4.3	2.8	2.2	1.7	1.24	.99	7
8	22.0	20.1	17.5	15.5	13.4	10.2	7.3	5.1	3.5	2.7	2.2	1.65	1.3	8
9	23.6	21.7	19.0	16.9	14.7	11.4	8.3	5.9	4.2	3.3	2.7	2.09	1.7	9
10	25.2	23.2	20.5	18.3	16.0	12.5	9.3	6.7	4.9	3.9	3.2	2.55	2.2	10
11	26.8	24.7	21.9	19.7	17.3	13.7	10.3	7.6	5.6	4.6	3.8	3.05	2.6	11
12	28.3	26.2	23.3	21.0	18.5	14.8	11.3	8.4	6.3	5.2	4.4	3.57	3.1	12
13	29.8	27.7	24.7	22.4	19.8	16.0	12.3	9.3	7.0	5.9	5.0	4.11	3.6	13
14	31.3	29.1	26.1	23.7	21.1	17.1	13.3	10.2	7.8	6.6	5.6	4.66	4.1	14
15	32.8	30.6	27.5	25.0	22.3	18.2	14.3	11.0	8.5	7.3	6.3	5.23	4.6	15
16	34.3	32.0	28.8	26.3	23.5	19.4	15.3	11.9	9.3	8.0	6.9	5.81	5.1	16
17	35.7	33.4	30.2	27.6	24.8	20.5	16.3	12.8	10.1	8.7	7.6	6.41	5.7	17
18	37.2	34.8	31.5	28.9	26.0	21.6	17.3	13.7	10.9	9.4	8.2	7.02	6.3	18
19	38.6	36.2	32.9	30.1	27.2	22.7	18.3	14.6	11.7	10.1	8.9	7.63	6.9	19
20	40.0	37.6	34.2	31.4	28.4	23.8	19.3	15.5	12.4	10.9	9.6	8.26	7.4	20
21	41.4	38.9	35.5	32.7	29.6	24.9	20.3	16.3	13.2	11.6	10.3	8.9	8.0	21
22	42.8	40.3	36.8	33.9	30.8	26.0	21.3	17.2	14.0	12.3	11.0	9.5	8.6	22
23	44.2	41.6	38.1	35.2	32.0	27.1	22.3	18.1	14.8	13.1	11.7	10.2	9.3	23
24	45.6	43.0	39.4	36.4	33.2	28.2	23.3	19.0	15.7	13.8	12.4	10.9	9.9	24
25	46.9	44.3	40.6	37.7	34.4	29.3	24.3	19.9	16.5	14.6	13.1	11.5	10.5	25
26	48.3	45.6	41.9	38.9	35.6	30.4	25.3	20.8	17.3	15.4	13.8	12.2	11.2	26
27	49.6	47.0	43.2	40.1	36.7	31.5	26.3	21.7	18.1	16.2	14.6	12.9	11.8	27
28	51.0	48.3	44.5	41.3	37.9	32.6	27.3	22.7	18.9	16.9	15.3	13.6	12.5	28
29	52.4	49.6	45.7	42.6	39.1	33.7	28.3	23.6	19.8	17.7	16.0	14.3	13.1	29
30	53.3	50.9	47.0	43.8	40.3	34.8	29.3	24.5	20.6	18.5	16.8	15.0	13.8	30
40	66.8	63.7	59.3	55.8	51.8	45.6	39.3	33.7	29.1	26.5	24.4	22.2	20.7	40
60	92.0	88.4	83.3	79.1	74.4	67.0	59.3	52.3	46.5	43.2	40.5	37.5	35.5	60
100	140.2	135.8	129.6	124.3	118.5	109.1	99.3	90.1	82.4	77.9	74.2	70.0	67.3	100

* Abridged from *Biometrika Tables for Statisticians*, Vol. I. Pearson, E. S., and Hartley, H. O., (eds.) Cambridge Univ. Press, 1954, pp. 130–31. By permission of the editors and publisher.

Table F*
Confidence Intervals for the Median

N	Largest k	α ≤ .05	Largest k	α ≤ .01	N	Largest k	α ≤ .05	Largest k	α ≤ .01
6	1	.031			36	12	.029	10	.004
7	1	.016			37	13	.047	11	.008
8	1	.008	1	.008	38	13	.034	11	.005
9	2	.039	1	.004	39	13	.024	12	.009
10	2	.021	1	.002	40	14	.038	12	.006
11	2	.012	1	.001	41	14	.028	12	.004
12	3	.039	2	.006	42	15	.044	13	.008
13	3	.022	2	.003	43	15	.032	13	.005
14	3	.013	2	.002	44	16	.049	14	.010
15	4	.035	3	.007	45	16	.036	14	.007
16	4	.021	3	.004	46	16	.026	14	.005
17	5	.049	3	.002	47	17	.040	15	.008
18	5	.031	4	.008	48	17	.029	15	.006
19	5	.019	4	.004	49	18	.044	16	.009
20	6	.041	4	.003	50	18	.033	16	.007
21	6	.027	5	.007	51	19	.049	16	.005
22	6	.017	5	.004	52	19	.036	17	.008
23	7	.035	5	.003	53	19	.027	17	.005
24	7	.023	6	.007	54	20	.040	18	.009
25	8	.043	6	.004	55	20	.030	18	.006
26	8	.029	7	.009	56	21	.044	18	.005
27	8	.019	7	.006	57	21	.033	19	.008
28	9	.036	7	.004	58	22	.048	19	.005
29	9	.024	8	.008	59	22	.036	20	.009
30	10	.043	8	.005	60	22	.027	20	.006
31	10	.029	8	.003	61	23	.040	21	.010
32	10	.020	9	.007	62	23	.030	21	.007
33	11	.035	9	.005	63	24	.043	21	.005
34	11	.024	10	.009	64	24	.033	22	.008
35	12	.041	10	.006	65	25	.046	22	.006

* From Nair, K. R. Table of confidence interval for the median in samples from any continuous population, *Sankhyā*, 4, 1940, 551–8. By permission of the author and editor.

Table G*
Confidence Bands for Cumulative Percentage Histograms

N	$1 - \alpha$				
	.80	.85	.90	.95	.99
5	.45	.47	.51	.56	.67
10	.32	.34	.37	.41	.49
20	.23	.25	.26	.29	.35
25	.21	.22	.24	.26	.32
30	.19	.20	.22	.24	.29
35	.18	.19	.20	.23	.27
40	.17	.18	.19	.21	.25
45	.16	.17	.18	.20	.24
50	.15	.16	.17	.19	.23
For larger values..	$\dfrac{1.07}{\sqrt{N}}$	$\dfrac{1.14}{\sqrt{N}}$	$\dfrac{1.22}{\sqrt{N}}$	$\dfrac{1.36}{\sqrt{N}}$	$\dfrac{1.63}{\sqrt{N}}$

* From Dixon, W. J., and Massey, F. J. Jr. *Introduction to Statistical Analysis*, New York, McGraw-Hill, 1951, p. 360. By permission of the authors and publisher.

Table H*
Critical Values for the Number of Runs ($u_{.025}$)

m \ n	2	3	4	5	6	7	8	9	10	11	12	13	14	15	16	17	18	19	20
2											2	2	2	2	2	2	2	2	2
3				2	2	2	2	2	2	2	2	2	3	3	3	3	3	3	3
4			2	2	2	3	3	3	3	3	3	3	3	4	4	4	4	4	4
5		2	2	3	3	3	3	3	4	4	4	4	4	4	4	5	5	5	5
6	2	2	3	3	3	3	3	4	4	4	4	5	5	5	5	5	5	6	6
7	2	2	3	3	3	3	4	4	5	5	5	5	5	6	6	6	6	6	6
8	2	3	3	3	3	4	4	5	5	5	6	6	6	6	6	7	7	7	7
9		2	3	3	4	4	5	5	5	6	6	6	7	7	7	7	8	8	8
10		2	3	3	4	5	5	5	6	6	7	7	7	7	8	8	8	8	9
11		2	3	4	4	5	5	6	6	7	7	7	8	8	8	9	9	9	9
12	2	2	3	4	4	5	6	6	7	7	7	8	8	8	9	9	9	10	10
13	2	2	3	4	5	5	6	6	7	7	8	8	9	9	9	10	10	10	10
14	2	2	3	4	5	5	6	7	7	8	8	9	9	9	10	10	10	11	11
15	2	3	3	4	5	6	6	7	7	8	8	9	9	10	10	11	11	11	12
16	2	3	4	4	5	6	6	7	8	8	9	9	10	10	11	11	11	12	12
17	2	3	4	4	5	6	7	7	8	9	9	10	10	11	11	11	12	12	13
18	2	3	4	5	5	6	7	8	8	9	9	10	10	11	11	12	12	13	13
19	2	3	4	5	6	6	7	8	8	9	10	10	11	11	12	12	13	13	13
20	2	3	4	5	6	6	7	8	9	9	10	10	11	12	12	13	13	13	14

* From Swed, F. S., and Eisenhart, C. Tables for testing randomness of grouping in a sequence of alternatives, *Ann. Math. Stat.*, 14, 1943, 66. By permission of the authors and editor.

Table I*
5 Percent Critical Points of Rank Sums

n_2 \ n_1	2	3	4	5	6	7	8	9	10	11	12	13	14	15
						5 Per Cent Level								
4			10											
5		6	11	17										
6		7	12	18	26									
7		7	13	20	27	36								
8	3	8	14	21	29	38	49							
9	3	8	15	22	31	40	51	63						
10	3	9	15	23	32	42	53	65	78					
11	4	9	16	24	34	44	55	68	81	96				
12	4	10	17	26	35	46	58	71	85	99	115			
13	4	10	18	27	37	48	60	73	88	103	119	137		
14	4	11	19	28	38	50	63	76	91	106	123	141	160	
15	4	11	20	29	40	52	65	79	94	110	127	145	164	185
16	4	12	21	31	42	54	67	82	97	114	131	150	169	
17	5	12	21	32	43	56	70	84	100	117	135	154		
18	5	13	22	33	45	58	72	87	103	121	139			
19	5	13	23	34	46	60	74	90	107	124				
20	5	14	24	35	48	62	77	93	110					
21	6	14	25	37	50	64	79	95						
22	6	15	26	38	51	66	82							
23	6	15	27	39	53	68								
24	6	16	28	40	55									
25	6	16	28	42										
26	7	17	29											
27	7	17												
28	7													

* From White, C. The use of ranks in a test of significance for comparing two treatments, *Biometrics*, 8, 1952, 33–41. By permission of the author and editor.

Table J*
1 Percent Critical Points of Rank Sums

n_2 \ n_1	2	3	4	5	6	7	8	9	10	11	12	13	14	15
												1 PER CENT LEVEL		
5				15										
6			10	16	23									
7			10	17	24	32								
8			11	17	25	34	43							
9		6	11	18	26	35	45	56						
10		6	12	19	27	37	47	58	71					
11		6	12	20	28	38	49	61	74	87				
12		7	13	21	30	40	51	63	76	90	106			
13		7	14	22	31	41	53	65	79	93	109	125		
14		7	14	22	32	43	54	67	81	96	112	129	147	
15		8	15	23	33	44	56	70	84	99	115	133	151	171
16		8	15	24	34	46	58	72	86	102	119	137	155	
17		8	16	25	36	47	60	74	89	105	122	140		
18		8	16	26	37	49	62	76	92	108	125			
19	3	9	17	27	38	50	64	78	94	111				
20	3	9	18	28	39	52	66	81	97					
21	3	9	18	29	40	53	68	83						
22	3	10	19	29	42	55	70							
23	3	10	19	30	43	57								
24	3	10	20	31	44									
25	3	11	20	32										
26	3	11	21											
27	4	11												
28	4													

* From White, C. The use of ranks in a test of significance for comparing two treatments, *Biometrics*, 8, 1952, 33–41. By permission of the author and editor.

Table K*
Critical Values of r for the Sign Test

N	1%	5%	10%	25%	N	1%	5%	10%	25%
1					46	13	15	16	18
2					47	14	16	17	19
3				0	48	14	16	17	19
4				0	49	15	17	18	19
5			0	0	50	15	17	18	20
6		0	0	1	51	15	18	19	20
7		0	0	1	52	16	18	19	21
8	0	0	1	1	53	16	18	20	21
9	0	1	1	2	54	17	19	20	22
10	0	1	1	2	55	17	19	20	22
11	0	1	2	3	56	17	20	21	23
12	1	2	2	3	57	18	20	21	23
13	1	2	3	3	58	18	21	22	24
14	1	2	3	4	59	19	21	22	24
15	2	3	3	4	60	19	21	23	25
16	2	3	4	5	61	20	22	23	25
17	2	4	4	5	62	20	22	24	25
18	3	4	5	6	63	20	23	24	26
19	3	4	5	6	64	21	23	24	26
20	3	5	5	6	65	21	24	25	27
21	4	5	6	7	66	22	24	25	27
22	4	5	6	7	67	22	25	26	28
23	4	6	7	8	68	22	25	26	28
24	5	6	7	8	69	23	25	27	29
25	5	7	7	9	70	23	26	27	29
26	6	7	8	9	71	24	26	28	30
27	6	7	8	10	72	24	27	28	30
28	6	8	9	10	73	25	27	28	31
29	7	8	9	10	74	25	28	29	31
30	7	9	10	11	75	25	28	29	32
31	7	9	10	11	76	26	28	30	32
32	8	9	10	12	77	26	29	30	32
33	8	10	11	12	78	27	29	31	33
34	9	10	11	13	79	27	30	31	33
35	9	11	12	13	80	28	30	32	34
36	9	11	12	14	81	28	31	32	34
37	10	12	13	14	82	28	31	33	35
38	10	12	13	14	83	29	32	33	35
39	11	12	13	15	84	29	32	33	36
40	11	13	14	15	85	30	32	34	36
41	11	13	14	16	86	30	33	34	37
42	12	14	15	16	87	31	33	35	37
43	12	14	15	17	88	31	34	35	38
44	13	15	16	17	89	31	34	36	38
45	13	15	16	18	90	32	35	36	39

* From Dixon, W. J., and Massey, F. J. Jr. *Introduction to Statistical Analysis,* New York, McGraw-Hill, 1951, p. 324. By permission of the authors and publisher.

Table L*
Critical Values of χ^2 for the Friedman Test, Small r and k

r	$k = 3$		$k = 4$	
	$\alpha = .05$	$\alpha = .01$	$\alpha = .05$	$\alpha = .01$
2	—	—	6.0	—
3	6.00	—	7.4	9.0
4	6.5	8.0	7.8	9.6
5	6.4	8.4		
6	7.0	9.0		
7	7.143	8.857		
8	6.25	9.00		
9	6.222	8.667		

* Adapted from Friedman, M. The use of ranks to avoid the assumption of normality implicit in the analysis of variance, *J. Amer. Stat. Assn.*, 32, 1937, 688–9. By permission of the author and editor.

Table M*

Significance of r_0 for $N \leq 10$.

N	r_0	P
4	1.000	.0417
5	1.000	.0083
5	.900	.0417
5	.800	.0667
5	.700	.1167
6	.943	.0083
6	.886	.0167
6	.829	.0292
6	.771	.0514
6	.657	.0875
7	.857	.0119
7	.786	.0240
7	.750	.0331
7	.714	.0440
7	.679	.0548
7	.643	.0694
7	.571	.1000
8	.810	.0108
8	.738	.0224
8	.690	.0331
8	.643	.0469
8	.619	.0550
8	.595	.0639
8	.524	.0956
9	.767	.0106
9	.700	.0210
9	.650	.0323
9	.617	.0417
9	.583	.0528
9	.550	.0656
9	.467	.1058
10	.733	.0100
10	.661	.0210
10	.612	.0324
10	.576	.0432
10	.552	.0515
10	.527	.0609
10	.442	.1021

* From Edwards, A. *Statistical Methods for the Behavioral Sciences*, New York, Rinehart, 1954, p. 513. Values were computed by Edwards from Table IV of E. G. Olds, Distributions of sums of squares of rank differences for small numbers of individuals, *Ann. Math. Stat.*, 1938, 9, 133–48. By permission of A. Edwards, E. G. Olds, and the editor of *Annals of Mathematical Statistics*.

Table N*
Critical Values of t

| d.f. | Probability of a t as great as or higher than the tabled value | | | | | | | | d.f. |
	.25	.20	.10	.05	.025	.01	.005	.0005	
1	1.00	1.38	3.08	6.31	12.71	31.82	63.66	636.62	1
2	.82	1.06	1.89	2.92	4.30	6.96	9.92	31.60	2
3	.76	.98	1.64	2.35	3.18	4.54	5.84	12.94	3
4	.74	.94	1.53	2.13	2.78	3.75	4.60	8.61	4
5	.73	.92	1.48	2.02	2.57	3.36	4.03	6.86	5
6	.72	.91	1.44	1.94	2.45	3.14	3.71	5.96	6
7	.71	.90	1.42	1.89	2.36	3.00	3.50	5.40	7
8	.71	.89	1.40	1.86	2.31	2.90	3.36	5.04	8
9	.70	.88	1.38	1.83	2.26	2.82	3.25	4.78	9
10	.70	.88	1.37	1.81	2.23	2.76	3.17	4.59	10
11	.70	.88	1.36	1.80	2.20	2.72	3.11	4.44	11
12	.70	.87	1.36	1.78	2.18	2.68	3.05	4.32	12
13	.69	.87	1.35	1.77	2.16	2.65	3.01	4.22	13
14	.69	.87	1.34	1.76	2.14	2.62	2.98	4.14	14
15	.69	.87	1.34	1.75	2.13	2.60	2.95	4.07	15
16	.69	.87	1.34	1.75	2.12	2.58	2.92	4.02	16
17	.69	.86	1.33	1.74	2.11	2.57	2.90	3.96	17
18	.69	.86	1.33	1.73	2.10	2.55	2.88	3.92	18
19	.69	.86	1.33	1.73	2.09	2.54	2.86	3.88	19
20	.69	.86	1.32	1.72	2.09	2.53	2.85	3.85	20
21	.69	.86	1.32	1.72	2.08	2.52	2.83	3.82	21
22	.69	.86	1.32	1.72	2.07	2.51	2.82	3.79	22
23	.69	.86	1.32	1.71	2.07	2.50	2.81	3.77	23
24	.68	.86	1.32	1.71	2.06	2.49	2.80	3.74	24
25	.68	.86	1.32	1.71	2.06	2.48	2.79	3.72	25
26	.68	.86	1.32	1.71	2.06	2.48	2.78	3.71	26
27	.68	.86	1.31	1.70	2.05	2.47	2.77	3.69	27
28	.68	.85	1.31	1.70	2.05	2.47	2.76	3.67	28
29	.68	.85	1.31	1.70	2.04	2.46	2.76	3.66	29
30	.68	.85	1.31	1.70	2.04	2.46	2.75	3.65	30
40	.68	.85	1.30	1.68	2.02	2.42	2.70	3.55	40
60	.68	.85	1.30	1.67	2.00	2.39	2.66	3.46	60
120	.68	.85	1.29	1.66	1.98	2.36	2.62	3.37	120
∞	.6745	.842	1.282	1.645	1.960	2.326	2.576	3.291	∞

* Abridged from Fisher, R. A., and Yates, F. *Statistical Tables*, Edinburgh, Oliver and Boyd, 1957. By permission of the authors and publisher.

Table O*
Confidence Belts for the Correlation Coefficient, ρ

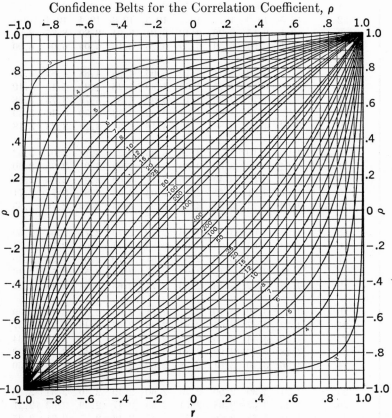

Numbers on the curves indicate sample size

* From David, F. N. Confidence belt for the correlation coefficient ρ when $\alpha = .05$. *Tables of the Correlation Coefficient*, The Biometrika Office, London. By permission of the author and the editor of *Biometrika*.

Table P*
F Distribution: 5 per cent Points

df₂ \ df₁	1	2	3	4	5	6	7	8	9
1	161	200	216	225	230	234	237	239	241
2	18.5	19.0	19.2	19.2	19.3	19.3	19.4	19.4	19.4
3	10.1	9.55	9.28	9.12	9.01	8.94	8.89	8.85	8.81
4	7.71	6.94	6.59	6.39	6.26	6.16	6.09	6.04	6.00
5	6.61	5.79	5.41	5.19	5.05	4.95	4.88	4.82	4.77
6	5.99	5.14	4.76	4.53	4.39	4.28	4.21	4.15	4.10
7	5.59	4.74	4.35	4.12	3.97	3.87	3.79	3.73	3.68
8	5.32	4.46	4.07	3.84	3.69	3.58	3.50	3.44	3.39
9	5.12	4.26	3.86	3.63	3.48	3.37	3.29	3.23	3.18
10	4.96	4.10	3.71	3.48	3.33	3.22	3.14	3.07	3.02
11	4.84	3.98	3.59	3.36	3.20	3.09	3.01	2.95	2.90
12	4.75	3.89	3.49	3.26	3.11	3.00	2.91	2.85	2.80
13	4.67	3.81	3.41	3.18	3.03	2.92	2.83	2.77	2.71
14	4.60	3.74	3.34	3.11	2.96	2.85	2.76	2.70	2.65
15	4.54	3.68	3.29	3.06	2.90	2.79	2.71	2.64	2.59
16	4.49	3.63	3.24	3.01	2.85	2.74	2.66	2.59	2.54
17	4.45	3.59	3.20	2.96	2.81	2.70	2.61	2.55	2.49
18	4.41	3.55	3.16	2.93	2.77	2.66	2.58	2.51	2.46
19	4.38	3.52	3.13	2.90	2.74	2.63	2.54	2.48	2.42
20	4.35	3.49	3.10	2.87	2.71	2.60	2.51	2.45	2.39
21	4.32	3.47	3.07	2.84	2.68	2.57	2.49	2.42	2.37
22	4.30	3.44	3.05	2.82	2.66	2.55	2.46	2.40	2.34
23	4.28	3.42	3.03	2.80	2.64	2.53	2.44	2.37	2.32
24	4.26	3.40	3.01	2.78	2.62	2.51	2.42	2.36	2.30
25	4.24	3.39	2.99	2.76	2.60	2.49	2.40	2.34	2.28
26	4.23	3.37	2.98	2.74	2.59	2.47	2.39	2.32	2.27
27	4.21	3.35	2.96	2.73	2.57	2.46	2.37	2.31	2.25
28	4.20	3.34	2.95	2.71	2.56	2.45	2.36	2.29	2.24
29	4.18	3.33	2.93	2.70	2.55	2.43	2.35	2.28	2.22
30	4.17	3.32	2.92	2.69	2.53	2.42	2.33	2.27	2.21
40	4.08	3.23	2.84	2.61	2.45	2.34	2.25	2.18	2.12
60	4.00	3.15	2.76	2.53	2.37	2.25	2.17	2.10	2.04
120	3.92	3.07	2.68	2.45	2.29	2.18	2.09	2.02	1.96
∞	3.84	3.00	2.60	2.37	2.21	2.10	2.01	1.94	1.88

* Abridged from Merrington, Maxine, and Thompson, Catherine. Table of percentage points in the inverted beta distribution, *Biometrika*, 33, 1943, 73–88. By permission of the authors and editor.

10	12	15	20	24	30	40	60	120	∞
242	244	246	248	249	250	251	252	253	254
19.4	19.4	19.4	19.4	19.5	19.5	19.5	19.5	19.5	19.5
8.79	8.74	8.70	8.66	8.64	8.62	8.59	8.57	8.55	8.53
5.96	5.91	5.86	5.80	5.77	5.75	5.72	5.69	5.66	5.63
4.74	4.68	4.62	4.56	4.53	4.50	4.46	4.43	4.40	4.36
4.06	4.00	3.94	3.87	3.84	3.81	3.77	3.74	3.70	3.67
3.64	3.57	3.51	3.44	3.41	3.38	3.34	3.30	3.27	3.23
3.35	3.28	3.22	3.15	3.12	3.08	3.04	3.00	2.97	2.93
3.14	3.07	3.01	2.94	2.90	2.86	2.83	2.79	2.75	2.71
2.98	2.91	2.84	2.77	2.74	2.70	2.66	2.62	2.58	2.54
2.85	2.79	2.72	2.65	2.61	2.57	2.53	2.49	2.45	2.40
2.75	2.69	2.62	2.54	2.51	2.47	2.43	2.38	2.34	2.30
2.67	2.60	2.53	2.46	2.42	2.38	2.34	2.30	2.25	2.21
2.60	2.53	2.46	2.39	2.35	2.31	2.27	2.22	2.18	2.13
2.54	2.48	2.40	2.33	2.29	2.25	2.20	2.16	2.11	2.07
2.49	2.42	2.35	2.28	2.24	2.19	2.15	2.11	2.06	2.01
2.45	2.38	2.31	2.23	2.19	2.15	2.10	2.06	2.01	1.96
2.41	2.34	2.27	2.19	2.15	2.11	2.06	2.02	1.97	1.92
2.38	2.31	2.23	2.16	2.11	2.07	2.03	1.98	1.93	1.88
2.35	2.28	2.20	2.12	2.08	2.04	1.99	1.95	1.90	1.84
2.32	2.25	2.18	2.10	2.05	2.01	1.96	1.92	1.87	1.81
2.30	2.23	2.15	2.07	2.03	1.98	1.94	1.89	1.84	1.78
2.27	2.20	2.13	2.05	2.00	1.96	1.91	1.86	1.81	1.76
2.25	2.18	2.11	2.03	1.98	1.94	1.89	1.84	1.79	1.73
2.24	2.16	2.09	2.01	1.96	1.92	1.87	1.82	1.77	1.71
2.22	2.15	2.07	1.99	1.95	1.90	1.85	1.80	1.75	1.69
2.20	2.13	2.06	1.97	1.93	1.88	1.84	1.79	1.73	1.67
2.19	2.12	2.04	1.96	1.91	1.87	1.82	1.77	1.71	1.65
2.18	2.10	2.03	1.94	1.90	1.85	1.81	1.75	1.70	1.64
2.16	2.09	2.01	1.93	1.89	1.84	1.79	1.74	1.68	1.62
2.08	2.00	1.92	1.84	1.79	1.74	1.69	1.64	1.58	1.51
1.99	1.92	1.84	1.75	1.70	1.65	1.59	1.53	1.47	1.39
1.91	1.83	1.75	1.66	1.61	1.55	1.50	1.43	1.35	1.25
1.83	1.75	1.67	1.57	1.52	1.46	1.39	1.32	1.22	1.00

F Distribution: 2.5 per cent Points

df₂ \ df₁	1	2	3	4	5	6	7	8	9
1	648	800	864	900	922	937	948	957	963
2	38.5	39.0	39.2	39.2	39.3	39.3	39.4	39.4	39.4
3	17.4	16.0	15.4	15.1	14.9	14.7	14.6	14.5	14.5
4	12.2	10.6	9.98	9.60	9.36	9.20	9.07	8.98	8.90
5	10.0	8.43	7.76	7.39	7.15	6.98	6.85	6.76	6.68
6	8.81	7.26	6.60	6.23	5.99	5.82	5.70	5.60	5.52
7	8.07	6.54	5.89	5.52	5.29	5.12	4.99	4.90	4.82
8	7.57	6.06	5.42	5.05	4.82	4.65	4.53	4.43	4.36
9	7.21	5.71	5.08	4.72	4.48	4.32	4.20	4.10	4.03
10	6.94	5.46	4.83	4.47	4.24	4.07	3.95	3.85	3.78
11	6.72	5.26	4.63	4.28	4.04	3.88	3.76	3.66	3.59
12	6.55	5.10	4.47	4.12	3.89	3.73	3.61	3.51	3.44
13	6.41	4.97	4.35	4.00	3.77	3.60	3.48	3.39	3.31
14	6.30	4.86	4.24	3.89	3.66	3.50	3.38	3.29	3.21
15	6.20	4.76	4.15	3.80	3.58	3.41	3.29	3.20	3.12
16	6.12	4.69	4.08	3.73	3.50	3.34	3.22	3.12	3.05
17	6.04	4.62	4.01	3.66	3.44	3.28	3.16	3.06	2.98
18	5.98	4.56	3.95	3.61	3.38	3.22	3.10	3.01	2.93
19	5.92	4.51	3.90	3.56	3.33	3.17	3.05	2.96	2.88
20	5.87	4.46	3.86	3.51	3.29	3.13	3.01	2.91	2.84
21	5.83	4.42	3.82	3.48	3.25	3.09	2.97	2.87	2.80
22	5.79	4.38	3.78	3.44	3.22	3.05	2.93	2.84	2.76
23	5.75	4.35	3.75	3.41	3.18	3.02	2.90	2.81	2.73
24	5.72	4.32	3.72	3.38	3.15	2.99	2.87	2.78	2.70
25	5.69	4.29	3.69	3.35	3.13	2.97	2.85	2.75	2.68
26	5.66	4.27	3.67	3.33	3.10	2.94	2.82	2.73	2.65
27	5.63	4.24	3.65	3.31	3.08	2.92	2.80	2.71	2.63
28	5.61	4.22	3.63	3.29	3.06	2.90	2.78	2.69	2.61
29	5.59	4.20	3.61	3.27	3.04	2.88	2.76	2.67	2.59
30	5.57	4.18	3.59	3.25	3.03	2.87	2.75	2.65	2.57
40	5.42	4.05	3.46	3.13	2.90	2.74	2.62	2.53	2.45
60	5.29	3.93	3.34	3.01	2.79	2.63	2.51	2.41	2.33
120	5.15	3.80	3.23	2.89	2.67	2.52	2.39	2.30	2.22
∞	5.02	3.69	3.12	2.79	2.57	2.41	2.29	2.19	2.11

F Distribution: 2.5 per cent Points

10	12	15	20	24	30	40	60	120	∞
969	977	985	993	997	1001	1006	1010	1014	1018
39.4	39.4	39.4	39.4	39.5	39.5	39.5	39.5	39.5	39.5
14.4	14.3	14.3	14.2	14.1	14.1	14.0	14.0	13.9	13.9
8.84	8.75	8.66	8.56	8.51	8.46	8.41	8.36	8.31	8.26
6.62	6.52	6.43	6.33	6.28	6.23	6.18	6.12	6.07	6.02
5.46	5.37	5.27	5.17	5.12	5.07	5.01	4.96	4.90	4.85
4.76	4.67	4.57	4.47	4.42	4.36	4.31	4.25	4.20	4.14
4.30	4.20	4.10	4.00	3.95	3.89	3.84	3.78	3.73	3.67
3.96	3.87	3.77	3.67	3.61	3.56	3.51	3.45	3.39	3.33
3.72	3.62	3.52	3.42	3.37	3.31	3.26	3.20	3.14	3.08
3.53	3.43	3.33	3.23	3.17	3.12	3.06	3.00	2.94	2.88
3.37	3.28	3.18	3.07	3.02	2.96	2.91	2.85	2.79	2.72
3.25	3.15	3.05	2.95	2.89	2.84	2.78	2.72	2.66	2.60
3.15	3.05	2.95	2.84	2.79	2.73	2.67	2.61	2.55	2.49
3.06	2.96	2.86	2.76	2.70	2.64	2.58	2.52	2.46	2.40
2.99	2.89	2.79	2.68	2.63	2.57	2.51	2.45	2.38	2.32
2.92	2.82	2.72	2.62	2.56	2.50	2.44	2.38	2.32	2.25
2.87	2.77	2.67	2.56	2.50	2.44	2.38	2.32	2.26	2.19
2.82	2.72	2.62	2.51	2.45	2.39	2.33	2.27	2.20	2.13
2.77	2.68	2.57	2.46	2.41	2.35	2.29	2.22	2.16	2.09
2.73	2.64	2.53	2.42	2.37	2.31	2.25	2.18	2.11	2.04
2.70	2.60	2.50	2.39	2.33	2.27	2.21	2.14	2.08	2.00
2.67	2.57	2.47	2.36	2.30	2.24	2.18	2.11	2.04	1.97
2.64	2.54	2.44	2.33	2.27	2.21	2.15	2.08	2.01	1.94
2.61	2.51	2.41	2.30	2.24	2.18	2.12	2.05	1.98	1.91
2.59	2.49	2.39	2.28	2.22	2.16	2.09	2.03	1.95	1.88
2.57	2.47	2.36	2.25	2.19	2.13	2.07	2.00	1.93	1.85
2.55	2.45	2.34	2.23	2.17	2.11	2.05	1.98	1.91	1.83
2.53	2.43	2.32	2.21	2.15	2.09	2.03	1.96	1.89	1.81
2.51	2.41	2.31	2.20	2.14	2.07	2.01	1.94	1.87	1.79
2.39	2.29	2.18	2.07	2.01	1.94	1.88	1.80	1.72	1.64
2.27	2.17	2.06	1.94	1.88	1.82	1.74	1.67	1.58	1.48
2.16	2.05	1.94	1.82	1.76	1.69	1.61	1.53	1.43	1.31
2.05	1.94	1.83	1.71	1.64	1.57	1.48	1.39	1.27	1.00

F Distribution: 1 per cent Points

df_2 \ df_1	1	2	3	4	5	6	7	8	9
1	4052	5000	5403	5625	5764	5859	5928	5982	6022
2	98.5	99.0	99.2	99.2	99.3	99.3	99.4	99.4	99.4
3	34.1	30.8	29.5	28.7	28.2	27.9	27.7	27.5	27.3
4	21.2	18.0	16.7	16.0	15.5	15.2	15.0	14.8	14.7
5	16.3	13.3	12.1	11.4	11.0	10.7	10.5	10.3	10.2
6	13.7	10.9	9.78	9.15	8.75	8.47	8.26	8.10	7.98
7	12.2	9.55	8.45	7.85	7.46	7.19	6.99	6.84	6.72
8	11.3	8.65	7.59	7.01	6.63	6.37	6.18	6.03	5.91
9	10.6	8.02	6.99	6.42	6.06	5.80	5.61	5.47	5.35
10	10.0	7.56	6.55	5.99	5.64	5.39	5.20	5.06	4.94
11	9.65	7.21	6.22	5.67	5.32	5.07	4.89	4.74	4.63
12	9.33	6.93	5.95	5.41	5.06	4.82	4.64	4.50	4.39
13	9.07	6.70	5.74	5.21	4.86	4.62	4.44	4.30	4.19
14	8.86	6.51	5.56	5.04	4.70	4.46	4.28	4.14	4.03
15	8.68	6.36	5.42	4.89	4.56	4.32	4.14	4.00	3.89
16	8.53	6.23	5.29	4.77	4.44	4.20	4.03	3.89	3.78
17	8.40	6.11	5.18	4.67	4.34	4.10	3.93	3.79	3.68
18	8.29	6.01	5.09	4.58	4.25	4.01	3.84	3.71	3.60
19	8.18	5.93	5.01	4.50	4.17	3.94	3.77	3.63	3.52
20	8.10	5.85	4.94	4.43	4.10	3.87	3.70	3.56	3.46
21	8.02	5.78	4.87	4.37	4.04	3.81	3.64	3.51	3.40
22	7.95	5.72	4.82	4.31	3.99	3.76	3.59	3.45	3.35
23	7.88	5.66	4.76	4.26	3.94	3.71	3.54	3.41	3.30
24	7.82	5.61	4.72	4.22	3.90	3.67	3.50	3.36	3.26
25	7.77	5.57	4.68	4.18	3.86	3.63	3.46	3.32	3.22
26	7.72	5.53	4.64	4.14	3.82	3.59	3.42	3.29	3.18
27	7.68	5.49	4.60	4.11	3.78	3.56	3.39	3.26	3.15
28	7.64	5.45	4.57	4.07	3.75	3.53	3.36	3.23	3.12
29	7.60	5.42	4.54	4.04	3.73	3.50	3.33	3.20	3.09
30	7.56	5.39	4.51	4.02	3.70	3.47	3.30	3.17	3.07
40	7.31	5.18	4.31	3.83	3.51	3.29	3.12	2.99	2.89
60	7.08	4.98	4.13	3.65	3.34	3.12	2.95	2.82	2.72
120	6.85	4.79	3.95	3.48	3.17	2.96	2.79	2.66	2.56
∞	6.63	4.61	3.78	3.32	3.02	2.80	2.64	2.51	2.41

Table P (Continued)
F Distribution: 1 per cent Points

10	12	15	20	24	30	40	60	120	∞
6056	6106	6157	6209	6235	6261	6287	6313	6339	6366
99.4	99.4	99.4	99.4	99.5	99.5	99.5	99.5	99.5	99.5
27.2	27.1	26.9	26.7	26.6	26.5	26.4	26.3	26.2	26.1
14.5	14.4	14.2	14.0	13.9	13.8	13.7	13.7	13.6	13.5
10.1	9.89	9.72	9.55	9.47	9.38	9.29	9.20	9.11	9.02
7.87	7.72	7.56	7.40	7.31	7.23	7.14	7.06	6.97	6.88
6.62	6.47	6.31	6.16	6.07	5.99	5.91	5.82	5.74	5.65
5.81	5.67	5.52	5.36	5.28	5.20	5.12	5.03	4.95	4.86
5.26	5.11	4.96	4.81	4.73	4.65	4.57	4.48	4.40	4.31
4.85	4.71	4.56	4.41	4.33	4.25	4.17	4.08	4.00	3.91
4.54	4.40	4.25	4.10	4.02	3.94	3.86	3.78	3.69	3.60
4.30	4.16	4.01	3.86	3.78	3.70	3.62	3.54	3.45	3.36
4.10	3.96	3.82	3.66	3.59	3.51	3.43	3.34	3.25	3.17
3.94	3.80	3.66	3.51	3.43	3.35	3.27	3.18	3.09	3.00
3.80	3.67	3.52	3.37	3.29	3.21	3.13	3.05	2.96	2.87
3.69	3.55	3.41	3.26	3.18	3.10	3.02	2.93	2.84	2.75
3.59	3.46	3.31	3.16	3.08	3.00	2.92	2.83	2.75	2.65
3.51	3.37	3.23	3.08	3.00	2.92	2.84	2.75	2.66	2.57
3.43	3.30	3.15	3.00	2.92	2.84	2.76	2.67	2.58	2.49
3.37	3.23	3.09	2.94	2.86	2.78	2.69	2.61	2.52	2.42
3.31	3.17	3.03	2.88	2.80	2.72	2.64	2.55	2.46	2.36
3.26	3.12	2.98	2.83	2.75	2.67	2.58	2.50	2.40	2.31
3.21	3.07	2.93	2.78	2.70	2.62	2.54	2.45	2.35	2.26
3.17	3.03	2.89	2.74	2.66	2.58	2.49	2.40	2.31	2.21
3.13	2.99	2.85	2.70	2.62	2.54	2.45	2.36	2.27	2.17
3.09	2.96	2.82	2.66	2.58	2.50	2.42	2.33	2.23	2.13
3.06	2.93	2.78	2.63	2.55	2.47	2.38	2.29	2.20	2.10
3.03	2.90	2.75	2.60	2.52	2.44	2.35	2.26	2.17	2.06
3.00	2.87	2.73	2.57	2.49	2.41	2.33	2.23	2.14	2.03
2.98	2.84	2.70	2.55	2.47	2.39	2.30	2.21	2.11	2.01
2.80	2.66	2.52	2.37	2.29	2.20	2.11	2.02	1.92	1.80
2.63	2.50	2.35	2.20	2.12	2.03	1.94	1.84	1.73	1.60
2.47	2.34	2.19	2.03	1.95	1.86	1.76	1.66	1.53	1.38
2.32	2.18	2.04	1.88	1.79	1.70	1.59	1.47	1.32	1.00

Table P (Continued)
F Distribution: 0.5 per cent Points

df₂ \ df₁	1	2	3	4	5	6	7	8	9
1	16211	20000	21615	22500	23056	23437	23715	23925	24091
2	198	199	199	199	199	199	199	199	199
3	55.6	49.8	47.5	46.2	45.4	44.8	44.4	44.1	43.9
4	31.3	26.3	24.3	23.2	22.5	22.0	21.6	21.4	21.1
5	22.8	18.3	16.5	15.6	14.9	14.5	14.2	14.0	13.8
6	18.6	14.5	12.9	12.0	11.5	11.1	10.8	10.6	10.4
7	16.2	12.4	10.9	10.0	9.52	9.16	8.89	8.68	8.51
8	14.7	11.0	9.60	8.81	8.30	7.95	7.69	7.50	7.34
9	13.6	10.1	8.72	7.96	7.47	7.13	6.88	6.69	6.54
10	12.8	9.43	8.08	7.34	6.87	6.54	6.30	6.12	5.97
11	12.2	8.91	7.60	6.88	6.42	6.10	5.86	5.68	5.54
12	11.8	8.51	7.23	6.52	6.07	5.76	5.52	5.35	5.20
13	11.4	8.19	6.93	6.23	5.79	5.48	5.25	5.08	4.94
14	11.1	7.92	6.68	6.00	5.56	5.26	5.03	4.86	4.72
15	10.8	7.70	6.48	5.80	5.37	5.07	4.85	4.67	4.54
16	10.6	7.51	6.30	5.64	5.21	4.91	4.69	4.52	4.38
17	10.4	7.35	6.16	5.50	5.07	4.78	4.56	4.39	4.25
18	10.2	7.21	6.03	5.37	4.96	4.66	4.44	4.28	4.14
19	10.1	7.09	5.92	5.27	4.85	4.56	4.34	4.18	4.04
20	9.94	6.99	5.82	5.17	4.76	4.47	4.26	4.09	3.96
21	9.83	6.89	5.73	5.09	4.68	4.39	4.18	4.01	3.88
22	9.73	6.81	5.65	5.02	4.61	4.32	4.11	3.94	3.81
23	9.63	6.73	5.58	4.95	4.54	4.26	4.05	3.88	3.75
24	9.55	6.66	5.52	4.89	4.49	4.20	3.99	3.83	3.69
25	9.48	6.60	5.46	4.84	4.43	4.15	3.94	3.78	3.64
26	9.41	6.54	5.41	4.79	4.38	4.10	3.89	3.73	3.60
27	9.34	6.49	5.36	4.74	4.34	4.06	3.85	3.69	3.56
28	9.28	6.44	5.32	4.70	4.30	4.02	3.81	3.65	3.52
29	9.23	6.40	5.28	4.66	4.26	3.98	3.77	3.61	3.48
30	9.18	6.35	5.24	4.62	4.23	3.95	3.74	3.58	3.45
40	8.83	6.07	4.98	4.37	3.99	3.71	3.51	3.35	3.22
60	8.49	5.80	4.73	4.14	3.76	3.49	3.29	3.13	3.01
120	8.18	5.54	4.50	3.92	3.55	3.28	3.09	2.93	2.81
∞	7.88	5.30	4.28	3.72	3.35	3.09	2.90	2.74	2.62

F Distribution: 0.5 per cent Points

10	12	15	20	24	30	40	60	120	∞
24224	24426	24630	24836	24940	25044	25148	25253	25359	25465
199	199	199	199	199	199	199	199	199	200
43.7	43.4	43.1	42.8	42.6	42.5	42.3	42.1	42.0	41.8
21.0	20.7	20.4	20.2	20.0	19.9	19.8	19.6	19.5	19.3
13.6	13.4	13.1	12.9	12.8	12.7	12.5	12.4	12.3	12.1
10.2	10.0	9.81	9.59	9.47	9.36	9.24	9.12	9.00	8.88
8.38	8.18	7.97	7.75	7.64	7.53	7.42	7.31	7.19	7.08
7.21	7.01	6.81	6.61	6.50	6.40	6.29	6.18	6.06	5.95
6.42	6.23	6.03	5.83	5.73	5.62	5.52	5.41	5.30	5.19
5.85	5.66	5.47	5.27	5.17	5.07	4.97	4.86	4.75	4.64
5.42	5.24	5.05	4.86	4.76	4.65	4.55	4.44	4.34	4.23
5.09	4.91	4.72	4.53	4.43	4.34	4.23	4.12	4.01	3.90
4.82	4.64	4.46	4.27	4.17	4.07	3.97	3.87	3.76	3.65
4.60	4.43	4.25	4.06	3.96	3.86	3.76	3.66	3.55	3.44
4.42	4.25	4.07	3.88	3.79	3.69	3.58	3.48	3.37	3.26
4.27	4.10	3.92	3.73	3.64	3.54	3.44	3.33	3.22	3.11
4.14	3.97	3.79	3.61	3.51	3.41	3.31	3.21	3.10	2.98
4.03	3.86	3.68	3.50	3.40	3.30	3.20	3.10	2.99	2.87
3.93	3.76	3.59	3.40	3.31	3.21	3.11	3.00	2.89	2.78
3.85	3.68	3.50	3.32	3.22	3.12	3.02	2.92	2.81	2.69
3.77	3.60	3.43	3.24	3.15	3.05	2.95	2.84	2.73	2.61
3.70	3.54	3.36	3.18	3.08	2.98	2.88	2.77	2.66	2.55
3.64	3.47	3.30	3.12	3.02	2.92	2.82	2.71	2.60	2.48
3.59	3.42	3.25	3.06	2.97	2.87	2.77	2.66	2.55	2.43
3.54	3.37	3.20	3.01	2.92	2.82	2.72	2.61	2.50	2.38
3.49	3.33	3.15	2.97	2.87	2.77	2.67	2.56	2.45	2.33
3.45	3.28	3.11	2.93	2.83	2.73	2.63	2.52	2.41	2.29
3.41	3.25	3.07	2.89	2.79	2.69	2.59	2.48	2.37	2.25
3.38	3.21	3.04	2.86	2.76	2.66	2.56	2.45	2.33	2.21
3.34	3.18	3.01	2.82	2.73	2.63	2.52	2.42	2.30	2.18
3.12	2.95	2.78	2.60	2.50	2.40	2.30	2.18	2.06	1.93
2.90	2.74	2.57	2.39	2.29	2.19	2.08	1.96	1.83	1.69
2.71	2.54	2.37	2.19	2.09	1.98	1.87	1.75	1.61	1.43
2.52	2.36	2.19	2.00	1.90	1.79	1.67	1.53	1.36	1.00

Table Q*
Critical Values of T for the Wilcoxon Test for Paired Replicates

N	α		
	Values of T required to reject hypothesis at significance level α by a two-tailed test.		
	.05	.02	.01
6	0	—	—
7	2	0	—
8	4	2	0
9	6	3	2
10	8	5	3
11	11	7	5
12	14	10	7
13	17	13	10
14	21	16	13
15	25	20	16
16	30	24	20
17	35	28	23
18	40	33	28
19	46	38	32
20	52	43	38
21	59	49	43
22	66	56	49
23	73	62	55
24	81	69	61
25	89	77	68

* From Wilcoxon, F. *Some Rapid Approximate Statistical Procedures*, New York, American Cyanamid Co., 1949, p. 13. Wilcoxon's values were obtained by rounding off values given by Tukey in Memorandum Report 17, *The simplest signed rank tests*, Statistical Research Group, Princeton University, 1949. By permission of F. Wilcoxon and J. Tukey.

Table R*
Random Sampling Numbers—I

	1 2	3 4	5 6	7 8	9 10	11 12	13 14	15 16
1	0 6	2 8	3 5	7 6	4 9	0 7	6 6	8 0
2	3 4	2 5	2 0	3 0	5 1	5 1	3 5	7 1
3	3 4	7 4	1 5	8 8	9 9	4 0	3 4	3 6
4	4 7	5 0	4 8	3 3	0 5	7 4	8 4	5 9
5	9 3	5 6	8 1	1 7	2 0	7 8	3 5	8 6
6	8 6	1 5	7 5	3 7	6 6	4 9	5 0	7 1
7	2 2	2 3	2 7	1 2	4 4	3 6	2 6	5 0
8	2 3	3 4	7 5	8 2	0 2	8 7	4 4	1 8
9	2 0	4 2	6 0	5 7	9 4	8 5	4 6	0 3
10	6 5	3 3	1 1	0 3	6 9	0 2	7 3	1 7
11	3 9	2 9	8 9	5 4	4 6	4 6	8 6	3 3
12	7 2	2 1	8 4	5 9	5 6	5 9	2 5	3 2
13	7 4	0 7	3 7	4 2	6 8	6 5	3 1	8 9
14	9 7	2 2	8 0	3 9	9 8	1 5	7 4	7 9
15	1 9	9 8	9 3	9 4	4 2	2 1	4 6	5 7
16	7 2	9 4	6 1	6 7	9 8	7 5	3 7	4 6
17	9 1	5 2	3 0	2 6	5 8	1 2	2 3	7 9
18	6 9	3 4	5 2	8 0	6 2	4 7	9 2	9 6
19	6 2	1 6	5 6	2 9	5 3	2 7	4 1	0 8
20	0 7	4 1	1 6	0 6	2 1	8 2	7 8	3 7
21	3 6	7 6	7 2	6 0	2 7	7 2	5 6	8 3
22	4 9	3 0	8 5	6 9	5 9	4 9	7 5	4 3
23	1 4	1 2	0 3	3 6	7 0	1 4	4 1	5 1
24	7 5	5 6	9 4	1 6	0 8	9 2	6 0	7 0
25	7 4	0 6	5 5	8 4	6 7	3 6	5 2	6 5
26	2 1	4 1	0 4	6 1	2 0	8 5	2 2	7 1
27	7 0	0 2	6 9	1 0	3 7	4 5	9 5	9 4
28	4 6	4 7	1 2	4 6	9 6	9 1	1 1	7 9
29	6 1	2 9	8 0	3 9	5 0	7 4	8 6	2 3
30	2 9	1 0	8 6	7 4	5 2	9 5	6 2	1 5
31	3 7	9 8	0 9	7 1	9 1	3 8	7 7	3 8
32	9 6	5 0	5 1	0 6	9 7	1 5	4 7	5 9
33	2 2	9 3	1 1	0 5	1 5	8 4	4 9	7 6
34	5 8	9 9	9 7	1 0	7 9	6 9	4 3	4 6
35	1 9	8 0	6 6	5 2	4 1	0 7	1 0	1 6
36	6 6	9 3	9 0	9 3	3 5	6 6	9 0	3 0
37	3 1	7 4	7 0	0 5	9 6	9 4	5 3	0 2
38	9 8	0 3	4 9	1 2	4 0	7 7	6 9	6 1
39	9 9	7 3	1 0	3 3	8 8	2 2	4 3	4 6
40	6 3	8 2	0 7	2 6	1 6	4 3	1 1	1 8

* From Hill, B. *Principles of Medical Statistics*, New York, Oxford Univ. Press, 1955, pp. 291–8. Used by permission.

	1 2	3 4	5 6	7 8	9 10	11 12	13 14	15 16
1	2 8	6 9	3 0	9 6	6 3	9 2	9 6	6 5
2	4 0	4 0	5 8	7 3	9 4	3 7	7 6	6 4
3	1 6	0 2	7 7	3 1	0 4	9 9	4 2	7 9
4	8 4	1 3	1 8	5 0	5 6	3 7	4 7	2 9
5	8 5	7 5	3 7	7 0	3 2	4 9	4 0	1 5
6	4 4	3 4	8 5	0 2	6 6	2 5	8 6	8 0
7	3 7	2 3	0 4	6 0	3 0	7 3	4 0	1 8
8	7 0	0 9	8 0	7 4	9 2	6 6	6 9	1 9
9	9 7	6 5	6 0	9 7	4 4	7 0	8 0	5 8
10.	3 2	5 9	9 3	9 7	8 3	6 1	8 1	0 4
11	9 8	3 6	0 3	8 9	7 4	5 0	4 9	4 2
12	1 8	2 9	0 1	3 2	1 4	6 8	2 6	9 8
13	2 1	2 6	4 9	8 3	0 4	6 1	9 8	0 6
14	9 5	1 4	7 5	6 4	1 4	0 3	2 7	4 3
15	0 5	1 0	5 5	2 9	4 8	8 7	7 8	2 1
16	2 8	8 4	5 9	7 8	7 4	2 3	3 7	4 9
17	6 5	6 3	2 6	0 5	0 0	4 9	6 6	7 0
18	8 8	8 0	1 6	9 6	1 8	6 8	6 3	3 3
19	3 1	9 3	5 3	3 6	5 0	9 6	5 0	1 8
20	4 1	4 6	6 7	1 1	4 4	5 1	0 0	5 9
21	4 7	4 0	7 5	0 6	8 5	6 6	4 4	4 2
22	1 8	7 5	4 8	2 6	7 1	3 0	6 2	3 7
23	8 0	3 6	6 5	2 5	9 9	3 9	0 8	8 9
24	4 4	7 0	2 1	8 1	9 7	8 5	7 5	3 5
25	2 9	1 9	8 6	2 0	4 5	0 3	5 4	4 1
26	0 3	4 2	5 9	4 8	6 2	1 5	7 2	7 2
27	9 1	5 9	4 6	8 6	4 5	2 0	4 8	7 6
28	0 1	9 6	8 5	3 7	3 1	5 9	4 7	0 8
29	6 1	6 2	0 1	3 6	9 6	6 0	1 1	8 7
30	5 9	3 6	0 5	4 9	4 8	9 2	9 1	8 5
31	0 9	0 2	7 8	9 9	0 4	6 7	1 2	0 7
32	7 5	0 3	5 8	7 2	7 6	8 3	8 7	4 5
33	6 4	0 4	7 3	6 1	3 7	2 7	1 2	7 4
34	3 8	5 1	4 5	2 4	5 0	8 2	2 9	1 5
35	4 4	8 1	9 7	6 9	4 0	5 7	4 6	2 9
36	3 1	2 3	9 6	2 2	1 4	6 8	8 5	1 2
37	1 4	1 9	4 7	1 8	6 4	7 3	1 3	2 6
38	3 3	3 9	5 5	6 0	5 3	2 0	6 7	6 3
39	1 8	4 8	5 6	3 8	4 3	7 8	2 2	7 7
40	8 8	3 5	8 6	3 9	0 6	0 3	4 7	4 5

Table R (Continued)
Random Sampling Numbers—III

	1 2	3 4	5 6	7 8	9 10	11 12	13 14	15 16
1	3 2	7 4	4 4	6 4	5 6	1 2	4 2	2 3
2	7 2	0 1	7 4	6 7	5 8	6 5	8 9	8 3
3	0 0	0 6	2 2	7 6	4 4	0 7	4 7	3 5
4	1 3	2 4	9 1	1 9	0 1	1 1	7 0	1 3
5	7 9	3 8	9 2	3 1	6 2	5 4	9 3	7 5
6	9 4	3 9	6 6	0 6	3 3	2 1	6 5	8 7
7	6 0	9 8	6 9	1 8	3 5	1 6	5 0	6 2
8	2 1	4 2	5 7	0 0	5 9	2 7	7 7	5 2
9	9 9	8 4	4 1	3 0	5 6	7 5	0 4	9 9
10	3 2	3 0	7 3	4 3	8 2	2 4	6 9	0 0
11	2 5	0 8	0 3	7 0	2 7	3 5	0 4	9 1
12	9 9	5 3	3 6	6 0	3 9	9 1	7 3	1 8
13	1 9	2 2	3 3	7 0	6 1	2 7	8 2	9 2
14	3 6	3 1	8 6	0 0	6 6	6 6	7 7	1 9
15	1 9	9 9	0 0	1 2	2 4	0 3	3 1	2 4
16	6 6	7 6	4 2	1 5	1 9	4 5	5 7	5 4
17	8 0	0 6	2 7	5 4	9 9	8 5	9 8	4 7
18	3 1	6 0	7 0	9 9	3 9	4 6	9 0	4 6
19	5 5	9 5	2 1	6 3	6 2	1 6	8 2	3 4
20	9 0	2 2	3 7	0 9	8 8	0 1	7 8	8 4
21	4 3	9 5	3 1	2 9	8 4	8 0	7 0	6 5
22	8 8	4 3	3 0	9 9	4 6	3 9	7 9	5 9
23	4 1	6 3	0 6	7 1	7 2	1 8	5 3	7 1
24	3 7	5 2	1 9	9 3	7 6	0 1	9 1	9 0
25	1 2	3 5	1 8	3 1	2 6	4 0	3 9	0 2
26	6 0	0 3	9 7	2 8	4 4	5 2	5 9	3 4
27	7 5	5 0	5 6	7 8	8 0	5 6	2 1	3 1
28	5 5	0 6	0 1	9 5	7 8	5 8	1 1	6 5
29	1 4	8 5	0 2	7 6	9 3	0 3	8 9	8 6
30	5 3	8 9	9 0	3 5	6 8	7 0	1 0	1 9
31	6 5	8 8	1 8	6 8	8 6	6 6	3 7	7 5
32	5 5	8 2	5 0	3 5	1 8	6 3	7 5	7 2
33	0 7	6 1	0 6	0 0	3 8	8 8	0 7	2 9
34	8 1	4 1	5 0	9 1	0 2	7 5	0 6	5 8
35	7 6	3 7	8 9	6 5	0 5	0 0	8 2	1 9
36	6 9	2 9	6 9	4 5	2 5	5 9	0 0	2 9
37	0 3	8 1	5 5	9 1	1 7	4 3	8 8	4 9
38	6 7	5 2	9 5	5 3	7 9	5 3	1 2	8 2
39	9 0	2 9	8 6	2 7	5 1	3 8	6 1	1 0
40	8 1	2 2	5 5	6 1	7 1	4 5	6 2	4 5

Table R (Continued)
Random Sampling Numbers—IV

	1 2	3 4	5 6	7 8	9 10	11 12	13 14	15 16
1	4 1	4 5	9 4	1 5	9 4	6 4	0 2	8 0
2	1 1	8 6	0 6	7 4	2 2	2 9	5 9	0 1
3	1 1	0 0	7 9	3 3	5 4	9 1	3 1	9 4
4	2 3	8 7	9 0	5 4	4 3	5 3	1 3	1 1
5	5 5	6 5	6 1	2 1	4 3	9 7	8 1	6 5
6	9 5	4 8	8 4	9 6	4 2	4 6	5 1	2 8
7	7 3	0 8	4 7	4 1	4 7	2 6	1 6	9 4
8	7 2	3 3	4 9	4 6	1 0	5 2	5 7	2 6
9	5 5	1 7	5 1	2 1	7 6	2 6	7 8	2 0
10	7 1	4 8	5 1	7 2	4 9	2 7	8 2	9 5
11	7 4	0 6	8 0	8 6	0 8	7 5	9 7	4 1
12	6 0	8 5	3 9	5 1	1 2	9 5	2 4	8 7
13	3 7	3 5	1 0	5 7	6 7	4 6	8 0	4 6
14	2 4	2 7	9 1	9 4	3 9	1 6	4 7	4 9
15	4 8	5 5	7 2	2 0	0 9	1 3	4 7	2 5
16	8 1	2 6	1 0	0 6	0 4	7 6	6 4	4 4
17	7 7	2 2	8 1	2 1	4 8	2 8	7 6	4 3
18	8 8	4 4	6 4	8 8	8 7	8 8	8 9	2 6
19	8 5	7 9	5 2	9 0	7 5	3 3	8 0	5 5
20	4 0	1 9	8 1	0 2	3 7	1 3	6 0	3 1
21	5 2	4 5	2 9	1 0	4 5	6 0	5 0	2 7
22	6 8	8 0	5 7	5 8	0 7	8 2	0 2	9 9
23	7 1	2 6	1 4	0 9	8 8	9 7	9 3	8 8
24	9 4	7 5	6 1	9 1	0 8	8 3	7 9	7 0
25	0 8	4 1	8 6	2 2	2 7	0 2	5 5	3 5
26	5 3	1 4	9 2	6 4	4 7	8 3	7 2	5 9
27	0 7	7 3	4 7	1 2	5 0	3 9	3 9	3 3
28	4 2	8 4	2 3	1 6	5 5	1 9	9 8	6 6
29	5 7	1 3	4 3	8 0	2 7	7 8	8 1	4 9
30	3 8	8 5	4 1	7 8	5 7	8 2	0 6	3 9
31	0 0	1 6	5 8	3 2	4 8	6 8	2 0	7 5
32	7 4	6 0	9 4	5 1	3 0	2 0	9 6	5 0
33	6 9	6 1	3 4	7 2	0 7	9 6	3 2	0 4
34	0 3	4 8	7 6	7 0	5 6	0 2	6 7	8 0
35	2 4	5 7	7 2	6 3	8 2	5 6	1 7	7 1
36	7 2	9 4	1 6	8 2	4 5	9 0	1 8	2 9
37	2 7	7 6	0 8	2 1	4 5	0 2	1 6	4 6
38	4 6	0 7	5 9	4 3	9 6	9 8	6 4	3 5
39	7 1	6 0	8 1	0 3	5 6	1 2	3 5	7 2
40	3 3	9 3	5 0	1 7	1 3	3 8	2 8	0 4

	1 2	3 4	5 6	7 8	9 10	11 12	13 14	15 16
1	7 8	7 4	4 6	0 9	3 6	7 3	9 9	8 4
2	7 8	0 4	0 8	0 4	7 9	8 5	0 5	9 6
3	5 6	9 9	1 4	9 9	4 3	8 6	5 6	8 4
4	8 0	7 7	6 0	2 0	7 1	4 5	8 6	0 7
5	5 4	2 0	4 4	2 8	9 0	2 8	8 9	3 3
6	7 1	7 5	9 2	5 2	3 7	0 3	5 9	5 6
7	6 7	1 2	9 4	1 0	1 1	9 3	4 2	4 4
8	1 2	1 8	2 8	9 3	7 9	9 7	1 1	6 0
9	7 0	5 6	1 1	4 2	1 3	2 0	5 3	8 9
10	3 6	4 3	6 5	3 8	1 1	3 5	9 3	9 1
11	4 6	2 0	3 6	3 5	4 8	7 5	2 4	7 9
12	4 3	2 6	4 9	2 2	3 0	6 6	2 4	9 6
13	1 5	7 3	1 6	1 3	3 8	7 0	2 8	7 7
14	9 1	1 3	3 2	7 6	9 2	1 7	5 2	0 9
15	5 6	1 5	9 4	6 8	8 6	9 6	1 2	5 5
16	1 2	7 3	7 3	3 9	6 5	4 0	7 0	1 1
17	1 8	7 1	2 7	4 8	5 5	7 5	3 3	4 0
18	0 7	5 5	8 2	3 8	2 2	1 2	9 7	0 6
19	6 1	8 1	6 3	2 7	2 6	2 0	1 8	4 0
20	4 1	5 1	3 4	5 9	2 8	5 9	5 3	0 9
21	2 9	2 9	1 3	0 7	8 8	6 5	2 8	7 9
22	9 0	9 8	9 9	9 2	8 6	4 3	6 1	8 2
23	9 3	1 8	2 3	6 2	2 4	0 0	8 1	2 4
24	5 9	3 0	4 8	1 0	3 9	7 5	7 0	8 7
25	4 1	6 3	3 7	8 1	5 7	9 3	4 4	7 1
26	9 2	4 8	8 4	7 9	4 7	3 9	3 3	6 6
27	4 0	7 1	3 1	1 3	6 0	3 4	2 6	1 0
28	1 3	6 5	2 7	8 6	2 5	3 0	7 1	8 1
29	3 9	5 7	1 1	1 7	5 9	1 2	6 9	9 0
30	1 2	4 2	5 7	3 0	1 5	7 0	7 4	6 6
31	1 8	0 5	7 6	8 6	4 0	9 1	0 9	7 6
32	5 8	3 1	2 1	0 8	5 4	0 3	6 4	6 9
33	9 4	6 0	5 1	9 9	4 4	6 6	4 1	7 7
34	4 3	0 7	7 9	9 2	7 5	6 9	5 1	8 0
35	9 1	0 5	8 4	9 0	8 9	0 2	3 4	2 7
36	0 8	1 6	7 9	9 4	3 3	4 3	1 8	0 8
37	2 0	8 0	0 4	6 7	6 5	7 8	1 4	1 9
38	1 0	1 2	2 4	6 2	5 7	4 7	1 1	5 7
39	4 2	5 7	2 3	1 3	5 0	9 8	6 7	1 7
40	6 0	9 9	3 9	7 4	9 3	1 6	5 5	4 9

Table R (Continued)
Random Sampling Numbers—VI

	1 2	3 4	5 6	7 8	9 10	11 12	13 14	15 16
1	9 3	3 1	5 3	8 6	8 5	8 2	5 6	2 8
2	5 6	6 7	4 4	8 4	1 2	1 1	9 7	4 8
3	4 5	3 0	8 9	6 9	6 7	0 2	1 1	2 1
4	3 3	3 8	5 8	3 3	6 0	2 2	3 8	9 1
5	7 3	6 4	9 6	6 7	2 9	1 1	1 8	1 6
6	5 9	3 4	4 4	8 3	2 3	9 6	7 8	8 4
7	7 2	5 2	3 7	0 8	9 9	9 6	3 3	9 2
8	0 4	7 7	2 8	5 3	3 7	7 3	4 9	6 2
9	4 9	5 6	3 3	6 2	6 4	6 9	8 2	7 1
10	3 1	3 3	0 5	4 0	5 9	3 3	3 5	8 4
11	4 1	0 8	2 5	8 8	7 8	2 8	4 6	4 2
12	3 3	6 3	4 0	1 5	1 5	6 1	2 0	0 5
13	1 6	2 6	2 4	6 6	0 7	6 7	3 8	0 7
14	2 4	8 5	4 8	6 3	5 6	2 6	1 4	5 7
15	9 0	3 8	8 8	3 1	2 1	5 6	9 9	4 0
16	8 2	8 5	2 3	2 6	2 5	6 7	2 4	2 6
17	5 7	8 8	1 2	2 3	6 1	1 3	5 2	4 6
18	2 1	2 4	6 2	7 4	5 7	9 7	1 8	5 6
19	5 7	3 4	9 1	4 4	5 6	6 0	2 4	1 0
20	9 7	3 1	7 1	3 6	2 5	1 9	4 2	5 8
21	2 2	3 8	1 7	6 8	0 3	5 0	0 1	6 3
22	7 7	8 4	0 1	4 4	5 8	1 2	1 7	6 1
23	5 2	7 9	7 3	5 3	4 0	0 7	0 6	8 6
24	4 8	7 7	1 8	1 2	9 3	0 6	7 7	8 0
25	3 8	8 6	9 1	9 7	4 5	4 7	3 4	4 2
26	2 7	3 5	8 8	8 0	9 6	9 7	2 4	7 7
27	5 9	0 5	9 4	9 5	7 3	4 2	2 5	1 6
28	4 4	7 6	9 2	9 5	8 3	0 4	0 7	3 1
29	1 3	3 8	1 3	3 8	3 2	4 8	4 2	0 2
30	9 0	2 8	1 3	3 0	1 5	5 9	4 0	6 0
31	8 0	5 7	0 0	1 4	9 5	9 5	5 1	8 5
32	2 6	5 3	8 8	6 4	3 2	6 6	9 9	3 4
33	2 8	8 3	2 4	2 8	0 6	1 4	6 6	2 7
34	3 4	8 0	1 9	9 7	2 0	9 8	8 1	7 4
35	5 8	1 4	2 4	5 7	0 2	3 7	9 3	7 1
36	1 4	8 1	6 6	9 2	5 9	0 8	4 6	5 3
37	1 1	0 6	6 7	0 1	2 2	3 2	2 5	3 3
38	7 5	3 1	4 5	1 7	1 4	8 4	8 5	8 1
39	7 8	1 7	9 3	9 5	8 9	0 3	9 8	0 9
40	9 0	9 3	6 4	3 4	1 9	4 0	9 9	9 9

	1 2	3 4	5 6	7 8	9 10	11 12	13 14	15 16
1	8 3	8 4	0 0	1 2	4 2	8 3	9 4	9 4
2	8 9	2 0	9 5	7 8	0 8	9 5	3 4	0 3
3	3 3	0 0	1 2	3 0	2 4	2 0	8 7	8 8
4	9 5	4 1	7 1	1 6	3 2	1 2	6 6	9 2
5	0 0	0 8	1 0	9 8	8 1	2 9	6 6	2 3
6	0 9	1 3	0 3	3 5	0 4	7 6	7 5	7 8
7	0 6	4 9	0 9	5 0	7 6	5 4	1 7	0 6
8	4 1	3 4	6 5	9 8	3 2	8 4	6 9	4 0
9	2 3	0 3	8 2	5 6	6 3	6 2	8 6	7 8
10	3 0	5 5	1 8	5 4	7 9	1 8	7 0	0 7
11	3 3	8 4	4 6	3 1	0 1	3 1	3 0	2 1
12	4 2	0 7	3 5	7 6	3 0	1 8	9 6	8 2
13	7 2	9 7	5 4	4 5	1 7	4 1	4 7	0 8
14	5 1	4 3	6 6	6 0	3 3	0 7	6 7	3 2
15	7 0	6 7	4 5	8 1	6 7	1 7	7 1	6 7
16	0 2	3 1	8 4	7 2	2 2	2 0	4 9	8 7
17	8 3	2 5	7 6	9 2	0 5	0 6	0 1	9 0
18	8 1	1 5	7 2	5 0	6 1	2 2	9 2	3 5
19	3 5	7 4	1 8	5 0	8 3	1 8	8 9	1 5
20	7 4	5 7	3 1	8 7	1 5	1 8	6 1	3 3
21	2 9	2 7	2 3	1 6	5 0	7 2	5 4	4 0
22	8 3	4 0	0 5	3 2	7 2	8 8	1 5	8 9
23	3 3	6 2	0 5	5 8	9 0	9 1	3 2	0 1
24	3 3	4 3	2 2	5 1	1 6	3 7	9 2	6 1
25	9 8	0 4	1 9	3 9	6 8	8 8	9 3	6 7
26	3 1	0 7	0 5	3 2	9 6	5 3	7 2	5 1
27	4 3	9 2	3 0	8 6	3 2	2 9	1 7	2 5
28	7 8	9 9	4 6	7 0	8 5	3 6	2 3	3 3
29	6 6	9 4	8 1	3 5	7 1	0 8	1 4	1 2
30	6 6	4 1	6 7	9 7	7 5	1 8	9 9	0 0
31	6 6	8 4	8 6	0 2	6 9	2 7	5 5	0 2
32	8 9	9 4	6 4	5 2	5 2	3 3	7 7	3 1
33	7 2	3 1	8 7	4 8	9 7	4 1	0 5	9 1
34	6 4	4 8	7 2	8 4	8 0	5 9	2 4	3 7
35	6 0	3 9	0 2	9 3	5 8	5 0	3 8	7 9
36	4 8	9 5	8 4	0 2	0 6	3 4	0 3	8 4
37	4 0	9 4	0 8	2 1	2 8	5 7	3 1	8 2
38	5 6	9 9	9 5	0 1	2 0	7 6	5 7	4 2
39	9 9	1 0	3 5	4 6	6 1	9 5	3 2	3 3
40	2 9	5 2	3 1	1 2	1 0	1 4	3 2	4 4

	1 2	3 4	5 6	7 8	9 10	11 12	13 14	15 16
1	1 0	0 2	5 7	3 5	0 5	2 3	2 0	1 7
2	1 7	5 0	7 4	9 9	6 0	2 5	2 9	6 5
3	9 9	7 0	3 4	0 5	7 2	4 6	0 1	7 2
4	2 4	3 6	7 0	4 7	9 0	9 2	1 9	4 8
5	6 5	1 2	9 0	9 1	9 2	3 3	5 6	4 0
6	1 0	1 4	3 7	3 2	5 3	9 0	9 3	3 5
7	3 1	5 3	3 1	0 8	6 6	6 8	4 4	4 9
8	6 7	3 1	1 4	2 7	5 1	9 0	2 8	0 4
9	2 2	6 3	6 2	7 4	2 2	1 7	2 9	7 8
10	6 7	1 7	8 4	3 5	9 2	3 4	7 7	2 9
11	5 0	9 7	4 2	5 9	6 4	8 3	9 7	2 1
12	5 1	5 1	9 7	8 0	6 6	5 2	5 0	3 1
13	6 2	4 7	2 4	4 0	7 5	4 6	3 2	9 5
14	4 7	3 6	9 0	1 2	1 4	5 3	2 9	9 7
15	7 1	7 8	6 3	7 5	7 2	7 6	6 7	4 7
16	0 2	0 9	5 3	9 5	9 9	5 2	8 4	4 6
17	2 7	6 1	3 7	0 2	0 5	2 7	8 0	5 1
18	8 2	6 4	3 0	5 0	8 4	0 6	2 9	5 5
19	8 6	2 2	4 8	1 0	9 2	8 2	1 5	3 5
20	4 9	0 6	3 8	2 6	4 2	4 5	4 5	7 4
21	8 7	1 7	3 6	3 1	9 8	2 9	1 4	0 3
22	2 4	8 4	1 0	3 9	6 2	5 5	3 7	0 1
23	2 2	4 6	4 3	1 4	3 9	7 2	1 2	1 5
24	6 4	5 5	5 5	0 5	7 9	8 1	2 3	2 1
25	1 1	2 3	8 6	1 6	5 5	9 6	0 2	1 5
26	0 5	6 9	9 1	9 3	7 5	9 4	2 6	3 1
27	3 6	8 0	7 5	8 3	9 7	1 3	8 4	9 2
28	4 2	2 8	9 0	1 8	1 0	9 9	9 7	4 1
29	8 5	2 8	1 7	6 3	9 6	3 0	2 2	7 0
30	9 2	6 4	9 0	1 5	2 7	2 7	1 4	2 1
31	9 9	1 5	3 0	6 8	1 7	8 3	9 4	3 5
32	1 5	4 7	8 1	4 2	1 3	8 7	9 3	6 8
33	3 0	7 8	4 7	2 4	7 8	7 0	5 1	7 8
34	2 3	5 6	8 8	0 1	9 1	8 0	2 5	9 7
35	2 3	7 2	5 6	9 0	3 7	6 1	0 6	0 3
36	2 3	0 1	0 8	7 7	9 9	1 1	6 6	0 6
37	7 2	2 5	6 8	1 6	4 5	4 1	8 5	6 9
38	0 2	3 5	3 6	4 0	7 8	4 1	1 3	0 7
39	8 7	2 0	4 1	8 9	8 0	0 5	2 1	5 9
40	9 9	4 5	2 5	3 8	1 3	4 0	0 2	5 9

	1 2	3 4	5 6	7 8	9 10	11 12	13 14	15 16
1	6 0	4 6	8 3	0 8	8 7	3 7	6 9	0 9
2	5 1	3 1	5 2	7 8	9 2	0 5	5 1	0 6
3	8 7	9 7	1 7	7 4	8 2	5 3	7 9	2 2
4	2 4	5 2	6 5	3 4	8 6	2 1	0 3	0 9
5	6 5	2 4	7 8	9 3	4 9	4 7	3 3	9 1
6	9 0	0 1	1 5	0 9	2 8	4 2	4 3	4 7
7	8 7	2 9	1 7	8 8	4 7	9 8	5 2	5 6
8	6 2	0 2	6 3	7 5	8 3	7 6	3 4	1 7
9	6 4	0 5	1 2	9 2	3 3	9 9	6 0	9 5
10	3 3	8 3	0 2	6 3	6 7	7 4	0 7	3 2
11	0 7	9 0	0 2	2 6	0 7	0 2	9 6	5 2
12	4 2	8 8	7 7	2 5	2 3	2 6	0 8	9 8
13	7 8	4 8	2 6	5 8	4 8	1 9	2 6	7 5
14	3 1	9 5	5 6	1 7	9 6	3 8	0 6	2 4
15	9 9	8 9	3 7	6 2	5 6	1 2	7 7	5 6
16	7 8	2 2	8 9	0 5	4 4	8 5	6 3	4 8
17	3 5	7 6	4 2	2 3	3 6	8 9	3 5	1 8
18	5 1	1 1	9 7	1 3	5 8	5 9	3 8	4 3
19	9 6	3 8	1 3	1 7	2 6	2 8	9 7	1 9
20	9 2	6 0	8 4	1 7	1 4	6 1	0 2	6 5
21	5 2	3 0	8 9	7 6	1 4	3 5	7 5	6 8
22	3 3	8 0	7 6	0 3	9 1	6 1	3 6	1 4
23	6 8	3 0	5 8	2 1	0 3	3 8	9 9	5 1
24	2 9	5 9	8 0	1 4	6 6	0 7	9 7	3 6
25	7 5	2 8	7 5	8 4	6 5	5 5	8 0	2 4
26	5 5	4 2	1 1	0 5	5 3	7 9	6 2	9 0
27	5 3	4 2	6 6	8 9	8 8	0 6	2 9	0 8
28	3 3	5 5	3 8	3 4	3 2	3 7	0 1	6 9
29	5 3	9 4	2 1	8 6	0 3	4 2	9 8	2 0
30	0 8	0 5	2 1	7 7	4 3	1 5	5 1	3 5
31	2 9	0 8	5 6	0 8	5 1	3 2	3 8	5 7
32	4 2	7 5	8 9	0 9	1 1	8 9	9 0	0 1
33	7 5	2 8	9 7	6 9	9 3	4 2	3 0	2 3
34	4 3	3 5	2 9	5 8	9 1	1 8	2 9	3 2
35	2 3	5 8	7 7	1 9	3 4	5 9	3 3	0 4
36	4 3	4 6	9 0	1 8	4 4	6 1	3 2	6 8
37	0 8	4 9	1 7	0 1	1 4	9 5	9 4	9 7
38	6 4	6 7	1 5	9 7	2 3	1 4	8 1	1 1
39	0 1	9 8	8 2	6 6	8 0	6 1	9 1	6 8
40	5 1	3 6	2 6	9 9	0 8	2 6	0 6	5 2

Table S*
Squares and Square Roots of Numbers

Number	Square	Square root	Number	Square	Square root
1	1	1.0000	41	16 81	6.4031
2	4	1.4142	42	17 64	6.4807
3	9	1.7321	43	18 49	6.5574
4	16	2.0000	44	19 36	6.6332
5	25	2.2361	45	20 25	6.7082
6	36	2.4495	46	21 16	6.7823
7	49	2.6458	47	22 09	6.8557
8	64	2.8284	48	23 04	6.9282
9	81	3.0000	49	24 01	7.0000
10	1 00	3.1623	50	25 00	7.0711
11	1 21	3.3166	51	26 01	7.1414
12	1 44	3.4641	52	27 04	7.2111
13	1 69	3.6056	53	28 09	7.2801
14	1 96	3.7417	54	29 16	7.3485
15	2 25	3.8730	55	30 25	7.4162
16	2 56	4.0000	56	31 36	7.4833
17	2 89	4.1231	57	32 49	7.5498
18	3 24	4.2426	58	33 64	7.6158
19	3 61	4.3589	59	34 81	7.6811
20	4 00	4.4721	60	36 00	7.7460
21	4 41	4.5826	61	37 21	7.8102
22	4 84	4.6904	62	38 44	7.8740
23	5 29	4.7958	63	39 69	7.9373
24	5 76	4.8990	64	40 96	8.0000
25	6 25	5.0000	65	42 25	8.0623
26	6 76	5.0990	66	43 56	8.1240
27	7 29	5.1962	67	44 89	8.1854
28	7 84	5.2915	68	46 24	8.2462
29	8 41	5.3852	69	47 61	8.3066
30	9 00	5.4772	70	49 00	8.3666
31	9 61	5.5678	71	50 41	8.4261
32	10 24	5.6569	72	51 84	8.4853
33	10 89	5.7446	73	53 29	8.5440
34	11 56	5.8310	74	54 76	8.6023
35	12 25	5.9161	75	56 25	8.6603
36	12 96	6.0000	76	57 76	8.7178
37	13 69	6.0828	77	59 29	8.7750
38	14 44	6.1644	78	60 84	8.8318
39	15 21	6.2450	79	62 41	8.8882
40	16 00	6.3246	80	64 00	8.9443

* Reproduced from Guilford, J. P. Fundamental Statistics in Psychology and Education, 2nd ed., 1950, pp. 590–62. By permission of McGraw-Hill, Inc.

Table S (Continued)
Squares and Square Roots of Numbers

Number	Square	Square root	Number	Square	Square root
81	65 61	9.0000	121	1 46 41	11.0000
82	67 24	9.0554	122	1 48 84	11.0454
83	68 89	9.1104	123	1 51 29	11.0905
84	70 56	9.1652	124	1 53 76	11.1355
85	72 25	9.2195	125	1 56 25	11.1803
86	73 96	9.2736	126	1 58 76	11.2250
87	75 69	9.3274	127	1 61 29	11.2694
88	77 44	9.3808	128	1 63 84	11.3137
89	79 21	9.4340	129	1 66 41	11.3578
90	81 00	9.4868	130	1 69 00	11.4018
91	82 81	9.5394	131	1 71 61	11.4455
92	84 64	9.5917	132	1 74 24	11.4891
93	86 49	9.6437	133	1 76 89	11.5326
94	88 36	9.6954	134	1 79 56	11.5758
95	90 25	9.7468	135	1 82 25	11.6190
96	92 16	9.7980	136	1 84 96	11.6619
97	94 09	9.8489	137	1 87 69	11.7047
98	96 04	9.8995	138	1 90 44	11.7473
99	98 01	9.9499	139	1 93 21	11.7898
100	1 00 00	10.0000	140	1 96 00	11.8322
101	1 02 01	10.0499	141	1 98 81	11.8743
102	1 04 04	10.0995	142	2 01 64	11.9164
103	1 06 09	10.1489	143	2 04 49	11.9583
104	1 08 16	10.1980	144	2 07 36	12.0000
105	1 10 25	10.2470	145	2 10 25	12.0416
106	1 12 36	10.2956	146	2 13 16	12.0830
107	1 14 49	10.3441	147	2 16 09	12.1244
108	1 16 64	10.3923	148	2 19 04	12.1655
109	1 18 81	10.4403	149	2 22 01	12.2066
110	1 21 00	10.4881	150	2 25 00	12.2474
111	1 23 21	10.5357	151	2 28 01	12.2882
112	1 25 44	10.5830	152	2 31 04	12.3288
113	1 27 69	10.6301	153	2 34 09	12.3693
114	1 29 96	10.6771	154	2 37 16	12.4097
115	1 32 25	10.7238	155	2 40 25	12.4499
116	1 34 56	10.7703	156	2 43 36	12.4900
117	1 36 89	10.8167	157	2 46 49	12.5300
118	1 39 24	10.8628	158	2 49 64	12.5698
119	1 41 61	10.9087	159	2 52 81	12.6095
120	1 44 00	10.9545	160	2 56 00	12.6491

Table S (Continued)
Squares and Square Roots of Numbers

Number	Square	Square root	Number	Square	Square root
161	2 59 21	12.6886	201	4 04 01	14.1774
162	2 62 44	12.7279	202	4 08 04	14.2127
163	2 65 69	12.7671	203	4 12 09	14.2478
164	2 68 96	12.8062	204	4 16 16	14.2829
165	2 72 25	12.8452	205	4 20 25	14.3178
166	2 75 56	12.8841	206	4 24 36	14.3527
167	2 78 89	12.9228	207	4 28 49	14.3875
168	2 82 24	12.9615	208	4 32 64	14.4222
169	2 85 61	13.0000	209	4 36 81	14.4568
170	2 89 00	13.0384	210	4 41 00	14.4914
171	2 92 41	13.0767	211	4 45 21	14.5258
172	2 95 84	13.1149	212	4 49 44	14.5602
173	2 99 29	13.1529	213	4 53 69	14.5945
174	3 02 76	13.1909	214	4 57 96	14.6287
175	3 06 25	13.2288	215	4 62 25	14.6629
176	3 09 76	13.2665	216	4 66 56	14.6969
177	3 13 29	13.3041	217	4 70 89	14.7309
178	3 16 84	13.3417	218	4 75 24	14.7648
179	3 20 41	13.3791	219	4 79 61	14.7986
180	3 24 00	13.4164	220	4 84 00	14.8324
181	3 27 61	13.4536	221	4 88 41	14.8661
182	3 31 24	13.4907	222	4 92 84	14.8997
183	3 34 89	13.5277	223	4 97 29	14.9332
184	3 38 56	13.5647	224	5 01 76	14.9666
185	3 42 25	13.6015	225	5 06 25	15.0000
186	3 45 96	13.6382	226	5 10 76	15.0333
187	3 49 69	13.6748	227	5 15 29	15.0665
188	3 53 44	13.7113	228	5 19 84	15.0997
189	3 57 21	13.7477	229	5 24 41	15.1327
190	3 61 00	13.7840	230	5 29 00	15.1658
191	3 64 81	13.8203	231	5 33 61	15.1987
192	3 68 64	13.8564	232	5 38 24	15.2315
193	3 72 49	13.8924	233	5 42 89	15.2643
194	3 76 36	13.9284	234	5 47 56	15.2971
195	3 80 25	13.9642	235	5 52 25	15.3297
196	3 84 16	14.0000	236	5 56 96	15.3623
197	3 88 09	14.0357	237	5 61 69	15.3948
198	3 92 04	14.0712	238	5 66 44	15.4272
199	3 96 01	14.1067	239	5 71 21	15.4596
200	4 00 00	14.1421	240	5 76 00	15.4919

Table S (Continued)
Squares and Square Roots of Numbers

Number	Square	Square root	Number	Square	Square root
241	5 80 81	15.5242	281	7 89 61	16.7631
242	5 85 64	15.5563	282	7 95 24	16.7929
243	5 90 49	15.5885	283	8 00 89	16.8226
244	5 95 36	15.6205	284	8 06 56	16.8523
245	6 00 25	15.6525	285	8 12 25	16.8819
246	6 05 16	15.6844	286	8 17 96	16.9115
247	6 10 09	15.7162	287	8 23 69	16.9411
248	6 15 04	15.7480	288	8 29 44	16.9706
249	6 20 01	15.7797	289	8 35 21	17.0000
250	6 25 00	15.8114	290	8 41 00	17.0294
251	6 30 01	15.8430	291	8 46 81	17.0587
252	6 35 04	15.8745	292	8 52 64	17.0880
253	6 40 09	15.9060	293	8 58 49	17.1172
254	6 45 16	15.9374	294	8 64 36	17.1464
255	6 50 25	15.9687	295	8 70 25	17.1756
256	6 55 36	16.0000	296	8 76 16	17.2047
257	6 60 49	16.0312	297	8 82 09	17.2337
258	6 65 64	16.0624	298	8 88 04	17.2627
259	6 70 81	16.0935	299	8 94 01	17.2916
260	6 76 00	16.1245	300	9 00 00	17.3205
261	6 81 21	16.1555	301	9 06 01	17.3494
262	6 86 44	16.1864	302	9 12 04	17.3781
263	6 91 69	16.2173	303	9 18 09	17.4069
264	6 96 96	16.2481	304	9 24 16	17.4356
265	7 02 25	16.2788	305	9 30 25	17.4642
266	7 07 56	16.3095	306	9 36 36	17.4929
267	7 12 89	16.3401	307	9 42 49	17.5214
268	7 18 24	16.3707	308	9 48 64	17.5499
269	7 23 61	16.4012	309	9 54 81	17.5784
270	7 29 00	16.4317	310	9 61 00	17.6068
271	7 34 41	16.4621	311	9 67 21	17.6352
272	7 39 84	16.4924	312	9 73 44	17.6635
273	7 45 29	16.5227	313	9 79 69	17.6918
274	7 50 76	16.5529	314	9 85 96	17.7200
275	7 56 25	16.5831	315	9 92 25	17.7482
276	7 61 76	16.6132	316	9 98 56	17.7764
277	7 67 29	16.6433	317	10 04 89	17.8045
278	7 72 84	16.6733	318	10 11 24	17.8326
279	7 78 41	16.7033	319	10 17 61	17.8606
280	7 84 00	16.7332	320	10 24 00	17.8885

Squares and Square Roots of Numbers

Number	Square	Square root	Number	Square	Square root
321	10 30 41	17.9165	361	13 03 21	19.0000
322	10 36 84	17.9444	362	13 10 44	19.0263
323	10 43 29	17.9722	363	13 17 69	19.0526
324	10 49 76	18.0000	364	13 24 96	19.0788
325	10 56 25	18.0278	365	13 32 25	19.1050
326	10 62 76	18.0555	366	13 39 56	19.1311
327	10 69 29	18.0831	367	13 46 89	19.1572
328	10 75 84	18.1108	368	13 54 24	19.1833
329	10 82 41	18.1384	369	13 61 61	19.2094
330	10 89 00	18.1659	370	13 69 00	19.2354
331	10 95 61	18.1934	371	13 76 41	19.2614
332	11 02 24	18.2209	372	13 83 84	19.2873
333	11 08 89	18.2483	373	13 91 29	19.3132
334	11 15 56	18.2757	374	13 98 76	19.3391
335	11 22 25	18.3030	375	14 06 25	19.3649
336	11 28 96	18.3303	376	14 13 76	19.3907
337	11 35 69	18.3576	377	14 21 29	19.4165
338	11 42 44	18.3848	378	14 28 84	19.4422
339	11 49 21	18.4120	379	14 36 41	19.4679
340	11 56 00	18.4391	380	14 44 00	19.4936
341	11 62 81	18.4662	381	14 51 61	19.5192
342	11 69 64	18.4932	382	14 59 24	19.5448
343	11 76 49	18.5203	383	14 66 89	19.5704
344	11 83 36	18.5472	384	14 74 56	19.5959
345	11 90 25	18.5742	385	14 82 25	19.6214
346	11 97 16	18.6011	386	14 89 96	19.6469
347	12 04 09	18.6279	387	14 97 69	19.6723
348	12 11 04	18.6548	388	15 05 44	19.6977
349	12 18 01	18.6815	389	15 13 21	19.7231
350	12 25 00	18.7083	390	15 21 00	19.7484
351	12 32 01	18.7350	391	15 28 81	19.7737
352	12 39 04	18.7617	392	15 36 64	19.7990
353	12 46 09	18.7883	393	15 44 49	19.8242
354	12 53 16	18.8149	394	15 52 36	19.8494
355	12 60 25	18.8414	395	15 60 25	19.8746
356	12 67 36	18.8680	396	15 68 16	19.8997
357	12 74 49	18.8944	397	15 76 09	19.9249
358	12 81 64	18.9209	398	15 84 04	19.9499
359	12 88 81	18.9473	399	15 92 01	19.9750
360	12 96 00	18.9737	400	16 00 00	20.0000

Number	Square	Square root	Number	Square	Square root
401	16 08 01	20.0250	441	19 44 81	21.0000
402	16 16 04	20.0499	442	19 53 64	21.0238
403	16 24 09	20.0749	443	19 62 49	21.0476
404	16 32 16	20.0998	444	19 71 36	21.0713
405	16 40 25	20.1246	445	19 80 25	21.0950
406	16 48 36	20.1494	446	19 89 16	21.1187
407	16 56 49	20.1742	447	19 98 09	21.1424
408	16 64 64	20.1990	448	20 07 04	21.1660
409	16 72 81	20.2237	449	20 16 01	21.1896
410	16 81 00	20.2485	450	20 25 00	21.2132
411	16 89 21	20.2731	451	20 34 01	21.2368
412	16 97 44	20.2978	452	20 43 04	21.2603
413	17 05 69	20.3224	453	20 52 09	21.2838
414	17 13 96	20.3470	454	20 61 16	21.3073
415	17 22 25	20.3715	455	20 70 25	21.3307
416	17 30 56	20.3961	456	20 79 36	21.3542
417	17 38 89	20.4206	457	20 88 49	21.3776
418	17 47 24	20.4450	458	20 97 64	21.4009
419	17 55 61	20.4695	459	21 06 81	21.4243
420	17 64 00	20.4939	460	21 16 00	21.4476
421	17 72 41	20.5183	461	21 25 21	21.4709
422	17 80 84	20.5426	462	21 34 44	21.4942
423	17 89 29	20.5670	463	21 43 69	21.5174
424	17 97 76	20.5913	464	21 52 96	21.5407
425	18 06 25	20.6155	465	21 62 25	21.5639
426	18 14 76	20.6398	466	21 71 56	21.5870
427	18 23 29	20.6640	467	21 80 89	21.6102
428	18 31 84	20.6882	468	21 90 24	21.6333
429	18 40 41	20.7123	469	21 99 61	21.6564
430	18 49 00	20.7364	470	22 09 00	21.6795
431	18 57 61	20.7605	471	22 18 41	21.7025
432	18 66 24	20.7846	472	22 27 84	21.7256
433	18 74 89	20.8087	473	22 37 29	21.7486
434	18 83 56	20.8327	474	22 46 76	21.7715
435	18 92 25	20.8567	475	22 56 25	21.7945
436	19 00 96	20.8806	476	22 65 76	21.8174
437	19 09 69	20.9045	477	22 75 29	21.8403
438	19 18 44	20.9284	478	22 84 84	21.8632
439	19 27 21	20.9523	479	22 94 41	21.8861
440	19 36 00	20.9762	480	23 04 00	21.9089

Squares and Square Roots of Numbers

Number	Square	Square root	Number	Square	Square root
481	23 13 61	21.9317	521	27 14 41	22.8254
482	23 23 24	21.9545	522	27 24 84	22.8473
483	23 32 89	21.9773	523	27 35 29	22.8692
484	23 42 56	22.0000	524	27 45 76	22.8910
485	23 52 25	22.0227	525	27 56 25	22.9129
486	23 61 96	22.0454	526	27 66 76	22.9347
487	23 71 69	22.0681	527	27 77 29	22.9565
488	23 81 44	22.0907	528	27 87 84	22.9783
489	23 91 21	22.1133	529	27 98 41	23.0000
490	24 01 00	22.1359	530	28 09 00	23.0217
491	24 10 81	22.1585	531	28 19 61	23.0434
492	24 20 64	22.1811	532	28 30 24	23.0651
493	24 30 49	22.2036	533	28 40 89	23.0868
494	24 40 36	22.2261	534	28 51 56	23.1084
495	24 50 25	22.2486	535	28 62 25	23.1301
496	24 60 16	22.2711	536	28 72 96	23.1517
497	24 70 09	22.2935	537	28 83 69	23.1733
498	24 80 04	22.3159	538	28 94 44	23.1948
499	24 90 01	22.3383	539	29 05 21	23.2164
500	25 00 00	22.3607	540	29 16 00	23.2379
501	25 10 01	22.3830	541	29 26 81	23.2594
502	25 20 04	22.4054	542	29 37 64	23.2809
503	25 30 09	22.4277	543	29 48 49	23.3024
504	25 40 16	22.4499	544	29 59 36	23.3238
505	25 50 25	22.4722	545	29 70 25	23.3452
506	25 60 36	22.4944	546	29 81 16	23.3666
507	25 70 49	22.5167	547	29 92 09	23.3880
508	25 80 64	22.5389	548	30 03 04	23.4094
509	25 90 81	22.5610	549	30 14 01	23.4307
510	26 01 00	22.5832	550	30 25 00	23.4521
511	26 11 21	22.6053	551	30 36 01	23.4734
512	26 21 44	22.6274	552	30 47 04	23.4947
513	26 31 69	22.6495	553	30 58 09	23.5160
514	26 41 96	22.6716	554	30 69 16	23.5372
515	26 52 25	22.6936	555	30 80 25	23.5584
516	26 62 56	22.7156	556	30 91 36	23.5797
517	26 72 89	22.7376	557	31 02 49	23.6008
518	26 83 24	22.7596	558	31 13 64	23.6220
519	26 93 61	22.7816	559	31 24 81	23.6432
520	27 04 00	22.8035	560	31 36 00	23.6643

Squares and Square Roots of Numbers

Number	Square	Square root	Number	Square	Square root
561	31 47 21	23.6854	601	36 12 01	24.5153
562	31 58 44	23.7065	602	36 24 04	24.5357
563	31 69 69	23.7276	603	36 36 09	24.5561
564	31 80 96	23.7487	604	36 48 16	24.5764
565	31 92 25	23.7697	605	36 60 25	24.5967
566	32 03 56	23.7908	606	36 72 36	24.6171
567	32 14 89	23.8118	607	36 84 49	24.6374
568	32 26 24	23.8328	608	36 96 64	24.6577
569	32 37 61	23.8537	609	37 08 81	24.6779
570	32 49 00	23.8747	610	37 21 00	24.6982
571	32 60 41	23.8956	611	37 33 21	24.7184
572	32 71 84	23.9165	612	37 45 44	24.7385
573	32 83 29	23.9374	613	37 57 69	24.7588
574	32 94 76	23.9583	614	37 69 96	24.7790
575	33 06 25	23.9792	615	37 82 25	24.7992
576	33 17 76	24.0000	616	37 94 56	24.8193
577	33 29 29	24.0208	617	38 06 89	24.8395
578	33 40 84	24.0416	618	38 19 24	24.8596
579	33 52 41	24.0624	619	38 31 61	24.8797
580	33 64 00	24.0832	620	38 44 00	24.8998
581	33 75 61	24.1039	621	38 56 41	24.9199
582	33 87 24	24.1247	622	38 68 84	24.9399
583	33 98 89	24.1454	623	38 81 29	24.9600
584	34 10 56	24.1661	624	38 93 76	24.9800
585	34 22 25	24.1868	625	39 06 25	25.0000
586	34 33 96	24.2074	626	39 18 76	25.0200
587	34 45 69	24.2281	627	39 31 29	25.0400
588	34 57 44	24.2487	628	39 43 84	25.0599
589	34 69 21	24.2693	629	39 56 41	25.0799
590	34 81 00	24.2899	630	39 69 00	25.0998
591	34 92 81	24.3105	631	39 81 61	25.1197
592	35 04 64	24.3311	632	39 94 24	25.1396
593	35 16 49	24.3516	633	40 06 89	25.1595
594	35 28 36	24.3721	634	40 19 56	25.1794
595	35 40 25	24.3926	635	40 32 25	25.1992
596	35 52 16	24.4131	636	40 44 96	25.2190
597	35 64 09	24.4336	637	40 57 69	25.2389
598	35 76 04	24.4540	638	40 70 44	25.2587
599	35 88 01	24.4745	639	40 83 21	25.2784
600	36 00 00	24.4949	640	40 96 00	25.2982

Number	Square	Square root	Number	Square	Square root
641	41 08 81	25.3180	681	46 37 61	26.0960
642	41 21 64	25.3377	682	46 51 24	26.1151
643	41 34 49	25.3574	683	46 64 89	26.1343
644	41 47 36	25.3772	684	46 78 56	26.1534
645	41 60 25	25.3969	685	46 92 25	26.1725
646	41 73 16	25.4165	686	47 05 96	26.1916
647	41 86 09	25.4362	687	47 19 69	26.2107
648	41 99 04	25.4558	688	47 33 44	26.2298
649	42 12 01	25.4755	689	47 47 21	26.2488
650	42 25 00	25.4951	690	47 61 00	26.2679
651	42 38 01	25.5147	691	47 74 81	26.2869
652	42 51 04	25.5343	692	47 88 64	26.3059
653	42 64 09	25.5539	693	48 02 49	26.3249
654	42 77 16	25.5734	694	48 16 36	26.3439
655	42 90 25	25.5930	695	48 30 25	26.3629
656	43 03 36	25.6125	696	48 44 16	26.3818
657	43 16 49	25.6320	697	48 58 09	26.4008
658	43 29 64	25.6515	698	48 72 04	26.4197
659	43 42 81	25.6710	699	48 86 01	26.4386
660	43 56 00	25.6905	700	49 00 00	26.4575
661	43 69 21	25.7099	701	49 14 01	26.4764
662	43 82 44	25.7294	702	49 28 04	26.4953
663	43 95 69	25.7488	703	49 42 09	26.5141
664	44 08 96	25.7682	704	49 56 16	26.5330
665	44 22 25	25.7876	705	49 70 25	26.5518
666	44 35 56	25.8070	706	49 84 36	26.5707
667	44 48 89	25.8263	707	49 98 49	26.5895
668	44 62 24	25.8457	708	50 12 64	26.6083
669	44 75 61	25.8650	709	50 26 81	26.6271
670	44 89 00	25.8844	710	50 41 00	26.6458
671	45 02 41	25.9037	711	50 55 21	26.6646
672	45 15 84	25.9230	712	50 69 44	26.6833
673	45 29 29	25.9422	713	50 83 69	26.7021
674	45 42 76	25.9615	714	50 97 96	26.7208
675	45 56 25	25.9808	715	51 12 25	26.7395
676	45 69 76	26.0000	716	51 26 56	26.7582
677	45 83 29	26.0192	717	51 40 89	26.7769
678	45 96 84	26.0384	718	51 55 24	26.7955
679	46 10 41	26.0576	719	51 69 61	26.8142
680	46 24 00	26.0768	720	51 84 00	26.8328

Table S (Continued)
Squares and Square Roots of Numbers

Number	Square	Square root	Number	Square	Square root
721	51 98 41	26.8514	761	57 91 21	27.5862
722	52 12 84	26.8701	762	58 06 44	27.6043
723	52 27 29	26.8887	763	58 21 69	27.6225
724	52 41 76	26.9072	764	58 36 96	27.6405
725	52 56 25	26.9258	765	58 52 25	27.6586
726	52 70 76	26.9444	766	58 67 56	27.6767
727	52 85 29	26.9629	767	58 82 89	27.6948
728	52 99 84	26.9815	768	58 98 24	27.7128
729	53 14 41	27.0000	769	59 13 61	27.7308
730	53 29 00	27.0185	770	59 29 00	27.7489
731	53 43 61	27.0370	771	59 44 41	27.7669
732	53 58 24	27.0555	772	59 59 84	27.7849
733	53 72 89	27.0740	773	59 75 29	27.8029
734	53 87 56	27.0924	774	59 90 76	27.8209
735	54 02 25	27.1109	775	60 06 25	27.8388
736	54 16 96	27.1293	776	60 21 76	27.8568
737	54 31 69	27.1477	777	60 37 29	27.8747
738	54 46 44	27.1662	778	60 52 84	27.8927
739	54 61 27	27.1846	779	60 68 41	27.9106
740	54 76 00	27.2029	780	60 84 00	27.9285
741	54 90 81	27.2213	781	60 99 61	27.9464
742	55 05 64	27.2397	782	61 15 24	27.9643
743	55 20 49	27.2580	783	61 30 89	27.9821
744	55 35 36	27.2764	784	61 46 56	28.0000
745	55 50 25	27.2947	785	61 62 25	28.0179
746	55 65 16	27.3130	786	61 77 96	28.0357
747	55 80 09	27.3313	787	61 93 69	28.0535
748	55 95 04	27.3496	788	62 09 44	28.0713
749	56 10 01	27.3679	789	62 25 21	28.0891
750	56 25 00	27.3861	790	62 41 00	28.1069
751	56 40 01	27.4044	791	62 56 81	28.1247
752	56 55 04	27.4226	792	62 72 64	28.1425
753	56 70 09	27.4408	793	62 88 49	28.1603
754	56 85 16	27.4591	794	63 04 36	28.1780
755	57 00 25	27.4773	795	63 20 25	28.1957
756	57 15 36	27.4955	796	63 36 16	28.2135
757	57 30 49	27.5136	797	63 52 09	28.2312
758	57 45 64	27.5318	798	63 68 04	28.2489
759	57 60 81	27.5500	799	63 84 01	28.2666
760	57 76 00	27.5681	800	64 00 00	28.2843

Table S (Continued)
Squares and Square Roots of Numbers

Number	Square	Square root	Number	Square	Square root
801	64 16 01	28.3019	841	70 72 81	29.0000
802	64 32 04	28.3196	842	70 89 64	29.0172
803	64 48 09	28.3373	843	71 06 49	29.0345
804	64 64 16	28.3049	844	71 23 36	29.0517
805	64 80 25	28.3725	845	71 40 25	29.0689
806	64 96 36	28.3901	846	71 57 16	29.0861
807	65 12 49	28.4077	847	71 74 09	29.1033
808	65 28 64	28.4253	848	71 91 04	29.1204
809	65 44 81	28.4429	849	72 08 01	29.1376
810	65 61 00	28.4605	850	72 25 00	29.1548
811	65 77 21	28.4781	851	72 42 01	29.1719
812	65 93 44	28.4956	852	72 59 04	29.1890
813	66 09 69	28.5132	853	72 76 09	29.2062
814	66 25 96	28.5307	854	72 93 16	29.2233
815	66 42 25	28.5482	855	73 10 25	29.2404
816	66 58 56	28.5657	856	73 27 36	29.2575
817	66 74 89	28.5832	857	73 44 49	29.2746
818	66 91 24	28.6007	858	73 61 64	29.2916
819	67 07 61	28.6082	859	73 78 81	29.3087
820	67 24 00	28.6356	860	73 96 00	29.3258
821	67 40 41	28.6531	861	74 13 21	29.3428
822	67 56 84	28.6705	862	74 30 44	29.3598
823	67 73 29	28.6880	863	74 47 69	29.3769
824	67 89 76	28.7054	864	74 64 96	29.3939
825	68 06 25	28.7228	865	74 82 25	29.4109
826	68 22 76	28.7402	866	74 99 56	29.4279
827	68 39 29	28.7576	867	75 16 89	29.4449
828	68 55 84	28.7750	868	75 34 24	29.4618
829	68 72 41	28.7924	869	75 51 61	29.4788
830	68 89 00	28.8097	870	75 69 00	29.4958
831	69 05 61	28.8271	871	75 86 41	29.5127
832	69 22 24	28.8444	872	76 03 84	29.5296
833	69 38 89	28.8617	873	76 21 29	29.5466
834	69 55 56	28.8791	874	76 38 76	29.5635
835	69 72 25	28.8964	875	76 56 25	29.5804
836	69 88 96	28.9137	876	76 73 76	29.5973
837	70 05 69	28.9310	877	76 91 29	29.6142
838	70 22 44	28.9482	878	77 08 84	29.6311
839	70 39 21	28.9655	879	77 26 41	29.6479
840	70 56 00	28.9828	880	77 44 00	29.6648

Squares and Square Roots of Numbers

Number	Square	Square root	Number	Square	Square root
881	77 61 61	29.6816	921	84 82 41	30.3480
882	77 79 24	29.6985	922	85 00 84	30.3645
883	77 96 89	29.7153	923	85 19 29	30.3809
884	78 14 56	29.7321	924	85 37 76	30.3974
885	78 32 25	29.7489	925	85 56 25	30.4138
886	78 49 96	29.7658	926	85 74 76	30.4302
887	78 67 69	29.7825	927	85 93 29	30.4467
888	78 85 44	29.7993	928	86 11 84	30.4631
889	79 03 21	29.8161	929	86 30 41	30.4795
890	79 21 00	29.8329	930	86 49 00	30.4959
891	79 38 81	29.8496	931	86 67 61	30.5123
892	79 56 64	29.8664	932	86 86 24	30.5287
893	79 74 49	29.8831	933	87 04 89	30.5450
894	79 92 36	29.8998	934	87 23 56	30.5614
895	80 10 25	29.9166	935	87 42 25	30.5778
896	80 28 16	29.9333	936	87 60 96	30.5941
897	80 46 09	29.9500	937	87 79 69	30.6105
898	80 64 04	29.9666	938	87 98 44	30.6268
899	80 82 01	29.9833	939	88 17 21	30.6431
900	81 00 00	30.0000	940	88 36 00	30.6594
901	81 18 01	30.0167	941	88 54 81	30.6757
902	81 36 04	30.0333	942	88 73 64	30.6920
903	81 54 09	30.0500	943	88 92 49	30.7083
904	81 72 16	30.0666	944	89 11 36	30.7246
905	81 90 25	30.0832	945	89 30 25	30.7409
906	82 08 36	30.0998	946	89 49 16	30.7571
907	82 26 49	30.1164	947	89 68 09	30.7734
908	82 44 64	30.1330	948	89 87 04	30.7896
909	82 62 81	30.1496	949	90 06 01	30.8058
910	82 81 00	30.1662	950	90 25 00	30.8221
911	82 99 21	30.1828	951	90 44 01	30.8383
912	83 17 44	30.1993	952	90 63 04	30.8545
913	83 35 69	30.2159	953	90 82 09	30.8707
914	83 53 96	30.2324	954	91 01 16	30.8869
915	83 72 25	30.2490	955	91 20 25	30.9031
916	83 90 56	30.2655	956	91 39 36	30.9192
917	84 08 89	30.2820	957	91 58 49	30.9354
918	84 27 24	30.2985	958	91 77 64	30.9516
919	84 45 61	30.3150	959	91 96 81	30.9677
920	84 64 00	30.3315	960	92 16 00	30.9839

Table S (Continued)
Squares and Square Roots of Numbers

Number	Square	Square root	Number	Square	Square root
961	92 35 21	31.0000	981	96 23 61	31.3209
962	92 54 44	31.0161	982	96 43 24	31.3369
963	92 73 69	31.0322	983	96 62 89	31.3528
964	92 92 96	31.0483	984	96 82 56	31.3688
965	93 12 25	31.0644	985	97 02 25	31.3847
966	93 31 56	31.0805	986	97 21 96	31.4006
967	93 50 89	31.0966	987	97 41 69	31.4166
968	93 70 24	31.1127	988	97 61 44	31.4325
969	93 89 61	31.1288	989	97 81 21	31.4484
970	94 09 00	31.1448	990	98 01 00	31.4643
971	94 28 41	31.1609	991	98 20 81	31.4802
972	94 47 84	31.1769	992	98 40 64	31.4960
973	94 67 29	31.1929	993	98 60 49	31.5119
974	94 86 76	31.2090	994	98 80 36	31.5278
975	95 06 25	31.2250	995	99 00 25	31.5436
976	95 25 76	31.2410	996	99 20 16	31.5595
977	95 45 29	31.2570	997	99 40 09	31.5753
978	95 64 84	31.2730	998	99 60 04	31.5911
979	95 84 41	31.2890	999	99 80 01	31.6070
980	96 04 00	31.3050	1000	100 00 00	31.6228

Table T
Four Place Common Logarithms of Numbers

	0	1	2	3	4	5	6	7	8	9
10	·0000	0043	0086	0128	0170	0212	0253	0294	0334	0374
11	·0414	0453	0492	0531	0569	0607	0645	0682	0719	0755
12	·0792	0828	0864	0899	0934	0969	1004	1038	1072	1106
13	·1139	1173	1206	1239	1271	1303	1335	1367	1399	1430
14	·1461	1492	1523	1553	1584	1614	1644	1673	1703	1732
15	·1761	1790	1818	1847	1875	1903	1931	1959	1987	2014
16	·2041	2068	2095	2122	2148	2175	2201	2227	2253	2279
17	·2304	2330	2355	2380	2405	2430	2455	2480	2504	2529
18	·2553	2577	2601	2625	2648	2672	2695	2718	2742	2765
19	·2788	2810	2833	2856	2878	2900	2923	2945	2967	2989
20	·3010	3032	3054	3075	3096	3118	3139	3160	3181	3201
21	·3222	3243	3263	3284	3304	3324	3345	3365	3385	3404
22	·3424	3444	3464	3483	3502	3522	3541	3560	3579	3598
23	·3617	3636	3655	3674	3692	3711	3729	3747	3766	3784
24	·3802	3820	3838	3856	3874	3892	3909	3927	3945	3962
25	·3979	3997	4014	4031	4048	4065	4082	4099	4116	4133
26	·4150	4166	4183	4200	4216	4232	4249	4265	4281	4298
27	·4314	4330	4346	4362	4378	4393	4409	4425	4440	4456
28	·4472	4487	4502	4518	4533	4548	4564	4579	4594	4609
29	·4624	4639	4654	4669	4683	4698	4713	4728	4742	4757
30	·4771	4786	4800	4814	4829	4843	4857	4871	4886	4900
31	·4914	4928	4942	4955	4969	4983	4997	5011	5024	5038
32	·5051	5065	5079	5092	5105	5119	5132	5145	5159	5172
33	·5185	5198	5211	5224	5237	5250	5263	5276	5289	5302
34	·5315	5328	5340	5353	5366	5378	5391	5403	5416	5428
35	·5441	5453	5465	5478	5490	5502	5514	5527	5539	5551
36	·5563	5575	5587	5599	5611	5623	5635	5647	5658	5670
37	·5682	5694	5705	5717	5729	5740	5752	5763	5775	5786
38	·5798	5809	5821	5832	5843	5855	5866	5877	5888	5899
39	·5911	5922	5933	5944	5955	5966	5977	5988	5999	6010
40	·6021	6031	6042	6053	6064	6075	6085	6096	6107	6117
41	·6128	6138	6149	6160	6170	6180	6191	6201	6212	6222
42	·6232	6243	6253	6263	6274	6284	6294	6304	6314	6325
43	·6335	6345	6355	6365	6375	6385	6395	6405	6415	6425
44	·6435	6444	6454	6464	6474	6484	6493	6503	6513	6522
45	·6532	6542	6551	6561	6571	6580	6590	6599	6609	6618
46	·6628	6637	6646	6656	6665	6675	6684	6693	6702	6712
47	·6721	6730	6739	6749	6758	6767	6776	6785	6794	6803
48	·6812	6821	6830	6839	6848	6857	6866	6875	6884	6893
49	·6902	6911	6920	6928	6937	6946	6955	6964	6972	6981
50	·6990	6998	7007	7016	7024	7033	7042	7050	7059	7067
51	·7076	7084	7093	7101	7110	7118	7126	7135	7143	7152
52	·7160	7168	7177	7185	7193	7202	7210	7218	7226	7235
53	·7243	7251	7259	7267	7275	7284	7292	7300	7308	7316
54	·7324	7332	7340	7348	7356	7364	7372	7380	7388	7396

Table T (Continued)
Four Place Common Logarithms of Numbers

	0	1	2	3	4	5	6	7	8	9
55	·7404	7412	7419	7427	7435	7443	7451	7459	7466	7474
56	·7482	7490	7497	7505	7513	7520	7528	7536	7543	7551
57	·7559	7566	7574	7582	7589	7597	7604	7612	7619	7627
58	·7634	7642	7649	7657	7664	7672	7679	7686	7694	7701
59	·7709	7716	7723	7731	7738	7745	7752	7760	7767	7774
60	·7782	7789	7796	7803	7810	7818	7825	7832	7839	7846
61	·7853	7860	7868	7875	7882	7889	7896	7903	7910	7917
62	·7924	7931	7938	7945	7952	7959	7966	7973	7980	7987
63	·7993	8000	8007	8014	8021	8028	8035	8041	8048	8055
64	·8062	8069	8075	8082	8089	8096	8102	8109	8116	8122
65	·8129	8136	8142	8149	8156	8162	8169	8176	8182	8189
66	·8195	8202	8209	8215	8222	8228	8235	8241	8248	8254
67	·8261	8267	8274	8280	8287	8293	8299	8306	8312	8319
68	·8325	8331	8338	8344	8351	8357	8363	8370	8376	8382
69	·8388	8395	8401	8407	8414	8420	8426	8432	8439	8445
70	·8451	8457	8463	8470	8476	8482	8488	8494	8500	8506
71	·8513	8519	8525	8531	8537	8543	8549	8555	8561	8567
72	·8573	8579	8585	8591	8597	8603	8609	8615	8621	8627
73	·8633	8639	8645	8651	8657	8663	8669	8675	8681	8686
74	·8692	8698	8704	8710	8716	8722	8727	8733	8739	8745
75	·8751	8756	8762	8768	8774	8779	8785	8791	8797	8802
76	·8808	8814	8820	8825	8831	8837	8842	8848	8854	8859
77	·8865	8871	8876	8882	8887	8893	8899	8904	8910	8915
78	·8921	8927	8932	8938	8943	8949	8954	8960	8965	8971
79	·8976	8982	8987	8993	8998	9004	9009	9015	9020	9025
80	·9031	9036	9042	9047	9053	9058	9063	9069	9074	9079
81	·9085	9090	9096	9101	9106	9112	9117	9122	9128	9133
82	·9138	9143	9149	9154	9159	9165	9170	9175	9180	9186
83	·9191	9196	9201	9206	9212	9217	9222	9227	9232	9238
84	·9243	9248	9253	9258	9263	9269	9274	9279	9284	9289
85	·9294	9299	9304	9309	9315	9320	9325	9330	9335	9340
86	·9345	9350	9355	9360	9365	9370	9375	9380	9385	9390
87	·9395	9400	9405	9410	9415	9420	9425	9430	9435	9440
88	·9445	9450	9455	9460	9465	9469	9474	9479	9484	9489
89	·9494	9499	9504	9509	9513	9518	9523	9528	9533	9538
90	·9542	9547	9552	9557	9562	9566	9571	9576	9581	9586
91	·9590	9595	9600	9605	9609	9614	9619	9624	9628	9633
92	·9638	9643	9647	9652	9657	9661	9666	9671	9675	9680
93	·9685	9689	9694	9699	9703	9708	9713	9717	9722	9727
94	·9731	9736	9741	9745	9750	9754	9759	9763	9768	9773
95	·9777	9782	9786	9791	9795	9800	9805	9809	9814	9818
96	·9823	9827	9832	9836	9841	9845	9850	9854	9859	9863
97	·9868	9872	9877	9881	9886	9890	9894	9899	9903	9908
98	·9912	9917	9921	9926	9930	9934	9939	9943	9948	9952
99	·9956	9961	9965	9969	9974	9978	9983	9987	9991	9996